Concepts in physics

Concepts
in physics *by*

Robert K. Adair

YALE UNIVERSITY

Academic Press

NEW YORK

ACADEMIC PRESS, INC.
111 Fifth Avenue, New York, New York 10003

United Kingdom Edition published by
ACADEMIC PRESS, INC. (LONDON) LTD.
Berkeley Square House, London W.1

LIBRARY OF CONGRESS CATALOG CARD NUMBER: 69-13481

PRINTED IN THE UNITED STATES OF AMERICA

I HAVE BEEN deeply interested for some time in the problems of scientific education for the able student not planning to major in physics, and this textbook thus represents implicitly my view concerning the kind of teaching of science which I feel is most important. The text is internalist inasmuch as the internal importance and internal consistency of physics is emphasized, necessarily at the expense of both historic perspective and the connection of physics to technology. This is not to say that either the history of science or technology is unimportant, but that I believe that neither the history of physics nor the subject of technology is easily coupled to the study of physics without obscuring the unity we have achieved in our view of the physical universe.

In the text and in the course I have attempted to convey some of the attitudes which a contemporary physicist has toward physics, by trying to present something of the basic concepts which dominate our view of the physical universe. In particular, I have attempted to give the student a reasonably sophisticated understanding of quantum mechanics, the special and general theories of relativity, and the importance of classifying the symmetries which we seem to observe in the universe.

Being dubious about the value of discussion alone, I have attempted to place as much of the foundations of the physical concepts on as logical a basis as possible. There are obvious limitations to what one can do without the use of any mathematics except elementary algebra and the fundamentals of geometry; but I hope I have kept largely within the bounds of good taste even if some precision in thought must be discarded. In line with this view, the students are supplied with a large number of quantitative problems. The mathematics is generally extremely elementary though the physics can be difficult.

I might add here that only the most exceptional student can be expected to follow all the logical steps in all the derivations, even though each step is simple enough. But I have found that it is useful to have these derivations available as a kind of proof that the ideas are accessible on an elementary basis. I cover in detail only about sixty percent of the formal logic which is presented, and, indeed, I only cover about eighty percent of the material in the text in any one year, although I cover different areas occasionally.

The text results from my experience with a specific course which I have taught for some years at Yale. A discussion of the character of that course and of the students who have attended it may be useful in setting goals of the text and defining the areas in which it may be useful.

The course is the basic physics course we offer for nonphysics majors. The students have a considerable variety of academic backgrounds: Some are quite sophisticated mathematically; some have no more than the minimum mathematical requirements for entrance to the University. Some have had excellent secondary school courses in physics, while many have had no physics or any other physical science course. It is then necessary to prepare a course which demands little in the way of previous work in either mathematics or science and yet is sufficiently sophisticated to interest those with a considerable background.

I am indebted to my colleagues and especially to my students for the benefit of innumerable suggestions, corrections, and criticisms. Mr. David Flory read the manuscript critically and his contributions were invaluable.

New Haven, Connecticut   *Robert K. Adair*

Contents

sixteen The phenomenology of heat

seventeen The kinetic theory of gases

eighteen The second law of thermodynamics—order to disorder

Concepts in physics

1|1   *The nature of understanding*
in physics

IT IS obvious to us that there is a great deal of order in the universe; the world we live in, our life itself, would be vastly different if all events were random. We might express this fact by stating that it is evident that relations exist between the observations of the universe. The study of all possible relations between objects of a set constitutes the body of mathematics; the study of the relations between the real observations we can make on our universe constitutes the body of science. The relations between the observations of the physical universe is the subject matter of *physics*. It is not important to define the extent of the physical universe or the extent of physics precisely; it is enough to state that the primary concerns of physics are the relations between particles and forces that lead naturally to inquiries into the nature of space and time. Although chemistry, astronomy, and geology have historical origins different from those of physics per se, in a broad sense they are now parts of physics. On the other hand, although biology and even, as a rather futuristic vision, the social sciences might be fundamentally understandable in terms of physical principles, at this time physics contributes little to biology and is nearly irrelevant to the social sciences.

The study of the set of observations of the physical universe entails, implicitly, asking questions. As a matter of practical procedure the observations must be considered in some context. It is essential, then, to consider carefully the character and the limitations of the questions as well as the content of the answers. A story is told of an ichthyologist who examined the fish collected after the seining of a lake. A primary conclusion of a study of his data was the interesting result that all fish that lived in the lake were more than four inches long. The moral is, of course, one must examine the seine as well as the fish, the questions as well as the answers.

The questions one asks in physics—and almost everything one says here refers to the biological sciences as well as the physical sciences—are never concerned with *how* something works. One can only ask how one observation relates to another. This limitation is a part of the implicit philosophy of science which is essentially a kind of *logical positivism*. Although the personal philosophy of scientists is varied, as scientists, considering science, they proceed according to the rule that the only questions that are admitted are questions that can be answered *in principle* by observation or by the controlled observations we call experiments.

If you consider your conversations with small children, it is clear that the limitation of answers to relations rather than ultimate causes is common, if not completely pervasive, in other aspects of experience. If a child asks why the sun comes up in the morning and goes down at night, you can answer that the sun is stationary and the earth turns. This pattern you have defined for the child may satisfy him. With your greater sophistication you realize that you have not answered his question in any absolute manner at all: you have only diverted his question to a further problem: Why does the earth turn? In the context of science we know no end to the chain of relations that could follow.

If this is always the case, then what is it that we do accomplish in science? We consolidate and integrate our knowledge by developing an understanding of the relations between phenomena. Yeats tells of a wise man who "found similarities between things long thought different, and differences between things long thought similar." This carries something of the spirit of science.

Let us consider the character of the class of events that we can call "falling bodies" in order to illustrate the character of the generalizations and their usefulness. We might collect a large number of observations of falling bodies. We find, for example, that a large stone falls 64 (ft) in 2 (sec). In the course of another observation we notice that an apple falls 16 ft from a branch of a tree in 1 sec. We could accumulate an enormous number of individual data. Each individual datum in this collection could be true, and the whole would certainly constitute a body of knowledge, albeit terribly unwieldy. We are now prepared to make a considerable intellectual step; we can make a generalization of all of these data. A simple generalization would be that all bodies fall down. A much more subtle generalization is that different bodies fall the same distance in the same time. These generalizations are generalizations of physics. You notice we have said nothing causal: we have not said how bodies fall or why bodies fall. Our contribution is to relate the fall of one body to the fall of another. The generalization we have produced consolidates a considerable amount of knowledge. It is consolidations, generalizations, and distillations of this nature that are the essence of all the important conclusions of physics. To professional physicists these consolidations have an aesthetic quality.

It seems unlikely that the methods used in science or in physics to arrive at these distillations are particularly different from the methods used in solving any other problem in human experience. We so often hear the phrase *scientific method.* Is there a scientific method? That is to say, is there a scientific method that is different from any other procedure of arriving at truth? There is little evidence that there is any qualitative difference between the reasoning of a scientist, a physicist, concerned with the problems of physics, and the reasoning of a theologian, a lawyer, a business man, or a farmer, concerned with problems of good and evil, legality or illegality, profit or loss, or of famine or plenty. There is probably some quantitative difference that follows from one special feature of the logic of the physical sciences, the practicability of the use of long complex logical constructions. Physics is narrow, precise, and simple in much the same way as history, sociology, psychology, or the study of literature is broad, hazy, and difficult. Because of this simplicity the premises used as the foundations of logical construction in physics are few and well defined, and very often their validity is well established. With so strong a foundation, reliable logical structures leading to far reaching conclusions and generalizations can be constructed.

In contrast, it is very difficult to establish any small but complete set of reliable premises in other areas of scholarship. The great generalizations of historians such as Toynbee or psychologists such as Freud are simply not reliable or useful in the sense of established physical laws. Their premises cannot support any extensive logical extropolations.

1 | 2   *The place of mathematics*
in physics

Even as physics is the study of the relations between the set of all possible observations of the real universe, these relations must be a part of all of the possible relations between the objects of any set, which is the body of mathematics. The logical structure of physics is therefore a part of the logical structure of mathematics and is couched in mathematical language. Mathematics is essentially formal logic. The immense human effort devoted to mathematics has resulted in crystallizations of large blocks of logic. We use these blocks in total as a saving of incalculable effort. One uses the results of the Pythagorean theorem without deriving it from the premises of plane geometry each time it is used. In the same way we use other mathematical results. The Pythagorean theorem contains, implicitly, certain assumptions concerning geometry—for example, it is valid only on a plane surface—and it is essential that we have some understanding of these assumptions; it is not necessary that we be prepared to derive the theorem at a moment's notice. Mathematical notation is also extremely important because it is so precise and compact. Since each basic mathematical symbol and basic mathematical operation can be defined using language alone, it is obviously possible, in principle, to substitute a discussion in English for any mathematical relation. There have been occasional attempts to do this, rather as a tour de force; typically, several pages of carefully phrased English are required to replace a simple mathematical relation.

We must not, however, confuse physics with mathematics. Nor should we conclude that the relation between physics and mathematics is other than the relation between physics and logic. Any

lem that is solvable by logical analysis can be put into a
 such that the problem can be solved using mathematical
edures. Indeed, such a statement is intrinsically tautological.
ematics and logic are the same. Mathematics is more im-
nt in physics than in biology, for example, only because
ics is simpler and more easily defined than biology and
vs more complex logical extensions. The importance of
logical extensions is, however, immense and it is certainly
that the existence of the mathematical or logical structures
have been developed by mathematicians has been essential
e development of our picture of the physical universe.

ere has been a division in physics between those who spe-
ze in the conducting of experimental measurements and those
 are primarily occupied with the logical constructions derived
 those experimental results. Einstein is an example of a
rist; Albert Michelson, who conducted some of the experi-
ts that led Einstein to construct the Theory of Relativity, is
xample of an experimental physicist. This division of labor
esents no division of the science, which is a unified disci-
. Further, the brilliance of the theoretical or logical work
en, such as Einstein and Bohr should not obscure the fact
 physics is based on experimentally obtained knowledge of
particular universe. Although many physicists believe, like
niz, that there can be only one logically consistent universe
ch Liebniz, as a theologian, considered the best of all possible
ds), we are very far from being able to deduce the structure
is universe from logical principles alone. The particular set
ll possible observations of the universe must be extracted
 the mathematician's complete and infinite set by inspection.
 must then rely on observation to determine, at least, which of
plausible universes is ours. Physics, then, is founded in ob-
ation and in the controlled observations we call experiments.
 is interesting to note that these two parallel parts of our
iries into the character of the universe—experiment and
ry—have different, though rather well defined, historical
ins. Although abstract mathematical thought existed in
ent Egypt and more particularly in Babylon, the contributions
e Greeks were so very great that we can reasonably consider
 the Greeks invented modern abstract thinking of this kind
 much as we know it today. Though the Greeks certainly per-

formed experiments, the systematically prepared observations of nature that correspond to the scientific experiments of today seem to have developed rather abruptly in the Europe of the Renaissance.

1|3   *The importance of idealizations in physics*

It is essential to construct reasonable idealizations as a part of most good reasoning and certainly as a part of the construction of physical theory. The idealizations of physics are not particularly different from the idealizations made in other aspects of human affairs. We consider, as an example, the idealizations made in the consideration of the description of a falling body. Previously, we made the familiar statement that all bodies fall at the same speed. This, of course, is completely incorrect. One only has to hold up a feather and a coin and let them drop to see that the feather drifts very slowly to the floor and the coin falls quickly. You might say that this is an unfair demonstration because the air resistance is much greater on the feather than it is on the coin. But for a real coin and a real feather in a real situation, the resistance of the air (if we wish to call it that) is a part of our real world and does not change the observation that this coin and feather do not fall at the same rate. We are only able to relate these experiences by considering an idealization, the idealization being that all heavy, dense particles, under situations where the air resistance is not important, would fall in such a way that they would travel any specific distance in the same time. This particular idealization or abstraction is by no means trivial. It is clear that Galileo understood the character and importance of this idealization very well; Aristotle and the Greeks probably did not.

We learn very early in life to make similar idealizations in our concern with less abstract problems. If we ask a child how many rabbits he might have in April if he were given 50 rabbits in January and 50 rabbits in February he will likely answer, "100 rabbits." If you then tell him that his answer is wrong and that he might have instead several hundred rabbits, and explain your reasoning, he will likely answer, "Oh, you're not being fair!" He has idealized the problem according to convention, and you have not.

1 | 4   *The character of experiments and theories*

Almost all experiments designed to obtain information of interest in physics can be described as measurements. If the results are to be useful, both the procedures used in the measurement and the measured quantity itself must be well defined. Although the measurements may be difficult in practice, the experimental methods and the interpretation of the results are almost always simple in principle. Compared to the behavioral sciences, and even much of the biological sciences, physics is simple in that it is nearly always possible to provide a complete and precise description of the goals, the procedures, and the conclusions of an experiment. As a result of this simplicity, experiments in physics are reproducible in a comparatively straightforward and noncontroversial way. This reproducibility provides a considerable discipline to experimental physics.

The study of physics is an endeavor conducted by human beings and is subject to the usual human frailties of dishonesty, stupidity, and carelessness, in much the same manner as other human pursuits. Experimental results in physics are accepted as the results of honest and vigorous attempts to determine the character of nature, not because physicists have many illusions about either the nobility or the infallibility of the profession, but because errors are inevitably detected and punished by the disapproval of society. Occasional cases of clearly fraudulent works have been linked to mental illness.

The problem of unconscious bias is more common and a concern of every experimental physicist. Such biases definitely have distorted broad categories of experiments, and seemingly no one can be certain that he is immune. A particular example of a type of bias that is easily illustrated is the "bandwagon effect." Experiments designed to check a prediction of a particular theory or to check the results of previous measurements are often subconsciously biased so as to agree with the predicted or previous result. The graph of Fig. 1 | 1 shows an example of data that might be presumed to be affected by such biases. The quantity measured in these investigations was the binding energy of the deuteron—the energy required to break up a deuteron into its constituents, a neutron and proton. The exact value of the energy was considered to be quite important, since it provides a rather

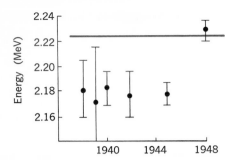

FIG. 1|1
Measured value of the binding energy of the deuteron plotted against the time of publication of the result. The solid line represents the value that is known to be correct today.

precise measure of the strength of nuclear forces. The values of the measurements, together with their assigned errors, are plotted as a function of the time when the results of the measurement were published. The solid line represents the very accurate value accepted today. It seems clear that many of the investigators were influenced by the previous values. The 1948 measurement, by Bell and Elliot in Canada, broke the hypnosis, and all subsequent measurements were near the value we accept today, which is certainly very nearly correct.

A possibly apocryphal story is told concerning an attempt to avoid this kind of bias. A well-known physicist was supposedly conducting a measurement of a fundamental constant, and his experiment was so designed that the value of the quantity he was measuring would be proportional to the length of a certain part of his apparatus. The physicist had a colleague make a precise measurement of that length and lock the results of the measurement in a safe without disclosing the result. Months later the measurement was completed and the value of the constant was determined in terms of the missing length. The experimenter then wrote the paper that described the measurement. Then, just before the paper was sent off for publication, he obtained the missing length, finished the calculation, inserted the final result, and mailed the paper, certain that, whatever other errors he had made, he was not biased by knowing the value he might expect to get.

It is often puzzling to the layman that the results of certain types of inquiries are not accepted by scientists in general. For example, the results of most psychical research, and in particular the work concerned with extrasensory perception, has met with very little acceptance. An important reason for the reluctance of the scientific community to accept these results is that the results are not simply reproducible by disinterested or hostile investigators. No experiment illustrating extrasensory perception has ever been proposed that is guaranteed to work. Some theories of extrasensory perception suggest that the interference from a hostile witness makes the perceptory channels inoperative so that extrasensory perception cannot be observed, *in principle*, by anyone who does not believe in it! Experience has taught scientists that it is a very difficult matter to conduct reliable and unbiased experiments and that, as a matter of record, only results that are subject to the discipline of reproducibility are reasonably reliable: scientists are therefore most reluctant to adopt radical postulates on the basis of weaker evidence.

Theories must also follow conventions that have been established through experience so as to require a reasonable discipline in the construction and dissemination of hypotheses. It is difficult to define a precise set of rules that is not, on occasion, usefully violated, but in general a new theory should be well defined so that precise consequences of the theory can be deduced. The consequences should not be in conflict with well established observations, and the theory should be new in that it differs from some previously accepted view and predicts some new and different result, or in that it reformulates and extends some previously accepted view. Furthermore, it is an unwritten law of the community that it is the obligation of the creator of the new idea to show that it is new and complete and that it is correct in that consequences of the theory do not violate what is already known to be true. As a matter of practice and of economics, the community has no obligation to disprove a carelessly formulated hypothesis. It is very easy to propose a radical idea; skill and effort are required to establish the consequences of the idea and to determine the relation of these consequences to the results of experiments. Most of the effort of theoretical physicists is concerned with this examination of the consequences of ideas, and not with any random generation of untested hypotheses.

Theories that do not fulfill professional requirements of completeness, logical correctness, and validity, in the sense that the obvious consequences of the theory are in accord with observation, are produced voluminously. The editor of a major physics journal can expect to receive a "crackpot" manuscript about once a week, and an established physicist can expect to receive a communication of this nature about once a month. A large number of books are published containing such theories, some of which are rather amusing. It is not uncommon for one of these to come to the attention of a reviewer, ignorant and antipathetic towards science and scientists, who reviews the book favorably. Such pseudoscience has caused only minor difficulties in most of Western society, though in the U.S.S.R. the idealistic and un-scientific genetics of Lysenko and his followers resulted in serious damage to Russian agriculture. Although science is too important to be left entirely to scientists, this does not mean that it should be turned over to fools.

1 |5   *The scale of the universe and the scale of perception*

A source of difficulty and of great interest in physics is the ex-tension in dimension that is involved. We are concerned with the very, very small and the very, very large. Both the microcosm and the macrocosm are very far from our direct experience. The whole structure of our experience, and then the whole structure of our reasoning, has been developed by considering magnitudes of things that are in our immediate sensory grasp. Our language, English, as well as most European languages, probably developed from the primitive speech of a primitive tribe that lived, perhaps, somewhere near the Elbe River in what is now Germany or Poland. This language was developed for the purpose of discuss-ing cows, women, children, the flight of game, the growth of grain, the variations of weather, and perhaps, most abstractly, the wrath of the gods. Both the vocabulary and the structure of the language limit us to things near our direct perception if we wish to discuss these things in any very precise way. We cannot expect that the structure of our language is well adapted to allow us to describe the very large and the very small, the macrocosm and the microcosm that lie so far from our immediate presence in di-mension, concisely and with precision. In order to deal with these extensions in dimension in a practical manner, it is essential that we have recourse to a carefully defined abstract logic (we use *abstract* here in a special way in which it carries the implication that we cannot rely upon intuition or common sense). Though the elements of this abstract logic (of mathematical physics) must be defined in terms of language, the whole logic represents an extension of verbal language as we know it.

The universe, which is our subject of inquiry, extends over an enormous scale of magnitude. Most of the universe is as far from our direct experience as fairyland from middle earth. And as the laws of fairyland are strange to us, and not like our laws, so is it with the laws of the very large and very small; we can understand them only through our ability to construct other, abstract, logics.

A scale is established in Fig. 1|2 that shows the relative sizes of various typical objects of our universe. On this logarithmic scale a distance of 1 unit represents a change of a factor of 10 in the mass of the object. We start at the far left with the electron, the smallest finite particular mass we know. A little more than 3 units to the right of the electron we have the proton, which has a mass about 2000 times as large as the electron. Eight units to the right, 10^8 times as heavy as an electron, is a typical large protein molecule such as DNA, the molecule that appears to be primarily responsible for the transmission of heredity. Twenty units to the right we have an ant having a mass about 10^{20} greater than that of an electron. Thirty-one units to the right we have man; 43 units to the right a typical mountain; and 54 units to the right, with a mass of 10^{54} times an electron, there is the earth. The sun has a mass of about 10^{60} times the mass of the electron; the whole galaxy, our milky way, is about 71 units to the right on our scale, and 83 units to the right, with a mass about equal to 10^{83} times that of an electron, is the whole universe as we know it.

One cannot directly perceive or determine the mass of an object if it is much more than ten times the mass of a man or if it

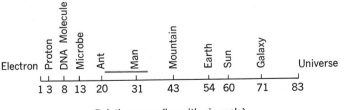

FIG. 1|2
Logarithmic scale of the masses of various objects. One unit represents a factor of 10 in mass.

is much less than one millionth of the mass of a man. As a result, all of our direct experience relates to that very small interval of magnitude suggested by the colored line in Fig. 1.2. All of our primitive concepts and ideas, and our language itself, can relate only to that small extent of mass. To consider anything larger or smaller we must extrapolate from our limited primitive experience.

The extrapolation to the macrocosm of the galaxy and to the universe as a whole is seen to be very great. It is then hardly surprising that our descriptions of the behavior of things of this magnitude are not simply accessible to us on terms of primitive ideas or even easily expressed by our primitively derived language. It should not, then, be expected that the General Theory of Relativity could be easily understood on elementary bases. It is possible that a precise statement of the General Theory of Relativity is beyond the limits of any elementary understanding. It is, then, eminently reasonable that we must extend our ideas through the use of rather abstract (that is, nonprimitive) analogies between such abstract concepts as four-dimensional space–time and concepts such as the directly perceived, and primitively accessible, geometry of three-dimensional space. Of course, these analogies must be, at best, imperfect shadows of an accurate map of reality.

For much the same reasons, we cannot properly describe the microcosm in terms of primitive ideas. We speak of the elementary subdivisions of matter as *particles* and as *waves:* they are neither particles nor waves, but in a limited way they behave a little like primitive particles and primitive waves; a little like stones and a little like ripples on the surface of a pond. We have no better words and no better language to use as a description of these entities, but we must be very careful to recognize the limitations of that language.

We can place only limited trust in language and in verbal description for still other reasons. It seems most likely that the detailed structure of the language we use influences the way we think. The grammar of English and all other Indo-European languages distinguishes quite precisely between past, present, and future in the conjugation of the verbs. Further, except for rare and generally archaic examples (such as "three days' journey from here"), English discriminates sharply between space and time. We hold the concept of an event, which takes place at a particular place at a specific time. This obviously can only have meaning only if we conceive of time and space as being completely separate. We accept the view that events at different places can take place at the same time in a well-defined and absolute way, independent of the state of any observer. Simultaneity is an absolute concept. We assume that the statement that two events have occurred at the same time but at different places is an essentially complete description of the time relation between the events. We now know that such a statement can have only a very limited validity and that the times of the two events will be different as the events are considered by different observers. This conclusion, which is deduced as a consequence of particular observations or experiments in the body of logic we call the Special Theory of Relativity, is difficult for most of us to accept intuitively. Perhaps this is connected with the character of the grammar of the languages most of us use. The claim has been made that speakers of languages that have quite different grammars—Hopi, for example—do not have such a barrier to acceptance of these conclusions from the Special Theory of Relativity.

1|6 *Dimensions and the logic of dimensional analysis*

There can be no understanding of physical phenomena, and perhaps any other phenomena, that is not quantitative. There can be no quantitative measurements without some insight into the intrinsic character or dimension of the quantities to be measured. Our primitive insights suggest to us that time, length, and mass are somehow fundamental and independent of each other. Actually, we recognize force, not mass, through direct sensory perception, but the acceleration of gravity is so constant and continual a part of our environment that the relation between the weight of an object, which is the force of gravity on the object, and its mass, which is the quantity of matter, is, considered primitively, so fundamental and invariant that it is ignored. It would appear that mass, not force, is somewhat closer to the primitive meaning of weight.

We can define length rather easily in essentially primitive terms. Once we have selected a standard unit—perhaps the length of a man's foot or the distance between the outstretched fingers and the nose of a king—we measure the length of an object in terms of the number of times we must lay out our standard to cover the distance. Time is not so easily defined. We notice that the relative readings of various natural clocks, such as the turning of the earth on its axis, the rotation of the earth about the sun, or a man's pulse, keep the same relative time. There are 365 and a fraction days in every solar year; the moon's phases recur in 28-day patterns again and again; if a man keeps his health, his pulse does not change very much from day to day or even from year to year. We might, then, choose any of these as a measure of time; but clearly we prefer clocks that belong to a set of time-keepers that always agree. We suspect that such clocks as the rotational period of the earth might have a more general significance than the pulse rate of some standard high priest. We will discuss the definition of mass later, when we construct a basis for dynamics, the description of the interaction of bodies.

As long as we deal with phenomena in which no velocity approaches the velocity of light, the simple idea that mass, length, and time can be used as the fundamental measures is correct. We can describe the character of a very large class of phenomena in terms of magnitudes of these three quantities. Certain other sets of three quantities can be used in principle; for example, force, velocity, and acceleration constitute a complete, though clumsy, set. An important reason for using mass, length, and time as fundamental units is found in the purely technical reason that it is relatively easy to set up standard measures of these three quantities for comparison in the establishment of a measurement scale. Later, for convenience, we will add electric charge to the list of basic dimensions.

All physical quantities can now be expressed in terms of the basic dimensions L for length, M for mass, and T for time. A few of the more complex quantities have obvious dimensions: area is L^2, volume is L^3, and velocity is L/T, as in miles per hour.

Important problems can be solved, and important inferences drawn, using little beyond the dimensional character of the relevant quantities. For example, is an ant stronger, relatively, than a man? Would a giant ant, out of a science-fiction novel, increased in scale to a length of ten feet, have enormous strength? No; he would be too feeble even to move. On the other hand man, decreased to a height of an inch, would wreak havoc in the insect kingdom. He would be appreciably stronger than almost any insect. We can deduce all of these from purely dimensional considerations. The strength of bone, muscle, and tendons, increases with the cross sectional area of the member. The mass of the animal increases with the volume of the animal. If the scale is held constant the strength varies as L^2, the weight as L^3, and the ratio of strength to weight varies as $1/L$. As L increases, the strength-to-weight ratio decreases. The spindly legs of the giant ant could not even hold him up. The compact frame of the Lilliputian man, with its high proportion of muscle tissue, easily equips him to withstand an insect enemy.

A less trivial but rather striking result of dimensional analysis among animals is the result concerning the height to which they can jump. It can be shown that this result should be independent of size. In fact, there is striking agreement on the height to which all animals can raise their center of gravity. It is no accident that a grasshopper, a frog, a dog, a man and a horse, can all jump about the same height. They can each raise their center of gravity about three feet.

1 | 7   *The choice of dimensional units*

It is necessary to have units of the basic quantities as an essential part of communication. With the existence of units, quantities can be expressed in terms of ratios to a standard. To the extent that the standard is universally accepted and available, the measure has a universal meaning. The statement that a man is 6 feet tall means that the ratio of the man's height to a standard measure called a "foot" is the number 6. If we have a primary, or more likely, a secondary standard available, we can deduce the height of the man knowing the unit, feet, and the ratio number, 6.

The choice of unit is essentially arbitrary. It is of primary importance that the different units of a particular dimensional measure be simply commensurate and, preferably, multiples of one another. It is of secondary importance that the ratios of the subunits be well chosen. A ratio of 10, that is, the decimal system, is most popular. Certain other ratios—6, 12, and 60—also have advantages, because there are a large number of factors in these numbers; for example, $\frac{1}{2}$, $\frac{1}{3}$, $\frac{1}{4}$, and $\frac{1}{6}$ of a unit are all integers in a scale of 12.

Ancient peoples used the cubit, which is the distance from the

elbow to the end of the extended finger, and the foot with surprising unanimity as their units of length. A cubit of 20.6 in. was
used by such disparate civilizations as the Egyptians, the Babylo-
nians, the ancient British, and the Pueblo Indians of prehistoric
New Mexico. A foot of about 11.6 in. was used in the building
of the Parthenon and in the construction of Stonehenge.

Until the end of the eighteenth century, all of the measures in
use were standardized versions of these ancient measures. The
rationalism accompanying the French Revolution then led to a
complete revision of the basic measuring system so that it rested
upon a comparatively rational basis. A basic length was established so that 10,000,000 of these lengths would reach from the
pole to the equator. This length was called the *meter.* Other
units were constructed using the meter and the properties of
water as a base. Subunits were defined using the decimal system.

This general system of units, the *metric system,* is used, for
almost all scientific work. There are several different basic ways
of using the metric system. If we exclude electrical measurements, there are two popular sets of units: the centimeter, gram,
and second, which are the basis of the *cgs system,* and the meter,
kilogram, and second, which are the basic units in the *mks system.*
There are advantages and disadvantages to each system, and
scientists sometimes feel strongly about the choice of units. The
mks system was adopted by the International Committee on
Weights and Measures in 1946, and we will use this system exclusively. The quantities used in any basic expression will be
meters (m), kilograms (kg), and seconds (sec).

The meter is now defined in terms of the length of a number of
wave lengths of monochromatic light from a particular source.
The kilogram is now defined as the mass of a standard kilogram
kept in Paris. The second is defined, now, as 1/86,400 of the
average solar day in the year 1900. In the near future the kilogram and the second will probably be redefined in terms of atomic
constants. At the moment, the relative masses of atoms and a
kilogram cannot be measured with sufficient accuracy. More
reliable measures of time than the turning of the earth are already available.

PROBLEMS

It is very important for a scientist to be able to estimate the magnitudes of quantities from the information he has available. This facility in estimation is also useful to a layman in dealing with the general problems of civilization. Using only the general information you should have available, you should be able to estimate such quantities as the following. You should be able to estimate these quantities to a factor of three. Of course there are many ways of proceeding in such estimates.

1|1   What percentage of the United States is paved?

1|2   How many gasoline service stations are there in the United States?

We seldom consider the arbitrary character of our definition of time.

1|3   Discuss the possibility that the rates of all mechanical and physiological mechanisms are speeding up. Could we detect such an effect? If not, could such a proposition have any meaning?

1|4   Assume that the universe is contracting evenly so that every natural and artificial length is reduced in size to the same extent. Could we detect such an effect? What would be the meaning of the effect if we could not detect it?

   Many interesting properties of nature can be understood to some extent solely through dimensional considerations and a little common sense. You should be able to deduce the answers to the following questions by considering the dimensional characteristics of the production and dissipation of heat by the animals. It is reasonable to assume that the production of heat will be roughly proportional to the volume or mass of the animal, while the dissipation will be proportional to the area of the skin of the animal. Although these factors are modified by differences in metabolic rate and the effect of insulation, they should be a useful guide to possible differential advantages of different sizes, and so on.

1|5   The ecological niches occupied by large fish have been invaded by warm blooded mammals such as the whales and dolphins. Why are there no small aquatic mammals?

1|6   There is some biological evidence that indigenous tropical animals tend to be taller and more slender than related arctic species. Assume that this is true and explain it on a dimensional basis.

two

*Falling bodies and
accelerated motion*

2|1 *Qualitative conclusions concerning
falling bodies*

ACCORDING TO legend, the concept that all bodies take the same
time to fall a given distance was developed by Galileo following
some experiments in which he dropped bodies of different masses
off the Leaning Tower of Pisa. The story is probably apocryphal;
there is no convincing evidence that Galileo ever dropped anything systematically from the tower, though he certainly thought
about it; and the significance of such an experiment is exaggerated in the implication that it could constitute any kind of
proof that all bodies will take the same time to fall any given
distance. If the experiment was a good deal less than has been
recorded, the ideas are a good deal more. First, as we mentioned
in Chapter 1, not all bodies fall at the same velocity or take the
same time to fall a specific distance. Feathers do fall more slowly
than coins in the real world.

Clearly we are going to have to make some kind of idealization
or simplification of this real world if we are going to reduce our
disparate experimental results, the different behaviors of different
falling objects, into any unified view. We can do this by performing a comparatively subtle experiment. We can drop a large
variety of objects from the Leaning Tower of Pisa, or some more
readily available building, and measure the time that elapses
before they hit the ground. We might then construct a graph in

which the time of fall is the ordinate and the abscissa is a property of the falling object that we will name "sectional density." We need not use any very precise definition of sectional density or even assign a numerical value to the quantity. We need only order the objects, and we can do this using only our common sense. We might order a feather, a piece of paper, a small wooden shingle, a larger wooden block, a stone about the same size as the block, and a piece of metal about the same size as the stone, in that order, and number the objects, 1, 2, 3, 4, 5, and 6, in the order in which they "feel" more dense to us.

The graph that would result might look something like that shown in Fig. 2 | 1. The very light objects take a long time to fall. The heavier objects generally take a shorter time to fall: as we increase the density of the object, the time required to hit the ground becomes smaller. But there is a limit to this trend; there comes a point of density such that the very heavy, very dense objects, even as we use the terms in a qualitative sense, all fall at the same velocity. Our general conclusion, couched in the language of modern physics, is that all objects fall at the same rate in the limit of great or infinite density. This is an important generalization that implicitly includes large varieties, or all varieties, of objects.

Other experiments can be performed to refine these ideas. For example, one can measure the time it takes for one of the lightest objects—a feather, for example—to fall a certain distance as the amount of air is reduced. This would be a test of the hypothesis

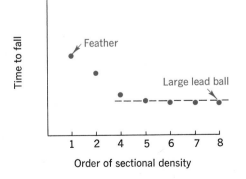

FIG. 2 | 1
The time required for a body to fall a certain distance plotted against an ordering of the sectional density.

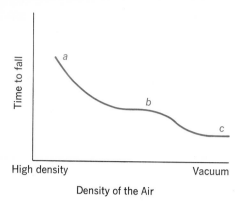

Time to fall

High density   Vacuum

Density of the Air

FIG. 2|2

The time required for a feather to fall a given distance as a function of the density of the atmosphere.

that the presence of air impeded the fall of the light bodies. The plot of Fig. 2|2 shows this time plotted as a function of the density of air, where the curve is meant to be considered only qualitatively.

This is a more complicated result than we might have anticipated. The part of the curve labeled *a* represents a region in which the feather's passage stirs up currents of air. As the density of the air is reduced, the energy dissipated in producing these currents is reduced and the feather falls faster. At the part of the curve marked *b*, the currents are no longer important; the main impedance afforded to the feather is from the viscosity or friction of the air. This friction is independent of the amount of air, or density of the air, over a wide region of densities. If our experiments were conducted only in this region of density we might come to the erroneous conclusion that the velocity of the feather is independent of the presence of the air, and that the fact that the feather falls slower than the heavy objects must result from some other cause. However, if we continue to decrease the density of the air by pumping it out of the experimental region, we will find that, at a certain point, the feather will again fall faster and finally reach the same velocity as that reached by the heaviest objects in the presence of air. We will have established that it is the air that causes the objects of small sectional density to fall slower than those that are massive. We can then restate our fundamental principle in the following form: All objects fall at the same rate in the absence of air.

2|2   *Quantitative conclusions concerning falling bodies*

Although qualitative conclusions are immensely important, it is essential to obtain a quantitative description of this phenomenon —the falling body. To understand something is to measure it.

It would seem that it would be a reasonable procedure to measure the position of a falling body as a function of elapsed time and examine the results in search of some regularity. In order to obtain the maximum generality, we consider the flight of a body (perhaps a ball) that has a certain initial velocity and initial position above the ground. We do, however, limit our discussion at this time to motion in one direction or dimension; we consider only the distance from the ground or the direction up and down. We might determine the position of the ball as a function of time by taking a time exposure of the flight of the ball in conjunction with a stroboscopic light source that flashes once a second. The resultant picture will look somewhat like the diagram of Fig. 2|3. A certain regularity is evident.

We investigate the character of the regularity by determining the position of the body every second by making measurements on the photograph and recording these positions as a function of time in Table 2|1. The first column of the table represents the time elapsed after the first flash, the second column lists the position of the body at that time. We choose 1-sec intervals for convenience; the essential results would be similar if we were to choose some other interval.

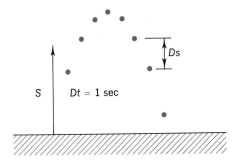

FIG. 2|3
The results of a stroboscopic time exposure of a ball in flight. The light is flashed once per second.

TABLE 2|1 *Position of the ball as a function of time together with the first and second differences of position with respect to time*

Time, t (sec)	Height, s (m)	First difference, Ds/Dt (m/sec)	Second difference, D^2s/Dt^2 (m/sec²)
0	50	—	—
$\frac{1}{2}$	—	25	—
1	75	—	−10
$1\frac{1}{2}$	—	15	—
2	90	—	−10
$2\frac{1}{2}$	—	5	—
3	95	—	−10
$3\frac{1}{2}$	—	−5	—
4	90	—	−10
$4\frac{1}{2}$	—	−15	—
5	75	—	−10
$5\frac{1}{2}$	—	−25	—
6	50	—	−10
$6\frac{1}{2}$	—	−35	—
7	15	—	−10

The third column lists the difference between adjacent values of distance recorded in the second column, divided by the time elapsed between the distance measurements, which is the difference between the times listed in the first column. We label this column Ds/Dt, where Ds represents the difference of the values of s from the second column and Dt is the difference in the values of t in the first column: Ds/Dt is the *first difference* of position with respect to time. The dimension of this quantity is L/T; in the mks system the units are meters per second (m/sec). By definition we call this the average *velocity* of the body during the time Dt.

The fourth column lists the differences between the adjacent values in the third column divided by the differences between the corresponding values of time in the first column. We call this the *second difference* of the position with respect to time. In the notation we have adopted, we could write this as $D(Ds/Dt)/Dt;$ the difference between the values of the third column $D(Ds/Dt)$ divided by the difference between the values of time in the first column Dt; here D is the symbol representing difference. It is the custom to use an abbreviated notation and write this second difference as D^2s/Dt^2; the dimensions of this quantity are L/T^2 and the units are meters per second squared (m/sec²). The meaning of the quantity is "change in the meters per second (velocity) during 1 sec." We name the quantity the average *acceleration* during the time Dt.

The most striking aspect of the table is the constant value of the second difference. If we make similar tables for a large number of heavy falling bodies projected from different initial heights with different initial velocities, the second differences will be constant in each case and, further, will have the same value: -10 m/sec². (Actually the values will be near -9.8 m/sec² and vary slightly from place to place. For our purposes, we ignore the slight variations and use the rounded-off value of -10 m/sec² for numerical convenience.) We have now a sophisticated quantitative relation that is valid for all heavy falling bodies; the second difference of height with respect to time is equal to -10 m/sec². We state this as a *difference equation*

$$\frac{D^2s}{Dt^2} = -10 \quad \text{m/sec}^2 \tag{2|1}$$

The results summarized by Eq. (2|1) are complete only if we add the information that the interval Dt was 1 sec. However, if we had made the measurements at 0.1-sec intervals, the values of the second differences D^2s/Dt^2 would be the same: -10 m/sec². Further, the values of Ds/Dt, taken at the $\frac{1}{2}$-sec intervals, would be very nearly the same as the values listed in the third column of the table. If the measurements were taken every $\frac{1}{1000}$ sec, so that Dt would be equal to $\frac{1}{1000}$ sec, the values of the first and second differences would agree with the values of Table 2|1. The solid points on the graphs of Fig. 2|4 represent the values of s, Ds/Dt, and D^2s/Dt^2 taken from the table. The solid lines can be considered to represent the loci of the points from such a table where the interval Dt was taken to be very small.

In the limit, where we take infinitesimally small time intervals for the differences, we use the term *differential* instead of *difference* and write the substance of Eq. (2|2) in a slightly different notation;

$$\frac{d^2s}{dt^2} = -10 \quad \text{m/sec}^2 \tag{2|2}$$

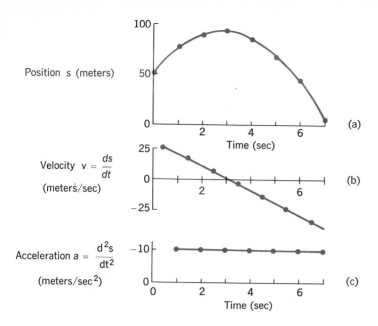

Position s (meters)

Velocity $v = \dfrac{ds}{dt}$
(meters/sec)

Acceleration $a = \dfrac{d^2s}{dt^2}$
(meters/sec^2)

FIG. 2|4
*The position, velocity,
and acceleration, of the
ball as a function of
time. The points shown
on the curves are taken
from Table 2|1.*

As Eq. (2|1) is a difference equation, Eq. (2|2) is a *differential equation*. Just as D^2s/Dt^2 and Ds/Dt are second and first differences of distance with respect to time, d^2s/dt^2 and ds/dt are second and first *differentials* of distance with respect to time. In general, a differential equation is an equation that involves relations between rates of change. We will drop the notation of using Dx and Dt for finite intervals and use dx and dt for both finite intervals and infinitesimals, assuming implicitly that we will choose such small intervals that the difference is not important. This is poor mathematics, but results in an improved simplicity of description. The solid lines of Figs. 2|4b and 2|4c then represent the values of the differentials d^2s/dt^2 and ds/dt.

Since d^2s/dt^2 is equivalent to $d(ds/dt)/dt$, and ds/dt is equal to v, the velocity, d^2s/dt^2 is equivalent to dv/dt, the rate of change of the velocity. In summary, the acceleration is the rate of change of the velocity, and the velocity is the rate of change of the position: the acceleration is then the rate of change of the rate of change of position. Of course, all changes are with respect to time.

2|3   *Differential equations*

A most obvious characteristic of the universe is that, at least on a local scale, it is not homogeneous in space or time. The character of any local environment changes with respect to changes in location and with respect to changes in time. Any attempt to describe the character of the universe must then be concerned with the character of change. In particular, relations between rates of change and other properties must be understood. The formal, or mathematical, description of any relation concerning rates of change takes a form called a *differential equation*. Even as one cannot study the character of the physical universe without considering change, one cannot engage in such a study, the study of physics, without using differential equations.

The study of the properties of differential equations in general is a part of the calculus, a specific area of mathematics introduced independently by Newton and Leibniz—although at least as far back as Archimedes specific problems of the type handled by the calculus had been considered. Although it is not important to us to gain any facility in the techniques of the calculus, nor are we in a position to study the broad properties of differential equations, it is important that we have a limited understanding of the character of a very few differential equations that are essential to the development of the most elementary understanding of the universe. Although this can be done, and often is, without mentioning the words *differential equation,* such ostrich-like behavior is not really necessary. It is not difficult to understand the character of the few differential equations that are essential to an elementary survey of physics.

It is useful to consider some of the general properties of differential equations by examining the particular situation of a particle moving a distance s as a function of time t according to some pattern that is not necessarily the pattern that describes the motion of a falling body. Instead of considering the motion of a body where the variables s and t, representing distance and time, are used to describe the possible observations, we might have analyzed a completely different kind of physical situation and been concerned with a variation of electric field with temperature, or the variation of the probability of a nuclear reaction with the energy of a bombarding particle. In any case, the character of the

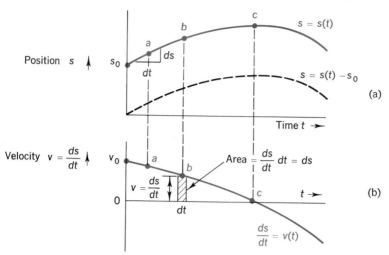

FIG. 2|5
The relations between the position and the velocity of a body moving in an arbitrary manner. Position and velocity are plotted as a function of time.

discussion and the character of the conclusions will be very much the same; all of these problems, describable as differential equations, are subject to the same logical, or mathematical, treatment. Our conclusions, then, are quite general.

We assume that the variation of the position, s, of the object with time, t, can be written in the form of an equation of the type

$$s = s(t)$$

where the symbol $s(t)$ stands for the particular variation of position with time that is determined by the physical situation. The specific form of $s(t)$ may be some simple expression in t such as

$$s = s(t) = a + bt + ct^2$$

or

$$s = a \cos bt + c \sin bt$$

where a, b, and c are constants; or the form may be much more complicated. The solid line of Fig. 2|5a is meant to represent the position of the object as a function of time according to some prescription, $s = s(t)$. The dashed line represents the same curve displaced downward on the diagram (toward lower values of the position s) by an amount s_0, the value of $s(t)$ at the time $t = 0$. The curve of Fig. 2|5b represents the slope of the curve of Fig. 2|5a as a function of time. The slope of the curve at a particular time *t* is defined as *ds/dt*, or the ratio of an infinitesimal increment of distance *ds* to the corresponding increment *dt* at the particular value of *t*. The elements of this ratio are shown graphically in the diagram of Fig. 2|5a for the particular time *t* = *a*. In this particular situation, where we are dealing with the position of a particle, *ds/dt* is the velocity of the particle. At the time *t* = *b*, where the slope of the curve of Fig. 2|5a is zero, the value of the curve of 2|5b is zero: the slope of the curve of 2|5a at the time *a* is equal to the value of the curve of 2|5b at the time *t* = a.

Even as the ordinates of Fig. 2|5b represent the slope of the curve of 2|5a, there is a converse relation: the area under the curve of 2|5b is related to the ordinates of 2|5a. Consider the shaded area of Fig. 2|5b: the height of this nearly rectangular area is equal to the ordinate of 2|5b, which is *ds/dt* at the time *t* = *c*. The width of the rectangle is equal to the time interval *dt*. The area of the rectangle is then equal to the base, *dt*, times the height, *ds/dt*, and

$$\text{Area} = \frac{ds}{dt} \, dt = ds$$

The area is equal to the change in position *ds* during the time *dt*. Then, by extension, the area under the curve between any two points or two times is equal to the distance the object travels during this time. Obviously, we can break up the total area into a large number of nearly rectangular areas as suggested in Fig. 2|6, and the total area under the curve will be equal to the sum of the areas under each individual rectangle. The sum of all of these areas will be equivalent to the sum of all of the distances traveled

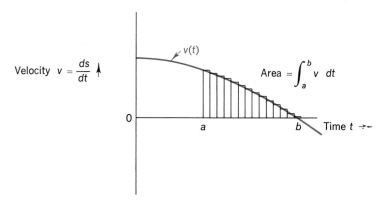

Velocity $v = \dfrac{ds}{dt}$

Area $= \displaystyle\int_a^b v \; dt$

FIG. 2|6
The velocity of a body plotted against time. The area under the curve is shown to be related to the distance the body travels. (The area under the curve from a to b is approximately equal to the total area of the rectangles.)

during all of the times dt. The sum of all of those times is obviously equal to $t_b - t_a$. Then the area under the curve of Fig. 2|5b between the times $t = a$ and $t = b$ is equal to the total distance the object traveled between these times.

We can write this relation concisely using the notation of the calculus:

$$s(b) - s(a) = \int_a^b \left(\frac{ds}{dt}\right) dt$$
$$= \int_a^b v\, dt \qquad \text{since} \quad v = \frac{ds}{dt}$$

which means that the distance the object travels from time a to time b is equal to the sum (or, for infinitesimals, the infinite sum or *integral*) of all the quantities $v\, dt$ for all of the time elements dt that make up the time between a and b. Obviously, the distance traveled between the times a and b is equal to the difference in position of the object at time b, which is $s(b)$, and the position at time a, $s(a)$.

For the simple systems that we will discuss, the notation

$$\int_b^a y\, dx$$

will always mean the area under the curve that represents the values of y as they depend on x, from the value $x = a$, to the value $x = b$.

These reciprocal relations—the slope of the curve of Fig. 2|5a, which shows the variation of s with respect to t, is equal to the value of the curve of 2|5b, which shows the variation of v or d/dt with respect to t, for any value of t; and the area under the curve of 2|5b between any two points is equal to the difference between the values of the ordinates of the curve 2|5a at these points—constitute an example that expresses the *fundamental theorem of the calculus*.

The operation of finding the slope of a curve is called *differentiation;* the operation of finding the area under a curve is called *integration*. The "fundamental theorem of the calculus," when used in the limited way that is of interest to us at this time, is an expression of the relation between the slopes, values, and areas of curves such as those of Fig. 2|5a and 2|5b, are therefore of the relations between differentiation and integration.

2|4   *Solution of the differential*
equation $\dfrac{d^2s}{dt^2} = a$

The differential equation

$$\frac{d^2s}{dt^2} = a \qquad\qquad (2\,|\,2)$$

where *s* is the position of some point, *t* is time, and *a*, the acceleration, is constant, represents the motion of any body moving with a constant acceleration equal to *a*: this is the relation that defines the character of the motion of a falling body near the surface of the earth: then the value of *a* is about equal to -10 m/sec², where *s* is height—that is, upward is taken as positive. We are interested in constructing, from Eq. (2|2), the relation between the position *s* of the body and the time *t*. This relation will represent the *solution* of the differential equation. It is particularly convenient to develop this relation, and some further relations, using graphical analyses of the sort suggested by the previous section.

The variation of acceleration (d^2s/dt^2 or dv/dt) with time, as defined by Eq. (2|2), is displayed by the graph of Fig. 2|7. We can express the change in velocity, *dv*, in a very short time, *dt*, as

$$dv = \frac{dv}{dt}\, dt$$

which is equal to the area of the small shaded rectangle in Fig. 2|7, where the height of the rectangle is dv/dt and the width is *dt*. The change in velocities over larger times, such as the change from the velocity at the time zero, which we label v_0, to the velocity at *any* later time *t*, which we label simply as *v*, will be equal

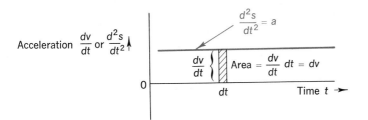

FIG. 2|7
The acceleration of a body moving with constant acceleration plotted against time. The velocity is equal to the area under the curve.

to the sum of the areas of rectangles that occupy the area under the curve from 0 to t, and is then equal to the area under the curve from 0 to t. That area is equal to

$$\frac{dv}{dt}(t-0) = \frac{dv}{dt}t$$
$$= at$$

and the general expression for the variation of velocity with time for a point moving with constant acceleration a is

$$v = v_0 + at \qquad\qquad (2 | 3)$$

Knowing the variation of the velocity with respect to time, we can now determine the position of the particle as a function of time by using the same kind of analysis that allowed us to determine the velocity from a knowledge of the acceleration. The result, Eq. (2|3), which expressed the variation of velocity with respect to time, is shown on the graph of Fig. 2|8. Since the acceleration was constant, the slope of the curve is constant; that is, the curve is a straight line. Recalling that the velocity v is defined as ds/dt, we see that the distance ds that the particle travels in a very short time dt can be expressed as

$$ds = \frac{ds}{dt}dt = v\,dt$$

which is equal to the area of a rectangle with height v and width dt. The change in position of the particle over larger times, such as the change from the position at time zero, which we write as s_0, to the position at any later time t, which we write simply as s, will be equal to the area under the curve from time 0 to t.

The calculation of the area is made by dividing the area under the curve into two parts; the area of a rectangle of the height v_0

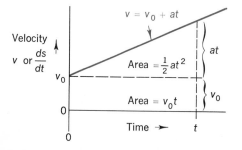

Velocity
v or $\dfrac{ds}{dt}$

$v = v_0 + at$

Area $= \frac{1}{2}at^2$

Area $= v_0 t$

at

v_0

Time $\longrightarrow$ t

FIG. 2|8

The velocity of a body moving with constant acceleration plotted against time. The distance the body moves is determined from the area under the curve.

and of length t, and the area of the triangle which lies upon the rectangle. Since the height of the rectangle is v_0 and the length of the rectangle is t, the area of the rectangle is just $v_0 t$. The area of the triangle is calculated using the relation that the area is equal to one-half the length of the base times the altitude. The base is t, the altitude is at, where a is the acceleration, and the area is then $\frac{1}{2}at^2$. The distance that the particle has moved, $s - s_0$, is equal to the sum of the two areas and

$$s - s_0 = v_0 t + \tfrac{1}{2} at^2$$

or

$$s = s_0 + v_0 t + \tfrac{1}{2} at^2 \tag{2|4}$$

Here the first term represents the position of the particle at time zero, the second term represents the distance the particle would have traveled if the initial velocity v_0 had not changed, and the third term represents the increased distance the particle traveled resulting from the acceleration.

In the treatment of this section we started with the relation of Eq. (2|2) expressing the value of the acceleration and showed that Eqs. (2|3) and (2|4), describing the variation of velocity and position with time, followed logically from the knowledge of the acceleration expressed in (2|2). This reverses the original discussion of Section 2|2, where we started with the positions of the body—essentially the results of Eq. (2|4)—and derived our knowledge of the velocity and acceleration. Indeed, any two of the three equations can be deduced from the third.

Although Eqs. (2|2), (2|3), and (2|4) are the basic equations concerning accelerated motion, it is convenient to add here an important auxiliary equation: the equation formed by eliminating the time between Eqs. (2|3) and (2|4). Equation (2|3) relates the velocity at any time to the initial velocity and the acceleration. Equation (2|4) relates the distance at any time to an initial distance, an initial velocity, and the acceleration. We would like to construct an equation that relates distance, velocity, and acceleration, but does not contain time explicitly. From Eq. (2|3), $v = v_0 + at$, we have

$$t = \frac{v - v_0}{a}$$

We substitute for t in Eq. (2|4) and obtain

$$s = s_0 + \frac{v_0(v - v_0)}{a} + \frac{\frac{1}{2}(v - v_0)^2}{a}$$

With a little algebraic simplification,

$$2a(s - s_0) = v^2 - v_0^2 \tag{2|5}$$

These results, expressed in Eqs. (2|2)–(2|5) describe the *kinematic* properties of any body undergoing constant acceleration in a straight line, irrespective of the source of the motion. The term *kinematics* refers to the characteristics of motion independent of the origin of the forces causing or initiating the motion.

Equations (2|3) and (2|4) can be considered to be the solutions of the differential equation (2|2), though any two of the relations follows from the third: the three equations are essentially equivalent logically. Even as they represent logical relations, the equations are valid independent of the physical character of the variables s and t. We will use these relations, then, to describe other physical phenomena; phenomena where motion, per se, is not involved. This is the first of three differential equations we will consider in our description of physical phenomena. For mnemonic reasons, and for easy reference, we will label this set of equations as DE-CA, for the Differential Equations representing Constant Acceleration.

2|5   *Boundary conditions*

It is important to notice that even a complete knowledge of ds/dt, the rate of change of position with respect to time, does not allow us to determine completely the variation of distance with time. The solid and dashed curves of Fig. 2|5a both have the same slope at every point, and the value of that slope is represented correctly by the single curve of Fig. 2|5b, which shows the slope as a function of time. The two curves of 2|5a and 2|5b differ only by a constant. In general, the knowledge of the rate of change of a quantity determines an infinite family of variations of the quantity with time; the members of this family are differentiated by different values of one constant.

We can understand this easily enough by considering simple physical situations such as position of a body traveling on a one-dimensional manifold with constant velocity. If we know that an automobile is traveling west on the Pennsylvania Turnpike at a constant velocity of 60 mph, we will still not know the position of the car at any particular time unless we have the position at some particular time. If, for example, we know that it passed Exit 18, near Harrisburg, at 9:00 a.m. on some particular day, we can figure out where it was at any other time during the trip. We needed one more piece of information—the constant, or time it passes by Exit 18—to differentiate that trip from an infinite number of other possible trips. Since this extra information very often relates to a boundary of the problem—in the case of the trip, when the car left its original location or when it reached its destination—these extra conditions are usually called *boundary conditions*.

The measurements made on the falling body that were tabulated in Table 2 | 1 refer to a particular situation. As far as the investigator is concerned, he came upon the situation at a time set at zero according to his clock. At this time the body was at a height of 50 meters from the ground and was traveling upward with a velocity of about 30 m/sec (we extrapolate from the first value in the table, which is 25 m/sec at a mean time of about $\frac{1}{2}$ sec). We call these values *initial conditions* or, more generally, *boundary conditions* because they represent conditions at the boundary of the problem; in this case, the boundary at time $t = 0$. If we had observed some different object propelled with a different velocity from a different height at a different time, the boundary conditions would be different, but the acceleration would be the same; Eq. (2 | 2) would still hold. There is an infinite number of initial velocities, initial positions, and initial times. Further, we can also define the problem by observing the velocity and position of the object at the end of some period of time, or at a time that is neither at the beginning or end of some period of interest. There is an infinite number of possible velocities and positions at an infinite variety of times possible for a body in free fall under the influence of the earth's gravitational field. But in all cases, the acceleration will be the same. It is essential that we be able to select the general and to discard that which is special. We will find that in much of physics, as well as in this rather trivial case, this means discarding the boundary conditions and extracting the relation between rates of change—the differential equation.

Boundary conditions are only unimportant if the basic relation is independent of the conditions, or *invariant* with respect to that parameter. The acceleration of gravity is independent of time, so the absolute value of the time is not of fundamental importance; the acceleration of gravity near the surface of the earth is independent of height, so the absolute value of the height is not of fundamental importance; the acceleration of gravity is independent of the velocity of the object, so the absolute value of the velocity is not important. In other words, the acceleration of gravity is (in the approximation we are using for this example) invariant with respect to time, height, or velocity. The selection of the general from the mass of particular data, which is so important to us in physics, thus demands a considerable attention to the invariances of nature.

2 | 6   The dimensional consistency of equations

The quantities distance, velocity, and acceleration, as well as having quantitative values, have specific dimensions. Distance has a dimension of length. Area has a dimension of length squared. We measure area, for example, in square feet as we measure distance in feet. Volume has a dimension of length cubed: we of course measure volume in cubic feet or the cube of some other length. Velocity has dimensions of length divided by time: we talk about feet per second, meters per second, miles per hour, kilometers per hour. Acceleration is the change in velocity per unit time and has, then, dimensions of length divided by time squared. The acceleration of gravity at the surface of the earth is about 32 ft/sec^2. If we look at Eq. (2|3) or Eq. (2|4), we find that the dimensions of all the terms of the equations are the same. For example, in Eq. (2 3) we note that the quantity v on the left of the equals sign, the velocity, has dimensions of length divided by time L/T. The first term on the right of the equals sign, which is the velocity at time zero, also has dimensions of length divided by time, L/T. The second term to the right of the equals sign, representing the acceleration times time, also has dimensions of length divided by time. (The acceleration has dimensions of length divided by time squared, L/T^2, which, multiplied by time, is then just length divided by time L/T.) The equation, then, is dimensionally consistent. Equation (2|4) is also dimensionally consistent. We have, on the left-hand side of the equals sign, s, which has a dimension of distance, L; the first

term on the right hand side—the distance at time equals zero—
is also of course a distance, L. The second term $v_0 t$ also has the
dimension distance, as does the third term, $\frac{1}{2}at^2$.

Although it is not essential that all relations be dimensionally
consistent, relationships that are dimensionally consistent are
more general than those that are not. For example, let us consider a possible particular situation in which we find by the course
of measurement of a falling body under a specific condition that
the distance traveled in feet is equal to the time in seconds. We
could then define this condition by the equation $s = t$. If there is
no initial velocity or initial displacement, we can solve the equa-
tion for the value of t: since s is equal to $\frac{1}{2}at^2$ and $t = s$, t is equal
to $2/a$. If the acceleration is 32 ft/sec², we find that t is equal to
$\frac{1}{16}$ sec. But this is true only in the English system of units. Consider the same equation in the metric system of units, where a
is equal to 10 m/sec². In this case t, equal to $2/a$, is equal to $\frac{1}{5}$ sec.
The results of our equation are not the same if the units are
changed; thus, the equation is not invariant under a change in
units. This equation, then, cannot be any very general representation of a property of our universe. The results are dependent
upon our choice of units, and our choice of units is determined
more by social and historical processes than physical processes.
The dimensionally consistent relations, such as Eqs. (2|3), (2|4),
and (2|5), are independent of the choice of units. These equations
are valid in the English system or in the mks system, which we
use in this course, or in any other consistent unit of units. In
physics we concern ourselves almost exclusively with dimensionally consistent equations. As a calculational aid, it is very useful
to carry the units through the calculation; certain classes of
errors are avoided by doing this.

The dimensional relations between quantities can be used
themselves to give some insight into the solutions of certain
difficult problems. We can illustrate this by considering a problem that is not difficult; one we have just solved in detail—that
is, the problem of the distance traversed by a body under constant
acceleration. Let us assume we do not know the exact relation
between distance, acceleration, and time, but wish to know the
general way in which the distance will vary with time. We have
these quantities at our disposal: distance, acceleration, and time.
We want to construct an equation of the type "distance is equal
to a function of the acceleration and time." The dimension on

the left-hand side of the equation will then be length. We must therefore construct a quantity with the dimension length out of the two quantities acceleration and time. The dimensions of acceleration are L/T^2, length over time squared, and the dimension of time is, of course, T. From these we must construct a combination, or function, with the dimension L. The only simple combination that satisfies this requirement is at^2, with the dimensions $(L/T^2)T^2 = L$. This suggests that the relation will likely have the form

$$s \propto at^2$$

This suggests that the displacement of a body under constant acceleration will vary with the square of the time and linearly with the value of acceleration. These correct conclusions were drawn wholly from the dimensional properties of the quantities.

PROBLEMS

2|1   An automatized explorer rocket lands upon a small moon of a distant planet. A device shoots a ball straight upwards from the surface of the airless planet while a camera photographs the ball once a second. The camera breaks down and takes only three photographs: the first shows the ball 9 meters above the surface, the second shows the ball 16 meters above the surface, and the third shows the ball 21 meters high.

(*a*) What is the value of the acceleration of gravity on the moon?

(*b*) How high did the ball go?

(*c*) What was the initial velocity of the ball?

2|2   The graph represents the reading of an automobile speedometer as a function of time. (The values are given in meters per second for convenience.)

(*a*) Draw a graph showing the acceleration as a function of time.

(*b*) Calculate the total distance traveled in the 700 sec.

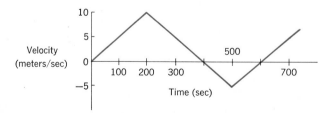

2|3 Take the acceleration of gravity at the earth's surface as $g = -10$ m/sec². A ball is thrown upward from the ground with an initial velocity of 20 m/sec.

(*a*) How high will the ball go?

(*b*) What will be the value of the velocity of the ball when the ball is at its highest point?

(*c*) What will be the value of the acceleration when the ball is at its highest point?

(*d*) What will be the value of the velocity just before the ball hits the ground?

(*e*) How long will the ball be in the air?

2|4 A toy rocket is launched so that the rocket shoots straight up in the air. The motor of the rocket is designed so that it gives the rocket a constant acceleration with respect to the ground of 20 m/sec². The motor runs for 5 sec and then shuts off. The air resistance is negligible.

(*a*) How high is the rocket when the motor shuts off?

(*b*) How fast is it going when the motor shuts off?

(*c*) How long does it continue to travel upward?

(*d*) How high does it go?

(*e*) How fast is it going when it strikes the earth?

(*f*) How much time elapses between the time it takes off and the time it lands?

2|5 A rocket is designed to operate so that the acceleration of the rocket increases linearly with time according to the relation $a = a_0 + kt$ where a_0 is the acceleration at the time the main rocket motor is turned on and k is a constant. Write an equation that expresses the variation of the velocity of the rocket with respect to time.

2|6 (*a*) Two balls are thrown into the air at the same time, with the same initial velocity of 100 m/sec. One ball is thrown from the ground and one from a height of 20 m. Which ball will strike the ground first? How high will the second ball be at the time the first ball hits the ground?

(*b*) Two balls are released at the same time from the top of the Empire State Building, which is about 300 m high. One ball is given an initial velocity of 10 m/sec downward, and the other is given a velocity of 10 m/sec upward. What will be the difference between the velocities of the balls at the time the first ball hits the ground?

2|7 (Dimensional Analysis) The acceleration of a body oscillating as a result of the force exerted by a spring can be measured and shown to have the form $a = -kx$, where a is the acceleration, x is the displacement from the equilibrium position, and k is a constant depending upon the stiffness of the spring and the mass of the body. How will the time of oscillation depend upon the value of k?

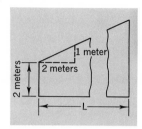

2|8 A series of wooden sections are cut following the pattern shown in the diagram, but of varying lengths L. If the wood weighs 10 kg/m², express the weight of the sections as a function of the length L.

2|9 (Dimensional Analysis) Neglecting air resistance, the distance that a mortar shell will travel depends on the angle of inclination θ, the muzzle velocity v, and the acceleration of gravity g. Angles have no dimension; they are numbers. If the muzzle velocity is doubled, how much will the range change? If the acceleration of gravity were $\frac{1}{6}g$, as on the moon, what would be the effect on the range?

2|10 (*a*) Engineers are considering diverting a river into a reservoir. The flow of the river in gallons per day has been measured for an average year and is shown on graph (a). If the river is diverted into the reservoir on January 1 and the year is average, how much water will flow into the reservoir during the year? Assuming evaporation to be negligible, draw a graph showing the contents of the reservoir in gallons as a function of time during the next year. (An accuracy of about 20 percent is sufficient.)

(*b*) A river has been diverted to a reservoir on January 1. The contents of the reservoir in gallons have been measured during the year and are shown on graph (b). Draw a graph of the flow of the river in gallons per day as a function of time during the year. (Again an accuracy of 20 percent is adequate).

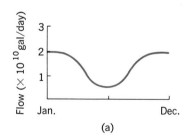

(a)

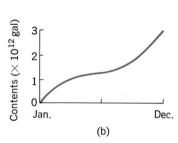

(b)

three *Scalars, vectors,*
and covariance

3 | 1 *Scalars, vectors, and tensors*

IN THE PREVIOUS chapter we emphasize the importance of the classification of physical quantities according to their dimensions. Further, we showed that it is necessary that any expression (that is, equation) that is designed to represent a general relation between physical quantities must be dimensionally consistent if it is to have a meaning independent of the choice of units; a choice that is always largely arbitrary. It is equally important that we classify quantities according to the precise way in which their description depends on the "viewpoint" of the observer who measures the quantities. We use *viewpoint* here in a narrow sense; for the problems we consider in this chapter, the different views will be limited to the use of variously oriented coordinate systems or maps by the observers. When we consider the Special Theory of Relativity we will also discuss the relations between measurements made by observers moving with different velocities.

To illustrate the classification of various quantities, let us examine the observations made by two observers who have summarized their measurements by constructing different maps of the northeastern part of the United States (Fig. 3 | 1). Let us assume that one surveyor defined north as the direction toward the North Pole, while the other used a magnetic compass bearing, made while he was in Boston, to define north. Although we usually adopt the convention that north is the direction towards

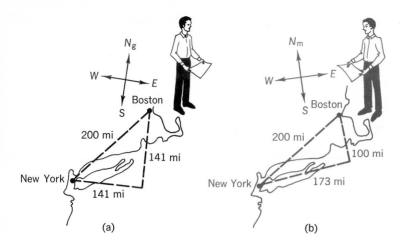

FIG. 3|1
A map showing the distance between New York and Boston using two different coordinate systems: (a) using geographic north; (b) using magnetic north.

the geographic North Pole, neither convention is wrong—both are admissible. The two maps then differ in the orientation of their coordinate system; magnetic north will lie about 15° west of polar north.

On each map the distance between New York and Boston will be 200 mi. The two surveyors will have measured the distance to be the same, though they have used different coordinate systems. In general, the distance measured between any two points is independent of, or invariant with respect to, the orientation of the coordinate system. Quantities that are described in a manner independent of the orientation of the coordinate system of the observer are called *scalars*. Only one number, in this case 200, is necessary to define the magnitude of a scalar.

According to the map that uses geographic north, Boston is 200 mi northeast of New York; or more precisely, Boston is 200 mi from New York in a direction that is 45° east of north. The direction is 60° east of north according to the other map, which uses the magnetic system implicitly. Using a Cartesian coordinate system and the map that uses geographic north, we find Boston to be 141 mi north and 141 mi east of New York. From the other map, using magnetic north, Boston is 100 mi north and 173 mi east of New York. The description of the relative position of the two points is different in the two coordinate systems in that the two numbers used to describe the quantity are different. It is reasonably obvious that the two descriptions are rationally related to each other and to the angle that defines the difference between the two coordinate systems. Quantities that have this character are called *vectors*. Relative position is a vector. Two numbers are required to describe a vector in a two-dimensional space: in this case, the distance north and the distance east, or the total distance and the direction angle. Three numbers are required to describe a vector in a three-dimensional space: for example, distance north, east, and up. Four numbers are needed in a four-dimensional space, and so on.

For the sake of completeness we introduce a third class of quantities that require a more complicated description. For this purpose we adopt the conventional mathematical labels x and y for the coordinate system. Figure 3|2a shows a square of rubber with two arbitrarily selected points a and b marked on the rubber. The relative position of b with respect to a is a vector that we describe by the two numbers s_x and s_y, where s_x is the distance of b from a in the x-direction and s_y is the distance in the y-direction. Figure 3|2b shows the same piece of rubber now distorted by some stress. The relative position of the two points is now different and the new relative-position vector is described by the new numbers s'_x and s'_y. The two sets of numbers, the results of two sets of measurements, are related by a set of equations.

$$s'_x = u_{xx}s_x + u_{xy}s_y$$

$$s'_y = u_{yx}s_x + u_{yy}s_y$$

If the square of rubber is small enough (presumably it is part of a large sheet that is stretched), the four numbers u_{xx}, u_{xy}, u_{yx}, and u_{yy} are the same for any pair of points and then completely represent the distortion in the rubber at the position of the small square. In this case the distortion represents a combination of stretch (or strain) and rotation of the square. Such a set of four numbers is called a *tensor*.

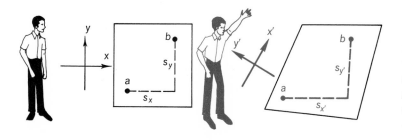

FIG. 3|2
The relative position of two nearby points on a piece of rubber before and after the rubber is stretched.

The particular values of the components of the tensor, the numbers u, depend upon the choice of coordinate system. If we had chosen to describe the situation using a coordinate system that was rotated, such as that labelled x'' and y'' in Fig. 3|2, the numbers s and s' defining the vectors and the numbers u describing the tensor would all be different. The physical situation would be unchanged, and we can be confident that the change in the numbers depends upon the angle between the coordinate systems in some rational way.

In three dimensions a tensor of this character is described by nine numbers, in four dimensions by sixteen numbers, and so on. There are also quantities that require even more complicated descriptions, such as tensors of third order, which require eight numbers for a description in two dimensions. We will not concern ourselves with quantities more complex than vectors.

3|2 *The arithmetical properties of vectors*

In the previous section the relative-position vector was described in two different ways: both a polar coordinate system and a Cartesian coordinate system were used. There are many coordinate systems that have particular advantages for specific problems: we will limit our discussions primarily to the Cartesian system for simplicity. Furthermore, we will no longer use the labels north, south, east, and west, but instead will use the

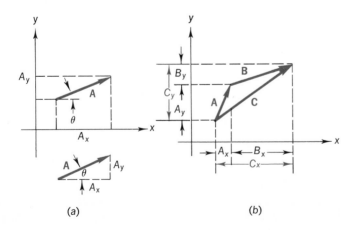

(a) (b)

FIG. 3|3
(a) *The resolution of a vector into components.*
(b) *The addition of vectors* **A** *and* **B** *to form the vector* **C**.

more usual algebraic labels x, y, and z. Again in the interests of maximum simplicity, we will use only two-dimensional vectors for most of our illustrations; the three- and four-dimensional extension are generally obvious. Since directed lines on a plane piece of paper are two-dimensional vectors (representing the vector distance between the two ends of the line), we will often represent other vectors graphically as lines on paper.

Figure 3|3 shows a typical vector, which we label **A**. Bold-faced type will be used for vectors when we intend to emphasize or make special use of their vector properties: thus **A** will represent the vector, while A will represent the magnitude of the vector when the vector property is irrelevant.

Perpendiculars dropped from the ends of the vector **A** define intervals on the axes, which are labeled A_x and A_y: these are the *components* of the vector: they are positive if the perpendicular from the end of the vector (shown as the head of an arrow) falls at a larger value of the coordinate than the perpendicular from the beginning of the vector (the tail of the arrow). This is the case for the components of **A** in Fig. 3|3; both components are positive. This procedure is called *resolving a vector into its components*. As a matter of notation, it is sometimes convenient to signify a vector as $\mathbf{A}(A_x, A_y)$, listing the components specifically.

The components can be expressed in terms of the length of the vector and the angle the vector makes with the x-axis, which is an implicit use of a polar coordinate system.

$$A_x = A \cos \theta \qquad \text{and} \qquad A_y = A \sin \theta$$

where A is the length of the vector. One can also calculate the length of the vector in terms of its components by using the Pythagorean theorem. We see that we can consider **A** as the hypotenuse of the right triangle in which A_x and A_y are the sides. Then,

$$A^2 = A_x{}^2 + A_y{}^2$$

Vectors can be added and subtracted: more precisely, there are operations involving two or more vectors that are very much like the operations of addition and subtraction as applied in ordinary arithmetic. There are also several operations that have a character similar to that of multiplication. The addition of two vectors, $\mathbf{A}(A_x, A_y)$ and $\mathbf{B}(B_x, B_y)$, follows the rule

$$\mathbf{A}(A_x, A_y) + \mathbf{B}(B_x, B_y) = \mathbf{C}(C_x, C_y)$$

where

$$C_x = A_x + B_x \quad \text{and} \quad C_y = A_y + B_y$$

The vector that is the sum of the vectors **A** and **B** is the vector with components that are equal to the sum of the components of **A** and **B**. These relations are illustrated graphically in Fig. 3|3b.

The addition operation on vectors follows the associative law

$$(\mathbf{A} + \mathbf{B}) + \mathbf{C} = \mathbf{A} + (\mathbf{B} + \mathbf{C})$$

and the commutative law

$$\mathbf{A} + \mathbf{B} = \mathbf{B} + \mathbf{A}$$

These rules become almost self-evident when one considers the special case of displacement. If one walks 3 mi east and 5 mi north on the first day of a hike across a flat plane, 10 mi east and 5 mi north on the second day, and 13 mi north and 7 mi west on the third day, the total displacement is certainly the same whether we consider the first two days as the first part of the trip and add it to the last day's traverse, or consider the first day's travel alone as the first part of the trip and add to it the sum of the distances traveled on the last two days (the associative law). Similarly, the total distance and place of arrival would be the same if the mileage schedules for the three days were interchanged (the commutative law).

The subtraction of vectors, such as the relation

$$\mathbf{A} - \mathbf{B} = \mathbf{C}$$

is equivalent to the addition of a negative vector:

$$\mathbf{A} + (-\mathbf{B}) = \mathbf{C}$$

where $(-\mathbf{B})$ is the vector with components that are the negative of the components of **B**. That is, **B** is changed to $-\mathbf{B}$ by reversing the signs of the components of **B** or multiplying each component by (-1). This is just a special case of the multiplication of a vector by a scalar. The product $a\mathbf{A}$, where a is a scalar and **A** is a vector, is equal to the vector $\mathbf{A}'$, where the components of $\mathbf{A}'$ are equal to the components of **A** multiplied by a:

$$a\mathbf{A} = \mathbf{A}'$$

or

$$a\mathbf{A}(A_x, A_y) = \mathbf{A}'(aA_x, aA_y)$$

There are also two operations concerning pairs of vectors that have somewhat the character of multiplication. These will not be discussed in this section.

The rules for the addition of vectors approach our intuitive concepts closely when we consider the addition of vectors representing displacement or distance: the conclusion that 2 mi east plus 3 mi east is equal to 5 mi east is easy to accept. The conclusion that 4 mi north plus 3 mi north is equal to 7 mi north is also easy to accept. The next extension, a distance that can be represented as 2 mi east and 4 mi north added to a distance that is represented as 3 mi east and 3 mi north is equal to a distance defined as 5 mi east and 7 mi north, is then again acceptable to us on essentially primitive bases. This is just the addition of two vectors, one of which has the components 2 and 4 and the other the components 3 and 3, in a system where the coordinate labels are *north* and *east*.

It seems somehow more difficult to accept the idea that a vector is defined in such a way that the position or origin of the vector is irrelevant. The vector *15 mi northeast* is the same whether the point of origin is New York, New Haven, or Boston (disregarding the curvature of the earth). This does not imply that a 15-mile journey from the center of any of these cities is physically identical to that from any other; the vector contains only part of the information. The limitation in the definition seems a little more sensible when we discuss the vector velocity. The idea of an airplane traveling 500 mph straight down is easily pictured, independent of the precise position of the plane—though, again, the position can be physically important.

The diagrams of Fig. 3|4 partially illustrate the freedom one has in handling vectors, together with the simple graphical techniques that are available. Since displacement is a vector, any vector can be represented by a spatial displacement. The vectors

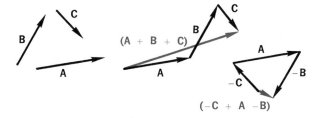

FIG. 3|4
The addition of vectors **A**, **B**, *and* **C**, *and the sum of the vectors* −**C**, **A**, *and* −**B**, *shown graphically.*

A, **B**, and **C** in Fig. 3|4 might represent velocity, electric field, momentum, or any other physical quantity that has the character of a vector. These vectors can then be added and subtracted graphically as suggested by the diagrams: to add two vectors one simply transposes one of the vectors so that the tail of the arrow representing the second vector is fitted to the head of the arrow representing the first vector. To subtract a vector one reverses the sense of the vector and adds it.

The application of the rules of vector addition to quantities such as velocity and acceleration is less obvious than for displacement. Nevertheless, velocity and acceleration are vectors. If the position of a moving body is measured at the beginning and end of a short time interval dt, the displacement, $d\mathbf{s}$, is obviously a vector. Since the velocity is the vector displacement multiplied by the scalar $(1/dt)$, the product $d\mathbf{s}/dt$ is a vector. If velocity, $\mathbf{v} = d\mathbf{s}/dt$, is a vector, a change in velocity, $d\mathbf{v}$, during a very short time interval will also be a vector. Again the vector $d\mathbf{v}$ is multiplied by a scalar $(1/dt)$; the product is an acceleration: $\mathbf{a} = d\mathbf{v}/dt$. Implicit assumptions concerning the nature of length and time are made in this discussion—assumptions that are approximately valid only for velocities that are small compared to the velocity of light. At this time we will limit our discussion to these classical (nonrelativistic) velocities.

Physically, the addition of velocity vectors is usually relevant to situations concerning observers in different natural systems. If a boy who can throw an apple with a velocity of 20 m/sec throws the apple from the bed of a truck traveling 30 m/sec with respect to the highway, the velocity of the apple with respect to an observer beside the highway will be equal to the vector sum of the velocity of the truck with respect to the highway and the velocity of the apple with respect to the truck.

From the rules concerning the addition of vectors, we see that the relation

$$\mathbf{A} + \mathbf{B} = \mathbf{C} - \mathbf{D}$$

implies that

$$A_x + B_x = C_x - D_x \qquad \text{and} \qquad A_y + B_y = C_y - D_y$$

An equation that relates two-dimensional vectors is equivalent to two equations relating the components of the vectors. In general, an equation relating N-dimensional vectors is equivalent to N equations relating the components of the vectors.

3 | 3   *The transformation properties of vectors*

We have emphasized the importance of classifying quantities according to the way their description changes as the coordinate system is changed. A quantity described in a manner that is independent of the orientation of the coordinate system is called a scalar. As the coordinate system is changed in orientation, the detailed description of a vector quantity does change; however, the changes are well defined, and they take place in a very particular way that is independent of any property of the quantity in question except that it is a vector. These changes in description are summarized in *transformation equations*, which are equations that relate the measurements of a quantity by one observer to the measurements of another observer who is using a different coordinate system.

Figure 3 | 5a shows a vector **A** in a coordinate system such that the axes are labeled x and y. Since the position of the vector is irrelevant, we can choose to put the origin of the coordinate system at the origin of the vector. Another coordinate system,

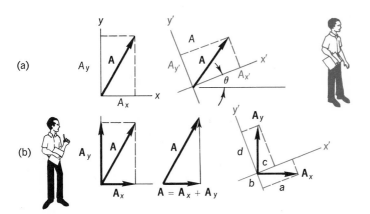

FIG. 3 | 5
(*a*) *The resolution of a vector into its components in two different coordinate systems.* (*b*) *The relation between the components of the vector in one system and the components in another system.*

labeled x' and y', is superimposed on the first system. The x', y' system differs from the x, y system by the angle of rotation θ. Since we are not concerned with the positions of points with respect to the origin, coordinate systems in a two-dimensional space can differ only by the angle of orientation. Our object is to find the relations between the description of the vector **A** by the two different observers, one using the x, y system and the other using the x', y' system. Their descriptions of the vector will differ in that they will assign different values to the components of the vector. The transformation equations we will develop will relate the components measured by one observer to the values of the components measured by the other. It is obvious from an inspection of the diagrams of Fig. 3 | 5a that the two sets of components, A_x, A_y and $A_{x'}, A_{y'}$, are related in some simple geometric manner.

Although the relations between the two sets of components can be calculated in a number of closely related ways, we choose to determine the transformation equations by analyzing the diagrams of Fig. 3 | 5b. We see that the vector **A**, with components A_x and A_y, can be considered as the sum of two vectors $\mathbf{A}_x$ and $\mathbf{A}_y$, where the x and y components of $\mathbf{A}_x$ are A_x and 0, and the components of $\mathbf{A}_y$ are 0 and A_y.

$$\mathbf{A}(A_x, A_y) = \mathbf{A}_x(A_x, 0) + \mathbf{A}_y(0, A_y)$$

This relation is illustrated by the construction of Fig. 3 | 5b.

Each of these vectors, $\mathbf{A}_x$ and $\mathbf{A}_y$, can be resolved into components in the x', y' system, as shown in Fig. 3 | 5b. Here the components of $\mathbf{A}_x$ are labeled a and b, and those of $\mathbf{A}_y$ are labeled c and d. So in the x', y' system,

$$\mathbf{A}_x = \mathbf{A}_x(a, b) \qquad \text{and} \qquad \mathbf{A}_y = \mathbf{A}_y(c, d)$$

From the geometry of the Figs. 3 | 5a and 3 | 5b,

$$a = A_x \cos \theta \qquad b = -A_x \sin \theta$$
$$c = A_y \sin \theta \qquad d = A_y \cos \theta$$

The measurements of the vectors $\mathbf{A}_x$ and $\mathbf{A}_y$ in terms of their components in the two coordinate systems are then related as

$$\mathbf{A}_x(A_x, 0) \rightarrow \mathbf{A}_x(a, b) = \mathbf{A}_x(A_x \cos \theta, -A_x \sin \theta)$$
$$\mathbf{A}_y(0, A_y) \rightarrow \mathbf{A}_y(c, d) = \mathbf{A}_y(A_y \sin \theta, A_y \cos \theta)$$

In the primed coordinate system, the vector **A** will be represented by two components: $\mathbf{A} = A(A_x, A_y)$. Since the relation $\mathbf{A} = \mathbf{A}_x + \mathbf{A}_y$ will be valid in any coordinate system, including the primed coordinate system, the components of **A** will be equal to the sum of the components of $\mathbf{A}_x$ and $\mathbf{A}_y$ in any coordinate system. In the primed coordinate system this leads to

$$A_{x'} = A_x \cos \theta + A_y \sin \theta$$
$$A_{y'} = -A_x \sin \theta + A_y \cos \theta$$

$$(3\,|\,1)$$

These equations represent the relations between the description of any vector **A** in the x, y coordinate system and the description in the x', y' coordinate system. The equations are called *transformation equations;* they describe the transformation of the components of the vector as the coordinate system is rotated. It is useful to consider that they represent the relation between observations or measurements made by an observer using one coordinate system (and written down in his notebook) with the measurements (and records) of another observer using a different coordinate system.

Equations (3 | 1) can be solved for the inverse transformation:

$$A_x = A_{x'} \cos \theta - A_{y'} \sin \theta$$
$$A_y = A_{x'} \sin \theta + A_{y'} \cos \theta$$

$$(3\,|\,2)$$

The form is the same as Eqs. (3 | 1) except that θ goes to $-\theta$, since the angular difference between the two systems is now in the opposite direction.

We now have a more complete definition of a vector: in a two-dimensional Cartesian coordinate system, a vector is a set of two numbers that transform into each other under a rotation of the coordinate system. More generally, a vector in an N-dimensional space is a set of N numbers that transform into each other according to transformation equations that depend upon $N - 1$ parameters. A vector in three dimensions is thus a set of three numbers, for which the transformation equations contain two parameters that can be considered to correspond to two angles of rotation in the three-dimensional space.

3|4   *Affine coordinate systems*

Not all sets of numbers are vectors. Consider the three-dimensional position of a point in the United States, such as the peak of a mountain. We can define this position by the latitude, longitude, and height, which are essentially an x coordinate, y coordinate, and a perpendicular z coordinate. The three numbers will represent components of a vector in a three-dimensional coordinate system. A relief map presents such a three-dimensional coordinate system. However, we may also have a very similar map in which we present the latitude, the longitude, and the temperature or the barometric pressure. The three numbers that represent the barometric pressure at a particular point—the value of the latitude, the value of the longitude, and the value of the barometric pressure—do not represent the components of a vector. We see that this is the case because they do not transform into one another under a change of coordinate systems. Latitude, longitude, and height can be represented, though inconveniently, in a coordinate system such as is shown in Fig. 3|6, where the coordinates make some angle with the earth's surface. In this case the old latitude will be some linear combination of the new latitude, the new longitude, and the new height. The old height will again be a linear combination of the new latitude, new longitude, and new height. The distance between two points is invariant under this change of coordinate system and will then be the same in the two coordinate systems.

We cannot do the same thing for latitude, longitude, and barometric pressure. We cannot conceive of any sensible coordinate system in which our new latitude would be a function of the old latitude, longitude, and barometric pressure. Barometric pressure is an entirely different kind of quantity than latitude or longitude: it does not have a dimension of length; it cannot follow transfor-

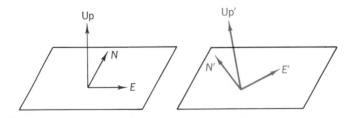

FIG. 3|6
A normal three-dimensional coordinate system and a rotated coordinate system.

mation equations in any meaningful fashion; the distance between two points has no meaning. So the set of three numbers, latitude, longitude, and barometric pressure, does not make up a vector. The coordinate system is very useful, but it does not admit the construction of vectors. Such a coordinate system is called an *affine* coordinate system.

Most of the vectors that concern us in classical mechanics can be completely described by stating the magnitude and direction of the quantity. This is implicitly a description of the vector in a polar coordinate system. The inverse statement "A quantity that has a magnitude and a direction is a vector" must be used with care. A 110-lb woman traveling south is not a vector. Although observers who are differently oriented may note different aspects of the girl, the relations between these different observations will be more complex than those suggested by the transformation equations (3|1).

3|5 *Covariance*

We will emphasize the importance of the various symmetries of the universe. It appears that, aside from purely local effects, observers moving at different velocities view the universe in the same way; observers at different places view the universe in the same way; observers view the universe the same way at different times; and observers who look in different directions or use coordinate systems that are differently oriented see very much the same thing. Any general description of the universe must therefore be independent of the velocity and position of the observer, and must not depend upon the time of the observations or the directions chosen to define the coordinate system. Any general relations, or equations, must then be independent of the choice of coordinate system.

By requiring that all general equations be dimensionally consistent, we found that we could write equations that are valid or invariant regardless of the choice of units. Our equations for accelerated motion are dimensionally consistent and therefore are equally valid for the metric system, the English system, or any other system of consistent units. A general relation or equation should also be invariant with respect to the choice of coordinate system. The separate quantities in the equation must then transform in the same way under the operation of changing the coordinate system. Therefore, we are restricted to general relations between scalars and scalars and between vectors and vectors, and also, for completeness, relations between quantities with more complex transformation properties, which we called tensors.

When all of the terms of an equation transform in the same way, we say that the equation is *covariant*. Equations that are not covariant can be useful and correct, but they are generally valid in only one particular coordinate system. For example, we might state that a ball, in free fall near the surface of the earth, will fall straight "down" with an acceleration of 10 m/sec². If we adopt a standard coordinate system such that the direction "up" is labeled y, as suggested by the sketch of Fig. 3|7, we can state the relation a little more elegantly by writing

$$a_y = g \tag{3|3}$$

where g is a constant equal to -10 m/sec². The quantity a_y is a component of a vector. Let us assume that the observations are made by an observer in Peoria, Illinois, and then that the coordinate system is set up so that the y-direction is "up" at Peoria. Then the description of falling bodies expressed by Eq. (3|3) is hardly adequate for observers in Montevideo or in Osaka, where the y-direction, up in Peoria, no longer represents up in Osaka.

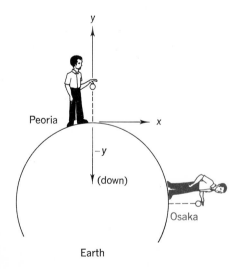

FIG. 3|7
Coordinate systems used by observers at different places on the earth.

However, if we represent the relation describing the acceleration of falling bodies as

$$\mathbf{a} = \left(\frac{g}{r}\right)\mathbf{r} \tag{3|4}$$

where a is the vector acceleration, r is the magnitude of the radius of the earth and $\mathbf{r}$ is the vector distance between the center of the earth and the observer, we will have a relation that is correct and meaningful to any observer, be he a resident of Osaka, of Montevideo, or of Peoria, Illinois. Now we say, covariantly, the ball falls with an acceleration of 10 m/sec² toward the center of the earth. Equation (3|4) is a covariant relation between the vectors $\mathbf{a}$ and $(g/r)\mathbf{r}$; Eq. (3|3), which singles out one component of a vector, is not covariant and is therefore valid only in one coordinate system.

The relation between the importance of covariant expressions and the existence of symmetries in nature is made apparent by this example. If the universe were intrinsically anisotropic, there would be important descriptions of nature that would depend upon the values of specific components of a vector, and covariant descriptions of such phenomena would not be useful or even possible. If we restrict ourselves to a universe that consists only of a small region on the surface of the earth, such as a laboratory, that universe is definitely anisotropic; down is definitely different from up or north or east. The correct description of the effects of gravity that states that all bodies fall "down" will not hold for the observer who uses a map such that the coordinate system is rotated and down is replaced by east.

In the whole universe, as we know it, isotropy rules and observers using differently oriented maps are equivalent. This symmetry is contained or expressed by the covariance of general descriptions of nature. Each term in such a covariant relation must have the same transformation properties.

We might now consider the transformation properties of the equations we used to describe uniformly accelerated motion: can these equations be written in a covariant form? Equations (2|2), (2|3), and (2|4) were developed to describe motion in one direction and are thus valid for each direction separately. If a body accelerates in an arbitrary direction, we can consider motion in an x-direction and in a y-direction separately: that is,

$$s_x = s_{0x} + v_{0x}t + \tfrac{1}{2}a_xt^2 \quad \text{and} \quad s_y = s_{0y} + v_{0y}t + \tfrac{1}{2}a_yt^2 \quad (3\,|\,5)$$

where s_x and s_{0x} represent displacements in the x-direction, v_{0x} is the initial velocity in the x-direction, and a_x is the acceleration in the x-direction. The quantities in the y-direction. It is easily seen that s_x and s_y are the components of a vector $\mathbf{s}$, s_{0x} and s_{0y} are the x- and y-components of the vector $\mathbf{s}_0$, and similarly v_{0x} and v_{0y}, and a_x and a_y, are the components of vectors $\mathbf{v}_0$ and $\mathbf{a}$. Since time, t, is a scalar, independent of the orientation of the coordinate system, and since a scalar times a vector is a vector, the products $v_{0x}t$ and $v_{0y}t$, and $\tfrac{1}{2}a_xt^2$ and $\tfrac{1}{2}a_yt^2$, are the components of the vectors $\mathbf{v}_0t$ and $\tfrac{1}{2}\mathbf{a}t^2$. Then from our discussion of the relations between the additions of the components of vectors and the addition of vectors, we can write the covariant vector relation

$$\mathbf{s} = \mathbf{s}_0 + \mathbf{v}_0t + \tfrac{1}{2}\mathbf{a}t^2 \tag{3\,|\,6}$$

where each term in the equation transforms as a vector.

Since the general form of the equation holds for each component of the vector, as expressed by Eqs. (3|5), the vector equation (3|6) is valid and the relation is covariant. Or we can say the same thing in reverse: a covariant expression is valid for each component of a vector (or a tensor) taken separately. Since each term of Eq. (3|6) is a vector, each term transforms in the same way. Although two different observers using different coordinate systems will describe any event that conforms to Eq. (3|6) in somewhat different ways, their different descriptions (that is, different values of the x- and y-components) of the various vector quantities will differ in just the same manner and Eqs. (3|5) and (3|6) will still be valid.

The same arguments can be applied to the expressions relating the components of velocity to the acceleration and the relation

$$\mathbf{v} = \mathbf{v}_0 + \mathbf{a}t$$

3|6   *The scalar product of two vectors*

The kinematic equation written as

$$v^2 - v_0^2 = 2a(s - s_0)$$

serves to introduce the concept of an invariant or scalar constructed from two vectors. This relation is valid for each separate component of the vectors. For example, setting $v_0 = 0$ and $s_0 = 0$ for simplicity and considering motion in only two dimensions,

$$v_x^2 = 2a_x s_x \qquad \text{and} \qquad v_y^2 = 2a_y s_y$$

It then follows that

$$v_x^2 + v_y^2 = 2(a_x s_x + a_y s_y)$$

We will now show that the quantities

$$v_x^2 + v_y^2 = v_x v_x + v_y v_y$$

and

$$a_x s_x + a_y s_y$$

retain the same value in differently oriented coordinate systems: they are invariant with respect to the rotation of the coordinate system and are therefore scalars.

Since **s**, **v**, and **a** are vectors, the transformation equations apply to their components. If we consider a coordinate system x', y' rotated by an angle θ, the relations (3|1) and (3|2) hold:

$$a_{x'} = a_x \cos \theta + a_y \sin \theta \qquad a_{y'} = -a_x \sin \theta + a_y \cos \theta$$

$$v_{x'} = v_x \cos \theta + v_y \sin \theta \qquad v_{y'} = -v_x \sin \theta + v_y \cos \theta$$

$$s_{x'} = s_x \cos \theta + s_y \sin \theta \qquad s_{y'} = -s_x \sin \theta + s_y \cos \theta$$

By direct substitution and nominal algebraic simplification,

$$a_{x'} s_{x'} + a_{y'} s_{y'} = (a_x s_x + a_y s_y)(\sin^2 \theta + \cos^2 \theta)$$

and

$$v_{x'} v_{x'} + v_{y'} v_{y'} = (v_x v_x + v_y v_y)(\sin^2 \theta + \cos^2 \theta)$$

Since

$$\sin^2 \theta + \cos^2 \theta = 1$$

we see that

$$a_{x'} s_{x'} + a_{y'} s_{y'} = a_x s_x + a_y s_y$$

and

$$v_{x'}^2 + v_{y'}^2 = v_x^2 + v_y^2$$

independent of the value of the angle of rotation θ. These quantities are then *invariants* or *scalars*.

In general, for any two vectors **A** and **B**, the quantity

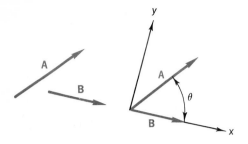

FIG. 3|8
*Two vectors, and a
coordinate system
aligned with one of the
vectors.*

$$(\mathbf{A} \cdot \mathbf{B}) = A_x B_x + A_y B_y$$

is an invariant or scalar and is known as the *scalar product* of
the vectors **A** and **B**. Using this notation, we can write the kinematic equation as

$$(\mathbf{v} \cdot \mathbf{v}) = 2(\mathbf{a} \cdot \mathbf{s})$$

Since the quantities on both sides of the equals sign are scalars,
the equations are covariant; they are valid in any coordinate
system.

　We can consider the scalar product of two vectors in another
simple manner. Two vectors, **A** and **B**, are shown in Fig. 3|8,
where the coordinate system is chosen such that the abscissa is
parallel to **B**. The scalar product of the two vectors is

$$(\mathbf{A} \cdot \mathbf{B}) = A_x B_x + A_y B_y$$

Since B_y is zero,

$$(\mathbf{A} \cdot \mathbf{B}) = A_x B_x$$

Since

$$A_x = A \cos \theta$$

where A is the magnitude or length of the vector **A**, θ is the angle
between the vector **A** and the x-axis, and is also equal to the
angle between **A** and **B**, and B_x is equal to B, the magnitude of
the vector **B**, we can write

$$(\mathbf{A} \cdot \mathbf{B}) = AB \cos \theta$$

　In summary, the scalar product of the two vectors **A** and **B**,
$(\mathbf{A} \cdot \mathbf{B})$, can be written as $AB \cos \theta$, where θ is the angle between
A and **B**, and A and B are the invariant lengths of the vectors.

We will usually use the form $AB \cos \theta$ rather than the more elegant and abstract form $(\mathbf{A} \cdot \mathbf{B})$. The invariant character of the scalar product is intuitively clear in this form, since the lengths of the vectors and the angle between them are all independent of the orientation of an observer.

3 | 7   *Choices of coordinate systems*

Since general descriptions of nature can be expressed in covariant form, one has a choice of coordinate systems for the investigation of particular problems. Although solution of a problem cannot depend upon the choice of system, an appropriate choice often simplifies the calculation or even results in delineating some general principle. Often the best choice is rather obvious: for most falling-body problems, it is most convenient to use a system such that one of the Cartesian axes is up or down. Sometimes, however, the use of other coordinate systems is more convenient.

We consider a particular problem to illustrate the simplifications that may result through a careful choice of coordinate system. Figure 3 | 9 shows a mortar firing a shell onto a hill. We have certain input information: the hill rises at an angle of 30°, starting from a point 1000 m from the gun; the gun fires at an angle of 30°; and the acceleration of gravity is 10 m/sec². We ask: How long will the shell be in the air?

From the definition of addition for vectors, we know that if a

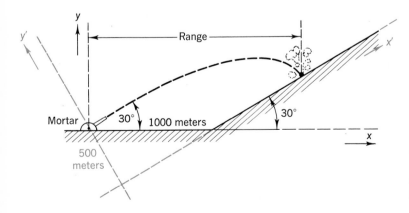

FIG. 3 | 9
A kinematic description of the flight of a mortar shell that lands on a hill.

vector **C** is equal to the sum of two vectors **A** and **B**, it follows that $C_x = A_x + B_x$ and $C_y = A_y + B_y$. From this result and from the equation of accelerated motion,

$$s = s_0 + \tfrac{1}{2}at^2$$

which represents the distance a particle travels when it is moving with uniform acceleration, we have two equations that hold for the components:

$$s_x = s_{0x} + \tfrac{1}{2}a_x t^2 \qquad \text{and} \qquad s_y = s_{0y} + \tfrac{1}{2}a_y t^2$$

Since the equations of motion are covariant, any coordinate system may be used: we choose the system x', y' of Fig. 3|9. Then, considering only components in the y'-direction,

$$s' = s_0' + v_0't + \tfrac{1}{2}a't^2 \qquad (y'\text{-components}) \tag{3|7}$$

Here s' is the position of the shell in the y'-direction when the shell lands: from Fig. 3|9 we see that $s' = 0$. The value of s_0', the distance of the gun from the origin of the coordinate system in the y'-direction, is 500 m, and the acceleration a', the component of acceleration in the y'-direction, is given by

$$a' = -10 \cos 30°$$
$$= -8.66 \text{ m/sec}^2$$

Substituting the numbers into the relation (3|7) we have

$$0 = 500 \text{ m} - (4.33 \text{ m/sec}^2)t^2$$
$$t^2 = 155 \text{ sec}^2$$
$$t = 10.7 \text{ sec}$$

The value of the time the shell was in the air was calculated rather painlessly, and the bases of the important qualitative conclusion—that the time is necessarily independent of the muzzle velocity—are nearly transparent.

The same calculation could be made using the normal coordinate system x, y. The course of the calculations will be less obvious in this case, though the final results will certainly be the same.

For completeness we note that we can find the range of the shell, or the position on the hill where the shell will land, if we are given the muzzle velocity. For this part of the calculation it is simpler to use the x, y coordinate system, now that we know the value of the time of flight t. Using only the x-component of velocity

$$v_{0x} = v_m \cos 30°$$

where v_m is the muzzle velocity. The acceleration of gravity has no component in the x-direction. Then the basic relation is

$$s_x = s_{0x} + v_{0x}t$$

The quantity s_0, the initial position of the shell or the position of the gun, is equal to zero from the construction of Fig. 3|9. If the muzzle velocity is 200 m/sec,

$$v_{0x} = 200 \cos 30°$$
$$= 173 \text{ m/sec}$$

and the range is

$$s_x = v_{0x}t$$
$$= 173 \times 10.7$$
$$= 1850 \text{ m (in the } x\text{-direction)}$$

PROBLEMS

$\sin \theta = O/H, \quad \cos \theta = A/H,$

$\tan \theta = O/A$

$\sin 30° = 0.5,$

$\cos 30° = 0.866 = \sqrt{3/4}$

$\sin 45° = \cos 45° = 0.707 = \sqrt{1/2}$

$\sin 60° = 0.866, \quad \cos 60° = 0.5$

$\sin 0° = 0, \quad \cos 0° = 1$

$\sin 90° = 1, \quad \cos 90° = 0$

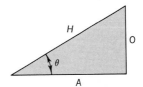

3|1 (a) A town b is 3 mi north and 4 mi west of town a; a town c is 7 mi north and 6 mi west of b. What is the position of c with respect to a? What is the straight-line distance between a and c?

(b) A town b is 12 mi north and 5 mi east of a; a town c is 5 mi

north and 2 mi west of *a*. Where is *c* with respect to *b*? How far
is it from *c* to *b*?

(*c*) A ship is traveling north with a velocity of 20 mi/hr as a traveler on the ship is running from the port rail to the starboard rail
(from west to east) directly across the deck at a velocity of 10
mi/hr. What is the direction (approximately) and the velocity of
the passenger from the view of an observer on a nearby island?

(*d*) Another ship is traveling due west with a velocity of 20 mi/hr.
From the view of an observer on this ship, how fast is the ship of
part (*c*) traveling? (That is, what is the relative velocity of the
two ships?)

3|2   In Newfoundland a village *b* is 86 mi north and 50 mi west of an-
other village *a* according to a standard map of the region designed such
that north is the direction towards the geographic pole. If the magnetic
compass points 30° west of north in this region:

(*a*) What is the direction of *b* with respect to *a* according to the
compass?

(*b*) What is the distance between the villages according to the magnetic map? According to the geographic pole map?

3|3   Express all of the quantitative results in terms of the unit spacing
of the grid in the figure.

(*a*) What are the components and the invariant lengths of the
vectors **a**, **b**, **c**, **d**, **e**, **f**, **g**, and **h**?

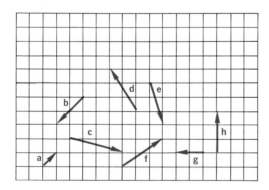

(*b*) Construct the following vectors and determine their components and their invariant lengths:

$a + c + f$ $a + c - f$ $-a + h - g + c$

$d + g - e$ $-d - g + e$ $g + b - d - a$

3 | 4   The diagram shows the position of a body at 1-sec intervals. The grid spacing is 1 m. Assume that we know that the acceleration is constant.

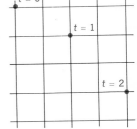

(*a*) What is the magnitude and direction of the acceleration of the body?

(*b*) What is the average velocity of the body during the time interval from 0 sec to 1 sec?

3 | 5   A space ship is traveling parallel to the ground over the surface of a planetoid, where both gravity and the atmosphere are negligible. The ship is traveling at a velocity of 30,000 m/sec and fires a tracer shell directly downward from a gun with a muzzle velocity of 40,000 m/sec.

(*a*) What is the absolute value of the velocity of the shell with respect to an observer on the ground?

(*b*) The observer sees that the shell is in flight for 1 sec. How high is the ship?

(*c*) Where is the ship with respect to the target when the shell hits the target?

(*d*) Show that the observer on the ground sees the path of the shell as a straight line. (A rigorous formal treatment is not necessary here.)

3 | 6   (*a*) An airplane is flying slowly over a train at a height of 1 km. It is traveling in the same direction and at the same speed as the train, 150 km/hr. A heavy bomb is dropped from the plane. With respect to their positions at the time the bomb is released, where will the plane, bomb and train be when the bomb strikes? Neglect air resistance.

(*b*) Answer the same questions for the condition such that the bomb is fired downwards with respect to the plane with a velocity of 100 m/sec.

3 | 7 A car is rolling down a steep slope that is at an angle of 60° with the horizontal. There is no friction. The acceleration of a cart in such a situation is just the component of the acceleration of gravity in the direction of motion of the cart. A man in the cart drops a ball from a point 10 m "above" the floor of the cart. When and where will the ball strike the floor?

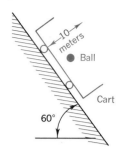

3 | 8 (*a*) A cart starts up a narrow 30° incline with an initial velocity of 20 m/sec. The only acceleration is due to the component of gravity parallel to the incline. How far along the incline will the car travel before it stops and rolls back?

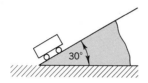

(*b*) Immediately after the cart starts, a bolt falls off the cart and lands on the flat surface beside the incline. Where does it hit?

3 | 9 A ball on the end of a string 1 m long moves in a circle about a point at which one end of the string is secured at a frequency of 1 revolution/sec.

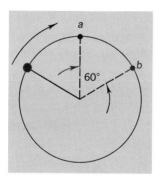

(*a*) What is the magnitude of the velocity of the ball at any time?

(*b*) What is the direction of the velocity of the ball when the ball reaches point *a*?

(c) If **s** is the position of the ball with respect to some arbitrary point, D**s**/D*t* is the average velocity over an interval of time D*t*, where D**s** is the difference in position. Find the average velocity of the ball as it moves from *a* to *b*.

(d) The average acceleration of the ball over a time interval D*t* will equal D**v**/D*t*, where D**v** is the change in velocity during the interval D*t*. What is the magnitude and direction of the average acceleration of the ball as it moves from *a* to *b*?

3|10 An automobile is traveling along a winding road at a constant speed—that is, the reading of the speedometer is constant. Draw vectors that represent the direction of the average acceleration of the car over the intervals between the labeled points.

3|11 The following seven quantities, **F, A, S, V,** *M, E,* and *T*, are vectors and scalars. Their dimensions in terms of mass, *m*, length, *L*, and time, *t*, are as follows: **F** (mL/t^2), **S** (L), **V** (L/t), **A** (L/t^2), M (m), E (mL^2/t^2), and T (t). Construct covariant, dimensionally consistent, equations relating:

(a) **F** in terms of **A** and *M*

(b) *E* in terms of **A**, *M*, **S**

(c) **S** in terms of **A**, *T*

(d) *E* in terms of **V**, *M*

3|12 A beetle is crawling on a piece of paper marked as shown. An observer says that it is crawling in the *y*-direction. Why is this statement not covariant? Restate the description of the beetle's motion in a covariant way.

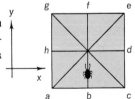

3|13 Using the diagram of problem 3|3, what are the values of the following invariant products?

(a) (**a** · **b**)   (d) (**c** · **d**)

(b) (**b** · **g**)   (e) (**d** · **g**)

(c) (**h** · **g**)   (f) (**g** · **d**)

4|1   *The relative character of time
and position*

WE HAVE emphasized the invariance properties of the universe: the descriptions of the general properties of nature appear to be independent of some aspects of the observer's situation. It appears that physical laws, which are statements that describe the relations between observations of the universe, are independent of time. Observers operating at different times will deduce the same laws of behavior. The laws are invariant with respect to (the passage of) time. This invariance has the consequence that there is no absolute time. Time differences can be measured in a laboratory, but no absolute time can be measured, and the concept of absolute time is meaningless. In an enclosed laboratory without access to an external world, the question whether the laboratory clock is correct can have no meaning. No measurement can be made in the laboratory that can detect absolute time. This, of course, is equivalent to stating that the results of an experiment cannot depend upon absolute time.

It is also possible that the laws of physics are invariant with respect to position. If this is the case, there can be no absolute position, only differences in position. We can discuss our position with respect to the earth, with respect to the sun, and with respect to the galaxy; these, however, are all relative positions. We have implicitly defined our position relative to the center of the earth, or relative to the sun, or relative to the center of the galaxy. We have no way of establishing an absolute position. Again, if we are in an enclosed laboratory without any access to the outside world, we cannot detect any absolute position. The results of any experiment we perform in our laboratory will not depend, and cannot depend, upon the position of the laboratory. If this is true, we state that the laws of physics are invariant with respect to position or invariant with respect to displacement from one position to another.

Although we may not have an absolute origin of displacement or an absolute origin of time, we are still interested in establishing relations between different relative systems. If the clock in laboratory a is an hour ahead of the clock in laboratory b, we know we have no method of determining whether the clock in a or the clock in b is correct. Indeed, it is not even possible to define what is meant by the "correct" time in a way that is not arbitrary and essentially capricious. Parenthetically, for matters of convenience, we do establish an arbitrary reference time, namely Greenwich Mean Time, which we then can use to relate observations between different laboratories. But in general, if laboratory b is an hour ahead of laboratory a, we can say that the time in b is equal to the time in a plus 1 hour: $t_b = t_a + 1$, where the units are hours. Using this equation one can relate observations of laboratory a to observations of laboratory b. If each laboratory times the observance of an eclipse of the moon, we can determine whether these observations are in fact simultaneous using this equation of time.

In a similar manner we can determine the position of laboratory b with respect to laboratory a. Again we have no absolute position, except by convention. We conventionally use a coordinate system based on the geographic poles of the earth and the position of the observatory at Greenwich, England. The poles determine our latitude scale and the point at Greenwich determines our longitude scale, establishing a coordinate system for all points on the earth's surface. We can add height above sea level to establish a complete three-dimensional (though non-Cartesian) coordinate system.

4 | 2   *Invariance with respect to velocity—the Galilean transformation*

We might ask whether the laws of physics are invariant with respect to velocity. Most of us have had occasion to be seated in a train in the yards waiting to depart from the station. Noticing from our window the motion of the train on the next track, we have wondered whether the other train was moving or whether we were moving. Only the relative velocity of our train and the train on the next track was easily discernible. Furthermore, when our train is in motion there is no gross difference between our relation with our near environment and the relation with that environment when the train was stationary. Nothing near us is obviously changed by any motion of the train; if we were juggling oranges, the precision of our movements and the flight of the oranges would not be different if the train were stationary or moving smoothly. If the roadbed were ideally smooth and the windows were made opaque, there would be no obvious way in which we could tell whether the train is moving or not. This suggests to us that a general principle may exist to the effect that we cannot, under any circumstance, determine whether the train is moving. If this is true, the movement of the train can have no absolute significance. Indeed if we establish a laboratory on the train, we will find that, within the accuracy of our present techniques, there are no experimental results that depend upon the absolute velocity of the train. The laws of physics, our description of the universe, then seem to be invariant with respect to velocity. Relative velocity, of course, still exists, even as relative displacement or relative time exists. Even as it appears that absolute position or absolute time does not have any significance, then absolute velocity cannot have any significance. If we cannot measure absolute velocity it cannot have any meaning.

We can determine the relative velocity between moving systems or moving laboratories by various conventional means. We can, for example, measure the distance between such laboratories as a function of time. Again there is no intrinsic absolute velocity, although again it is convenient to consider the earth's surface as having zero velocity. This convention is of the same nature as our conventions concerning zeros of time and the latitude–longitude coordinate system on the surface of the earth.

In order to relate events in one laboratory with events in another laboratory when the laboratories are moving, we need relations between the displacements and times in the two laboratories. The illustration in Fig. 4|1 shows such a pair of laboratories.

A laboratory S' is on a car of a train moving with velocity v in the x-direction, and a laboratory S is constructed on the platform. An observer O' who is equipped with a clock that reads time t' and a meter stick L' directs proceedings in the laboratory S'. The observer O in the stationary laboratory S has a clock that reads time t and a meter stick L. We make the classical assumption that a second in the laboratory S' is the same as a second in the laboratory S and a meter in S' is the same as a meter in S. This is a very good approximation if v is much less than the velocity of light.

We are now prepared to develop the relations between the measurements of the two observers concerning the distance between the two events and the time that elapses between the two events. The first event will be a spark that occurs when an electrode on the train at the position marked x_0' passes an electrode on the platform marked x_0: the second event is a similar spark that occurs when an electrode at x_1' passes an electrode at x_1. Although this rather odd choice of events was made to emphasize the equivalent standing of the two systems, events that might nominally be considered to be a natural part of one system or the other could have been chosen with no resulting change in principle. Each observer will record the time that

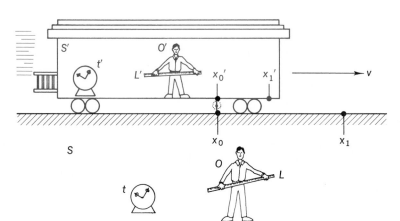

FIG. 4 |1
Observers in different coordinate systems measuring the distance between two events.

elapses between the two events with his clock. The elapsed time will be the difference in the reading of the clock as the two events are perceived. We implicitly assume either that the signal takes no time at all to travel from the event to the observer or that some satisfactory correction can be made for the time required for transmission of the signal. If the observer detects the event by observing the light emitted from the spark, we can safely neglect the correction if the velocity of the train is very small compared to the velocity of light. If t_1 is the time that observer O reads on the clock as he sees the second spark and t_0 is the time of the first spark, the difference in time will be

$$dt = t_1 - t_0$$

In the same way, the time difference recorded by observer O' will be

$$dt' = t'_1 - t'_0$$

Since the clocks are the same in the two systems, the times will be the same

$$dt' = dt \qquad\qquad (4|1)$$

The two men will not record the same distance, however. Each will measure, at his leisure, the distance between the two electrodes in his system. An inspection of the diagram of Fig. 4|1 shows that the distance between the two electrodes on the platform, $x_1 - x_0$, will be greater than the distance between the two electrodes attached to the train, $x'_1 - x'_0$.

The observer on the platform may take an egocentric position and say that his measurement of the distance between events is correct and the measurement of O', the man on the train, is in error because O' did not take into account the "fact" that the train was moving during the time that elapsed between the two events and therefore the electrode at x'_1 moved during this time. According to O, O' should have added this distance to his measured distance to get the "correct" value of the space between the two events, which is the value O measured and recorded in his notebook. According to O, the distance he measured, $x_1 - x_0$, will be equal to the distance between the electrodes on the train, which were measured correctly by O', $x'_1 - x'_0$, plus the distance the train (and the electrode x'_1) moved during the elapsed time;

this will be equal to $v(t_1' - t_0')$. Then

$$(x_1 - x_0) = (x_1' - x_0') + v(t_1' - t_0')$$

If he expresses the difference between the displacements measured in the two systems as dx and dx', and the differences in elapsed time as dt and dt'

$$dx = dx' + v\, dt' \qquad\qquad (4|2)$$

Independent of the question of which observer is "correct," the equations do express correctly the relations between the measurements made, and recorded in their notebooks, by the two observers.

If absolute velocity has no meaning, it is equally permissible, if less conventional, for the observer on the train to consider that his system is preferred. He might then adopt an egocentric position and claim that his measurements are correct and the results of the man on the platform are wrong. From the view of O', the man on the train, the platform is moving backwards with a velocity of $-v$ with respect to the "stationary" train. According to O' the measurements of O are incorrect, because he did not take into account the "fact" that his platform was moving with the velocity of $-v$ during the time that elapsed between the events. According to O', the electrode x_1 moved backwards an amount equal to $v(t_1 - t_0)$ during this time. According to O', observer O should have subtracted this from his measurement of the distance between the electrodes, $x_1 - x_0$, and then he would have obtained the "correct" result that O' obtained. Or

$$(x_1' - x_0') = (x_1 - x_0) - v(t_1 - t_0)$$

Expressing the differences as dx, dx', dt, and dt',

$$dx' = dx - v\, dt \qquad\qquad (4|3)$$

Again, independent of the results of any judgement as to which observer is "correct," the equations do correctly express the relations between the two sets of measurements.

Equations (4|1), (4|2), and (4|3) have very much the character of the equations that related the observations (or records) of two observers who used differently oriented coordinate systems. Like those equations, these relations are important because there is no preferred system; as there is no preferred direction of orientation of a coordinate system, there is no absolute velocity of a reference system. Just as the equations that relate the components of a vector in one system to the components in another system are called transformation equations, the equations that relate intervals of time and distance in two systems are called transformation equations—in this case, the equations of the *Galilean transformation*. These are the equations of classical or Galilean relativity, where the term *relativity* refers to the relative character of reference frames moving at different velocities. When we include properly the finite velocity of light, these will be superseded by the equations of the Lorentz transformation of Einstein's Special Theory of Relativity.

4|3 *Acceleration and gravity—*
the equivalence principle

We have noted formal similarities between displacement, velocity, and acceleration. They are all vectors; all transform in the same way under a change in coordinate system. Further, we have found that only relative position is important, and only relative velocity is important: there is no absolute position; there is no absolute velocity. We can well ask whether only relative acceleration is important: is there such a thing as absolute acceleration?

The question of the absolute or relative character of acceleration is not a question to be decided from any logical or mathematical procedure; one must decide this by observation or by the controlled observations we call experiments. Excluding any special local characteristics, it appears that we cannot determine any absolute position, absolute velocity, or absolute time through experiment. It appears that time, position, and velocity have only a relative meaning. Though neither time nor velocity has an absolute meaning, it does not follow necessarily that acceleration, the rate of change of velocity with time, has only a relative significance.

The question of the absolute or relative character of acceleration must, then, be answered by observation. Here our accumulated experience suggests that there *is* such a thing as absolute acceleration. If we are sitting in a train in the yards, we *can* determine whether our train is starting to move from the station rather than the train next to us, if our train begins to move with an appreciable acceleration. If we restrict our observations to measurements of space and time alone, we cannot differentiate between the two possibilities (1) that our train is moving forward out of the station and (2) that the other train is moving backward out of the station. The distance between the trains will change with time in the same manner for the two possible situations. However, the behavior of a simple accelerometer, a weight hanging from the end of a string, will differentiate between the two possibilities (see Fig. 4 │2). If our train is accelerating, the weight will swing back in the opposite direction to the direction of acceleration; if our train is stationary and it is the other train that is moving, the weight will not move but will continue to hang straight down towards the floor.

An observer in an enclosed laboratory can, then, determine the absolute acceleration of the laboratory by using such simple accelerometers. If absolute acceleration exists, the state of zero acceleration must have some absolute meaning in terms of a reference system. What is the preferred frame of reference that has no acceleration?

Again we must eventually have recourse to experiment, and the most meaningful thing we can say is that our zero of acceleration is the fixed stars. Acceleration with respect to the average distribution of mass in the universe, defined empirically as the average positions of the fixed stars, appears to establish a zero for measurements of acceleration.

Frames of reference that are not accelerating play a particularly important part in our formulations of mechanics and are called *inertial systems*.

An observer in an enclosed laboratory on earth can measure the acceleration of the laboratory using various techniques. He might determine the acceleration by dropping a ball a specific

Train accelerating   Train moving with constant velocity

FIG. 4 │2
Observers in different coordinate systems with simple accelerometers.

distance and measuring the time elapsed between the release of
the ball and the instant it hits the floor. If he drops the ball from
a height of 5 meters and finds that it hits the floor 1 sec later,
he can use the equations of accelerated motion to deduce that
the acceleration is 10 m/sec².

Now let us consider another laboratory very far from the
earth in interstellar space, where gravity is negligible. Assume
that some kind of rocket drive is attached to the laboratory and
the laboratory is accelerating, in a direction perpendicular to
the floor, upward with an acceleration of 10 m/sec². Now an
observer can measure the acceleration in that laboratory by
releasing a ball from a definite height above the surface of the
floor and measuring the time it takes until the floor and the ball
meet. If the ball is released 5 meters above the floor and the
floor and ball meet 1 sec later, we can deduce that the acceleration of the floor—and the rest of the laboratory—is 10 m/sec²,
exactly the value measured on earth.

Now we might ask the same kind of question we asked in the
cases of the laboratories established at different positions or

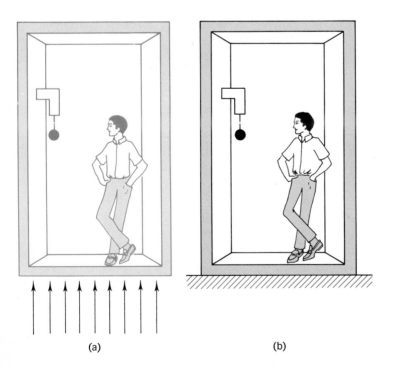

(a)   (b)

FIG. 413

*An observer in an
accelerating system* (a)
*and an observer in a
gravitational system* (b)
*considering the behavior
of a body released in the
system.*

established with different velocities: Can we make any measurement in the laboratories that will differentiate between the laboratory of Fig. 4|3a, which is accelerating in interstellar space, and the laboratory of Fig. 4|3b, which is stationary in the earth's gravitational field on the surface of the earth? This is an experimental question, and it appears that the answer is no. The effect of the gravitational field appears to be the same in every respect as the effects induced by the acceleration of the system. It is impossible to tell which laboratory we are in by measurements confined to the laboratory. This is the *principle of equivalence*, first formulated clearly by Einstein, and is one of the most important clues to our understanding of the basic relationships between space and matter. The effects that result from an acceleration of the reference system are indistinguishable from the effects of gravity. Then gravity and acceleration must be the same!

An apocryphal story is told about Einstein. It seems that he was supposed to have seen a construction worker fall from a tall building to be miraculously saved by landing on a pile of soft refuse. The worker told Einstein that it seemed that he was at rest (while he was falling) and that the ground was moving up to strike him. The effects we call gravity appeared to him to be identical to the acceleration of the ground towards him. According to the principle of equivalence it does not just *seem* that way, it *is* that way.

4|4   *The bending of light in a*
gravitational field

The equivalence between acceleration and gravity provides us with some further insights. We first pose a problem of an essentially trivial nature to introduce important consequences of the equivalence theorem. Suppose a gun is fired at a ball at the moment the ball is released to fall from some height. We assume that the activity takes place on the earth's surface, at normal gravity, and that we can neglect air resistance. Figure 4|4 illustrates the situation. Both ball and bullet will undergo an acceleration resulting from gravity. The bullet will follow some kind of curved path. Our question is: How should the gun be aimed so that the bullet will strike the ball?

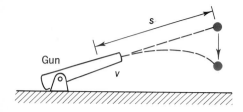

FIG. 4|4
A gun firing at an object that is released as the gun fires.

Without knowing the original height of the ball, the distance from the gun, the muzzle velocity, or even the value of the acceleration of gravity, we can state that the gun should be aimed directly at the ball just as if there were no gravity at all.

Although one can prove the validity of this conclusion without using the equivalence theorem explicitly, we can see how this result obtains in a particularly transparent fashion by using the equivalence principles. According to this principle, we can consider the effects of the gravitational field of the earth as an upward acceleration of the earth. We have a choice of two convenient systems of reference then. One, the usual one, is based on the earth's surface, considering it as an accelerating platform. Or we can use the frame of reference of the nonaccelerating objects, the ball and bullet. From this view we, as observers in that frame of reference, are stationary and the earth is accelerating toward us. In this coordinate system, with only the earth accelerating, the ball is stationary and obviously the gun should be aimed directly at the ball. The bullet will strike the ball later after a time, $t = s/v$, has elapsed, where s is the distance from gun to ball and v is the muzzle velocity. For the purpose of this calculation, it does not matter that the earth is accelerating toward us. Of course, knowing the acceleration of gravity, which is the acceleration of the earth in our frame of reference, we can calculate the distance the earth has "moved" during the time t and find where, with respect to the earth, the ball was struck.

We can use much the same kind of reasoning to consider the behavior of a light beam in a gravitational field. Let us assume that we have available a laboratory in interstellar space, far from the gravitational influence of any star or planet. Figure 4|5 shows such a laboratory 300,000 km long. The ridiculously large length is chosen for computational convenience; the speed of light is 300,000 km/sec, and a ray of light will cross the room in 1 sec.

We first assume that the room is at rest with respect to some far-off source of light, perhaps a star, and the light from the star enters the room parallel to the floor through a hole in the wall of the laboratory that is 5 m above the floor. The observer in the laboratory measures the height of the beam above the floor and finds that the beam is 5 m above the floor at every point and strikes the far wall of the laboratory at a point 5 m above the floor.

Then some sort of motors are started that give the room an upward acceleration of 10 m/sec². After 0.5 sec the room will have moved upwards 1.25 m. Light that entered the room at the time t_0, when the motors started and the acceleration began, will have reached the center of the room at that time, and the light will be only 3.75 m above the floor; the floor has moved 1.25 m. One second after the motors started, the light that entered the room at that time will have reached the far wall. By this time the room will have moved upward 5 m, and the ray of light will hit the far wall at floor level. Figure 4|5b shows the path of the beam *from the view of the observer in the laboratory:* from that observer's view the light has curved.

It is easy to calculate the angle through which the light was bent according to the measurements of the observer in the laboratory. The light entered the room with a velocity c, equal to 3×10^8 m/sec, traveling parallel to the floor: after 1 sec the velocity of the floor will be 10 m/sec upward, as measured by a stationary observer outside of the laboratory. From the view of the observer in the laboratory, the light has a component of velocity downward v_d, equal to 10 m/sec, as it reaches the far wall. At this time, according to him, the light is then traveling at an angle θ with respect to the floor. The value of θ, in radians (rad), is

FIG. 4|5
The path of light rays passing through a stationary system (a) and an accelerating system (b).

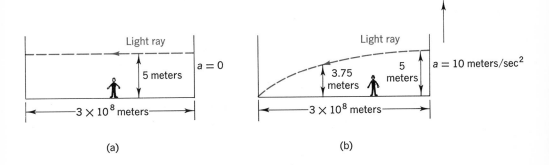

(a)   (b)

$$\theta = \frac{v_d}{c}$$

$$= 3.3 \times 10^{-8} \text{ rad}$$

Assuming that he has no source of information beyond his own measurements, the observer in the laboratory will not know whether the laboratory has accelerated as the result of the ignition of rocket motors attached to it or whether the laboratory has suddenly come under the influence of a gravitational field. If the equivalence principle is valid, it is *impossible* for him to tell the difference. Then a ray of light must be bent in a gravitational field, just as it "seems" to be bent from the view of an observer in an accelerating frame of reference. If light behaved differently in the two cases, an observer could make measurements on a beam of light and deduce whether he was in a gravitational field or merely in an accelerating reference frame: but according to the equivalence principle, this is impossible. The bending of light in a gravitational field, then, follows from the equivalence principle.

According to this method of calculating the bending of light, light acts very much as a material object and "falls" in a gravitational field like a material object. We can use this method of thinking about the curvature to estimate the magnitude of curvature of light caused by the gravitational field of the sun. In particular, we will estimate the bending of light from a star where the path of the light just grazes the surface of the sun. The actual gravitational effects are important even very far from the star, and we would need to know the strength of the field everywhere as well as have some facility at calculation in order to derive a precise answer. However, if we approximate the effect of the sun by assuming the

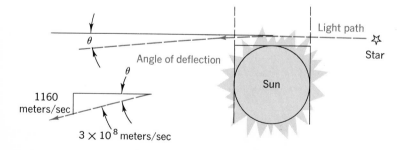

FIG. 4|6

A schematic description of the bending of light that passes near the sun.

acceleration of gravity is equal to that at the surface of the sun along a path equal to the diameter of the sun and is negligible beyond this, we will make no serious mathematical error. The character of the approximation is shown in Fig. 4|6. The light, grazing the surface of the sun, is unaffected by any gravitational effect until it reaches the region of the sun shown in the diagram where the maximum gravitational acceleration found at the surface of the sun is effective. The light ray remains under the influence of this gravitational field for a time equal to the diameter of the sun divided by the velocity of light. Since the diameter of the sun is about 1.3×10^6 km, and the speed of light is 3×10^5 km/sec, the time the light spends in this gravitational field in this model is

$$t = \frac{1.3 \times 10^6 \text{ km}}{3 \times 10^5 \text{ km/sec}}$$

$$= 4.3 \text{ sec}$$

The acceleration of gravity at the surface of the sun, a_s, is about 270 m/sec—about 27 times greater than at the surface of the earth. This gravitational field will introduce a component of the velocity of the light ray, v_d, perpendicular to the original direction of the light ray. The magnitude of the velocity is then

$$v_d = a_s t$$

$$= (270 \text{ m/sec}^2)(4.3 \text{ sec})$$

$$= 1160 \text{ m/sec}$$

The change in direction of the light can be expressed by an angle of deflection. Since the transverse velocity is very much smaller than the velocity of light, the value of the angle in radians is very nearly equal to the ratio of the transverse velocity to the velocity of light.

$$\theta = \frac{v_d}{c}$$

$$= \frac{1160 \text{ m/sec}}{3 \times 10^8 \text{ m/sec}}$$

$$= 3.9 \times 10^{-6} \text{ rad}$$

This represents a deflection of about a quarter of an inch in a mile.

There are flaws in our handling of the problem of the gravitational deflection of the light passing the sun. Although an observer stationed at the position of the surface of the sun would notice a curvature of the passing light of the magnitude we have calculated if the sun were suddenly moved into position, the relation between that observation and any observation of a man on the earth is not simple. Indeed, that relation depends upon the details of theories concerning the structure of space that are contained in theories of *general relativity*. According to Einstein's General Theory of Relativity, the deflection should be twice as large as the result from our calculation. This deflection is usually stated in units of seconds (sec) of arc, where 1 sec is $\frac{1}{3600}°$. In these units the deflection from our calculation is 0.87 sec; the result of a precise calculation using general relativity gives 1.75 sec of arc—twice as large as our result.

Values of the deflection of light by the gravitational field of the sun that are in agreement with the calculated value of 1.75 sec of arc have been made by measuring the change in apparent position of stars so placed that the light from the stars to earth passes very close to the sun. Such stars are visible only during the phenomenon of a total eclipse.

4|5   *Gravity and the curvature of space*

The distortion of the path of the light rays by a gravitational field is generally considered to represent the effects of a distortion of space itself. It is instructive to first consider distortions of a two-dimensional space. We might consider a race of observers, perhaps flatworms, who are cognizant only of the surface on which they crawl and cannot even conceive of a third dimension —up or down. On this surface they will define a straight line as the shortest path between two points. We will call these shortest paths *geodesics*. If they live on a plane surface, a theorem of their geometry is that the sum of the internal angles of a triangle will be 180°. Now if this surface is not plane but curved—perhaps the surface of a globe—the flatworms will find that the sum of the angles of large triangles, constructed, of course, from three geodesics, will be greater than 180°. This is illustrated in Fig. 4|7. The two-dimensional geometry is changed if the two-dimensional surface is curved in three dimensions.

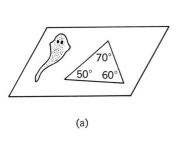

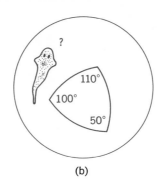

(a)

(b)

FIG. 4 |7
*Flatworms determining
the geometry of their
universes: (a) a satisfied
flatworm geometer on a
plane surface; (b) a
puzzled flatworm
geometer on a spherical
surface.*

This suggests that we can investigate any possible curvature of our universe by examining the geometry. In order to study the geometry, we must use straight lines. Like any other concept in science, straight lines, the geodesics of our universe, must be operationally defined in terms of some particular technique of measurement. Our experience suggests strongly to us that nothing travels faster than light and that the path of a light ray in vacuum between two points therefore defines the shortest distance between these points and thus defines the geodesics of our space. We can then examine the curvature of our space by examining figures constructed by these goedesics.

It was early in the last century that it was recognized, particularly by the great mathematician C. F. Gauss, that geometry was then an experimental science and the character of the geometry pertaining to our universe must be determined experimentally. Gauss therefore performed the flatworm experiment in 1823, using beams of light as geodesics, but found, within the accuracy of his measurements, that for a triangle of the order of 100 km on a side, the angles did add up to 180°.

Then if light is bent by a gravitational field, we must either give up the idea that the beam of light still represents a geodesic, the shortest distance between two points, or conclude that space itself is warped or curved by the source of the gravitational field. However, the change in geometry occasioned by the presence of matter does not demand that the light beam no longer be a geodesic: we certainly know of no other shortest path. It is therefore attractive to consider that it is space that is curved.

The curvature of space in the presence of matter has been measured by an analysis of the curvature of light near the most mas-

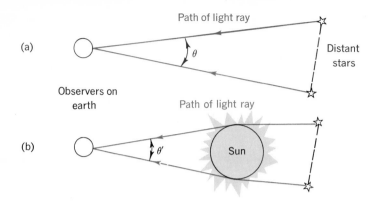

FIG. 4|8
Paths of light rays from distant stars as seen (a) when the sun is not near the path of the light as it travels to the earth and (b) when the sun is near the path of the light.

sive body in our vicinity—the sun. The diagram of Fig. 4|8a shows a triangle formed by two distant stars and a point on the earth in the absence of the sun. The sides of the triangles are the geodesics defined by the paths of light from the stars to the observer on the earth. Figure 4|8b represents the same configuration at a time when the sun is between the earth and the two stars. The new geodesics are shown. It is a matter of observation that the angle θ' is greater than θ. If the angles of the triangle in Fig. 4|8a add up to 180°, the angles in 4|8b surely add up to more: the excess is just $\theta' - \theta$.

Our space, then, is distorted or warped by the presence of mass. Our three-dimensional space is curved in a space of higher order—perhaps having four or more dimensions. In the General Theory of Relativity, Einstein explains or relates the acceleration of gravity to the geometry of this curved space.

4|6   *The distortion of time in a gravitational field*

Even as the equivalence principle leads naturally to the conclusion that space is curved or distorted by a gravitational field, the postulated equality between an accelerating reference frame and a similar system in a gravitational field shows that the flow of time is changed by gravity. In particular, an observer in a gravitational field, such as the field at the surface of the earth, will find that a clock below him will run slow and a clock held

above him will run fast: time will pass more slowly below him
and more quickly above him.

Again we use the assumed equivalence of gravitation and acceleration and examine the observations of a man in an elevator
car, where the elevator is on some planetoid where gravity is
negligible, so we can analyze the character of these dilations and
compressions of time. Figure 4|9 shows the position of such an
elevator car at four different times spaced at intervals of a second.
We assume that the elevator was stationary at the time $t = 0$, but
is accelerating upward at a rate of 10 m/sec². The height of the
car (the distance from floor to ceiling) is taken, conveniently for
us if not for the elevator manufacturer, as $h = 3 \times 10^8$ m. Light,
which travels at a velocity of 3.10^8 m/sec, will then pass from the
floor to the ceiling of the car in 1 sec. We postulate the existence
of a clock at the floor of the elevator car and an observer near the
ceiling who watches the clock on the floor through a telescope
and compares its readings with the readings of a similar clock set
beside him. The clocks had been compared, side by side, before
the observer climbed to his perch near the ceiling and they were
found to run at the same rate. We complete the setting of the stage
by stating that we anticipate the observations and reasoning that
make up the Special Theory of Relativity and presume that it is
understood that no signal can be transmitted faster than light and
that the velocity of light is the same in any inertial system.

Let us assume that the clock on the floor emits a flash of light
once per second as it measures off the seconds, the first flash
appearing at a time $t = 0$, just as the elevator leaves from its

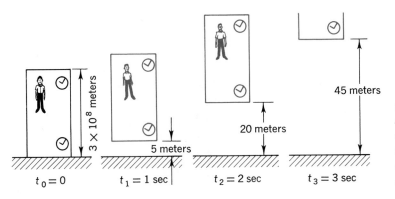

FIG. 4|9
*An observer in an
accelerating elevator
reading a clock near him
and a clock far below
him.*

ground position in Fig. 4|9. The light will arrive at the ceiling of the elevator car at a time equal to

$$t_0' = t_0 + \frac{h}{c}$$

where $h/c = 1$ sec if the elevator car is not moving. Since the car is accelerating upward during this time with an acceleration of 10 m/sec², the car will have moved upward an amount equal to 5 meters during the second the light signal is traveling toward the ceiling. The signal will take a little longer to reach the ceiling, since it has a little further to go; the extra time will be equal to the extra distance divided by the speed of the signal, or 5 m, divided by c, where c is the speed of light. Then the time of arrival will be

$$t_0' = t_0 + \frac{h}{c} + \frac{5 \text{ m}}{c}$$

$$= 0 \text{ sec} + 1 \text{ sec} + \frac{5 \text{ m}}{c}$$

If the second pulse starts at a time $t_1 = 1$ sec, the floor of the elevator will be 5 meters above ground. By the time the signal reaches the ceiling about 1 sec later, the ceiling will have moved a total of 20 m from its original position. The signal will then have to travel an extra distance equal to 20 m − 5 m and will reach the observer at a time t_1' that is equal to t_1 plus 1 sec plus the extra time, which will again be equal to the extra distance divided by the speed of light:

$$t_1' = t_1 + \frac{h}{c} + \frac{(20 \text{ m} - 5 \text{ m})}{c}$$

$$= 1 \text{ sec} + 1 \text{ sec} + \frac{15 \text{ m}}{c}$$

Similarly

$$t_2' = t_2 + \frac{h}{c} + \frac{(45 \text{ m} - 20 \text{ m})}{c}$$

The time intervals between the reception of the signals by the observer near the ceiling will be

$$t_1' - t_0' = 1 \text{ sec} + \frac{10 \text{ m}}{c}$$

$$t_2' + t_1' = 1 \text{ sec} + \frac{10 \text{ m}}{c}$$

$$t_3' - t_2' = 1 \text{ sec} + \frac{10 \text{ m}}{c}$$

and in general

$$t_{n+1}' - t_n = 1 \text{ sec} + \frac{10 \text{ m}}{c}$$

where n is any integer.

The observer will receive the signals at intervals that are larger than 1 sec. If he is watching the hands of the clock instead of the flashes, he will see the clock on the floor count out the seconds as if the clock were running too slowly. Time has meaning only in terms of measurements, so from the view of the man at the ceiling time will be running more slowly on the floor of the elevator car. If the principle of equivalence is valid, he cannot determine in any way, whether he is on an elevator that is accelerating in a region where there is no gravity or whether he is in a stationary elevator car in a gravitational field. So time must run slowly at the bottom of a gravitational field. As you stand on the earth, time must run more slowly at your feet than at your head.

We could have examined the converse situation where the observer was at the floor of the elevator and the clock was on the ceiling. We would have found then that the clock appeared to run fast. Time proceeds more quickly at the top of the elevator, or over your head in a gravitational field.

Are these effects real, or are they illusive effects of the particular observations? If the two clocks are brought together again, will they agree or will the lower clock have fallen behind permanently? If the acceleration is carried on for a sufficiently long time, the lower clock will fall behind the upper clock by a certain amount—let us say an hour for definiteness. Then if the acceleration is stopped, the clocks will keep time in unison— though the lower clock still seems slow by an hour to the observer at the top of the elevator car. Since light travels at the same speed c in any inertial system, the light takes only 1 sec to go from the lower clock to the upper clock, and the correction that takes place as the two clocks are brought together, is only 1 sec. The two clocks are still (almost) 1 hr apart. The time is lost irretrievably. If two twins are stationed at the positions of the two clocks, the lower twin will have aged 1 hr less than the upper twin: after all, aging is a biological clock and will not proceed differently than a mechanical clock.

We should emphasize, in summary, that the differential flow of time in an accelerating system follows from the axiom of relativity applied to the velocity of light. The velocity of light is the same in any inertial (that is nonaccelerating) reference system. If this were not true, one could measure the velocity of light and determine the absolute velocity of the system. The extension to gravitational fields then follows from the equivalence principle.

Our discussion of the distortion of time in the elevator emphasized a particular situation in which we could use numerical values in an attempt to gain some conceptual clarity. For completeness we should establish a more general relation, using the same logic, which will include the special situation we examined. Here we assume that the elevator car begins to accelerate upward from a stationary position at time $t = 0$, and again we examine the passage of time at the floor of the car from the view of an observer at the ceiling.

At a time t a signal is emitted by a device at the bottom of the elevator; the signal will be received at a time

$$t' = t + \theta + \frac{1}{2} \frac{a(t + \theta)^2}{c} - \frac{1}{2} \frac{at^2}{c} \qquad (4\,|\,4)$$

where θ is the uncorrected time it would take the light to reach the ceiling of the elevator ($\theta = h/c$, where h is the height of the elevator), the third term represents the correction that results from the motion of the ceiling, which makes the path longer than h, and the last term is the correction that results from the motion of the floor, which makes the path shorter. A signal emitted at a time $t + dt$ will be received at a time

$$t' + dt' = t + dt + \theta + \frac{1}{2} \frac{a(t + dt + \theta)^2}{c} - \frac{1}{2} \frac{a(t + dt)^2}{c} \qquad (4\,|\,5)$$

Subtracting (4 | 4) from (4 | 5),

$$dt' = dt + \frac{a\,dt\,\theta}{c}$$

$$= dt \left(1 + \frac{a\theta}{c}\right)$$

$$= dt \left(1 + \frac{ah}{c^2}\right)$$

Since accelerating frames of reference and systems in a gravitational field are equivalent, a can represent either the conventional acceleration of a reference frame or the acceleration of gravity in the frame or a combination of both.

Then in an accelerating frame of reference, whatever the source of the acceleration, as 1 sec elapses as measured by the watch on the wrist of an observer,

$$\frac{1}{1 + (ah/c^2)} \tag{4|6}$$

passes as measured by the clock h m below him, where a is the acceleration. A clock h' m above him ticks off

$$\left(1 + \frac{ah'}{c^2}\right) \tag{4|7}$$

Though the effects on the earth's surface are small—over a vertical distance of 10 m the dilation factor is only 10 m $\times$ g/c^2, where g is equal to 10 m/sec², or about 1 part in 10^{15}—this change in the rate of flow of time has been accurately measured and is in accord with these calculations.

PROBLEMS

4|1 In interstellar space (no gravity) at time t_0, a space ship (a) is moving upward with a velocity of 100 m/sec and an acceleration upward of 5 m/sec², with respect to a stationary observer (b) who is not accelerating.

A ball in ship (a) is projected upward from the floor with an initial velocity with respect to (a) of 20 m/sec. For *each* observer, find the acceleration and velocity of the ball at each of the following times:

(*a*) Just after the ball left the projector.

(*b*) Just before the ball struck the floor.

(*c*) At a time half way between that for (a) and (b).

(a) (b)

4|2 A man (i) standing on a platform on earth drops a ball from a height of 1.25 m. The ball falls to the floor of the platform. This action

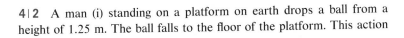

is observed by a second man (ii) who is in an elevator that is descending at a velocity of 5 m/sec and is at a position 5 m below the platform at the instant the ball is released. The elevator is in the process of *slowing down* to stop. The deceleration is 10 m/sec². From the view of (ii):

(a) What was the acceleration of the ball?

(b) How far did it fall?

4 | 3   A man standing on a platform on earth throws a ball into the air over his head with a velocity of 20 m/sec. The ball lands at his feet on the platform. An observer is in an ascending elevator that passes the platform. At the instant the ball is thrown, the floor of the elevator car is level with the floor of the platform, and the elevator is moving upward with a velocity of 5 m/sec and has an upward acceleration of 5 m/sec².

From the view of each man, using his floor as a reference:

(a) How high did the ball go?

(b) How long did the ball remain in flight?

(c) What was the acceleration of the ball when it reached its maximum height?

(Neglect the height of the first man: that is, assume that the ball was thrown from the floor of the platform.)

4 | 4   A missile is traveling parallel to the surface of the moon with a velocity of 100 m/sec. As it passes over a gun emplacement at a height of 10,000 m, its fuel is exhausted. A gun fires at an angle of 45° and shoots down the missile.

(a) What is the muzzle velocity of the gun?

(b) How long after the gun is fired does the shell hit the missile?

(c) What is the height of the missile from the surface of the moon when the shell strikes it?

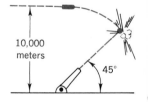

(Neglect the curvature of the surface of the moon.) On the moon $g = 1.0$ m/sec².

4 | 5   A missile and an antimissile are moving above the earth with their fuel exhausted at a time $t = 0$, as shown. They are above the atmosphere, but the acceleration of gravity is still 10 m/sec².

(a) Show that they will collide.

(b) When will they collide?

(c) Where will they collide with respect to their initial positions at time $t = 0$?

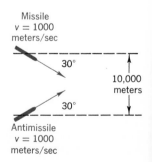

4|6   A small two-stage rocket is designed so that when the whole rocket reaches its maximum height (at which time the velocity upward is zero) the second stage is shot upward out of the barrel of a gun. The muzzle velocity of this gun has been measured to be 100 m/sec. The first stage falls to the earth, striking 1000 sec after ejecting the second stage. How high is the second stage when the first stage hits the ground? (Neglect air resistance.)

4|7   It appears that there are stars (white dwarfs) that are composed of extremely dense matter. Such a star might be as small as the earth but have a mass a million times greater; the acceleration of gravity at the surface of the star would be a million times greater than that of the earth, or about 10^7 m/sec^2.

(*a*) What would be the angle of deflection of light that travels 1 km over the surface of such a star?

(*b*) If the radius of the star is the same as that of the earth (6400 km) what must the acceleration of gravity be to cause a ray of light parallel to the surface to continue about the star in a circle (and thus never leave the star)? (The surface of the star will fall away from a tangential line at a rate of $\frac{1}{6400}$ rad/km; therefore the light must be deflected $\frac{1}{6400}$ rad as it travels 1 km.)

4|8   From the view of an observer far away, how much will time be slowed on the surface of a white dwarf star the size of the earth that has a surface gravity a million times greater than the earth? Explicitly, as 1 hr passes on the earth, how much time passes on the surface of the star? (Make the same kind of approximation considering the extent of the gravitational field as we used to consider curvature of light near the sun. Assume that the gravitational field extends only to a distance from the surface equal to the radius of the star—6400 km—and that the acceleration of gravity has the same value as at the surface throughout this region.)

4|9   In our discussion of the flow of time in accelerating systems, we stated that the velocity of light is the same in any inertial system, in accordance with the postulate that the velocity of an inertial system is not detectable. (We will review direct evidence for this property of nature when we consider the Special Theory of Relativity in Chapter 15.) Show that the velocity of light is not the same in accelerating systems as in inertial systems. (Consider the arguments of Section 4|6.)

five Mass, force, and the conservation of momentum

5 | 1 *The conservation of momentum and the definition of mass*

WE HAVE emphasized the importance of classifying properties of the universe in terms of invariances. Within the accuracy of our observations, the basic character of the universe appears to be independent of time, position, and velocity. Observers who reside at different times or at different places or in reference frames moving with different velocities see the universe in essentially the same way. The description of any particular event or series of events can then be divided into two parts: One part depends upon local circumstances and thus upon the particular place, time, and velocity of the reference system—for example, the boundary conditions that define the particular flight of a particular falling body. The second part is independent of these local circumstances—for example, the differential equation that is valid for all falling bodies—and constitutes a part of the collection of generalizations that makes up our physical theory. We will find that we can also select physical quantities that remain unchanged throughout any physical process—quantities that are *conserved*. The conservation laws that apply to these quantities are related to the existence of the invariances or symmetries we have already discussed. These relations are subtle, however, and we will not discuss them at this time.

The first conserved quantity we consider is momentum. For clarity we construct a set of thought experiments, which are idealized versions of experiments that could actually be carried out. We define quantities that we call *mass* and *momentum*, which help us describe regularities in our observations of the results of these experiments and, by extension, regularities in our observations of the physical universe itself.

Our set of experiments consists of observations of collisions between quantities of water. Although we are interested at this time in the collisions of pure samples of water, we must bow to practicality and place our water in very light containers that are designed to move on a flat surface, perhaps on very light ball bearings, with negligible friction. In a real experiment we would have to draw upon other experiences in order to make corrections for these departures from our ideal. However, in the spirit of thought experiments, we will neglect these complications.

For reasons that will become evident later, we construct or invent a property that we call *mass*; for water, mass and volume are essentially equivalent, though we use different units for the two quantities; a volume of 1 liter of water has, by definition, a mass of 1 kg; $\frac{1}{2}$ liter of water has a mass of $\frac{1}{2}$ kg, and so on. Mass, defined in this manner, has only a very narrow meaning. We will extend the meaning of mass later; the concept is useful in describing the interactions of other materials besides water, and this, of course, is why we have introduced this new quantity.

A typical collision between volumes, or masses, of water is represented schematically by the drawings of Fig. 5|1. Here a mass of water m_1 moving with a velocity $\mathbf{v}_1$ collides with a mass of water m_2 moving with a velocity $\mathbf{v}_2$. During the collision, water may spill from one container to the other, so the volumes, or masses, of water after the collision may not be the same in general. Then, typically, after the collision we find a mass m_1'

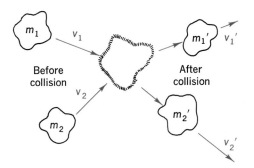

Before
collision

After
collision

FIG. 5|1
*Masses of water before
and after a collision.*

moving with a velocity v_1' and a mass m_2' moving with a velocity v_2'. We may make many observations of such collisions; in each case we will notice that there is a particularly striking relation between certain combinations of the measured quantities before the collision and after the collision; in all cases

$$m_1 v_1 + m_2 v_2 = m_1' v_1' + m_2' v_2' \qquad (5 \, | 1)$$

The sum of the quantities "mass times velocity" is unchanged by the collision or interaction of the volumes of water. We give a special name *momentum* to the product of mass and velocity and summarize our conclusions by stating that *momentum is conserved*; the total momentum of quantities of water, under the conditions of our experiment, is constant.

Although this summary of experimental results in terms of a conservation law would be relevant only for water, we are led to suspect that we might be able to form a much more general summary of experience of the same kind that would be valid for the interactions of all possible materials. After all, water is not a very special material. In order to define the quantity momentum for other materials, we will have to construct a more general definition of mass than that provided by a volume of water. We are interested in such a definition only if it will be useful, and at this time we have no reason to believe that it will be useful unless the conservation law can be extended to the other materials. We can therefore *attempt* to construct a definition of mass using the conservation law and then perform experiments with various materials to see whether the conservation law actually holds for our extended definitions.

For the sake of definiteness, let us examine the problem of defining a very particular mass, that of a piece of iron. We can easily do this by arranging a simple collision between the piece of iron and a known volume of water. If we measure the velocities of all of the quantities before and after the collision and assume the validity of a law of conservation of momentum, we can use the resultant mathematical relations to establish a value of the mass of the piece of iron. Let us examine in detail such a collision where we arrange, for simplicity, a head-on collision so that all of the velocities, before and after the collision, lie in the same line. Since the vector velocities are constrained in one dimension, we can treat them as algebraic quantities. The results of our measurements can then be expressed by the simple algebraic relation

$$m_i v_i + m_w v_w = m_i v_i' + m_w v_w'$$

where v_i and v_w are the measured velocities of the iron and water before the collision, and v_i' and v_w' are the measured velocities after the collision; m_w is the mass of the water and m_i is the unknown mass of the iron. With a little algebraic manipulation we can express the mass of the iron in terms of the known quantities:

$$m_i = m_w \frac{v_w' - v_w}{v_i - v_i'} \qquad\qquad (5 | 2)$$

We can use this kind of operational technique to *define* the mass, in kilograms, of any body made up of any material. By measuring the velocities in Eq. (5 | 2) we can determine the mass m_i of any body in terms of the mass of water m_w. A quantity of iron that acts like a kilogram of water in a collision in that a relation such as (5 | 1) is fulfilled is *defined* to have a mass of 1 kg.

It remains for us to establish the usefulness of this definition of mass. We can now examine the results of many interactions or collisions between various materials where the mass of the individual pieces is determined according to the foregoing procedures. We find, in general, that conservation laws such as expressed by the relation (5 | 1) hold now for all materials if mass is defined according to (5 | 2).

We can now summarize our conclusions. The vector quantity mass times velocity, which we will call *momentum*, is always conserved when mass is defined according to the procedure outlined in the previous paragraphs. We discussed the conservation of momentum in terms of a particular interaction—a collision. Since the history of any ensemble of masses is a history of interactions or collisions, we can expect that the rule that momentum is always conserved holds through the history of any ensemble, independent of the details of interaction. If we consider an initial system made up of a large number of quantities of matter with masses m_1, m_2, m_3, ... moving with velocities $\mathbf{v}_1$, $\mathbf{v}_2$, $\mathbf{v}_3$, ... and measure the final velocities $\mathbf{v}_a$, $\mathbf{v}_b$, $\mathbf{v}_c$, ... of the resultant quantities with masses equal to m_a, m_b, m_c, ... after the quantities interact according to some arbitrary history, we will find

$$m_1 \mathbf{v}_1 + m_2 \mathbf{v}_2 + m_3 \mathbf{v}_3 \cdots = m_a \mathbf{v}_a + m_b \mathbf{v}_b + m_c \mathbf{v}_c \cdots \qquad (5 | 3)$$

independent of the details of the interactions and independent of any details of divisions or consolidations of the various discrete portions of matter. Relation (5|3) is a general statement of the law of *conservation of momentum.*

It is important to notice that we define mass and momentum in such a way that the conservation law is valid. We could have defined mass in some other way; a kilogram might have been defined as the amount of material that occupies a volume of 1 liter. This would not be incorrect—we are at liberty to name things as we choose—but such a definition would not be very useful. Likewise, we might have constructed the quantity $m^2\mathbf{v}$ and named it momentum. It is a respectable, well-defined quantity, but it is not conserved and therefore not very useful. We selected useful quantities.

5|2 *Force*

It is convenient to use the law of conservation of momentum to define another useful quantity, which we call *force.* Even as our technically precise definition of mass is near the primitive concept of mass, the quantity we will define precisely and name *force* has properties similar to those we attribute to the primitive concept of force. It is, then, particularly useful to introduce force through the analysis of a familiar activity.

The diagram of Fig. 5|2 shows a man wearing skates standing

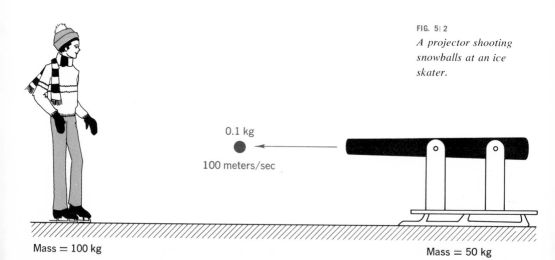

FIG. 5|2
A projector shooting snowballs at an ice skater.

0.1 kg

100 meters/sec

Mass = 100 kg

Mass = 50 kg

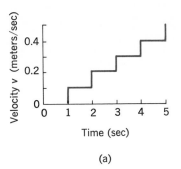

(a)

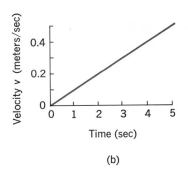

(b)

FIG. 5|3
The velocity of the skater as a function of time (a) when he is hit once per second by large snowballs and (b) when he is hit continuously by a stream of infinitesimal snowballs.

at rest on a surface of ice. We use ice and skates to emphasize the idealization we wish to make: we will neglect friction. The gun or projector at the right fires in this case snowballs at the man, who catches them. To be definite, we assume the man has a mass M equal to 100 kg and each snowball has a mass m of 0.1 kg and is traveling with a velocity v of 100 m/sec. Snowballs are fired, and caught, once per second. Each time the man catches one, the system of man and snowball must retain the momentum of the snowball according to the principle of conservation of momentum. If we label the velocity of the man as V and use dV for a change in velocity, we have

$$M \; dV = mv$$

or

$$(100 \text{ kg}) \; dV = (0.1 \text{ kg})(100 \text{ m/sec})$$

$$dV = 0.1 \text{ m/sec}$$

for each reception of a snowball. We neglect the small increment of mass the snowball adds to the mass of the man. Each time the man catches one, his velocity will then increase by 0.1 m/sec. Figure 5|3a shows a chart of the velocity of the man as a function of time. The velocity changes, discontinuously, at a rate of 0.1 m/sec every second, or 0.1 m/sec². Thus the average acceleration is 0.1 m/sec².

We have presented this transfer of momentum as a discrete manifestation: one pellet is caught every second. We might have pellets with half the mass traveling with the same velocity at a rate of two per second; or pellets with one tenth the mass coming at a rate of ten times per second; or a million pellets per second,

each with a mass one millionth as large. In that case the momentum transferred to the man every second would be the same, but
the transfer would be more nearly continuous; in the limit of a
very large number of very small momentum transfers, the variation of the velocity of the man with time will approach the graph
of Fig. 5|3b: the velocity will vary continuously with time at
the rate of 0.1 m/sec². The man will undergo an acceleration of
0.1 m/sec².

The man who is catching snowballs fired at the rate of one per
second might consider that he is being knocked backward by the
successive impacts. The man who is receiving a very large
number of very small pellets—a stream of powder snow—would
likely consider that he is being steadily pushed backward; he
would say that a *force* is pushing him. This primitive use of the
term *force* is closely related to the quantity we will define as
force. We define force as the rate of change of the transferred
momentum. Since momentum is a vector, force is a vector:

$$\mathbf{F} = \frac{d(m\mathbf{v})}{dt}$$

of, if the mass does not change, which is often the case,

$$\mathbf{F} = m\frac{d\mathbf{v}}{dt}$$

The rate of change of the velocity of the man on the skates was
0.1 m/sec². Since the mass of the man was 100 kg, the force on
the man was

$$\mathbf{F} = M\frac{dV}{dt}$$

$$= (100 \text{ kg})(0.1 \text{ m/sec}^2)$$

$$= 10 \text{ kg m/sec}^2 \quad \text{or} \quad 10 \text{ N}$$

where N, the *newton*, is the mks unit of force: $1 \text{ N} = 1 \text{ kg m/sec}^2$.

Since dv/dt is the acceleration **a**, the transfer of momentum
that constitutes a force can also be written as

$$\mathbf{F} = m\mathbf{a}$$

The effect of gravity near the surface of the earth results in the
transfer of momentum to a free body, causing an acceleration **g**;
the force of gravity on a body is then

$$\mathbf{F} = mg$$

where the direction of the force, like the direction of the acceleration, is down.

5|3 Action and reaction

It is interesting to extend the observations on the system of the man and projectiles to include the projector. Consider that the projector has a mass M' of 50 kg and slides freely on the ice, just as the skater does. Momentum must be conserved. Therefore, as the projector fires a pellet, the velocity V' of the projector must change as the projector recoils:

$$M' \, dV' = mv$$
$$= 10 \text{ kg m/sec}$$

Since M' equals 50 kg, dV', the change in the velocity of the projector that occurs with each shot, is 0.2 m/sec. Since this occurs once per second, the change in velocity is 0.2 m/sec every second, which corresponds to an average acceleration a' of 0.2 m/sec². When the projector is adjusted to shoot a very large number of very small pellets—a snow shower—with the same average transfer of momentum, the acceleration will be constant at the value of 0.2 m/sec². The recoil of the projector will occur as a result of a "force" on the projector. The magnitude of the force is

$$F = M'a'$$
$$= 10 \text{ kg m/sec}^2$$
$$= 10 \text{ N}$$

Even as the force on the skater was directed to the left in Fig. 5|2, the force on the projector is directed to the right.

As observers we might have been able to measure the acceleration of the skater and the projector, but we might not have been able to detect the flight of the projectiles. We would then be at liberty to say that the projector acts on the man through some medium, which we might not understand in detail, with a force of 10 N. There is also a reaction on the projector of a force of 10 N. The action of the projector on the man is thus countered by a reaction of the man on the projector, and the action is equal to the reaction. This general conclusion that *action equals reaction* follows directly from the concept of the conservation of momentum. For every force there is an *equal and opposite force.*

In Chapters 2 and 4 we considered *kinematics,* which is the description of the motion of bodies without reference to the forces on the bodies; we have now introduced *dynamics,* which is the study of the character of forces and their effects on bodies, by the analysis of a particular ideal situation that is implied to be representative of more general phenomena. We were led to define a quantity called *force,* where the force on a body is equal to the rate of change of the momentum of the body. In the example we have considered, the force between the projector and the skater resulted from the change of real particles that carried momentum. If we cannot observe the exchanged particles, we might as well consider that the projector and skater exert a force on each other over the distance between them, and that this "action at a distance" is a simple property of the skater–projector system. If we adopt this concept of a natural "action at a distance," we have no need of any intermediate agency (such as snowballs). Although it may be aesthetically unsatisfying to consider that two bodies can influence each other's motion when only empty space lies between them, this classical Newtonian view of forces is adequate up to the point at which propagation times becomes important; then some difficulties occur. Notice that action and reaction, as measured on the skater and projector, does not hold at the instant the projector begins to shoot at the skater (the projector may have been quickly moved into position) because the reaction on the projector will occur before the snowballs begin to strike the skater. When all factors are considered, it seems that the action-at-a-distance concept does not adequately describe nature, and we are led back to ideas that are very similar to the model in which we consider that the forces between bodies result from the exchange of particles between them.

Since a stationary object is not accelerating, the sum of all forces on the object is zero. Let us consider, for example, the skater receiving the pellets when he is up against a fence. The pellets striking the skater result in a force on the skater. Since the skater is not moving, the force on the skater from the pellets must be counteracted by a force the fence gives to the skater.

Since the fence is not moving, the corresponding force of the skater on the fence must be counteracted by a force the supports give to the fence, and so on. Likewise, an object moving at constant velocity without acceleration must be subject to a total force that is zero. It was really not necessary to consider separately stationary objects and objects moving with constant velocity, since we know that velocity has only a relative meaning: the stationary skater is moving with constant velocity from the viewpoint of someone passing in an automobile.

The basic results concerning the relations between force, mass, and acceleration that were developed as a consequence of the conservation of momentum were first stated precisely by Newton in the form of three laws. We will not attempt to make a literal translation of Newton's Latin, but state Newton's laws in our own words. Newton's first law states that *in the absence of a force, the velocity of an object remains unchanged.* The second law states that *the mass times the acceleration of a body is proportional to the force acting on the body.* And the third law states that *action is equal to reaction;* for every force there is an equal and opposite force.

Our discussion of the forces on the skater has been implicitly restricted to coordinate systems that are stationary or moving with constant velocity as measured with reference to the fixed stars. If a skater is standing on ice carried on a large railroad car while the train is moving at constant velocity, nothing will be changed in our treatment. The skater will obey Newton's laws; he will accelerate only if a force is applied to him, and the acceleration $\mathbf{a}$ will be proportional to the force $\mathbf{F}$ according to the relation $\mathbf{F} = m\mathbf{a}$, where m is the mass of the skater. We call this system, in which Newton's laws are valid, an *inertial* system.

If the train is accelerating, Newton's laws will not hold, according to measurements made by an observer using a coordinate system anchored to the train. If there is no force on the skater, he will be stationary or moving with a constant velocity as he is observed by an observer on the platform, which is nominally an inertial system. The observer on the platform sees the train accelerating, so that one end of the rink accelerates toward the skater. From the view of an observer on the train, the skater is accelerating toward the rear of the train. If the acceleration of the train is measured to be a' in the x-direction by the man on the platform, the observer on the train will measure the acceleration of the skater as $-a'$ in the x-direction, even though there is no force on the skater. The fundamental law of dynamics that takes the form of $\mathbf{F} = m\mathbf{a}$ in inertial systems must be modified to a form such as

$$\mathbf{F} = m\mathbf{a} - m\mathbf{a}'$$

in the train system, where $\mathbf{a}'$, the acceleration of the system with respect to the inertial system, is a constant of the train system.

An observer in the train system might describe the character of his universe by stating that there is a force on every object proportional to the mass of the object where the force is equal to $m\mathbf{a}'$. With this addition he can use Newton's laws and the relation $\mathbf{F} = m\mathbf{a}$. We will call this kind of force, which arises because of our choice of an accelerating coordinate system, a *fictitious force*. We should not be misled by the name, however; the force that throws you off your feet as a train starts or stops abruptly is a fictitious force if you prefer to use the train as your system of orientation, but the force can still knock you down: fictitious in this case does not mean imaginary.

It is interesting to restate our discussion of inertial accelerating systems in another form: We find experimentally that systems exist in which Newton's laws are valid. We find that these systems are all moving with constant velocity with respect to the fixed stars and that all systems that are moving with constant velocity with respect to those stars are inertial systems. What is the influence of these stars so very far away? We would like to know!

5|4   *Action and reaction—an example*

It is desirable to clarify the third law by noting that the conclusion that action is equal (and opposite) to reaction does not mean that the total forces on a body are zero: the action and reaction apply to different bodies. Consider, for example, the interaction of the skater and the projector. The third law, action equals reaction, is a statement concerning the equality of the force the projector exerts on the man with the force the man exerts on the projector. Neither the force on the man nor the force on the pro-

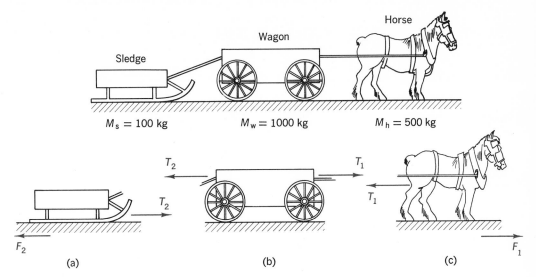

FIG. 5|4
*A horse drawing a
wagon and a sledge, and
the forces acting on the
horse, the wagon, and
the sledge.*

jector is zero, of course, but the force on the man is equal to the
force on the projector.

It is instructive and interesting to analyze the mutual interactions of a set of bodies that are connected by various constraints. It is attractive to illustrate the general considerations
that are involved by examining a particular, though represen-
tative, example. The diagram of Fig. 5|4 shows a horse pulling
a wagon that in turn is attached to a sledge that is dragged across
the ground. The relations that relate the force on a body to the
acceleration of the body apply to any individual particle or to
any set of particles.

We adopt the following symbols:

M_h = mass of the horse
M_w = mass of the wagon
M_s = mass of the sledge
T_1 = tension on the rope connecting the horse to the wagon
T_2 = tension on the rope connecting the wagon to the sledge
F_1 = the force the horse's hooves exert against the ground and,
     equally, the force the ground exerts on the horse.
F_2 = the force of friction on the sledge

We also assume that we can neglect the small amount of friction
from the wheels of the wagon and the smaller amount of air

resistance on the bodies. All of the forces that concern us in this problem lie along a line of motion parallel to the ground. The relation

$$F = ma$$

where F is the total force on a body of mass m and a is the acceleration of the body, can be applied to any one of the three separate bodies in the problem, or to any continuous group of two, or to all three together. Any combination of particles that are connected rigidly can be considered as a "body." As long as the ropes connecting the members of the train in Fig. 5|4 are taut, they are equivalent to rigid constraints.

We can, then, immediately write down relations for each one of the bodies separately. We begin by constructing an imaginary surface about a body of interest, in this case the horse, and find the sum of the forces acting on the body from outside the surface. Such a surface is suggested by the dashed line in Fig. 5|4. This total force will effect an acceleration of the body. The total force on the horse is the force resulting from the reaction of the ground on the horse's hooves, minus the force that results from the tension on the rope tied to the horse. Then

$$F_1 - T_1 = M_h a_h$$

where a_h is the acceleration of the horse. Performing a similar analysis of the forces on the wagon,

$$T_2 - T_1 = M_w a_w$$

where a_w is the acceleration of the wagon. In this case the tension of the rope between the horse and wagon is in a direction to cause the wagon to accelerate forward. The force the wagon exerts on the horse is equal to T_1 and is directed backward, while the force the horse exerts on the wagon is also equal to T_1 but is directed forward. Of course, this is just an example of action and reaction.

The analysis of the dynamics of the sledge leads to the relation

$$T_2 - F_2 = M_s a_s$$

where a_s is the acceleration of the sledge.

Since the horse, wagon, and sledge are all tied together and, if the ropes are taut, keep the same relative positions, the accelerations of the individual bodies must all be the same:

$$a_h = a_w = a_s$$

There are, then, three equations that connect eight quantities: three masses, four forces, and the acceleration. If we know any five of the quantities, we can determine the other three by solving the equations.

We could have divided the system into larger portions and carried on the analysis in the same way. For example, we can consider the wagon and sledge together. The total force on that system from outside the system is $T_1 - F_2$, and the total mass is $M_w + M_s$. Therefore,

$$T_1 - F_2 = (M_w + M_s)a$$

The force on the whole system of horse, wagon, and sledge is equal to $F_1 - F_2$ and the total mass is $M_h + M_w + M_s$, so

$$F_1 - F_2 = (M_h + M_w + M_s)a$$

If the mass of the horse is 500 kg, the mass of the wagon is 100 kg, and the mass of the sledge is 100 kg, we can calculate the acceleration of the system and the tension on the two ropes if we know the force the horse exerts (and then the reaction of the ground on the horse) and the frictional force between the ground and the sledge. Assume we determine that the horse's pulling power F_1 is 1000 N and that the friction drag of the sledge is 500 N. The total mass of the whole system is then equal to 1600 kg, and the total force is 500 N. The acceleration is

$$a = \frac{500 \text{ N}}{1600 \text{ kg}}$$

$$= 0.313 \text{ m/sec}^2$$

This must be the acceleration of each of the three discrete parts of the train. Then for the horse alone the force is $F_1 = T_1$, where $F_1 = 1000$ N, the acceleration is known to be $a = 0.313$ m/sec^2, and the mass is 500 kg. Then

$$-T_1 = (500 \text{ kg})(0.313 \text{ m/sec}^2) - 1000 \text{ N}$$

then

$$-T_1 = (156 \text{ N} - 1000 \text{ N})$$

$$= 844 \text{ N}$$

The tension in the second rope T_2 can now be determined by considering either the wagon or sledge alone. The mass of the sledge is 100 kg and the force on the sledge is $T_2 - F_2$, where F_2 is 500 N. The acceleration a is the same as in the rest of the system, 0.313 m/sec². Then

$$T_2 = (100 \text{ kg})(0.313 \text{ m/sec}^2) + 500 \text{ N}$$

$$= 531 \text{ N}$$

With this, all of the quantities are known.

5|5   *Inertial and gravitational mass*

Let us assume that we are able to construct a laboratory in a space ship that is able to travel deep into interstellar space, so far from any star or other massive body that gravitational effects are negligible. The rocket motors are set so that the acceleration of the ship is 10 m/sec². Any object in the laboratory must be accelerated along with the rest of the ship if it is to keep its relative position in the laboratory. This acceleration must be produced by some transfer of momentum to the object, and that transfer of momentum will constitute a force as we have defined force. Figure 5|5a shows such an object, a container holding 1 liter of water (the mass of the container is presumed to be negligible). The liter of water retains its position in the laboratory by virtue of the force exerted on it by the pan of the spring scale. The scale (which measures force) will read 10 N. If we put on the scale a piece of iron that has a mass of 1 kg according to our standard definition of mass, the scale will again read 10 N. In general, the

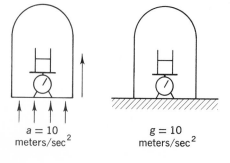

FIG. 5|5

A kilogram of water resting on a spring scale in an accelerating system and in a system in a gravitational field.

scale will read a value equal to ma, where m is the mass of the object on the scale and a is acceleration of the laboratory. Indeed, we can use this procedure to determine the mass of any object by comparing the reading of the scale, F_m, when the unknown mass m is in the pan with the reading F_{kg} when a liter of water in the pan: the water will have a mass m_{kg} of 1 kg by definition. We use the relations

$$F_m = ma \qquad \text{and} \qquad F_{kg} = m_{kg}a$$

or

$$m = m_{kg}\frac{F_m}{F_{kg}}$$

This is logically identical to the definitions of mass that we devised using the results of collisions in Section 5 | 1. We will call these masses *inertial* masses.

When the ship and laboratory return to rest on the surface of the earth, the pattern of measurements can be repeated. Now the liter of water on the pan of the scale is stationary. The force on the water due to gravity is counteracted by the force on the water from the pan on the scale. The reading on the scale will represent the force exerted by the pan on the water to keep the water stationary; this will be equal in magnitude to the force gravity exerts on the container of water. We find that the force is proportional to the mass of water in the pan, and in general we can describe the effects of gravity on water as

$$F_w = m_w g \tag{5 | 4}$$

where g is a constant that we call the *acceleration of gravity;* the value of g near the earth's surface varies from place to place, but is near 10 m/sec². Now we can assume that the relation holds for other materials and determine a *gravitational* mass for other materials by using the relation (5 | 4) together with readings of the force F on the scale. The gravitational mass will be defined as

$$m = \frac{F}{g}$$

or

$$m = m_w\frac{F}{F_w}$$

If we do this for the same set of materials for which we determined the inertial masses in space, we will find that the inertial masses and gravitational masses are equal. The inertial mass of an object is defined, with respect to a liter or kilogram of water, either by the analyses of collisions according to the procedures of Section 5|1, or according to the ratio of the force required to give the object a particular acceleration and the force required to give a standard liter or kilogram of water the same acceleration. The definitions are equivalent. The gravitational mass of an object is defined as the ratio of the force required to keep the object stationary in a gravitational field to the force required to keep a standard kilogram of water stationary in the same gravitational field.

We find, experimentally, that for all objects, the gravitational masses and inertial masses are equal. This conclusion that the force of gravity on an object is exactly proportional to the inertial mass is hardly obvious. The electrical forces are not proportional to mass; the nuclear forces on different particles are not proportional to mass. The extraordinary result comprises another view of the equivalence principle. We cannot use the force on masses to differentiate between laboratories that are being accelerated and laboratories under the influence of a gravitational field. Indeed this observation that gravitational masses and inertial masses are equivalent is the origin of the equivalence principle and ultimately the General Theory of Relativity.

PROBLEMS

5|1   A rocket having a mass of 10^6 kg is driven by a motor that acts to combine oxygen with hydrogen so as to eject water from the rocket tubes with an exhaust velocity of 5 km/sec. The rocket leaves the launching pad on the earth and ascends straight up with an acceleration of 10 m/sec^2. How much fuel is being exhausted per second?

5|2   A space ship having a mass of 50,000 kg, moving through space at a velocity of 5 km/sec, picks up by collision 1 gm of stationary cosmic dust per second. The dust sticks to the ship.

(*a*) What is the retarding force on the ship due to the dust collisions?

(*b*) If the exhaust velocity of the rocket fuel is 10 km/sec relative to the ship, how much fuel must the ship expend per second to maintain constant speed?

5|3 A hammer is used to drive a nail into a board. Assume that the mass of the hammer is 1 kg and is concentrated in the head, which is moving at a velocity of 2 m/sec when it strikes the nail. Assume that there is no recoil—the hammer follows the nail as it enters the board— and that the resistive force of the board on the nail is constant. If the nail is driven in 1 cm, what is the force the hammer exerts on the nail?

5|4 An automatic rifle weighing 5 kg shoots downward. The bullets, which weigh 25 gm, leave the gun with a muzzle velocity of 1000 m/sec. What is the rate of fire such that the recoil is just sufficient to keep the rifle suspended in air (the recoil balancing the weight)? (Neglect any change in mass of the rifle and magazine, and neglect effects of the momentum of ejected gas.)

5|5 A truck tractor is pulling a trailer. At a particular moment, the velocity of the truck is 20 m/sec, and the velocity is increasing so that the acceleration is 1 m/sec². The mass of the tractor is 2000 kg and that of the trailer is 10,000 kg. If air resistance and other friction on the trailer results in a retarding force of 1000 N, what force does the tractor exert on the trailer through the hitch between them?

5|6 A set of three blocks having masses of 1, 2, and 3 kg is at rest on the earth as shown ($g = 10$ m/sec²).

(*a*) What are the forces on each block?

(*b*) Assume that the blocks are fastened together and are somewhere in interstellar space where gravitation is negligible. Assume that a rope is attached to the 1-kg block and the whole set is pulled by the rope so that the acceleration is 10 m/sec². What are the forces on each block? What is the tension on each rope?

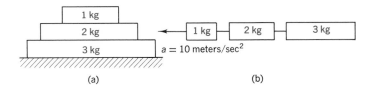

(a)   (b)

5|7 Describe or construct a set of experiments to be conducted on earth that would test the proposition that gravitational and inertial masses are equal.

5|8 A ball having a mass of 66 gm and the size of a billiard ball collides with a group of stationary billiard balls, each having a mass of 100 gm. After the collision one billiard ball moves in the direction of motion of the original ball with a velocity of 2 m/sec. Two other balls move away from the group in opposite directions at right angles to the direction of motion of the original ball. The velocity of one of these balls is 1 m/sec. All the other balls, including the original ball, are stationary. What is the velocity of the original ball? What is the velocity of the second ball that moves at right angles to the original direction of motion of the incident ball?

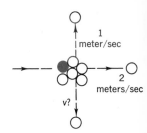

5|9 An astronaut's rocket motor has failed, and he is plunging toward Jupiter in free fall. His acceleration is 20 m/sec² and his velocity is 1000 m/sec. The astronaut weighs 100 kg. In exasperation he picks up a book having a mass of 1 kg and throws it to the floor with a velocity of 10 m/sec relative to him. The ceiling of the room is 20 m high. How long after he throws the book does his head hit the ceiling? (Neglect the height of the man.)

5|10 Guns are mounted on a rocket ship in interstellar space. The ship weighs 10,000 kg and travels at a velocity of 250 m/sec. The guns fire in the forward direction at a rate of 100 rounds/sec for 3 sec. The bullets weigh 100 gm apiece and the muzzle velocity is 1000 m/sec.

(a) What is the force on the rocket from the recoil of the guns?

(b) If the exhaust velocity of the rocket gases is 5 km/sec, how much fuel must be used to keep the rocket's speed constant?

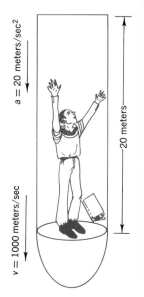

5|11 A shell fired from a gun in an environment where there is no gravity has a momentum **p**. If the shell explodes in flight, what will be the momentum of the total of the shell fragments? Justify your conclusion.

5|12 A chain 2 m long having a linear density of 1 kg/m slides off a table as shown in the diagram. At the instant half of the chain is off the table, what is the tensile force on the link that is just going over the edge? (Neglect friction.)

5|13 Each of the five weights shown has a mass of 1 kg. The mass of the string and pulley wheels is negligible.

(a) What is the value of the acceleration of the system?

(b) What is the tension on the section of rope marked *a*? On the section marked *b*?

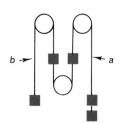

5|14   A projectile is passing directly overhead, parallel to the ground, with a velocity of 500 m/sec when it splits into two parts as a result of an explosive charge it carries. The mass of the explosive is negligible. One piece of the projectile falls straight down, landing 10 sec later at the feet of an observer, while the other piece is shot straight forward. The pieces are very heavy, so that air resistance is negligible; $g = 10$ m/sec².

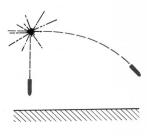

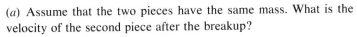

(*a*) Assume that the two pieces have the same mass. What is the velocity of the second piece after the breakup?

(*b*) How far away from the observer will the second piece hit the ground?

6 | 1   *Kinetic energy*

EVEN VERY SIMPLE collision processes are not completely defined by the law of conservation of momentum: we cannot predict
the consequences of simple collisions from the law of conservation of momentum alone. This suggests to us that there must
be additional constraints or laws relevant to such processes. It
is particularly easy to detect or define the character of such laws
by analyzing simple situations.

Figure 6 | 1 represents a particularly simple collision phenome-
non that results, nevertheless, in striking patterns. A number of
identical hard balls, such as billiard balls, each of mass m, are suspended by strings so that they touch one another in a manner
such that the centers of contact are in a straight line. If one
of the balls at the end of the group is drawn back a distance
s and let fall so that it collides with the set of balls with its velocity in line with the line of centers, one ball on the other end of
the set will rebound to approximately the height and distance s'
characteristic of the release of the first ball: $s = s'$. It is almost
obvious, even without more direct measurements, that the velocity of the final ball just after the collision is equal to the velocity
of the initial ball just before the collision. Since the balls are
identical, the mass of the first ball times its velocity before
collision is equal to the mass of the second ball times its velocity
after collision, which is what we expect from the law of conservation of momentum. If we pull two balls back from the group,

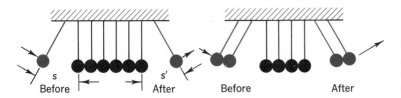

FIG. 6|1
*The character of
collisions of equal
elastic spheres.*

hold them together, and then let them fall and collide with the set, the two original balls will stop dead and two balls from the opposite end of the set will rebound together almost as a continuation of the motion of the first two balls. Again the velocity of the first set of balls v just before the collision will be equal to the velocity of the second set v' just after the collision. Again this is consistent with the conversation of momentum. If the mass of a ball is m,

$$(2m)v = (2m)v'$$

If we hold three balls back from the set and release them they will stop upon colliding with the set and three balls from the far end will rebound together. We will find the same kind of pattern with any number of balls.

We can observe the same patterns in the collisions of billiard balls with a line of other balls or the collisions of coins sliding on a table with lines of similar coins.

Although these results are consistent with the law of conservation of momentum, they are not uniquely determined by conservation of momentum. In the first case, where one ball was pulled back and released, the law of conservation of momentum would have been equally well satisfied if two balls had disengaged themselves from the set on the far end and proceeded with half the initial velocity; or three balls could have rebounded each with one third the initial velocity: an infinite number of other combinations could have ensued. Nevertheless, experimentally if one, two, or three balls are allowed to collide with the group, one, two, or three balls, respectively, will rebound. This suggests strongly to us that there must be another law of behavior operating in addition to the law of conservation of momentum. Further, the simplicity of the results suggests that this additional law of behavior might be simply described.

If the law is indeed simple, and if our experiment is indeed simple, we would expect that any quantitative description of this law can contain only the quantities mass and velocity: the total masses of the balls involved in the initial collision m and the total masses of the recoiling balls m', the velocity of the balls in the initial collision v and the velocity of the recoiling balls v'. We might examine the special case where one ball strikes the set and one ball recoils with the same velocity as the initial ball, rather than two balls recoiling, each with half the velocity. As we have said, both of these possibilities are in accord with the conservation of momentum. For one ball recoiling

(before)   (after)
$$mv = mv$$

for two balls recoiling

(before)   (after)
$$mv = (2m)(\tfrac{1}{2}v)$$

where in each case we compare the quantity before the collision on the left of the equality with the quantity after the collision on the right.

We can now attempt to construct other quantities that might be conserved in the hope of finding a conservation law that will allow one ball to recoil but forbid the recoil of two balls. We might guess that a conservation law holds such that the quantity m^2v is conserved. The for one ball

(before)   (after)
$$m^2v = m^2v$$

but for two balls

(before)   (after)
$$m^2v \neq (2m)^2(\tfrac{1}{2}v)$$

A conservation law of this kind would require that only one ball recoil rather than two; the recoil of two balls with half the velocity of the initial ball would violate the new conservation law we are suggesting. This is, then, very promising: we want a rule that forbids two balls recoiling.

However we should also investigate other possibilities. Perhaps the conserved quantity is mv^2; then for one ball

(before)   (after)
$$mv^2 = mv^2$$

but for two balls

(before)   (after)
$$mv^2 \neq (2m)(\tfrac{1}{2}v)^2$$

and the recoil of two balls with half the original velocity would again violate the conservation law. The existence of this new conservation law would also forbid the reaction that does not take place, which is just what we want.

But we have too many possibilities; indeed if we explored things further, we would find that the conservation of any quantity $m^a v^b$, where a and b are not both equal to one, would allow the result we see, one ball recoiling with the original velocity, and forbid the result we do not see, two balls rebounding with half the original velocity.

We must, then, test these various ideas further by proceding with a simple variation of the experiment. In this new setup, shown in Fig. 6|2, we use only three balls. We glue a two-ball set together to have a total mass of $2m$ and allow it to collide with the one remaining ball and measure all velocities before and after the collision. We can expect to gain some insight into the particular character of the additional law by examining the results. We might test the proposition that the conserved quantity is *mass times velocity squared*. If we write the initial velocity of the two-ball set as V, the final velocity of the two-ball set as V', and the final velocity of the single ball as v, we have Eq. (6|1) from the conservation of momentum and Eq. (6|2) from conservation of mass times velocity squared:

$$(2m)V = (2m)V' + mv \qquad\qquad\qquad (6|1)$$

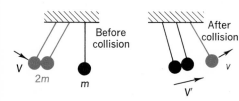

FIG. 6|2
The collision of two spheres glued together with one sphere.

$$(2m)V^2 = (2m)V'^2 + mv^2 \tag{6|2}$$

If we divide both sides of both equations by m, square both sides of Eq. (6|1) and then subtract from this result twice the value of the modified Eq. (6|2), we have

$$
\begin{array}{rcl}
4V^2 &=& 4V'^2 + 4V'v + v^2 \\
4V^2 &=& 4V'^2 + 2v^2 \\
\hline
0 &=& 0 + 4V'v - v^2
\end{array}
$$

Then

$$v = 4V' \qquad \text{and} \qquad v = \frac{4V}{3}$$

A measurement of the velocities in this experiment will show that they are in accord with these results calculated from the assumption that the quantity "mass times velocity squared" is a conserved quantity. The results will not be in agreement with the other possible assumptions: for example, the quantity m^2v will not be conserved.

We have avoided the necessity of considering whether the quantity mv^2 is a scalar or vector by restricting the collisions that were examined to head-on collisions, in which all the velocities lie in a line. We can construct a scalar of dimensions v^2 simply, from the vector quantities $\mathbf{v}$, by constructing the scalar product $(\mathbf{v} \cdot \mathbf{v})$. On the other hand, the vector $\mathbf{v}$ times the square root of the scalar product $(\mathbf{v} \cdot \mathbf{v})$, or $\mathbf{v}(\mathbf{v} \cdot \mathbf{v})^{1/2}$, will have the transformation properties of a vector and still have the dimension velocity squared. If we analyze the results of collisions of hard (elastic) particles that are not collinear, we find that the results are determined by the law of conservation of momentum and by the new relation, the conservation of the quantity, mv^2, where v^2 is indeed a scalar. This, then, is a scalar conservation law.

For convenience we are accustomed to considering the conservation of the quantity $\frac{1}{2}mv^2$, which we call *kinetic energy*. The introduction of the quantity $\frac{1}{2}$ results in no change in either principle or result. If the quantity mv^2 is conserved, of course, the quantity $\frac{1}{2}mv^2$ is also conserved.

In summary, we are now able to classify the results of a large set of collision phenomena in terms of two conservation laws, the conservation of momentum and the conservation of kinetic energy. The dimension of kinetic energy is seen to be equal to ML^2/T^2; the unit of energy is 1 kg m²/sec², a unit to which we give, for convenience, the special name *joule* (J).

6 | 2   *Elastic and inelastic collisions*

Most collision phenomena will not fit these simple conservation laws as they have been stated. Some simple examples of violations result if small bits of putty are placed between the balls of the experiment of Fig. 6 | 1, and the collision experiment is performed. After the first ball strikes the set, the other balls recoil at various small velocities with no obvious pattern. If we were to measure all of these velocities, we would find that the sum of mv for all balls after the impact would just equal the value of mv, the momentum, of the original ball. Momentum is still conserved as it should be, since no external force has acted along the line of the balls. However, the sum of the quantities $\frac{1}{2}mv^2$ for all of the balls after the collision will be much less than the value of $\frac{1}{2}mv^2$ of the original ball. So the kinetic energy of the original balls is not conserved. We give these two classes of collision phenomena particular names. We call collisions of the first class, defined so as to follow the two conservation laws, the conservation of energy and the conservation of momentum, *elastic* collisions. We call the second class of collisions, which conserve momentum but not kinetic energy, *inelastic* collisions. Kinetic energy is always lost in inelastic collisions; the resultant particles always have less kinetic energy than the incident particles.

We might ask whether these distinctions are not completely artificial. Of what importance is a conservation law if only very special classes of phenomena fit this law? Our answer is that the class of elastic collisions is a large class, differentiated qualitatively by its simplicity, and that we have reasons to hope that it is an ideal class, and that the conservation law may be intrinsically general and not less important because we understand how to apply it quantitatively only to this idealized class. This is similar to the restrictions on the law that all bodies fall at the same speed in a gravitational field, an idealization that suggests important general truths. We might anticipate that the conservation law may be extended to take into account all collision

phenomena, elastic and inelastic, and then to include all interactions of matter, when we understand these phenomena better.
In particular, we might expect that our defect in the application
of this law might lie in the limitations of our observations: perhaps our accounting system is faulty; perhaps kinetic energy is
conserved in all collisions, but some of this energy is transferred
to particles we do not count, such as the microscopic particles
that make up macroscopic matter.

6|3   *Potential energy*

A simple fundamental generalization of the limited rule concerning the conservation of kinetic energy can be made by introducing the concept of potential energy. We consider first a par-
ticularly simple situation. Figure 6|3 shows a ball falling from a
cliff where the height of the cliff is h_0. We assume that the ball
was originally thrown from the cliff with a velocity v_0 where the
positive direction is up, and we consider, for simplicity, only
motion up and down. We can then simplify the writing of the
equations concerning the vectors velocity and acceleration by
writing them as algebraic quantities. We are now prepared to
calculate the velocity of the ball at any point as it falls down the
cliff as a function of its height above the base of the cliff by using
one of the fundamental kinematic relationships developed pre-
viously (Eq. 2|5):

$$a(s - s_0) = \tfrac{1}{2}(v^2 - v_0^2)$$

where a is the acceleration and s is the displacement. The sub-

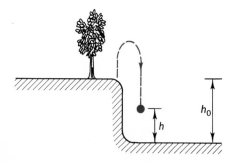

FIG. 6|3
*A path of a ball thrown
from a cliff.*

script zero marks the values of the quantities at $t = 0$, the time relevant to the beginning of the consideration of our problem. The acceleration is the acceleration of gravity g directed downward, so $a = -g$. The distance s is the height of the ball h; the initial distance is the height of the cliff h_0. The relation then has the form

$$-g(h - h_0) = \tfrac{1}{2}(v^2 - v_0^2)$$

Multiplying both sides of the equation by m, the mass of the ball, and rearranging terms, the equation is written

$$\tfrac{1}{2}mv^2 + mgh = \tfrac{1}{2}mv_0^2 + mgh_0 \qquad\qquad\qquad (6|3)$$

The right-hand side of the equation is a constant depending only on the initial height and initial velocity of the ball. Thus the sum of the quantities $\tfrac{1}{2}mv^2 + mgh$, which make up the left-hand side of the equation, is also constant or conserved. We give the name *potential energy* to the quantity that is equal to mgh in this case and extend the limited conservation law concerning kinetic energy in elastic collisions to the more general statement that the *total energy of the system is conserved,* where by total energy we mean the sum of kinetic and potential energy.

In the very particular system of a ball in a gravitational field, the potential energy has the form mgh. The potential energy will be described differently in other systems, depending in detail on the character of the forces involved. That is, we can very often construct a scalar quantity with the dimensions of energy that varies with some parameter (such as h, the height above the ground, for the falling body) in a way such that the sum of the quantity and the kinetic energy is always constant. And we call this quantity *potential energy*. The restricted law of the conservation of energy can now be extended to a more general statement: The sum of the kinetic energy and the potential energy of a closed system is conserved. We are implying that we either take into account dissipative mechanisms such as friction or that our statement is valid only in the absence of these types of energy losses.

You will notice that we have invented this concept of potential energy in order, again, to achieve a simple description of our observations of nature. This would be bad taste, at best, if we had to invent a large number of essentially arbitrary quantities and arbitrary relations. When we have as many quantities as observations, we are back to witchcraft. Of course that is not the case with the concepts of kinetic energy, potential energy, and momentum. These are simple and powerful constructs that can be used to classify very large numbers of different observations.

In certain specific cases it is possible to show that the macroscopic concept of potential energy can be understood in terms of the kinetic energy of microscopic particles. Even as compressing an air-filled tire, where the tire acts as a spring, can be considered to increase the potential energy of the tire, we know now that the energy stored by the tire, and called by us potential energy, is actually the increased kinetic energy of the air molecules in the tire. If we define carefully what we mean by particle, it seems that this exposition of potential energy can probably be extended to all forces; but these are subtle concepts, and we will usually find it convenient to talk about potential energy as if it were something apart from kinetic energy.

6|4   *Work*

The transfer of energy from one system to another, or from kinetic energy to potential energy or vice versa, involves a concept that is sufficiently specific that it is useful to give it a particular name, *work*. It is helpful to examine the description of the falling body as shown in Fig. 6|3 in order to demonstrate the utility of the concept of work. When the ball falls a short distance dh, the kinetic energy T (equal to $\frac{1}{2}mv^2$) changes a small amount, dT. From the law of conservation of energy the change in the kinetic energy of the ball (the ball-and-earth system) is equal in magnitude and opposite in sign to the change in potential energy

$$dT = -dV$$
$$= -mg\,dh$$

where we use the symbol V for the potential energy of the system.

The quantity mg, mass times the acceleration of gravity, has the dimensions of force and is the quantity we call the force of gravity on the ball. The relation can then be written

$$dT = -dV$$
$$= -mg\,dh$$
$$= -F\,dh$$

We give the name *work* to the quantity $F\,dh$, which has the dimensions of energy. In this case the increment of work, $F\,dh = dw$, is equal in magnitude to the change in kinetic energy. The sign of the work depends upon which transfer we are considering. As the ball falls, we might consider that the outside agency (the gravitational field) is doing work on the ball, increasing the kinetic energy of the ball. The ball is doing negative work on the field, reducing the energy stored—as potential energy—in the field. When the ball is rising, the reverse is true. In general, we will consider F as the force acting on some body (the ball) by some outside agency (here the gravitational field) and the work dw as being done by the outside agency on the ball. The signs are reversed when we consider the work done by the body on the agency. The sign conventions are not too important in practice, because for any real problem the directions of the forces and the directions of the energy transfer are usually obvious.

In order to express events in a space of more than one dimension, it is necessary to express the relations between force, distance, and work in a consistent covariant notation:

$$dw = (\mathbf{F} \cdot d\mathbf{s})$$
$$= F\,ds\,\cos\theta \qquad\qquad\qquad\qquad\qquad \textbf{(6|4)}$$

where $d\mathbf{s}$ is the vector displacement, $\mathbf{F}$ is the vector force, dw is the increment of work, and θ is the angle between the applied force and the displacement.

Work is a scalar quantity with the dimensions of energy even as kinetic energy and potential energy are scalar quantities with the dimensions of energy. The scalar *work* is made up of the scalar product of the vector *force* and the vector *distance*. As with other scalar products, it is sometimes more convenient to use the relation $dw = F\,ds\,\cos\theta$, where θ is the angle between the force and the distance, and the quantities in the relation are algebraic quantities.

We note some immediate simple properties of this relation: there is no work done when the force is perpendicular to the displacement. This approaches the obvious; consider some examples familiar to us on the basis of our general experience: When a mass of 1 kg mounted on frictionless bearings is moved 1 meter along a table, even though the force on the mass is 10 N, of course no work is done. On the other hand, if one lifts the mass of 1 kg 1 m, one does 10 units of work or 10 J of work in our mks system of units. In the first case the force was perpendicular to the displacement; in the second case the force was aligned with the displacement; in the first case cos θ was zero; in the second case cos θ was equal to 1—all consistent with the general relation (6|4).

In the example discussed, we considered the change in kinetic energy of the ball as a result of work done on the ball. It is customary to say the work was done by the gravitational field of the earth. At any rate, it is work done by an outside agency as far as the ball is concerned. After the ball rests on the ground, we may wish to return it to the top of the cliff. We can do this by lifting the ball against the force of gravity. If the ball has a mass m, the force required is equal to mg, where g is the acceleration of gravity. The amount of work done in lifting the ball 1 meter is equal to mg units of work, where m is measured in kg and g in m/sec^2. The units are units of force times distance, newton-meters or joules. The amount of work done to lift the ball from the base of the cliff to the top is equal, then, to mgh, where h is the height of the cliff. Again work is done on the ball, increasing the potential energy of the ball rather than the kinetic energy, and again the work is done by an outside agency. We need not define the outside agency; in this case it might be a crane, for example.

In summary, the detailed transfer of energy from one body to another, or from the kinetic energy of one body to potential energy of that body, or vice versa, invariably takes place through a mechanism that is describable in terms of a force acting through a distance. It is this transfer of energy that is called work. Work is a scalar invariant equal to the invariant product of the vectors force and distance; or the force times the distance times the cosine of the angle between the force and distance, where the quantities are treated algebraically.

6|5　*Force and potential energy*

Gravitational potential energy is only one of the forms of potential energy. As another example we consider the potential energy of an ideal compressed spring. The force a typical spring exerts is simply proportional to its change in dimension and opposite in direction to the change in dimension. For example, in a rubber band the force is approximately proportional to the distance the rubber band is stretched; in a compression spring, the force exerted is approximately proportional to the distance the spring is compressed. This simple relation is called Hooke's law and is written explicitly as

$$F = -kx \qquad\qquad (6|5)$$

where F is the force exerted by the spring on the restraining body, k is a proportionality constant called the *spring constant* and x is the displacement from equilibrium where the force is zero. The minus sign signifies that the force is directed opposite to the displacement.

The graph of Fig. 6|4b shows the force exerted by the spring on the restraining body as a function of the displacement x. The shaded area, equal to minus the force exerted by the spring on the body times an increment of displacement, is equal to the increment of work done by the spring on the body as the body is displaced:

$$dw = F \, dx \qquad \text{or} \qquad \frac{dw}{dx} = F$$

The expression that results can be recognized as having the same form as the differential equation $dV/dt = a$; (DE-CA). The area under the whole curve, equal to the work done by the spring as the body is displaced by an amount x', is expressed by the integral form 0 to x' of $F \, dx$. This area is equal to the area under the triangle with a base of x' and a height equal to $F' = -kx'$. The total work is then

FIG. 6|4
The variation of force and potential energy with respect to change in length of a coiled spring: w is the work done by the spring, V is the potential energy of the spring.

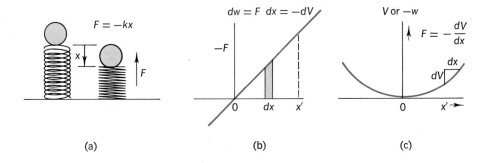

(a)　　　　　(b)　　　　　(c)

$$w = \int_0^{x'} F \, dx$$

$$= \int_0^{x'} (-kx) \, dx$$

$$= -\tfrac{1}{2}kx'^2$$

This is the work done by the spring on the body as the spring is compressed starting from an equilibrium position. The sign is negative, indicating that energy is transferred to the spring from the body and that the body does work on the spring. The energy stored by the spring is then the potential energy of the spring in the same way that the energy stored by the gravitational field as a body is lifted to a height is considered the potential energy of the system.

The total work done by the spring on the body—and then the negative of the work done by the body on the spring—is shown as a function of the displacement x' in the diagram of Fig. 6|4c. The slope of this curve, dV/dx, is then equal to $-dw/dx$, which is equal to the force F. This is a useful and therefore important relation:

$$F = -\frac{dV}{dx} \qquad \text{or} \qquad dV = -F \, dx \qquad \qquad (6|6)$$

In all of these relations the appropriate choice of sign can be confusing if one considers the relations only formally. In practice, this is of little concern because the appropriate sign will usually be obvious in any real problem.

Relation (6|6) is quite general, applying to the large variety of systems to which the concepts of force and potential energy are applicable. The interactions between elementary particles, between nuclei, between atoms, between molecules, between electrically charged macroscopic objects, between the earth and the moon, between the sun and the earth, between different stars, and between the different assemblies of stars that we call galaxies can all be described wholly or in part in terms of potential energies and forces, and the expressions of (6|6) then pertain to all of these interactions. If a curve of force versus displacement in some particular direction is plotted for the displacement of some atom with respect to another, or one star with respect to another, the area under the curve between two values of the displacement

represents the work done in effecting the displacement and thus
the change in potential energy. If a curve of potential energy
versus displacement in some direction is plotted for any physical
system, such as shown in Fig. 6|4b for a spring the slope of the
curve for any value of the displacement will be equal to the force
exerted in that direction by the system on the constraint.

It may be helpful to an understanding of the principles of this
kind of description of interactions to consider a particular
example very close to our experience. The illustration of Fig. 6|5
shows a cart that is allowed to roll on a surface in a uniform gravitational field. For definiteness we will assume that the surface is
on earth and then there is a force due to gravity on the cart where
g is 10 m/sec² directed downward. The potential energy of the
cart varies with its height; an increase in height of 1 m increases
the potential energy 10 J if the mass of the cart is 1 kg. It is obvious to us intuitively that the cart will be forced to the left by the
surface when it is on the surface c, and there will be a force on the
cart pushing it to the right when it is on the surface a. It is also obvious that the force will be greater in magnitude on the steeper
slope c than on a. As the cart moves to the right on c under an
external force directed on it, it will rise 1 m for every meter it
moves to the right; the potential energy will increase at the rate
of 10 J for each meter to the right in the x-direction. The force the
potential-energy surface exerts on the cart will be to the left, or
in a negative x-direction, and will be equal to $-dV/dx = -10$ N.
The force on the cart on the slope a will be $+5$ N, where plus and
minus have the meaning of to the right and left.

$g = 10$ meters/sec²
$V = Mgh = 10$ J/meter

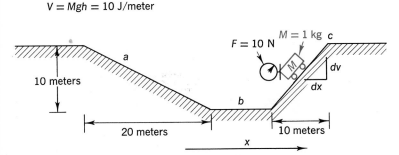

FIG. 6|5
*The relation between
force and the rate of
change of potential
energy is illustrated by
considering the force on
a cart rolling on a
surface in a uniform
gravitational field.*

6|6   *An example of energy transfers*

It is instructive to consider the energy transfers in a simple system as an illustration of the principles and definitions we have established. Such a system is shown in Fig. 6|6.

Initially a ball lies on the ground near an inclined plane. We can consider the total energy of the system in this state as zero: we are never interested in the absolute energy of a system—we do not know whether the concept of absolute energy has any operational meaning—we are interested only in differences of energy. Work is done from outside the system by some external agency that runs the pulley system on the inclined plane and moves the ball slowly up the plane (a). The force applied to the ball by the pulley system must counteract the force of gravity along the slope and must therefore be equal to (or infinitesimally greater than) the component of the force of gravity on the ball along the plane, namely, $mg \sin \theta$, where m is the mass of the ball, g is the acceleration of gravity, and θ is the angle the plane makes with the ground, taken here as 30°. Since the value of $\sin 30°$ is $\frac{1}{2}$, the force is $\frac{1}{2}mg$. This force is applied along the length of the incline, which is equal to the height of the incline, h, divided by $\sin \theta$, or $h/\sin \theta$, which is equal to $2h$. The total work done is equal to the force along the incline times the distance along the incline, or $\frac{1}{2}mg$ times $2h$, or mgh. The work done by the outside agency to bring the ball to the top of the plane, at a height h, is independent of the angle of the incline θ and is just equal to the potential energy of the ball, mgh, with respect to the ground.

Next (b) the ball falls off the top of the incline onto a spring, compressing the spring (c). As the ball falls, the potential energy changes to kinetic energy. Assuming that the height of the spring

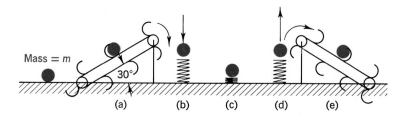

Mass = m

(a)   (b)   (c)   (d)   (e)

FIG. 6|6
An illustration of different forms of energy and the exchanges of energy.

is negligible, the kinetic energy of the ball as it hits the spring will be just equal to the potential energy of the ball at the top of the incline, which in turn is equal to the work done by the outside action. The ball now will be slowed to a stop by the force the spring exerts on the ball while the spring is being compressed. The spring does work on the ball, reducing its kinetic energy; the ball does work on the spring to compress the spring. At the moment the ball is stationary, all of the kinetic energy has passed to the potential energy of the spring: the potential energy of the spring at this point is equal to the original work done by the external source, of course.

Now if the spring is unlatched, it will propel the ball upward: (d): if the system is well designed, all of the energy of the spring will pass again into the kinetic energy of the ball. So the instant the ball leaves the spring, it will have the same magnitude of velocity as when it hit the spring, although in the opposite direction. This velocity and this kinetic energy were provided by the work the spring did on the ball. If the system is efficient, the ball will then rise to a height just equal to the height of the first incline. When it reaches this point it will have no kinetic energy, but it will have a potential energy again equal to the amount of work initially done on the ball by the outside agent. We might here say that the ball does work against the gravitational field in changing its kinetic energy to potential energy.

Then the ball rolls down this second incline (e), driving a pulley system similar to the pulley system that first drove the ball up. If this system is so designed that the ball goes down very slowly, having a negligible velocity and therefore a negligible kinetic energy at the bottom, the ball will have done work on the pulley that is just equal to the work done initially on the first pulley system to push the ball up the incline. Energy will have been conserved.

No system really works as well as the one described in the preceding paragraphs. Always some energy is lost from the simple sum of kinetic and potential energy. We now know that this energy is not lost physically, but only appears to be lost as a result of imperfections in our accounting system. The kinetic energy of some microscopic particles is increased, and hence energy is lost from the macroscopic description. These microscopic particles are the particles that make up the ball, spring, and so on. When we take into account energy lost to microscopic motion—energy finally accounted for in the form we term heat—we find that the total energy is completely conserved and that we have a general and far-reaching law of the total conservation of energy. Classically, we have a parallel law concerning the conservation of matter, which states that the total amount of matter in any closed system is constant. We now know from the theory of relativity and experiment that energy and matter are really different aspects of the same thing and can be expressed in terms of one another. Our law of the conservation of energy therefore implicitly contains the law of the conservation of matter.

6|7   *Power*

We may be interested in the rate of doing work as well as the work done. Through an appropriate pulley system and gears it is possible to arrange for a mouse, running in a treadmill, to lift a mass of a ton to a height of 10 meters. An elephant or a building crane could do the same. There is a considerable, and obvious, difference between the activity of a mouse and an elephant or a building crane, and it is important to recognize this quantitatively. The difference lies in the rate of doing work. The mouse in its little treadmill must work for a very long time to lift the ton 10 meters; to do 10^5 J of work with a well-designed treadmill it might take an industrious mouse about a month of hard work. A building crane would need but a few seconds. Each can supply a different rate of work, a different power.

Power is work per unit time. The unit of power in the mks system of units is the joule per second or watt (W). A man can deliver about 100 W for a reasonable length of time, a mouse about 0.1 W, and a typical motorized building crane can deliver about 50,000 W. In the English system we use horsepower (hp) as a unit of power. It is useful to remember that 1000 W, or 1 kW, is equal to about $\frac{4}{3}$ hp. Contrariwise, 1 hp is equal to about $\frac{3}{4}$ kW.

The definition of power leads to some simple auxilliary relations that are worth noting. Since power equals work per unit time, or $P = dw/dt$, and work equals force times distance, or $dw = F\,ds$, we have immediately

$$P = \frac{dw}{dt}$$

$$= \left(\mathbf{F} \cdot \frac{d\mathbf{s}}{dt} \right)$$

$$= (\mathbf{F} \cdot \mathbf{v})$$

$$= Fv \cos \theta$$

where θ is the angle between the direction of the force and the direction of the velocity.

PROBLEMS

6|1 The cart in the figure weighs 100 kg. From a stationary start, the cart rolls on very small wheels, with negligible *friction*, down the track. When the cart passes the point *i*:

(*a*) What is the kinetic energy of the cart?

(*b*) What is the velocity of the cart?

(*c*) What is the potential energy of the cart with respect to the starting point?

(*d*) What is the potential energy of the cart with respect to the ground?

(*e*) How high will the cart go in the air when it leaves the track at *ii*?

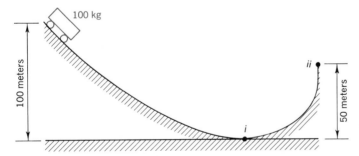

6|2 A bow is designed so that the force required to bend the bow varies with the distance the arrow is pulled back as shown by the solid line in the figure. The arrow has a mass of 50 gm and is pulled back 50 cm. If all of the energy stored in the bow is transmitted to the arrow and if air resistance can be neglected:

(*a*) How high will the arrow go if it is shot straight up?

(*b*) If the bow were designed so that the pull varied as shown by the dashed line on the figure how high would the arrow go?

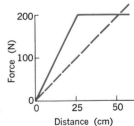

6|3   The curve shows the potential energy of two molecules as a function of the distance between the molecules. Plot a curve showing the approximate force between the molecules indicating clearly where the force is attractive and where it is repulsive.

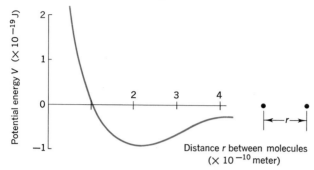

6|4   Assume that the cart rolls smoothly on the surface (that is, the discontinuities are smoothed out) and the mass of the cart is 2 kg. The acceleration of gravity is 10 m/sec².

(a) Draw a graph of the potential energy of the cart on the surface as a function of the distance x.

(b) If the cart rolls very slowly over the edge at g, what will be the velocity of the cart at the end of the segment marked a? at the end of b? at the end of c? at the end of d? at the end of e? (Ignore friction.)

(c) What is the value of the x-component of the force on the cart when the cart is on the segment a? b? c? d? e?

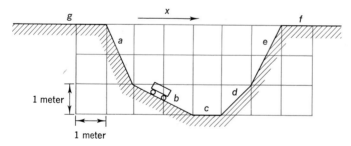

6|5   A heavy chain one meter long lies stretched out on a frictionless table so that its length is perpendicular to an edge of the table. The end of the chain slips over the edge and pulls the rest of the chain with it off the table. How fast is the chain moving when half its length is off the table?

6|6   An automobile is traveling on a level highway at a speed of 30 m/sec (about 70 mph). Measurements of the engine operating conditions show that 60 hp is being delivered to the rear wheels. One hp is equal to $\frac{3}{4}$ kW. The mass of the car is 1000 kg.

(*a*) What is the force exerted on the car by air resistance? (This is the main frictional force.)

(*b*) If the air resistance remains constant, what power is required for the car to travel 30 m/sec up a 10 percent grade? (As the car moves 100 m it goes up 10 m.)

6|7 A space vehicle is traveling through interstellar space in our galaxy with a constant velocity of 10,000 km/sec. The cross section of the ship is 100 m². Assume that all the matter the ship sweeps through on its journey sticks to it. The density of matter in space is about 10^{-20} kg/m³ (about one hydrogen atom/cm³).

(*a*) What is the effective retarding force on the ship resulting from the collection of this matter?

(*b*) How much power is required from the ship's motors to keep the velocity of the ship constant?

6|8 A heavy body is moving with constant velocity through a rarefied gas. Assume that the gas molecules bounce off the body elastically, and for further simplicity assume that the surface of the body is such that the "front" is flat and perpendicular to the direction of motion. Assume that the velocity of the body is *v* and that the gas molecules are stationary before being struck by the moving body.

(*a*) Show that the molecules bounce off the moving missile with a velocity equal to 2*v*. (It may help to consider this problem from the view of an observer on the missile who sees the gas molecules coming at him with velocity *v*.)

(*b*) Show that the work the body must do in traveling 1 meter against the friction of the gas is proportional to v^2.

(*c*) Show that the power required to overcome friction and keep the body moving at constant velocity is proportional to v^3.

6|9 A rocket having a mass of 10^4 kg is leaving the moon, where the acceleration of gravity is 1.5 m/sec². The acceleration of the rocket is 5 m/sec² and the exhaust velocity of the gas from the rocket engines is 10,000 m/sec.

(*a*) How much fuel must be expended per second?

(*b*) How much energy will be expended by the rocket (through its engines) in the first second after takeoff?

(c) What will be the value of the kinetic energy of the rocket 1 sec after takeoff? (Neglect the change in mass of the rocket that results from the burning of its fuel.)

6|10 The water in the tank shown is 1 m deep. Water flows into the large pipe at the top of the tank *very slowly* to keep the level constant. What is the velocity of the water flowing out the small hole near the bottom of the tank? Neglect the effects of viscosity (friction).

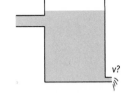

6|11   Certain simple machines, such as levers, are designed to multiply an input force or an input motion. If energy is conserved, the input work $f\,ds$ must be equal to the output work $f'\,ds'$, where f and f' are the input and output forces and ds and ds' are the distances through which the input and output forces act.

(a) Show that the mechanical advantage of the lever, f'/f, is equal to L/L'.

(b) The radius of the large cylinder in the hydraulic system is r', and that of the small cylinder is r. The oil is incompressible. Show that f'/f is equal to r^2/r'^2.

(c) A complex pulley system is designed so that a weight is lifted 1 ft as 10 ft of chain are payed out. If friction can be neglected, how much force is required to lift 100 kg using the pulley system?

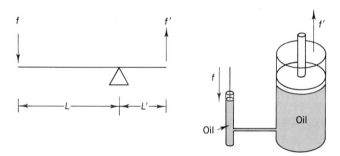

6|12   A ball the size of a billiard ball but of unknown mass collides with a group of stationary billiard balls, each having a mass of 100 gm. After the collision one billiard ball moves in the direction of motion of the original ball with a velocity of 1 m/sec. Two other balls also move away from the group, but in opposite directions at right angles to the original direction of motion. The velocity of one is 1.0 m/sec. All the other balls, including the incident ball, are stationary after the collision. What is the mass of the original ball?

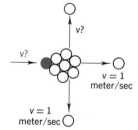

seven *Angular momentum and circular motion*

7 | 1 *The conservation of angular momentum*

OUR DAY-TO-DAY experience of nature suggests to us that there may be other constants of nature besides energy and momentum. A spinning wheel persists in its motion; not only does the rate of spin tend to remain constant, but the direction of the axis of the wheel has a definite tendency to remain unchanged as in a gyroscope. The length of the day—a measure of the rotation of the earth—remains very constant, and the northern extension of the axis of rotation continues to point very near the star Polaris as the earth travels in its orbit around the sun. And the time required to complete that orbit—the year—remains very constant. Although the conservation of *angular momentum* is most obvious when we consider circular orbits, the concept is more general and we introduce this conservation law by analyzing a characteristic of motion in a straight line.

Figure 7 | 1 shows the trajectory of a particle moving in a straight line and a point i that lies at a distance a from the straight line. If the particle moves at constant velocity, v, it will traverse equal distances in equal intervals of time. Two such displacements are displayed on Fig. 7 | 1: ds and ds'. The shaded areas, which are the areas subtended by the displacements ds and ds' from the point i, are then equal. Both areas have the form of triangles. The bases of these triangles, ds and ds', are equal from

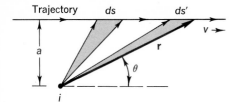

FIG. 7|1
The trajectory of a particle moving with constant velocity sweeps out equal areas with respect to a point i in equal times.

the condition that the particle is moving with constant velocity and the displacements represent displacements traversed in equal times; the height of each triangle is the distance a; the area of each triangle is therefore equal to $\frac{1}{2}a\ ds$. The path of the particle subtends equal areas with respect to any arbitrary point in equal intervals of time.

If the interval ds is sufficiently short, the vector representing the distance between the point i and the beginning of the interval will be almost the same as the vector connecting the point with the end of the interval. In the limit of an infinitesimal ds, the two vectors are the same and we label the vector $\mathbf{r}$. The distance a is now equal to $r \sin \theta$, where θ is the angle between $\mathbf{r}$ and $\mathbf{v}$. Since ds is equal to $v\ dt$, the area dA subtended by the path of the particle in a time dt is equal to $\frac{1}{2}v\ dt\ r \sin \theta$, or the area subtended per unit time is

$$\frac{dA}{dt} = \tfrac{1}{2}vr \sin \theta \tag{7|1}$$

and this quantity is a constant. If each side of Eq. (7|1) is multiplied by 2 for convenience, and by the mass of the particle m, the quantities will still be constant. This particular combination defines the *angular momentum j* of the particle about the point i.

$$j = mvr \sin \theta$$

Since $mv = p$, where p is the momentum of the particle, the relation can also be written as

$$j = pr \sin \theta \tag{7|2}$$

where θ is the angle between the vectors $\mathbf{p}$ and $\mathbf{r}$. Since the value of r to a point other than i will be different, it is clear that the angular momentum of the particle about another point will generally have a different value.

Even as the combination $pr \sin \theta$ can represent different geo-

metric constructions, the meaning of the combination can be
stated in different ways: the angular momentum of a particle at
a point *b* with respect to a point *a* is equal to the product of the
momentum of the particle *p* times the perpendicular distance
from *a* to the trajectory of the particle r_t as represented by the
cross-hatched area in Fig. 7|2a; or the angular momentum of a
particle at point *b* with respect to a point *a* is equal to *r*, the
distance between *a* and *b*, times the component of momentum
p_t of the particle perpendicular to *r*, as shown by the cross-
hatched area of Fig. 7|2b. The two cross-hatched areas are
equal, of course, and are equal to the quantity we have defined
as the angular momentum of the particle about the point *a*. In
the absence of any interaction, the angular momentum *j* of the
massive particle about any point in space is conserved: the
angular momentum about any point is a constant of motion even
as the momentum or energy of the particle.

The conservation law that has been described is not very interesting as long as it is restricted to the case of a particle moving
with constant velocity in a straight line. The law is important
only if angular momentum is conserved under more general
conditions such that collisions and other interactions between
particles are allowed. It is easy to show that the total angular
momentum of a pair of particles is conserved though the particles
interact.

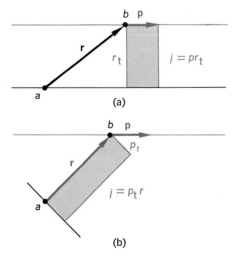

FIG. 7|2

*Two different
representations of the
angular momentum of a
particle with respect to
a point.*

In order to establish the validity of the conservation law in the presence of interactions, it is useful to examine a simple, but characteristic, interaction. Assume that two particle, moving with momenta **B** and **C**, collide and form one particle with momentum **A**. From the conservation of momentum

$$A = B + C$$

as shown in Fig. 7|3a. The magnitude of **A** can be expressed in terms of the magnitudes of **B** and **C** as

$$A = B \cos \theta_b + C \cos \theta_c \qquad (7\,|\,3)$$

where θ_b and θ_c are the angles between the vectors **A** and **B**, and **A** and **C**, respectively. We are interested in the relation of the angular momentum with respect to some arbitrary point of the particles with momenta **B** and **C** before the collision to the angular momentum of the particle with momentum **A** after the collision.

The angular momentum of the final particle after the collision is just Aa, where a is the distance from the particle to the point in a direction perpendicular to **A**. The magnitude of the angular momentum is then shown by the appropriate area of Fig. 7|3a. Likewise the angular momenta of the original particles is equal to Cc and Bb, where c and b are the distances from the particles to the reference point x in directions perpendicular to **C** and **B**. Again these angular momenta are equal to the appropriate areas of Fig. 7|3a. If angular momentum is conserved in the interaction,

$$Aa = Bb + Cc$$

or the areas of the two colored rectangles must equal the area of the other rectangle. It is easy to show that this is true.

Multiplying expression 7|3 by a, we have

$$Aa = Ba \cos \theta_b + Ca \cos \theta_c$$

But it is easily seen from the diagram of Fig. 7|3 that

$$b = a \cos \theta_b \qquad \text{and} \qquad c = a \cos \theta_c$$

Therefore

$$Aa = Bb + Cc$$

which is just what we wished to prove: that the total angular

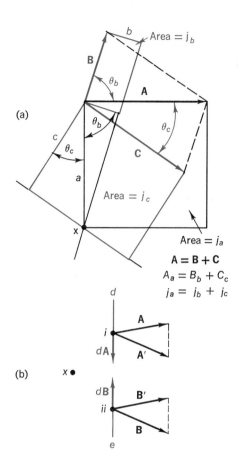

(a)

$$A = B + C$$
$$A_a = B_b + C_c$$
$$j_a = j_b + j_c$$

(b)

FIG. 7 | 3
*Diagrams showing that
total angular momentum
of a system is conserved
in the presence of
interactions.*

momentum after the interaction was the same as the angular momentum before the interaction.

A slightly more complex interaction is shown in Fig. 7 | 3b: two particles move with momenta **A** and **B** interact through a long-range attractive interaction at a time when they are at the points *i* and *ii*, respectively. At this instant, as a result of the interaction, the momenta of the two particles are altered by the addition of the components $d\mathbf{A}$ and $d\mathbf{B}$. The momentum of the first particle after the interaction is $\mathbf{A}' = \mathbf{A} + d\mathbf{A}$, and the momentum of the second particle is $\mathbf{B}' = \mathbf{B} + d\mathbf{B}$. From the conservation of momentum, $d\mathbf{A}$ and $d\mathbf{B}$ are equal in magnitude but opposite in direction.

We can now see that the angular momentum of the two par-

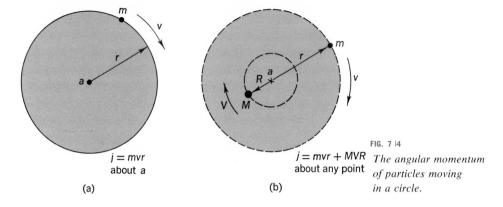

$j = mvr$
about a

(a)

$j = mvr + MVR$
about any point

(b)

FIG. 7 | 4 *The angular momentum of particles moving in a circle.*

ticles about the arbitrary point x will not be changed by the interaction. The change in angular momentum of the first particle will be equal to $d\mathbf{A}$ times the distance from x to the line d-e and the change in the angular momentum of the second particle will be equal to $d\mathbf{B}$ times the distance from x to the line d-e on Fig. 7|3b. Since $d\mathbf{A}$ and $d\mathbf{B}$ are oppositely directed, the total change in angular momentum about x (or any other point) is then zero: the interaction has not changed the total angular momentum of the two particles about the arbitrary point x.

Obviously, the situations we have discussed are hardly completely general. However, those results can be extended to any number of particles, interacting with one another in any possible way, without introducing any particularly different methods of calculation. The result is general, and it appears that the total angular momentum of any set of particles with respect to any arbitrary point is conserved through any history of interaction of the particles. This total angular momentum is thus a constant of nature.

It is now useful to consider the archetypical systems that suggested the importance of the conservation of angular momentum, systems that can be described adequately as mass points moving with constant velocity in a circle as in Fig. 7|4a. Here the angular momentum of the mass point with respect to the center of the circle is simply

$$j = pr$$

$$= mvr$$

where $p = mv$ is the magnitude of the linear momentum of the particle with mass m moving with a velocity v about the circle, and r is the radius of the orbit. Unless the whole system is considered as in Fig. 7|4b, including the bodies that act on the mass point to restrain its motion to the circle, the angular momentum of the system will be constant only with respect to the center of the circle. The angular momentum of the whole system will be the same with respect to any point at rest with respect to the center of the circle. Neglecting, for simplicity, the effect of other bodies, the angular momentum of the earth alone is constant only with respect to the center of its orbit (more precisely, with respect to one of the foci of its elliptical orbit.) But the angular momentum of the sun and earth is constant and has the same value with respect to any point that is stationary with respect to that focus.

7|2   *The transformation properties of angular momentum and torque*

The quantities momentum and displacement are vectors. In the definition of angular momentum we have used these only as algebraic quantities and have not concerned ourselves with the transformation properties of angular momentum. In Fig. 7|5a we show two vectors, **p** and **r**, in a two-dimensional coordinate system. Here **p** represents the vector momentum and **r** represents the vector distance between the position of the particle and an arbitrary axis of rotation, taken here as the origin of the coordinate system.

It is desirable to express the angular momentum in terms of the components of the two vectors **p** and **r**. Each of these vectors can be expressed as the sum of vectors that lie along the coordinate axes and have a magnitude equal to the components of

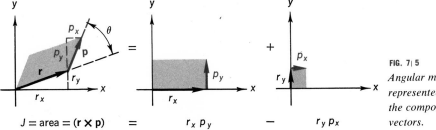

FIG. 7|5
Angular momentum represented in terms of the components of vectors.

p and **r**. We write these as

$$\mathbf{r} = \mathbf{r}_x + \mathbf{r}_y \quad \text{and} \quad \mathbf{p} = \mathbf{p}_x + \mathbf{p}_y$$

Then the relation

$$j = rp \sin \theta$$

where θ is the angle between the vectors **r** and **p**, can be written as

$$j = r_x p_x \sin \theta_{xx} + r_x p_y \sin \theta_{xy} + r_y p_x \sin \theta_{yx} + r_y p_y \sin \theta_{yy}$$

where θ_{xx} is the angle between $\mathbf{r}_x$ and $\mathbf{p}_x$, θ_{xy} is the angle between $\mathbf{r}_x$ and $\mathbf{p}_y$, and so on. It is immediately clear that

$$\sin \theta_{xx} = 0 \qquad \sin \theta_{xy} = 1 \qquad \sin \theta_{yx} = -1 \qquad \sin \theta_{yy} = 0$$

then

$$j = rp \sin \theta = (\mathbf{r} \times \mathbf{p}) = (r_x p_y - r_y p_x) \qquad (7\,|\,4)$$

where r_x and r_y are the components of **r** and p_x and p_y are the components of **p**. The relations (7 | 4), which are shown graphically in Fig. 7 | 5, define angular momentum in two dimensions.

The relation $(\mathbf{r} \times \mathbf{p})$, defined in Eq. (7 | 4) for vectors in a two-dimensional manifold, is called the *vector product* of **r** and **p**, in contrast to the scalar product $(\mathbf{r} \cdot \mathbf{p})$.

Even as total linear momentum is conserved, we believe that total angular momentum is conserved; even as we are interested often in the change in the linear momentum of a particular particle, we can be interested in the change of the angular momentum of a particular particle. The change in linear momentum per unit time is defined as force; $\mathbf{F} = d\mathbf{p}/dt$. A change in the angular momentum of a particle with respect to some particular point or axis of rotation will involve a change in the momentum of the particle. Considering, for simplicity, a situation where the radius r does not change, the change in angular momentum will reflect the change in linear momentum

$$\mathbf{j} = (\mathbf{r} \times \mathbf{p})$$

then

$$\frac{d\mathbf{j}}{dt} = \left(\mathbf{r} \times \frac{d\mathbf{p}}{dt} \right)$$

where

$$\frac{d\mathbf{p}}{dt} = \mathbf{F}$$

Then

$$\frac{d\mathbf{j}}{dt} = (\mathbf{r} \times \mathbf{F})$$

$$= rF \sin \theta$$

$$= L$$

where θ is the angle between $\mathbf{r}$ and $\mathbf{F}$, and $\mathbf{r}$ is the vector distance from the particle to the reference axis. We call this combination $\mathbf{L} = (\mathbf{r} \times \mathbf{F})$ a *torque*. Even as the change in linear momentum per unit time is equal to the applied force, the change in angular momentum per unit time is equal to the applied torque. In anticipation of an analysis of the transformation properties of torque and angular momentum in three dimensions, we write $\mathbf{L}$ and $\mathbf{j}$ as vectors.

The units of torque are units of force times distance, even as the units of work are units of force times distance. Are these then the same kind of quantity? Work is a scalar: what are the transformation properties of torque? If we limit our discussion to two dimensions, it would appear that torque is also a scalar. If we define torque as force times distance times the sine of the angle between the force and the distance, and confine ourselves to two dimensions, we see that the value of the torque is defined by one number that will remain the same if the coordinate system is rotated. This would suggest that the quantity torque is also a scalar. On the same basis angular momentum would seem to be a scalar.

Let us now consider, however, how the quantities work and torque are changed when reflected in a mirror. How does Alice find them "through the looking glass"? What happens if we change from a right-handed coordinate system to a left-handed coordinate system? Figure 7|6 illustrates torque and work in the real world and "through the looking glass" and shows clearly that work is not changed in the mirror world, but that the direction of the torque is reversed. Looking down, the torque is clockwise in the real world, counterclockwise in the mirror.

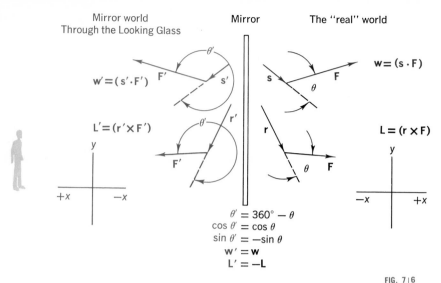

$$\theta' = 360° - \theta$$
$$\cos \theta' = \cos \theta$$
$$\sin \theta' = -\sin \theta$$
$$\mathbf{w'} = \mathbf{w}$$
$$\mathbf{L'} = -\mathbf{L}$$

FIG. 7|6
Work (the scalar product of two vectors) and torque (the vector product of two vectors) considered in mirrored coordinate systems.

Torque and work, then, have different properties when changed by the mirror transformation. If we merely rotate the coordinate system, each is unchanged. If we reflect the coordinate system in a mirror, changing our right-handed coordinate system to a left-handed one, work is unchanged, but the sign of the torque is reversed. We have a special name for this situation. We call torque, in two dimensions, a *pseudoscalar*. A pseudoscalar is a

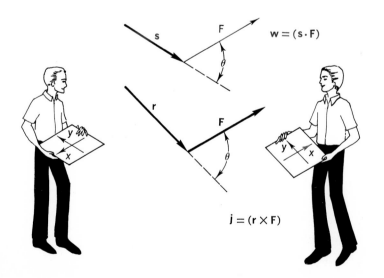

FIG. 7|7
Observers using left- and right-handed coordinate systems consider work and angular momentum.

quantity that remains the same under rotation of the axis, but changes its sign upon reflection.

Two observers who use maps that agree with the relative convention of x and y (or north, south, east, and west), but have their maps oriented differently, will agree on the magnitude and sign of a torque or an angular momentum. But if the two observers use mirror coordinate systems, such as in Fig. 7|7, they will measure torques or angular momenta to have the same magnitudes but different signs. They would both measure a unit of work to be the same. Since torque and work have different transformation properties, though the same dimensions, they are quite different kinds of quantities.

When we consider torque or angular momentum in three dimensions, it is clear that they are no longer unchanged upon rotation of the coordinate system. In two dimensions we can talk about only the magnitude and the sign of torque or angular momentum. The rotation or torque is either clockwise or counterclockwise. In three dimensions the plane of rotation or the plane of application of the torque, defined by two vectors, can lie in many different orientations. We find it convenient to define a direction of angular momentum in terms of the direction of a vector that is perpendicular to the plane defined by the vectors **r** and **p**; the direction then lies along the axis of rotation implied by the motion. There is still a question of a choice of sign, and we choose as a convention to take the positive direction as the direc-

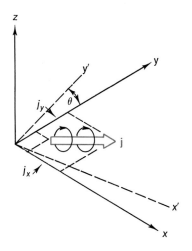

FIG. 7|8
Angular momentum in three dimensions transforms as a vector under rotation.

tion out of the paper for a counterclockwise rotation. If you position your right hand with the fingers curled and the thumb up-
right, held so the curl of the fingers is in the direction of rotation,
the direction of the thumb will represent the conventional direction of the angular momentum. Angular momentum or torque
defined in this way transforms like a vector under rotation. If
we consider an angular momentum vector that lies in the x, y
plane as shown in Fig. 7|8, under a rotation of the coordinate
system about the z-axis, the new coordinates of the angular
momentum will be related to the old according to the relations

$$j_{x'} = j_x \cos \theta + j_y \sin \theta \qquad \text{and} \qquad j_{y'} = j_y \cos \theta - j_x \sin \theta$$

These equations are just the transformation equations of a vector,
so we consider that angular momentum transforms like a vector
under a rotation of coordinate axes in three dimensions. That is,
two observers who use coordinate axes that differ only by angles
of rotation will have their description of angular momentum differ
in just the same way that their descriptions of displacement or
velocity will differ. The relations between the components of
angular momentum in the two systems will be the same as the
relations between the components of conventional vectors.

In three dimensions, the notation $(\mathbf{a} \times \mathbf{b})$ represents a vector
with a magnitude of $ab \sin \theta$, where θ is the angle between the
two vectors $\mathbf{a}$ and $\mathbf{b}$. The resultant vector is perpendicular to $\mathbf{a}$
and to $\mathbf{b}$ and has the direction shown in Fig. 7|9. Then we write
for torque $\mathbf{L}$ and angular momentum $\mathbf{j}$

$$\mathbf{L} = (\mathbf{r} \times \mathbf{F})$$

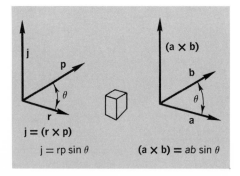

FIG. 7|9
The relation of the
vectors in the
construction of angular
momentum and other
vector products.

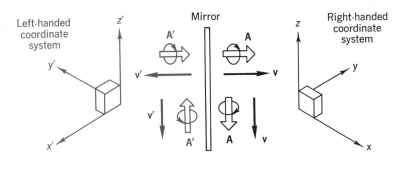

FIG. 7|10
*The behavior of vectors and axial vectors with respect to a mirror transformation. **A** is an axial vector such as the angular momentum of a mass point moving in a circle; **v** is a vector such as the velocity of a mass point.*

and

$$\mathbf{j} = (\mathbf{r} \times \mathbf{p})$$

where the torque **L** and the angular momentum **j** are axial vectors or pseudovectors.

Again, if we perform the mirror transformation, we find that angular-momentum vectors and ordinary vectors behave differently. For example, as shown in Fig. 7|10, the direction of an ordinary vector **v** is reversed when it is observed in a mirror mounted perpendicular to the vector. On the other hand, the direction of the angular-momentum vector **A** is unchanged; the reflected rotation is in the same direction. We call these special vectors, corresponding to torque and to angular momentum, *axial vectors* or *pseudovectors:* under rotations they transform like regular vectors, but under reflection in a mirror they behave differently than vectors.

The relations between the descriptions of pseudovectors or axial vectors by two observers who use coordinate systems that differ as mirror images will not be the same as the relations between their descriptions of ordinary vectors such as velocity or

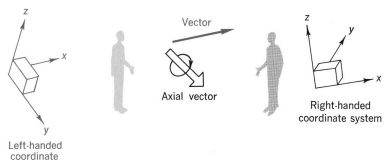

FIG. 7|11
Observers using left- and right-handed coordinate systems consider vectors and axial vectors in a three-dimensional space.

displacement (see Fig. 7|11). If the two observers, one using a right-handed coordinate system and the other a left-handed one, each measure the angular momentum of a particle about some origin and also measure the linear velocity of another particle, the relations between their measurements of the components of angular momentum will not be the same as the relations between their measurements of velocity. The axial vector *angular momentum* and the vector *velocity* will have different transformation equations. A man who uses a left-handed coordinate system will describe an axial-vector quantity in a different way than an observer using a right-handed coordinate system, though they will describe vectors in the same way. These different transformation properties are of particular importance to us when we consider the problem of describing the universe covariantly; if the universe is symmetrical in such a way that natural processes do not define the sense of a coordinate system, if the left-handed or right-handed character of a coordinate system is purely a convention, fundamental equations relating different quantities must be covariant in that the different quantities must have the same transformation properties from left-handed to right-handed systems. No relation equating a vector and an axial vector can be universally valid if the universe does not differentiate between left-handed and right-handed coordinate systems, since the equation would have different meanings to a man using a left-handed system and a man using a right-handed system.

7|3   *Circular motion*

The motion of a mass point in a circular path about an axial point *x*, as shown in Fig. 7|12, presents a simple example of the important class of circular motions. The position of the object on the circumference of a circle can be defined in terms of the angular displacement from some arbitrary origin on the circumference. In Fig. 7|12 the position of the point is defined by the value of the angle θ. The distance from the origin along the circumference is $s = r\theta$, where r is the radius of the circle and θ is measured in radians. The ratio s/r is the definition of angle where the units are radians; in degrees

$$\theta° = \left(\frac{360}{2\pi}\right)\left(\frac{s}{r}\right)$$

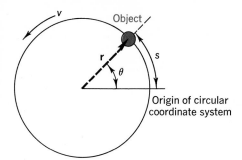

Origin of circular
coordinate system

FIG. 7|12
*The vectors describing
the motion of an object
in a circle.*

An increment of distance along the circumference of the circle
will correspond to an increment of angle

$$s = r\theta \quad \text{or} \quad ds = r\,d\theta$$

If the object is moving along the circumference of the circle with
a velocity of $v = ds/dt$, then

$$v = \frac{ds}{dt}$$

$$= r\frac{d\theta}{dt}$$

$$= r\omega$$

where

$$\omega = \frac{d\theta}{dt}$$

here ω is the angular velocity of the object even as θ is the angular
displacement. If the velocity of the object along the circumference
of the circle is changing, then

$$a = \frac{dv}{dt}$$

$$= \frac{d^2s}{dt^2}$$

$$= r\frac{d^2\theta}{dt^2}$$

$$= r\frac{d\omega}{dt}$$

$$= r\alpha$$

where α is the angular acceleration of the object.

Using the relations developed above, the relations $s = r\theta$, $v = r\omega$, and $a = r\alpha$, and the equations previously determined for accelerated linear motion, we can write down a set of parallel equations for accelerated circular motion.

$$s = s_0 + v_0 t + \tfrac{1}{2}at^2 \qquad\qquad r\theta = r\theta_0 + r\omega_0 + \tfrac{1}{2}\alpha t^2 \quad (7\,|\,5)$$

$$v = v_0 + t \qquad\qquad\qquad r\alpha = r\omega_0 + \alpha t \quad (7\,|\,6)$$

$$2a(s - s_0) = v^2 - v_0^2 \qquad 2r\alpha(r\theta - r\theta_0) = (r\omega)^2 - (r\omega_0)^2 \quad (7\,|\,7)$$

Dividing the right-hand equations of (7|5) and (7|6) by r, and that of (7|7) by r^2, we have

$$\theta = \theta_0 + \omega_0 t + \tfrac{1}{2}\alpha t^2$$

$$\omega = \omega_0 + \alpha t$$

$$2\alpha(\theta - \theta_0) = \omega^2 - \omega_0^2$$

The equations for accelerated angular motion have the same form as those for linear motion.

The dimensions of the angular quantities are different however; θ is the ratio of two lengths, s/r, and is therefore dimensionless. The dimensions of ω and α are seen to be $1/t$ and $1/t^2$ respectively.

There are further similarities worth notice:

$$T = \text{kinetic energy} = \tfrac{1}{2}mv^2$$

$$= \tfrac{1}{2}(mr^2)\left(\frac{v}{r}\right)^2$$

$$= \tfrac{1}{2}I\omega^2 \qquad\qquad\qquad\qquad (7\,|\,8)$$

where $I = mr^2$ is called the *moment of inertia* and plays much the same role in circular motion as mass does in linear motion. Equa-

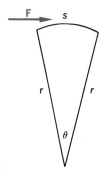

FIG. 7 |13
The relation of work to torque and angular displacement.

tion (7|8) relates to mass points. The equation that is relevant for solids has much the same form: in a solid, $I = m_1 r_1^2 + m_2 r_2^2$ ... for all the mass points that make up the body. We will not consider such problems in detail.

There is also a circular analogue to the basic dynamic relation $F = ma$:

$$F = ma \quad \text{(linear motion)} \qquad Fr = (mr^2)\left(\frac{a}{r}\right) \quad \text{(circular motion)}$$

Since Fr is equal to the torque L, mr^2 is I, the moment of inertia, and a/r is α, the angular acceleration, we have

$$L = I\alpha$$

The invariant product of the vectors force and distance is the scalar work. We are also interested in the relationship of torque to work. Figure 7|13 shows a force doing work by acting through a distance. The work done is the force times the distance s. This is equal algebraically to the torque, force times distance, times the quantity s/r. The quantity s/r, in the limit of small s, is just the angle of displacement of the vector $\mathbf{r}$, measured in radians. If we write that angle as θ, we find that the work done by application of a constant torque L is equal to the torque times the angle θ:

$$w = L\theta$$

In the same vein we can calculate the power required to transfer energy to a rotating system, or the power one can extract from such a systems. Since $w = L\theta$,

$$P = \frac{dw}{dt}$$

$$= L\frac{d\theta}{dt}$$

$$= L\omega$$

7|4   The transformation properties of some angular quantities

What are the transformation properties of θ, ω, and α? Are they vectors even as torque and angular momentum are vectors (properly, pseudovectors or axial vectors)? First we will show that θ is not a vector because vectors commute ($\mathbf{A} + \mathbf{B} = \mathbf{B} + \mathbf{A}$)

and angular displacements about different axis do not, in general, commute. The noncommutivity of the operation of rotation is shown by following the operations illustrated in Fig. 7|14.

The bricks are dark on three sides, light on the other three. The first row represents a brick first rotated 90° around the z-axis, then 90° around the x-axis. The second row shows the same brick rotated 90° around the x-axis and then 90° about the z axis. The final positions of the bricks are different. If we use the notation $\underline{\theta|}(x)$ for a rotation of an angle θ about the x-axis we can write our results as

$$\underline{90°|}\,(z) + \underline{90°|}\,(x) \neq \underline{90°|}\,(x) + \underline{90°|}\,(z)$$

The rotations do not commute, and angular rotation is not a vector.

Very small rotations actually act very much as vectors; they almost commute. We demonstrate this, again, by investigating the rotation of bricks, but now we rotate the bricks by very small amounts. In order to observe the small rotations conveniently, we use bricks with rods 1 m long baked into them as shown in Fig. 7|15. We rotate the brick a 0.01 rad about the z-axis and then 0.01 rad about the x-axis. In our operator notation we describe this as

$$\underline{0.01|}\,(z) + \underline{0.01|}\,(x)$$

the other brick is rotated according to the operations

$$\underline{0.01|}\,(x) + \underline{0.01|}\,(z)$$

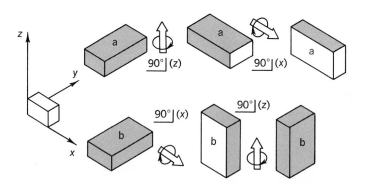

FIG. 7| 14
A demonstration that angular rotation is an operation that does not commute and is therefore not a vector.

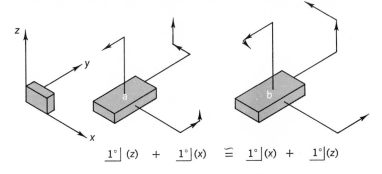

$$\underline{1^\circ|} (z) \quad + \quad \underline{1^\circ|}(x) \quad \stackrel{\scriptscriptstyle\sim}{=} \quad \underline{1^\circ|}(x) \quad + \quad \underline{1^\circ|}(z)$$

FIG. 7|15
*A demonstration that
infinitesimal rotations
commute.*

The displacements of the ends of the rods are shown, exaggerated for clarity, in the diagrams of Fig. 7|15. We consider in detail the positions of the rods that point along the *x*-axis. When brick *a* is rotated about the *z*-axis 0.01 rad, the end of the rod is moved 0.01 m, or 1.0 cm, as shown in the diagram. Then when the brick is rotated about the *x*-axis, the end of the rod moves very slightly—about 0.01 cm. This is equal to 1.0 m times the product of the two angles in radians.

When brick *b* is rotated about the *x*-axis, the end of the rod is not displaced in the *x*-direction at all. When the brick is then rotated about the *z*-axis, the rod is displaced as shown in the diagram a distance of 1.0 cm. The displacement of the rod in brick *a* is almost exactly the same as the displacement of the rod in brick *b*, although the order of the operations was reversed. The same kind of analysis can be used to show that the rods in the *y*-direction and the rods in the *z*-directions of the two bricks are displaced almost exactly the same. Since the position of the brick is determined completely by the position of the ends of the rods, it is clear the the rotated positions of the two bricks are almost identical. If the angles had been smaller, the proportional difference in the positions of the two bricks (0.01/1.0) would be smaller yet. In the limit of infinitesimal rotations $d\theta$, the rotations commute precisely and the infinitesimal angular displacements transform as vectors (or, more properly, as pseudovectors.)

Since angular velocities $\boldsymbol{\omega} = d\boldsymbol{\theta}/dt$ concern the change in such infinitesimal displacements with time and such displacements are vectors, angular velocity is a vector. By a similar argument angular acceleration $\mathbf{a} = d^2\boldsymbol{\theta}/dt^2$ is a vector. We will not usually differentiate between axial vectors and vectors.

7|5 *Centripetal force and centrifugal force*

The motion of a mass point moving with constant absolute velocity in a circular path about an axial point x is illustrated in Fig. 7|16. Since both the magnitude of **r**, the vector representing the distance between the axis and the mass, and the magnitude of **p**, the momentum of the particle, are constant, and the angle between them is constant—and 90°—the angular momentum $(\mathbf{r} \times \mathbf{p})$ is constant. Since the angular momentum is constant, the torque, $\mathbf{L} = (\mathbf{r} \times \mathbf{F}) = rF \sin \theta$, must be equal to zero. This will be the case if the direction of any force that bears on the mass point lies along the direction of the radius vector **r**. Then the value of the angle θ between the direction of the force and the direction of the radius vector will be zero and the torque will be zero. Though the magnitude of the velocity remains constant, the direction of the velocity vector changes as the particle moves around the circle. The change in the vector velocity per unit time represents an acceleration, and a force is required to cause the mass to accelerate. If there were no force, the mass would not travel in a circle, but would continue in a straight line. We proceed to determine the magnitude of this *centripetal* acceleration and then the centripetal force.

The change in position of the mass point in a small interval of time is shown in Fig. 7|16b. In this time the radius vector will

FIG. 7|16

Vectors used to determine the kinematics of a particle moving with constant velocity in a circle.

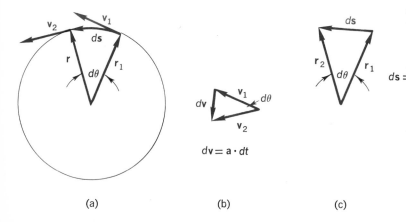

$$ds = \mathbf{v} \cdot dt$$

$$dv = \mathbf{a} \cdot dt$$

(a)   (b)   (c)

have passed through an angle $d\theta$, from $\mathbf{r}_1$ to $\mathbf{r}_2$. The orientation of the velocity vectors is also shown on Fig. 7|16b: the velocity vector will have changed from $\mathbf{v}_1$ to $\mathbf{v}_2$ in the time dt. The difference between the two radii is the vector labeled $d\mathbf{v}$. Separate vector diagrams are shown in Fig. 7|16c. From the general equations of motion.

$$\mathbf{a} = \frac{d\mathbf{v}}{dt} \quad \text{and} \quad \mathbf{v} = \frac{d\mathbf{s}}{dt}$$

Since $\mathbf{v}_2$ is perpendicular to $\mathbf{r}_2$, $\mathbf{v}_1$ is perpendicular to $\mathbf{r}_1$, $v_1 = v_2$, and $r_1 = r_2$, the two triangles of Figs. 7|16b and 7|16c are similar triangles. Then

$$\frac{dv}{v} = \frac{ds}{r}$$

Dividing by dt,

$$\frac{(dv/dt)}{v} = \frac{(ds/dt)}{r}$$

Since

$$\frac{dv}{dt} = a \quad \text{and} \quad \frac{ds}{dt} = v$$

then

$$\frac{a}{v} = \frac{v}{r}$$

$$a = \frac{v^2}{r}$$

which is the basic relation between the magnitude of the acceleration and the magnitude of the linear velocity and the radius of the circle. It is sometimes convenient to express the acceleration in terms of the angular velocity. Since $\omega = v/r$,

$$a = \omega^2 r$$

We see from the diagrams of 7|16b and 7|16c that the direction of the change in velocity of the acceleration is perpendicular to the velocity, collinear with the radius vector, and directed in the opposite direction; that is, toward the center axis. There is then a constant acceleration toward the center axis equal in magnitude to v^2/r. We can write this equation in a convariant form, using the formal vector notation, as

$$\mathbf{a} = -\frac{(\mathbf{v} \cdot \mathbf{v})}{(\mathbf{r} \cdot \mathbf{r})} \mathbf{r} \quad \text{or} \quad a = -(\boldsymbol{\omega} \cdot \boldsymbol{\omega})\mathbf{r}$$

If the mass of the particle moving in the circle is m, a force is required to provide the acceleration. The magnitude and direction of the force is determined by the relation $\mathbf{F} = m\mathbf{a}$. There must, then, be a force on the particle in the direction of the center of the circle equal to the mass of the particle times v^2/r. We call this a *centripetal* force, which merely means a force directed toward the center:

$$F = m\frac{v^2}{r} \quad \text{or} \quad F = m\omega^2 r$$

Centrifugal force is the reaction to the centripetal force. If a stone is swung on the end of a string, the string exerts a centripetal force on the stone, causing it to accelerate toward the center of the circle. The reaction to this force, the reaction of the stone on the string, is called the *centrifugal* force.

7|6 *The absolute character of circular motion*

We now ask the question: Does circular motion have an absolute meaning as does linear acceleration, or only a relative meaning as does linear motion? Let us consider the simple example of an object moving in a circle about an ovserver. The object might be a stone held on the end of a string, where an observer in the center of the circle holds the string. If the observer is standing on a platform that rotates at the same angular velocity—the same number of revolutions per second—as the stone, the spatial position of the stone with respect to the observer will remain constant. If the observer is initially facing the stone, he will continue to face the stone. The question we are asking concerning the possible relative character of circular motion is then the question: Is there any difference between this situation and a situation in which the observer is stationary, holding onto a string attached to a stone that is stationary? The relative position of the man and the stone is the same in the two instances. But we know by simple experience that there is a very considerable difference between the stationary and rotating systems. In the case of the rotating system, the string would be taut: a force would have to be applied to the stone to keep it in the circular path. No force would be required in the stationary situation; the string would be slack. If the string should break in the rotating system, the stone would move out away from the observer in a complex curved trajectory with respect to the observer's rotating coordinate system. The forces are quite different for the stationary observer of a stationary stone. The string is slack. If it were released or cut, there would be no difference whatsoever in the relation between the observer and the stone.

We see, then, that circular motion is not relative but absolute in character. Not only can we detect the rotation of an enclosed laboratory about an axis, but we can determine the rate of rotation by measuring the centrifugal forces on objects in the laboratory, and then establish an absolute zero of rotation without referring to anything outside the laboratory. When we establish this absolute zero of rotation, we still must ask the question: What is it that is *not* rotating about us; what is the basis for our exact zero of rotation? And when we ask this question, we are led to the same experimentally based answer as for the case of linear acceleration: Our zero of rotational motion appears to be the coordinate system defined by the fixed stars.

7|7 *Fictitious forces and the choice of coordinate system*

Although a rotating coordinate system has the unaesthetic property that it is an absolute system and not a relative one, and the equations of motion of an object in a rotating system are more complicated than in an inertial system, it is still most convenient for very many types of problems. The navigator of a ship on the ocean uses the earth as a coordinate system, though the earth is rotating about its axis as well as moving in a circle around the sun. The suggestion that he plot the absolute position of his ship with respect to some universal coordinate system based on some far-off galaxies, rather than on the cosmologically insignificant rotating ball we call the earth, is not likely to be attractive to him. Since rotating coordinate systems are important, it is essential

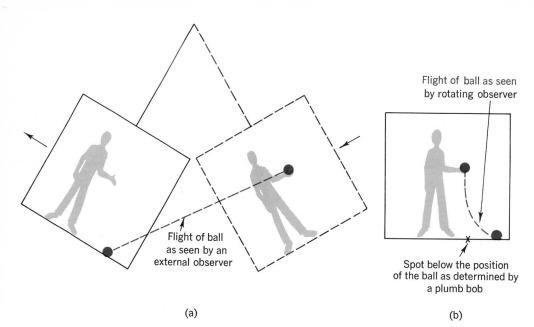

Flight of ball as seen by rotating observer

Flight of ball as seen by an external observer

Spot below the position of the ball as determined by a plumb bob

(a)   (b)

FIG. 7 | 17
Diagrams showing the relations between views of kinematics in a rotating coordinate system and an inertial system.

that we investigate the character of the descriptions of behavior, which we call physical laws, in such systems.

We can investigate the character of such physical laws in a rotating system of reference by considering simple phenomena from the view of an observer who is in an enclosed laboratory that is rotating about some axis in interstellar space far from any massive bodies and their gravitational fields. Such a laboratory is suggested by the drawing of Fig. 7 | 17.

An observer in the laboratory, situated as shown, releases a ball. The dashed line in Fig. 7 | 17a shows the position of the ball as a function of time from the viewpoint of a nonrotating coordinate system and a nonrotating observer. From that view, the ball will be acted on by no external force and will travel in a straight line with the velocity it had upon being released. We note, however, that from the viewpoint of the observer in the rotating laboratory, the ball will fall toward the floor of the laboratory. From his view, there will be a force acting on the ball. Indeed if he tries to hold the ball in his hand or suspend it from a string, he can measure the magnitude and direction of the force. Knowing he is in a rotating coordinate system, he will call the force on his hand, which seems to be exerted by the ball, a centrifugal force.

From the viewpoint of the observer outside of the rotating laboratory, this centrifugal force will be the reaction to the centripetal force applied by the hand of the observer in the laboratory that forces the ball to move in an orbit about the axis with the rest of the rotating laboratory.

The centrifugal force observed by the man in the rotating system is not the same as the usual force, inasmuch as it does not result from an interaction with another body in the system: we call it a fictitious force, and we must introduce it as a consequence of our choice of an accelerating coordinate system instead of an inertial system. Now let the observer in the rotating system release the ball. If the fictitious forces on the ball leaving the observer's hand were completely described by the centrifugal force, the ball would drop from the observer's hand to a spot on the floor directly below, just as if it were affected by gravitational force. Such a spot could be determined by dropping a plumb bob. But the falling ball will not follow this line. The straightline path of the ball seen by the external observer actually becomes a slightly curved line in the system of the rotating observer. The ball does not appear to drop straight down toward the spot directly below, the spot *a* that could be defined by the plumb bob suspended from the hand of the rotating observer; the ball's flight would follow a slightly curved path as shown in the diagrams of Fig. 7 | 17. From the view of the observer in the rotating system, another fictitious force will have acted on the ball, deflecting its flight so that it doesn't fall straight down. If he uses our vocabulary, he would call this part of the fictitious force a *Coriolis force*.

We can understand this Coriolis effect qualitatively by considering the activity in the rotating system from the view of an observer in a nearby inertial system. Since there are no external torques acting on the ball, the angular momentum of the ball with respect to the axis of rotation will remain constant. The angular momentum of the ball at the instant it leaves the observer's hand will be equal quantitatively to mvr, where r is the distance from the hand to the axis of rotation, v is the linear velocity of the ball or the hand at the moment of release, and m is the mass of the ball. It is easy to see that the spot on the floor just below the hand is not only at a larger distance from the axis, but must be moving with a higher velocity. So if the ball reaches that point with no transverse component of velocity parallel to the floor of the rotating system, it will have the velocity of that point on the floor, and the angular momentum of the ball will have increased. Since the angular momentum does not increase, the ball must have a component of velocity opposite to the direction of the velocity of the spot on the floor, and as a result of that velocity it will have drifted backward and landed back of the spot on the floor as shown in the diagram of Fig. 7|17b.

Figure 7|18 shows a disk that is rotating counterclockwise. This figure might also represent the Northern Hemisphere of the earth viewed from far above the North Pole. On this rotating system there resides an observer O' who is interested in constructing a description of phenomena that is valid in his "rotating" universe. Another observer O is stationary in a nonrotating system. We observe the flight of two projectiles, both of which are in free flight. One, a, is moving from the axis of the rotating disk; since it is acted on by no forces, it will move in a straight line with constant velocity from the view of the observer O in the nonrotating inertial reference system. The solid line marked a shows the trajectory as observed by O. Let us assume that this body was leaking paint, which marked the surface of the rotating disk. The trail of the paint would, of course, mark the path of the body on the rotating reference system; this would be the trajectory observed by O' in his system of reference. The observer O' might describe this by stating that a force F'_a acted on the body, causing it to be deflected into the curved path that was observed. If he used our nomenclature, he would call this "fictitious force" a Coriolis force.

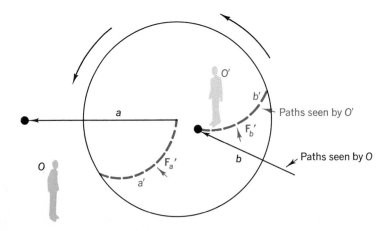

FIG. 7|18
Paths of a freely moving particle as determined in a rotating system and an inertial system.

The path of the second projectile *b* is directed toward the axis of rotation. Again its path appears to be a straight line from the view of *O*, but a curved path as seen by *O'*. Again the observer *O'* might postulate that a Coriolis force, F_b', caused the projectile to deflect from a straight line in the rotating system.

In general, if the paths of moving particles were to be straight lines on the rotating system, they would be curved lines in the inertial coordinate system. Particles move in curved paths in an inertial coordinate system only if there are forces on the particles. A particle moving in a straight line on the rotating surface can do so only if a force is provided: the reaction to that force is called a Coriolis force by the observer in the rotating system.

These fictitious forces are familiar to us through direct experience. It is hardly necessary to expand on our experience with centrifugal force, but the effects of Coriolis force are a little more obscure. If we are spinning on a piano stool, or on the tips of ice skates, with arms extended, and then pull our arms in close to our body we will "feel" a force that causes us to spin faster. This is particularly dramatic if we are holding weights in our hands: the weights appear to be pushing us around faster. The reaction of the weights against our hands in the direction to increase our angular velocity is the Coriolis force. The force is, of course, real; we can feel it. From the view of an observer on the sidelines, the force the weight exerts on our hand is the reaction to the force we are applying to the weight to force the weight to move in a curved path. From our egocentric view on the piano stool, we are moving the weight in a straight line but there is something about the character of our coordinate system such that a strong force must be applied to the weight (to counteract a Coriolis force) if the weight is to move in a straight line.

The study of kinematics in a rotating coordinate system is of particular interest to us because we live on a rotating body and all of our kinematics with respect to the earth's surface are in actuality kinematics in a rotating coordinate system. The earth rotates sufficiently slowly that these effects, the effects of our fictitious centrifugal force and Coriolis force, are quite small for most of our activities. In certain cases they are important. For example, the effect of Coriolis forces must be correctly accounted for in the aiming and firing of large naval guns. Of much more importance are the effects of Coriolis forces on meteorological problems. The counterclockwise rotation of cyclones and hurricanes in the Northern Hemisphere and the clockwise rotation of cyclones and hurricanes in the Southern Hemisphere result from the rotation of the earth.

Occasionally, choices must be made between coordinate systems: Are there coordinate systems that are correct and incorrect? If so what do we mean by correct and incorrect? Or do these coordinate systems only differ in complexity? In either an inertial coordinate system, an accelerating coordinate system, or a rotating coordinate system, we can construct precise, well-defined, and correct descriptions of all physical phenomena. In an inertial coordinate system the relations take a particularly simple form. For example, the basic equation of dynamics in an inertial system is

$$\mathbf{F} = m\mathbf{a}$$

In a rotating system the relation is more complicated:

$$\mathbf{F} + m\omega^2\mathbf{r} + 2m(\mathbf{v} \times \boldsymbol{\omega}) = m\mathbf{a}$$

where the second term on the left is the centrifugal force and third term is the Coriolis force. Although the relations or descriptions of physical phenomena take more complex forms in accelerating or rotating coordinate systems than in inertial systems, they are equivalent inasmuch as they all correctly represent nature and have the same descriptive value, and one cannot be considered more or less correct than another.

The Ptolemaic system considers the earth stationary, with the sun moving about the earth. The fixed stars also rotate about the earth, while the planets move in more complicated configurations called by the Ptolemaic astronomers *epicycles*. Is this description of nature incorrect? Our answer today is that it is not incorrect, it is merely complicated. In some applications it is not even complicated; it provides the simplest description of terrestial chronology, and is therefore the system we use for terrestial ñavigation. The Copernican system, which regards the sun as central and regards the earth moving about the sun, is an inertial system and has the advantage of simplicity. We must not consider it more or less correct than the Ptolemaic system; but the laws of nature take a much simpler form in the Copernican system, and for many purposes the Copernican system is the more convenient. We have then achieved the perhaps dubious end of reducing the great debate between Galileo and the conservatives of his day to a debate that is not about fundamental truths, but merely a debate about convenience.

Convenience and simplicity are extremely important, however: it is the simplicity of the Copernican system that makes it transparently obvious that the earth and the other planets are closely related—a result that is obscured in the Ptolemaic formulation.

PROBLEMS

7| 1 Two space ships, *i* and *ii*, are traveling freely in interstellar space with their rocket drives turned off. Gravity is negligible. The mass of *i* is 1000 kg, and it is traveling initially at a speed of 100 m/sec. The mass of *ii* is 2000 kg, and it is traveling initially at a speed of 150 m/sec. A shell is fired from ship *ii* straight ahead toward *i*, as shown in the diagram. The shell weighs 10 kg and the velocity of the shell is 5000 m/sec. The shell lodges in ship *i* when it is at position *b*, shown in the diagram. What is the angular momentum of each ship with respect to point *a*, and what is the total angular momentum of the two ships with respect to *a* under the following conditions:

(*a*) Before the gun is fired?

(*b*) After the gun is fired and the shell has struck ship *i*?

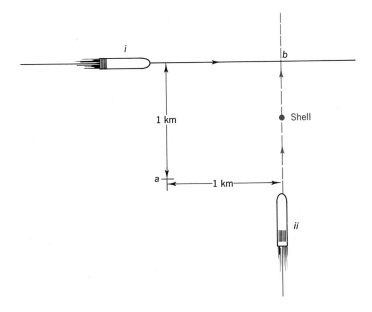

7|2 An automobile having a mass of 1000 kg is traveling at a speed of 100 m/sec around a circular track whose radius is 1000 m. When the car passes point *a* on the track:

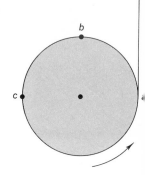

(*a*) What is the angular momentum of the car with respect to point *b*? With respect to point *c*? With respect to point *a*?

(*b*) What is the angular momentum of the car with respect to the center of the track?

(*c*) The car leaves the track on a road tangential to the track at point *a*. At the instant the car leaves the track and starts along the road, what is the angular momentum of the car with respect to point *a*? Point *b*? Point *c*? The center of the track?

7|3 Two rockets, *i* and *ii*, each weigh 10 kg; their motors produce a thrust of 10 N, using negligible fuel. One rocket is free to move in a straight line, the other is constrained by a light wire to travel in a circle 10 m in radius, as shown in the diagram. Starting when both rockets are at rest, after five seconds

(*a*) What is the magnitude of the velocity of *i*? Of *ii*?

(*b*) What is the angular velocity of *ii* about its center of rotation, *a*?

(*c*) What is the angular acceleration of *ii*?

(*d*) What is the kinetic energy of *i*? Of *ii*?

(*e*) What is the angular momentum of *i* about *b*? Of *ii* about *a*?

(*f*) What is the acceleration of *ii* in its direction of motion? Of *i*?

(*g*) What is the acceleration of *ii* toward *a*?

(*h*) What is the magnitude of the total acceleration of *ii*?

(*i*) What force does the wire exert on *ii*? What is the total magnitude of the force on *ii*?

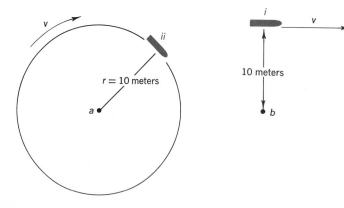

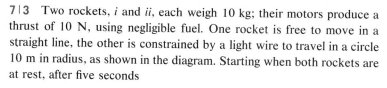

7|4 The grid spacing in the diagram is 1 unit. From the view of observer M using a right-handed coordinate system, and from the view of M' using a left-handed coordinate system, what are the values of the following?

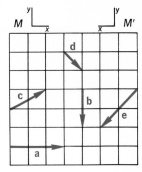

(*a*) $(\mathbf{a} \times \mathbf{c})$ and $(\mathbf{a} \cdot \mathbf{c})$.

(*b*) $(\mathbf{b} \times \mathbf{d})$ and $(\mathbf{d} \times \mathbf{b})$ and $(\mathbf{b} \cdot \mathbf{d})$ and $(\mathbf{d} \cdot \mathbf{b})$.

(*c*) $(\mathbf{e} \times \mathbf{a})$ and $(\mathbf{e} \cdot \mathbf{a})$.

7|5 A wheel is rotating at an angular velocity of 10 rev/sec. Friction provides a torque that reduces the angular velocity by 1 rev/sec every second. How many revolutions will the wheel turn before it stops?

7|6 A ball is swinging about on the end of a string. The string is slowly shortened by being pulled through a ring at the center of rotation.

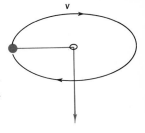

(*a*) Does the angular momentum at the ball change?

(*b*) Does the velocity of the ball change?

(*c*) Does the energy of the ball change? If so, does it increase or decrease? If the energy increases, what is the source of the energy? If the energy decreases, where does the energy go?

7|7 An automobile race track is banked at an angle of 45° as shown. A car traveling at a velocity of 100 m/sec shows no tendency to slide either up or down. What is the radius of the curve?

7|8 If the cart in the figure is started at a point just above h, it will "loop the loop," traversing the loop in the track with the wheels on the track. If it is started just below h, the cart will fall off the track near the top of the loop. What is the value of h? (The centripetal force will be equal to gravity plus the reaction of the track. The total energy will be conserved.)

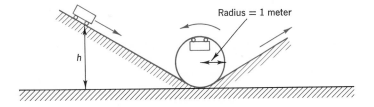

Radius = 1 meter

7|9 A wheel having all of its mass m in the rim rolls down an inclined plane. The height of the plane is h, the radius of the wheel is r.

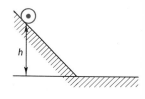

(*a*) Show that the moment of inertia of the wheel about the hub is mr^2.

(*b*) The total kinetic energy of a rotating body is the sum of the translational kinetic energy and the rotational kinetic energy. Show that the velocity of the wheel is equal to $\sqrt{gh}$ as the wheel reaches the bottom of the inclined plane (g is the acceleration of gravity).

(*c*) Will a wheel roll down a slope faster if the weight is concentrated in the rim or in the hub of the wheel?

7|10 A beetle weighing 1 gm is crawling from the hub of a rotating wheel to the rim. The wheel is rotating at a rate of $\frac{1}{2\pi}$ rev/sec. The beetle is crawling along a straight line painted on the wheel, at a rate of 1 cm/sec.

(*a*) How much does the angular momentum of the beetle change as it crawls from a point 9 cm from the hub to a point 11 cm from the hub?

(*b*) What is the value of the average torque on the beetle required to accomplish this change in angular momentum?

(*c*) What average transverse force does the beetle have to exert in order to resist the Coriolis force as it moves from the first point to the second?

(*d*) How much will this average transverse force be changed if the beetle crawls twice as fast? If the wheel rotates with twice the angular velocity?

7|11 A space station is to be designed so that men can live in the station for an appreciable length of time without serious deterioration of their skeletal and muscular systems. It is found that it is necessary to provide an artificial gravitation for the living quarters. This is accomplished by rotating the living quarters about the center of the station. The distance from these quarters to the control room and observatory at the hub of the system is 1000 m.

(*a*) What frequency of rotation is necessary so that earth's gravity is simulated?

(*b*) A ladder extends from the stationary hub of the system to the living quarters. How much work must a man weighing 100 kg exert to climb the ladder from the living quarters to the control room?

7|12 An observer O' resides in a universe S' that rotates about an axis with a frequency of 1 rev/min. Two weights, each having a mass of 10 kg, are at the ends of long telescoping rods that are connected to an axis with a frictionless bearing so that the weights are free to rotate. Initially, according to O', the weights are motionless. Then the rods contract from a length of 1 m to a length of $\frac{1}{2}$ m. Discuss the subsequent motion of the weights as viewed by the observer O'

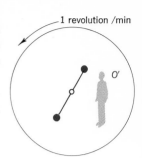

7|13 A space station in an orbit in space rotates in order to create an artificial gravity for the crew, who occupy a cabin 100 m from the center of rotation. In the cabin, a man holds a weight on a spring scale, which then registers 1.0 kg.

(*a*) The man then climbs a ladder toward the control room, which is at the center of rotation of the ship. When he stops to rest, he looks at the scale and the weight and finds that the scale reads 0.25 kg. How much farther does he have to climb to reach the control room? How much must the frequency of rotation be increased in order that the scale would again read 1.0 kg?

(*b*) As the man is climbing up the ladder toward the control room, he feels a transverse force on him, aside from the centrifugal force. What direction is this force? Explain the basis for your conclusion.

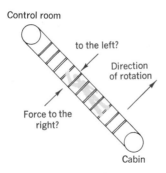

ALTHOUGH WE HAVE defined force as the rate of change of momentum, we have not considered the detailed character of any of the fundamental forces. Later we will discuss the view that the effects of gravitation can be considered to be a result of the curvature of space produced by the presence of matter: the curvature results in measurable consequences on matter, which we call the acceleration of gravity and the force of gravity. We regard these two views—the view that the force of gravity results from the exchange of momentum and the view that the force of gravity is geometric in nature—as two faces of a problem that is yet unsolved. This is essentially the problem on which Einstein spent the last years of his life: the Unified Field Theory. Einstein attempted to understand all forces, in particular the electromagnetic force, in geometric terms. In this section we will discuss the fundamental long-range forces of gravity, not in terms of the geometric space-distortion picture, but in terms of the transfer-of-momentum picture. In parallel with our discussion of gravity, we will touch upon electrostatic forces, the forces between stationary electric charges.

Although a detailed rigorous discussion of these phenomena is beyond the techniques available to us, we can construct some simple pictures that are designed to give some insight into the character of the long-range forces. We must, of course, recognize that these simple models can only be approximations of the truth as we know it. The fact that the simple models can only be a rough approximation to reality is not entirely a result of our imperfect knowledge of the exact phenomena, but is, to a large degree, a result of the limitations of both our language and the area of primitive experience to which we constrain our model.

Some of the most important characteristics of the long-range interactions depend more upon the simple geometric properties of space than on the specific characteristics of the interactions. It is because of this dependence on the properties of space that we can find very close parallels between the effects of gravitational forces and those of electrostatic forces. Weaker parallels can be drawn between these two forces and the nuclear forces. We will consider the character of nuclear forces much later.

We illustrate the relation between the variation of force with distance and the dimensionality of space by examining a very elementary model of a fundamental force, first in one dimension, then in two dimensions, and then in three dimensions. We consider two objects, A and B, in a one-dimensional manifold, where each object continuously emits particles that carry momentum. We might consider these as simple concrete particles, perhaps bullets, and our one-dimensional manifold could be a long tunnel with perfectly reflecting walls. The objects, A and B, are chosen to be the size of the tunnel and they block the tunnel so that all bullets fired by object A pass through the region occupied by B and vice versa. We assume that a bullet has a certain probability of hitting B when it passes through B, and that probability is a property of B. Likewise, the number of bullets fired per second by B is a property of B. Similarly the emission and absorption probabilities of A are a fundamental property of A. The exchange of the bullets results in an exchange of momentum, and this exchange constitutes a repulsive force between A and B. If the particles travel on forever—that is, the forces have an infinite range and are *long-range forces*—the force will be independent of distance. If we move the two objects A and B farther apart, there would still be the same number of momentum transfers per second. Every bullet fired from object A will pass through the region occupied by B, and every bullet starting from object B will pass through the region occupied by A, independent of the distance between them, and the force that acts between them will also be independent of that distance.

Now let us consider the same two objects in a two-dimensional manifold, such as a large plane surface. Now we will assume that the guns on the two objects will fire in random directions, parallel to the plane floor, and assume either that no gravity acts or that the floor is hard and frictionless so the bullets ricochet along. Again there will be an exchange of momentum; again there will be an effective repulsive force between the two objects. However, when the objects are far away from one another, the exchange of momentum will be smaller and the force will be smaller, since the randomly firing gunners will make fewer hits. The probability of making a hit, or the number of hits per second, will diminish linearly with the distance between the two objects. If the two objects are three times as far away there will be only one-third as many hits, and the momentum transfer will be reduced by a factor of one third. The force will then vary inversely with the distance.

If we now move the two objects to a three-dimensional manifold in interstellar space, where again we need not consider the effects of gravitational force, and again have the gunners fire at random in all directions, the number of hits will again decrease with distance, but now with the square of the distance. The momentum transfer will then diminish with the square of the distance, and the force will vary inversely with the square of the distance. Figure 8|1 illustrates the dependence on dimension and distance of the force from an object A acting on an object B, using this model, for the one-, two-, and three-dimensional cases. In the three-dimensional case the particles that pass through a certain area at a distance r pass through four times that area at a distance $2r$. The probability of hitting a particular object is thus reduced by a factor of 4 as the distance is doubled. In the two-

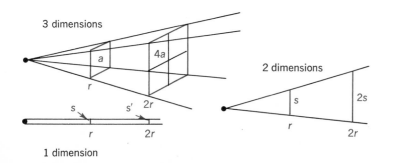

FIG. 8|1

The variation of the area subtended at a point with distance for spaces of different dimension.

dimensional case the particles that pass through a certain linear region s at a distance of r pass through a linear region $2s$ at a distance of $2r$. The probability of a particle hitting an object at a distance of r is twice that of the particle hitting the same object at a distance $2r$. The diagram in the one-dimensional case is not quite the same as the other two. The one-dimensional manifold is given, for artistic reasons, a certain width, even as the source is given width. It is nevertheless clear that particles emitted from the source contained by the one dimensional manifold will strike the object s or s' with equal frequency, even though s' is twice as far away from the source as s.

If we can describe forces adequately in terms of the exchange of momentum through the emission and absorption of particles, and if the range of the particles is unlimited, the long-range forces between two objects will vary as the inverse square of the distance between the two objects, and this particular variation with distance is a property of three-dimensional space and less particularly an intrinsic and special property of the force itself. It appears that we can describe all fundamental forces in such a manner, though only repulsive forces can be illustrated in models as elementary as those entertained here. By the use of less elementary logical constructs, or mathematical constructs, we are able to understand attractive forces as well as repulsive forces in this way. These attractive forces also come about through the exchange of momentum.

In the model of gravitation the particles that are supposed to be involved in the exchange of momentum in this picture are given the name *gravitons*. For electrostatic forces the particles involved in momentum exchange are called *photons*. In the gravitational case we can consider that the intensity of emission of gravitons is proportional to the mass of the emitting object A and that the probability of absorption by object B is proportional to the mass of B. Inversely, the probability of absorption by A is proportional to the mass of A, and the probability of emission by B is proportional to the mass of B. In a three-dimensional space the force between the two objects, taken as very small objects, is proportional to the product of the masses of the objects divided by the square of the distance between them:

$$F \propto \frac{M_A M_B}{r^2} \qquad\qquad (8\,|\,1)$$

where M_A and M_B are the masses of the two objects and r is the distance between them. For any particular set of units it is convenient to write the relation as an equality by introducing a constant of proportionality that is called the *gravitational constant* and written as G. Then the force between two masses m_1 and m_2, separated by a distance r, is

$$F = -G \, \frac{m_1 m_2}{r^2}$$

where the minus sign indicates that the force is attractive, in the direction opposite to the distance between the masses. The value of G has been measured to be $G = 6.67 \times 10^{-11}$ N m^2/kg^2.

The equation for electrostatic forces between two charges q_1 and q_2 has a form very similar to that for gravitational forces. The probability of an object emitting a photon is proportional to the charge of the object, and the probability of absorbing a photon is proportional to the charge. Then the relation representing the force between two charges is

$$F = k \, \frac{q_1 q_2}{r^2}$$

where q_1 and q_2 represent the charges of the two objects in appropriate units, k is a proportionality constant, and r is the distance between the two objects.

In either of these equations the force is in the direction of the line between the two particles—the two massive particles in the case of gravitation, and the two charges in the case of electrostatic forces. This is a consequence of our implicit assumption that the objects emitting these photons can be treated as infinitesimal points. If this is the case, we can see that the force can only be along the direction between the two points, simply because no other direction is defined by the problem. The symmetry of the problem allows no other direction.

8|2 *The superposition principle*

An important characteristic of the gravitational interactions of various objects is found in the independence of the interaction between two bodies with respect to the presence of other bodies. The force between two objects a and b is almost independent of the presence of a third body c. In particular, if the force on a from the presence of b is $\mathbf{f}_b$ when c is absent, and if the force on a from c is equal to $\mathbf{f}_c$ in the absence of b, the force $\mathbf{F}$ on a when both b and c are present is

$$\mathbf{F} = \mathbf{f}_b + \mathbf{f}_c$$

This is the principle of *superposition,* illustrated in Fig. 8|2.

We would expect that the superposition principle would hold in the projectile model of forces if the projectiles that carry the momentum, never, or almost never, collide with each other and if the objects absorb only an infinitesimal portion of the projectiles that pass through the region nominally occupied by the object: that is, if we assume that the density of the target objects is extremely low and that they are almost transparent. If the projectiles that pass from b to a never collide with the particles passing from c to a, and if the absorption of the projectiles by various sources and objects is sufficiently small that one object cannot effectively shield another, we would expect that the forces on a would be the simple vector sum of the forces from b and c. If there ever were collisions, we would expect them to be important when the density of projectiles was very high or when the forces were very large.

Although we have never observed any direct deviation from the principle of superposition in the measurement of gravitational forces or electromagnetic forces, we believe that the superposition principle breaks down near very dense stars, where the gravitational forces are enormous. A breakdown of the superposition principle in a related phenomenon—the scattering of light by a very strong electric field—has been observed for electromagnetic phenomena.

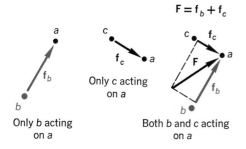

$$\mathbf{F} = \mathbf{f}_b + \mathbf{f}_c$$

Only b acting on a

Only c acting on a

Both b and c acting on a

FIG. 8|2
A diagram showing the additive character of forces on an object: the superposition theorem.

The superpositional property of gravitational forces leads immediately to some useful results concerning the nature of the forces that result from some particular configurations of matter. We consider, as a particularly interesting example, the calculation of the gravitational force on a small object, a, of mass m, that results from a spherically symmetric distribution of mass. Such a calculation would be relevant to the problem of the attraction of the earth on a satellite or the attraction of the sun on the earth. The simplest spherically symmetrical distribution of matter would be a homogeneous sphere. A spherical shell of constant thickness and density would be another example. A most general example would be a concentric set of such shells; each shell might be of a different thickness and made of different material with a different density. In any of these cases the density of material would depend only upon the distance from the center of the system and would be independent of any angular direction —that is what is meant by spherical symmetry.

The force of any test body, such as object a, near such a spherically symmetric body of matter, must lie along the line between the center of the body and the object a simply from the symmetry of the problem: no other direction is defined. We can use this symmetry, together with the long-range character of gravitational forces as expressed by the projectile model of forces, to suggest how the force on a test object a may vary with respect to the distance of a from the sphere.

We assume that every piece of matter of the sphere in Fig. 8|3 is emitting projectiles—gravitons—and the force on any object a results from the momentum transfer involved in absorbing these gravitons. Because of the symmetry of the problem, everywhere outside the sphere the momentum transfer is directed

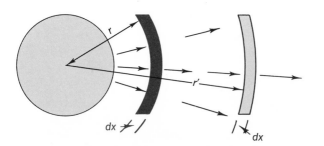

FIG. 8|3
A diagram used to discuss the momentum transfer to spherical shells at different distances from a central sphere.

outward, away from the center of the sphere. All components of momentum transfer in other directions must cancel when the contributions from the whole sphere are taken into account. Since the forces are long-range forces—the projectiles go on forever—all of the projectiles will pass through the spherical shell of radius r, which surrounds the central sphere, and there will be a certain momentum transfer to that sphere. Likewise, all the gravitons will pass through the larger spherical shell of radius of r', and if the two shells are of the same thickness, the momentum transfer to the two shells will be the same.

Since all gravitons emitted from any part of the central sphere will pass through any concentric shell, no matter what the size of the shell, the total momentum transfer to all shells of the same thickness will be equal. The total momentum transfer per second is then equal for all shells, and the force on the shells is the same. Since the area of a spherical shell is

$$A = 4\pi r^2$$

where r is the radius of the shell, and since the mass of the shell is

$$M = Axd$$

where d is the density of the material and x is the thickness of the shell, the force per unit mass is

$$\frac{F}{M} = \frac{F}{4\pi r^2 xd}$$

and varies inversely with the square of the distance from the center of the central sphere.

If the force on a certain shell of radius r is F, the total force on a shell of the same thickness but twice the radius will again be equal to F. But the area, and therefore the mass, of the larger sphere will be four times as great as that the smaller sphere. Then the force *per unit mass* on the larger sphere will be only one-fourth as great as the force per unit mass on the smaller sphere. We can consider that the force on any object, such as the object a, must then vary inversely with the square of the distance from the center of the attracting sphere. Of course, the force will be proportional to the mass of the object.

We can, then, write the force on the object in the form

$$F = K \frac{m}{r^2} \tag{8 | 2}$$

where m is the mass of the object, r is the distance of the object from the center of the attracting spherical object, and K is a constant of proportionality. If the object is at a great distance, the central sphere will appear as a point object. We know that the force can then be written as

$$F = -G \frac{Mm}{r^2} \qquad (8\,|\,3)$$

where G is the gravitational constant and M is now the mass of the central body. Since both the relations $(8\,|\,2)$ and $(8\,|\,3)$ must correctly describe the force on the body, we have

$$K = -GM$$

and the general conclusion that the force on a small object of mass m at a distance r from a spherically symmetric body of mass M will be equal to

$$F = -G \frac{Mm}{r^2} \qquad (8\,|\,4)$$

Although this result follows from the rather special model we have chosen to represent long-range forces, the conclusion can be derived from the basic relation $(8\,|\,1)$, which expresses the force between any two mass points as a function of the distance between them, and the superposition principle. The fact that the projectile model was successful does not demonstrate that it is a valid picture of the interaction. Although that description might well be reasonable, it has not been satisfactorily demonstrated yet—we are not certain that gravitons really exist.

We can also consider the force inside a sphere by analyzing the force inside a spherical shell of constant thickness. As an example, we calculate, explicitly, the force on the test mass m, in Fig. $8\,|\,4$, from the gravitational effects of the hollow sphere that surrounds it. Let us consider in particular the force on the test mass along an arbitrary direction denoted by the dashed line. Along this line, the test mass will be at a distance a from one surface of the sphere and a distance b from the other surface. The area s_a intercepted by any solid angle along the direction a is proportional to a^2; the area of the sphere s_b around the same solid angle in the direction of b will be proportional to b^2. The ratio of the area of the surface s_a to the area s_b will be equal to the ratio

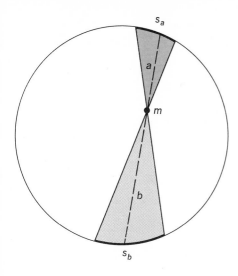

FIG. 8|4

A diagram showing the relative areas subtended at a point inside a spherical shell by the surface of the shell.

of a^2 to b^2. The force exerted on by m the mass in area s_a will be inversely proportional to a^2, and the force from s_b will be inversely proportional to b^2. The total force on the test body m will be the same from each of the small increments of surface s_a and s_b, but the force from s_a will be in the opposite direction from the force from s_b. If b is equal to twice a, the mass corresponding to s_n will be four times the mass corresponding to s_a. But the effect of the larger mass is exactly compensated by the greater distance: the force per unit mass on m from s_b will only be one-fourth as great as the force per unit mass from s_a, since s_b is twice as far from m as s_a. The forces on m from s_a and s_b will be equal in magnitude and opposite in direction; they will cancel each other, and the total force from the two segments of the sphere on m will be equal to zero.

Though we have discussed only the results along the direction denoted by the dashed line, this is clearly an arbitrary direction and the argument holds for any direction whatsoever. This leads us, then, to the final conclusion that the gravitational force on a mass inside a circular shell is zero. Since any homogeneous sphere is equivalent to a set of concentric shells, it immediately follows that the gravitational force on a test object inside a sphere is equal to the force from the matter that is nearer the center than the test object, and there is no total force from the matter that is farther from the center.

8|3 *Gravitational potential*

In the course of the previous discussions of potential energy, it was shown that the difference in potential energy of a mass point situated at two different points near the earth's surface was equal to the product of the acceleration of gravity near the earth's surface, the mass of the object, and the perpendicular distance between the two points. The potential energy of the mass at the higher point will be greater than the potential energy at the lower point by an amount

$$V = mgh$$

where V is the potential energy difference, m is the mass of the object, g the acceleration of gravity, and h is the difference in height of the two points. This relation is a good approximation for sets of points very near the earth's surface.

When we consider large distances—distances of the magnitude of the diameter of the earth—we must correctly account for the fact that the force varies inversely with the square of distance from the center of the earth. The calculation of potential energy then takes a more complicated form. In Fig. 8|5 the gravitational force on a 1-kg mass is shown as a function of distance from the earth's center. The curve follows the relation that was developed in the last section for regions away from the earth's surface:

$$F = -G \frac{M_e m}{r^2}$$

where G is the gravitational constant, M_e is the mass of the earth, m is the mass of the test object, and r is the distance from the

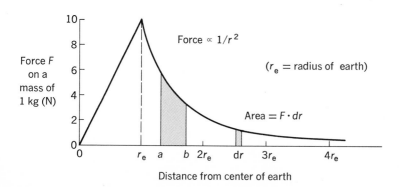

FIG. 8|5
The gravitational force on a 1-kg mass versus the distance from the center of the earth.

object to the center of the earth. If the earth were homogeneous (a rather poor approximation), the force of gravity below the surface of the earth would follow the straight line shown in the diagram.

We can use this curve to calculate the energy required to move the mass from a point a to a point b, where a and b are different distances from the earth's surface. The energy required will be the work done to move the mass *against* the force of gravity. Over an interval dr, where the interval is taken sufficiently small that the force of gravity does not vary substantially across it, the work done will equal the force F times the distance dr: that is, $dW = -F\,dr$. This represents a small increment of area under the curve of Fig. 8|5. It is easy to see that the amount of work done in moving an object over a larger distance, such as a to b, can be made up of such small intervals and small pieces of work each proportional to a small area under the curve. Therefore, the total area under the curve from a to b will equal the total amount of work done in moving the mass from a to b. Or

$$W_{ab} = \int_a^b -F\,dr$$

Since

$$F = -G\,\frac{M_e m}{r^2}$$

we can substitute to obtain

$$W_{ab} = \int_a^b G\,\frac{M_e m}{r^2}\,dr$$

In Fig. 8|5 the amount of work required to move the 1-kg object from a to b is represented by the cross-hatched area. Thus we could find the magnitude of the work by drawing a sufficiently careful graph and measuring the area under the curve. If we did so, we would find that the energy required to move the body from point a to point b is

$$W_{ab} = GM_e m \left(\frac{1}{r_a} - \frac{1}{r_b}\right) \tag{8|5}$$

where r_a and r_b are the initial and final distances between the object of mass m and the center of the earth. From the definition of potential energy, we are always interested in relative potential energy of the mass at point a and point b. The potential energy is higher at b.

If r_b is moved out very far, an infinite distance, the term $1/r_b$ in Eq. (8|5) will go to zero, and we will have the energy required to take a body from a radius a out to infinity. In the consideration of potential energy, we are always interested in relative potential energy. In problems considering situations near the earth's surface, it is often convenient to consider the potential energy at the earth's surface as the zero of potential energy. A more convenient choice for astronomical problems, and a choice that is more attractive intuitively for such problems, is to assign zero potential energy for the potential energy of particles infinitely far away from another, where there is no sensible residual of their gravitational attraction. In this case the potential energy is equal to the amount of work required to bring an object from infinity up to a point a, and for gravitational fields this energy will be quantitatively equal to

$$V(a) = -G\,\frac{M_e m}{r_a}$$

where $V(a)$ is the potential energy of the mass m with respect to a position very far from the earth. The minus sign occurs because energy must be supplied to the mass to move it out away from the earth from the point a. For any point at a distance r, the potential energy is

$$F(r) = -G\,\frac{M_e m}{r} \tag{8|6}$$

We can check formula (8|6) for the potential energy of a body of mass m as a function of distance r (or a) from a mass M, to determine whether that relation is consistent with the relation for the force on a particle. From the results of Section 6|5, we know that the force on the body in the radial direction will be equal in magnitude to the rate of change in the potential energy in the radial direction:

$$F = -\frac{dV}{dr}$$

This is equal to the difference between the potential energy of the body at a distance $r + dr$ from the central mass, minus the potential energy of the body at a distance r, all divided by the difference dr. Explicitly,

$$\frac{dV}{dr} = \frac{V(r+dr) - V(r)}{dr}$$

$$= \left(\frac{1}{dr}\right) \left(\frac{GMm}{r+dr} - \frac{GMm}{r}\right)$$

With a little algebraic manipulation,

$$\frac{dV}{dr} = \frac{GMm}{r^2 + r\, dr}$$

In the limit of a very small values of dr, the last term in the denominator can be neglected and

$$F = -\frac{dV}{dr}$$

$$= -\frac{GMm}{r^2}$$

which is expression (8 | 4) for the force on the particle as a function of distance r, and thus shows that expression (8 | 6) is valid.

In describing the character of forces such as the earth's force of gravity, a concept known as *potential* is useful. Expressions such as Eq. (8 | 4) and Eq. (8 | 6) do express the character of the gravitational force near the earth, but they include the mass of some test body. If we divide the formula for potential energy by the mass of the test body, we obtain a relation that depends only on the characteristics of the earth. We call this parameter, which has the dimensions of force per unit mass, *potential*. The gravitational potential near the surface of the earth is just $U = gh$, where the force on an object of mass m is $Um = mgh$. The potential of the earth in general is

$$U(r) = \frac{V(r)}{m}$$

$$= -G\frac{M_e}{r}$$

In the previous discussion we have implicitly considered only paths along a straight line from the center of the earth to infinity. Would it require more or less energy to move a particle x with a definite mass m from a to b along a more complicated path? Figure 8 | 6 shows two paths from point a to point b in the gravitational field of the earth. We note that the force of gravity on a

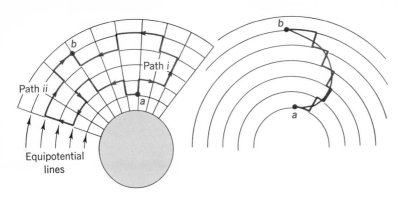

Equipotential lines

FIG. 8|6
*Paths in the
gravitational field of a
sphere.*

mass is always toward the earth and thus parallel to the radial lines. Then no work is required to move a mass along the circular paths, since the force is perpendicular to the direction of motion. The potential energy of the mass will not change as the mass is moved along these paths, and we call the paths *equipotential lines*. Work is done in moving the mass along a radial line; the same amount of work is done on the object as it is moved along any radial line from one equipotential line to another. This is clear from the symmetry of the situation—all radial lines are equivalent.

The same amount of work is done on the mass in moving it from *a* to *b* along either of the paths in Fig. 8|6, since the distance along the circular lines—the equipotential lines—can be disregarded and the two paths cover the same radial distance. If the two paths required a different amount of input energy—if, say, $W(i)$ were greater than $W(ii)$—we could complete a full circle clockwise, putting in an amount of energy equal to $W(ii)$ and taking out an amount $W(i)$, thus drawing energy from the system. But we have shown in detail why we cannot draw energy from the system: the energy difference between any two points is independent of the path between the points.

Though the particular paths of Fig. 8|6 are artificial in that they follow radial lines and equipotential lines exactly, the results illustrated by these special paths are general. Any irregular path can be considered to be infinitely close to a path made up entirely of elements that are equipotentials and radii. This is suggested by the right-hand part of Fig. 8|6, in which an irregular path is approximated by the path along radii and equipotentials.

If the character of the variation of a force with position is such that energy cannot be drawn from the system by moving an object through a closed path, we say that the force is a *conservative* force. If a force is conservative, the potential energy of a body under the influence of the force depends only on the position of the body, and a potential exists. The gravitational force is a conservative force, and we can therefore construct a gravitational potential.

We will use the results concerning gravitational potential near the earth in solving one particularly interesting problem, that of calculating the escape velocity from the earth—that is, the velocity a particle must have at the earth's surface in order to completely escape the gravitational field. We of course neglect air resistance. This result is pertinent to the design of interplanetary rockets.

The kinetic energy of the rocket very far from the earth, where the potential energy is negligible, must not be less than zero. Since energy is conserved, the kinetic energy plus the potential energy at the earth's surface must also be equal to or larger than zero. Then

$$\tfrac{1}{2}mv^2 - G\,\frac{M_e m}{r_e} = 0$$

or

$$\tfrac{1}{2}mv^2 = G\,\frac{M_e m}{r_e} \tag{8|7}$$

where m is the mass of the rocket, v is the velocity of the rocket, and r_e is the radius of the earth. We do not need to know the value of the gravitational constant G or the mass of the earth, because we do know the radius of the earth, about 6000 km, and the acceleration of gravity at the earth's surface, 10 m/sec². At the earth's surface,

$$F = mg$$
$$ = G\,\frac{M_e m}{r_e^2}$$

or

$$g = G\,\frac{M_e}{r_e^2}$$

or

$$GM_e = gr_e^2 \qquad (8|8)$$

Then from $(8|7)$ and $(8|8)$,

$$\tfrac{1}{2}mv^2 = gr_e m$$

or

$$v^2 = 2gr_e \qquad (8|9)$$

Substituting the numerical values $g = 10$ m/sec^2 and $r_e = 6 \times 10^6$ m, we have the escape velocity:

$$v = 11{,}000 \text{ m/sec}$$
$$ = 11 \text{ km/sec}$$

8|4   *The orbits of satellites*

The origin of the considerations that led us to understand that gravity follows an inverse-square law was derived from analyses of the measurements of the planetary orbits. Newton's great triumph was his ability to understand in detail the complexities of the planetary orbits, using precisely the same ideas he had formulated to describe the effects of gravitation at the earth's surface. He was able to understand the orbits of the moon around the earth and the orbits of the planets around the sun in terms of falling bodies.

In order to be specific, we follow Newton and discuss the moon's orbit around the earth. Even though the moon is con-tinually falling toward the earth, it is evident that it doesn't come any closer to the earth. This seemingly contradictory state of affairs is illustrated in Fig. $8|7$. In a period of time dt, the moon falls towards the earth the distance d. In that time it has moved perpendicular to a line between the earth and the moon a distance s equal to $v\,dt$ where v is the velocity of the moon in its orbit. One can see now how it is possible for the distance between the earth and moon to remain the same. If the moon had continued on a straight line it, of course, would be further from the earth. The distance it fell toward the earth just compensated for this effect, so that the distance from the earth to the moon remained constant. We can examine this relation quantitatively, using

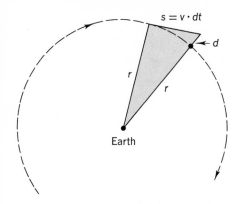

FIG. 8 | 7
*Kinematic quantities
concerning the moon's
orbit about the earth.*

Fig. 8 | 7. From the Phythagorean theorem we see that

$$(r + d)^2 = r^2 + s^2$$

or

$$r^2 + 2rd + d^2 = r^2 + s^2 \tag{8 | 10}$$

We should concern ourselves with a very small traverses, in which case d is very small compared with the other quantities, s and r. Therefore, d^2 is negligible compared to the other terms of (8 | 10), and we can drop it. Then, with a little manipulation,

$$d = \frac{s^2}{2r}$$

Since s is equal to $v\,dt$, where v is the velocity of the moon and dt is the time element we use, the distance the moon falls is

$$d = \frac{v^2\,dt}{2r}$$

Since the moon is a falling body, we can also use the relation for the distance a body falls in a time dt when the acceleration is g':

$$d = \tfrac{1}{2}g'\,dt^2$$

where g' is acceleration of gravity at the position of the moon's orbit. If we equate these two expressions for d we find that

$$g' = \frac{v^2}{r}$$

This is just the expression we derived previously for the centripetal acceleration of a body in a circular orbit: g' is thus the value of acceleration required to cause the moon to stay in a stable circular orbit.

This exposition of the acceleration of a body moving in a circle was familiar to Newton. Furthermore, the value of r, the distance from the moon to the earth, was known in Newton's time; and since the velocity is easily determined from the period of rotation of the moon around the earth, which is twenty-eight days, and the radius, the velocity was also known. Therefore, Newton could calculate g'. He found that the ratio g'/r^2 is equal to g/r_e^2, where g is the gravitational acceleration at the earth's surface and r_e is the radius of the earth. This suggested that a more general law of gravitation must hold, in which the gravitational force between two objects varies inversely with the square of the distance between the objects. Then in general, for any satellite in a circular orbit about a body of mass m,

$$\frac{Gm}{r^2} = \frac{v^2}{r} \tag{8|11}$$

The velocity of the moon in its orbit, v, is equal to the circumference of the orbit divided by the period, or the time T it takes to complete the orbit:

$$V = \frac{2\pi r}{T}$$

Using (8|11) with a little algebra,

$$T^2 = r^3 \left(\frac{4\pi^2}{GM_e}\right)$$

The square of the period of rotation is proportional to the cube of the radius of the orbit. This relation, which holds for the orbits about any body, was discovered by Kepler in the century before Newton, and is called Kepler's third law. The first of Kepler's laws is the observation that the planets move in elliptic orbits with with the sun at one focus. The second of Kepler's laws is the observation that the vector from the sun to a planet sweeps out equal areas in equal time. This is essentially the law of conservation of angular momentum, which we have discussed. Newton's detailed work showed that all three of Kepler's laws follow naturally from the assumption that the force of gravity varies inversely with the square of the distance.

PROBLEMS

8|1 (*a*) How would you expect a long-range force, such as gravity, to vary with distance in a four-dimensional universe?

(*b*) How would you expect it to vary in a three-dimensional universe with curved space? (Consider the variation of force with distance for a two-dimensional curved space, such as part of the surface of a globe.)

8|2 In the figure, the small inner sphere *a* has a mass of 1 unit; spherical shell *b* has a mass of 1 unit and a radius of 1 m; spherical shell *c* has a mass of 1 unit and a radius of 2 m. The force on mass *d*, which is 4 m from the center sphere, is 1000 N. (Take the potential energy at infinity as zero.)

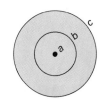

(*a*) Draw a graph of the force on *d* versus distance from the center of *a*.

(*b*) Show that the potential energy of *d*, 5 m from the center, is 4000 J.

(*c*) Draw a graph of potential energy versus the distance of *d* from the center of *a*.

8|3 Assume that the density of the earth is uniform. Show that the acceleration of gravity halfway to the center of the earth is exactly half the acceleration at the surface.

8|4 What is the escape velocity from the earth's gravitational field from a point at the distance of the moon (400,000 km)?

8|5 A 1-kg piece of iron (a meteorite) falls toward the earth from a stationary position very far away. Neglecting the effect of the sun and other planets:

(*a*) How fast will it be going when it strikes the earth?

(*b*) What will be the kinetic energy of the meteorite?

(*c*) What was its original potential energy with respect to the earth's surface?

8|6 A communication relay satellite is required to remain over one spot on the earth. What will be the radius of the orbit of such a satellite?

8|7 (*a*) The distance between earth and sun is about 92,000,000 mi in winter, 94,000,000 mi in summer. How will the velocity of the earth change between summer and winter?

(*b*) The mean radius of the orbit of Venus 68,000,000 mi, that of Mars is 142,000,000 mi; what is the length of the Venusian year? The Martian year?

8|8 What is the ratio between the kinetic energy of the moon and its potential energy with respect to a point very far from the earth?

8|9 What proportion of the angular momentum of the earth–moon system is stored in the rotation of the earth? (Estimate this within a factor of 2; the mass of the moon is about 1.2 percent of the mass of the earth.)

8|10 If the diameter of the sun is 100 times the diameter of the earth and the acceleration of gravity at the surface of the sun is 27 times that of the earth, what is the ratio of the mass of the sun and the mass of the earth?

8|11 The radius of the orbit of the moon, about the earth, is about $\frac{1}{400}$ of the radius of the orbit of the earth about the sun. There are 13 lunar months in a year. From these data calculate the ratio of the masses of the earth and sun.

8|12 The radius of the orbit of the moon about the earth is 400,000 km; the period of revolution is 28 days. The radius of the orbit of Dione, the fourth satellite of Saturn, is the same, but its period is 2.8 days. What are the relative masses of the earth and Saturn?

9|1 *The kinematics of simple*
harmonic motion

REPETITIVE MOTION, motion that repeats itself, is a common part of our everyday experience. The most common of repetitive motions are the motions of things traveling at constant speed in a complete circle like the spot on the edge of a rotating wheel, and the motion of things oscillating to and fro like the swing of the chandelier in the Cathedral at Pisa, which Galileo noticed and described over three hundred years ago. These two common repetitive motions are closely related. Oscillatory motion such as that of Galileo's chandelier is a projection of circular motion.

If a wheel is placed relative to the sun in such a way that the shadow of the wheel forms a straight line, the shadow of an extension fastened to the circumference of the wheel will represent a projection of a point on the wheel on the plane of the shadow (see Fig. 9|1). When the wheel rotates with constant velocity, the shadow of the extension will oscillate back and forth along the linear shadow of the wheel. The motion of the shadow will be identical to the motion of a pendulum or chandelier moving with the same amplitude and period. We call this particular motion *simple harmonic motion.*

Simple harmonic motion is the motion characteristic of the vibrations and oscillations of matter. The vibrations of a drumhead excited by the blow of a drumstick, the vibrations of the

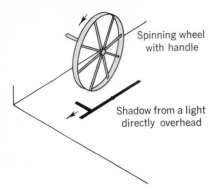

Spinning wheel
with handle

Shadow from a light
directly overhead

FIG. 9 1

*The projection of a
point on a wheel moving
with constant angular
velocity moves with
simple harmonic motion.*

surface of an atomic nucleus excited by the collision of a neutron,
and the oscillations of a cepheid variable star, which results in a
cyclic increase and decrease in the brightness of the star, are all
described in much the same manner. Though the frequency of
vibration of the nuclear surface is of the order of 10^{20} per second,
the vibrational frequency of the drumhead may be about 10^2 per
second, and the frequency of oscillation of the star will be of the
order of 10^{-6} per second, each of these phenomena is an example
of simple harmonic motion.

Waves that involve the motions of matter, such as water waves
and sound waves, are closely related to simple harmonic motion
in that as each piece of matter in a wave train moves with simple
harmonic motion: each drop of water or each molecule of air
moves with the same kind of motion as a pendulum bob moving
with the same amplitude and frequency. Since the same kind of

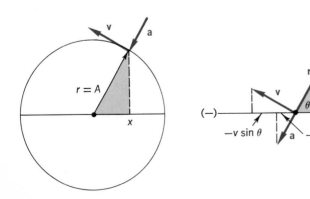

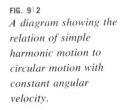

FIG. 9 2

*A diagram showing the
relation of simple
harmonic motion to
circular motion with
constant angular
velocity.*

description applies to electromagnetic waves and the de Broglie waves used to describe matter itself, although no overt motion is necessarily involved, we find that the concepts of simple harmonic motion dominate much of our description of nature.

The relation of simple harmonic motion to circular motion is shown with the help of Fig. 9|2. We will consider the relation between the position of a point on the circumference of the circle, moving with constant velocity v counterclockwise around the circle, and the projection of this point on the axis. If the absolute velocity of the particle moving on the circumference has the value v, the angular velocity will be equal to $\omega = v/r$. The position of the point is then defined by the angular displacement θ and, from the equations concerning circular motion, we can express the value of θ at any time t by the relation

$$\theta = \theta_0 + \omega t \qquad \text{or} \qquad \theta = \omega(t + t_0)$$

where $\theta_0 = \omega t_0$ is the angular position of the point at the time t_0. In order to make the equations a little simpler, we will choose the time scale such that $\theta_0 = 0$ so the equation will read

$$\theta = \omega t$$

It is convenient at this time to note two other useful relations. The period, T, or time it takes the point to move once around the circle, is

$$T = \frac{2\pi}{\omega} \qquad \text{so that} \qquad \omega = \frac{2\pi}{T}$$

and the frequency, f, the number of revolutions per unit time, is just the inverse of T:

$$f = \frac{1}{T} = \frac{\omega}{2\pi} \qquad \text{so that} \qquad \omega = 2\pi f$$

Now we can express the kinematic parameters of the projection on the x-axis. For the displacement of the projected point we use the symbol x. As we can see from the diagram of Fig. 9|2,

$$x = r \cos \omega t$$

where r is the radius of the circle. The x-component of the velocity of the point is seen from the figure to be

$$v_x = -v \sin \omega t$$

Since $v = \omega r$ we can also write this as

$$v_x = -\omega r \sin \omega t$$

The acceleration of the point moving around the circle is equal to v^2/r and is directed toward the center of the circle: this is the familiar centripetal acceleration of a particle moving in a circle with constant angular velocity. From an inspection of Fig. 9|2, the x-component of the acceleration is

$$a_x = -a \cos \omega t$$

or

$$a_x = -\left(\frac{v^2}{r}\right) \cos \omega t$$

We use the angular relation $v = \omega r$ to rewrite the expression as

$$a_x = -\omega^2 r \cos \omega t$$

Since $r \cos \omega t$ is equal to x,

$$a_x = -\omega^2 x$$

Since $a = d^2x/dt^2$, and $v = dx/dt$, we can also write these relations in the form

$$\frac{d^2x}{dt^2} = -\omega^2 x \qquad\qquad (9|1)$$

$$\frac{dx}{dt} = -\omega r \sin \omega t \qquad\qquad (9|2)$$

which emphasizes the fact that we have used the particular physical problem concerning the relations between the motion of the projection on a diameter of a point moving on the circumference of a circle with constant angular velocity to solve a second-order differential equation (9|1). The solutions of the equation are (9|2) and (9|3).

$$x = r \cos \omega t \qquad\qquad (9|3)$$

If we retract our original simplification that $\theta_0 = 0$ and replace t by $t + t_0$, where $\theta_0 = \omega t_0$, we obtain more general relations:

$$x = r \cos(\omega t + \theta_0)$$

$$v = -\omega r \sin(\omega t + \theta_0)$$

and

$$a = -\omega^2 x$$
$$= -\omega^2 r \cos(\omega t + \theta_0) \tag{9 | 4}$$

where

$$x_0 = r \cos \theta_0$$

is the displacement at the time $t = 0$.

Although these relations were developed from the analysis of a particular physical phenomenon, the motion of the projection of a point moving with constant speed on the circumference of a circle, the results are much more general. For any kinematic situation such that the acceleration is proportional to the displacement but oppositely directed, the motion is just like the motion of the projection of uniform circular motion, even when there is rather obviously no circular motion involved in the problem at all. Further, the three relations (9 | 1), (9 | 2), and (9 | 3) follow from one another. If the acceleration is described by (9 | 1), the velocity and position will vary with time according to the descriptions provided by (9 | 2) and (9 | 3). If the velocity is described by Eq. (9 | 2), the acceleration and position will follow from (9 | 1) and (9 | 3). If the position varies with time according to (9 | 3), the Eqs. (9 | 1) and (9 | 2) will describe the variation of the acceleration and velocity with time.

Even more generally, the equations may represent variations of quantities other than x and t, displacement and time. The relations between the three equations of (9 | 1)–(9 | 3) are mathematical or logical relations that must hold whatever the physical meaning of the variables. We will often refer to this differential equation developed to describe simple harmonic motion, and we will refer to it as DE-SHM, for Differential Equation of Simple Harmonic Motion.

It is useful to note a few simple characteristics of simple harmonic motion. Even though simple harmonic motions, in general, need not have anything to do with a physical circle, it is useful to keep in mind the equivalence between any simple harmonic motion and the motion of the projection of a point moving uniformly in a circle. By inspection of the relations (9 | 1)–(9 | 3), or by inspection of Fig. 9 | 2, we can see that when the displacement is zero ($x = 0$), the acceleration is also zero

($a = 0$), while the velocity is at its maximum value ($v = v_{\mathrm{m}} = \omega A = 2\pi f A$). When the displacement is at its maximum value ($x = A$, where we call A the *amplitude*), the acceleration is also at its maximum value ($a = -\omega^2 x = \omega^2 A = 4\pi^2 f^2 A$), while the velocity is zero ($v = 0$). We have now dropped the subscript x with a or v because this convention is no longer necessary when we are obviously discussing motion in a straight line.

It is interesting to compare the second-order differential equation DE-SHM of Eq. (9|1) with the second-order differential equation DE-CA representing motion under constant acceleration, which was discussed in Section 2|2. Even as the solutions of Eq. (2|2) (DE-CA) must have two constants that can be adjusted to meet all possible boundary conditions, the solutions of (9|1), as written in the general form (9|4), have two constants that can be adjusted to fit any boundary conditions. Even as the path of the flight of a ball that is thrown from an initial position x_0 with an initial velocity v_0 is described by the relation

$$x = x_0 + v_0 t + \tfrac{1}{2} g t^2$$

which is a solution to the differential equation $d^2 x / dt^2 = g$, where g is a constant determined by the physical character of the situation, the path of a particle moving with simple harmonic motion, where the initial position is x_0 and the initial velocity is v_0, is described by the relation

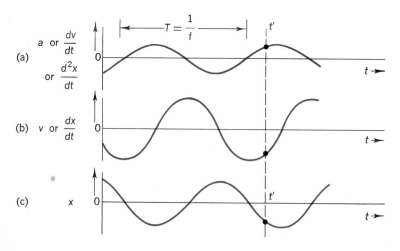

FIG. 9|3
The variation with time of the acceleration, velocity and position of a particle moving with simple harmonic motion.

$x = r \cos(\omega t + \theta_0)$

where

$x_0 = r \cos \theta_0$ and $v_0 = -r\omega \sin \theta_0$

The boundary conditions x_0 and v_0 determine the values of the parameters r and θ_0 in the solution of the differential equation $d^2x/dt^2 = \omega^2 x$, where ω is a constant determined by the physical character of the situation.

The diagrams of Fig. 9|3 further illustrate the character of simple harmonic motion. The slope of the curve representing the variation of x with respect to t and t_0 is equal to the value of v at the time t_0. In turn the slope of the curve representing the variation of v with respect to t, at the arbitrarily chosen time t_0, is equal to the value of the acceleration a at t_0.

9|2   *The dynamics of simple harmonic motion*

The kinematic equations of the last section describe the motion of a body moving with a particular acceleration. Such an acceleration must be induced by a force in the direction of the acceleration that has a value equal to the mass of the body times the value of the acceleration:

$a = -\omega^2 x$

$ma = -m\omega^2 x$

Since

$F = ma$

we can write

$F = -m\omega^2 x$

or

$F = -kx$

where

$$k = \omega^2 m \qquad \text{and} \qquad \omega = \sqrt{\frac{k}{m}} \qquad\qquad (9|5)$$

The relation (9|5) is the characteristic dynamical equation of simple harmonic motion. Even as the simple harmonic motion of a massive object leads to a relation between the force on the object and the displacement of the object from some equilibrium position of the form (9|5), the inverse also holds; any physical system such that the force on a mass and the displacement of the mass from an equilibrium position are related according to Eq. (9|5) will oscillate with simple harmonic motion with a frequency

$$f = \frac{1}{2\pi} \omega$$

$$= \frac{1}{2\pi} \sqrt{\frac{k}{m}}$$

The amplitude is determined by the character of the disturbance causing the oscillation: the amplitude may be zero, if there is no disturbance, or it might be quite large. The frequency is independent of the amplitude.

It is possible to show that many varieties of physical phenomena involve forces that vary with displacement according to a relation of the type $F = -kx$ for comparitively trivial reasons. We can gain some insight into the generality of the relation (9|5) by considering the potential energy of a typical system as a function of displacement, using the basic relations (9|5), $F = -kx$, as a starting point. In parallel with the general discussion, which is applicable to many varieties of systems, we will describe the application of the principles to two similar physical systems as illustrations.

Figure 9|4a shows a system in which a mass is held between two springs and a system in which a mass rolls on a curved surface. In each case an equilibrium position exists such that the total force on the mass is zero. For the mass between the springs, it is the position at which the springs exert equal but opposite forces on the mass; for the mass rolling on the curved surface, the equilibrium position is obviously at the lowest point of the surface. If the mass in either system is at any other point, a force is exerted on the mass in a direction so as to return the mass to the equilibrium position. The force, F, on the mass is thus always in the direction opposite to the displacement, and for the mass held by the springs the force is proportional to the displacement. Let us assume that the curved surface is so shaped that the restoring force is also proportional to the displacement (the curve

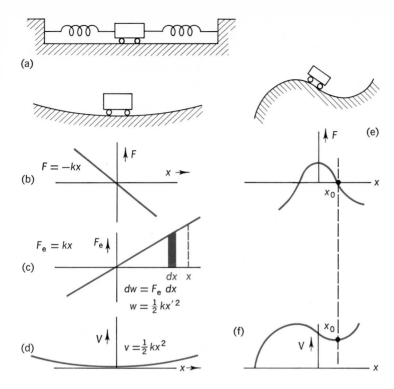

(a)

(b) $F = -kx$ $x \rightarrow$ $\uparrow F$

(c) $F_e = kx$ $F_e \uparrow$ dx x $dw = F_e\,dx$ $w = \frac{1}{2}kx'^2$

(d) $v \uparrow$ $v = \frac{1}{2}kx^2$ $x \rightarrow$

(e) $\uparrow F$ x_0 x

(f) x_0 $V \uparrow$ x

FIG. 9|4
*Descriptions of the
simple harmonic motion
of two systems.*

will be a parabola) and that the force, for any given displacement, is the same as the force exerted by the springs. Further, to emphasize the parallel, let us assume that the masses are equal. The force on the mass exerted by the springs, or the force on the mass derived from the reaction to the gravitational force by the curved surface, can be expressed as

$$F = -kx$$

where x is the displacement, and k, a proportionality constant, is a measure of the strength of the springs or the steepness of the curved surface. Figure 9|4b shows the variation of the force with the displacement.

If the mass is displaced from the equilibrium position to a point x', work must be done by some external source, or perhaps at the expense of kinetic energy of the mass. The external force, F_e, required to move the mass against the reaction of the springs, or to move the mass up the incline of the curved surface, must be equal in magnitude to the force exerted on the mass by these constraints and opposite in direction:

$$F_e = -F$$
$$= kx$$

Figure 9|4c shows the variation of the external force F_e with respect to the displacement x.

As the mass is moved from the equilibrium position, work must be done on the system to compress and stretch the springs or to lift the mass up against the force of gravity; this work represents an addition to the potential energy of the system. The small shaded area of Fig. 9|4c is equal to the increment of work dW_e done on the system in moving the mass through the interval dx and is thus equal to the increment of potential energy dV added to the system.

The total work done in displacing the mass from the point of equilibrium, where the force is zero, to a distance x' is equal to the area under the curve of force versus displacement:

$$V_e(0 \text{ to } x') = V(x')$$
$$= \int_0^{x'} F_e \, dx$$

Since $F_e = kx$, this takes the familiar form of DE-CA, discussed previously,

$$W_e(0 \text{ to } x') = V(x')$$
$$= \int_0^{x'} kx \, dx$$

and this is just equal to the area of the triangle of Fig. 9|4c with a base equal to x' and an altitude of kx'. The area is then $\frac{1}{2}kx'^2$, which is equal to the potential energy of the system when the mass is displaced by an amount x':

$$W_e(x') = V(x')$$
$$= \tfrac{1}{2}kx'^2$$

The potential energy of the system as a function of the displacement, now taken as x, is shown in Fig. 9|4d.

The curve of Fig. 9|4f represents the variation of potential energy with displacement for some arbitrary physical situation where a minimum of potential energy exists. The system will be at equilibrium at the position marked x_0. Sufficiently near this minimum the arbitrary curve will be very nearly the same as the curve of Fig. 9|4d, which represents potential energy as function of displacement from the equilibrium position for a system such that $F = -kx$. This curve follows the relation

$$V = \tfrac{1}{2}kx^2$$

which was shown to represent the variation of potential energy with distance characteristic of systems that oscillate in simple harmonic motion. Near the minimum in potential energy of Fig. 9|4f we can describe the curve by a power series in x, if the curve is smooth, no matter how complicated it may be:

$$V = a + bx + cx^2 + dx^3 \cdots$$

where x is the distance from the equilibrium point x_0. Since only differences in potential energy are important, we are not concerned with the magnitude of a, which is just the value of the potential energy at the minimum point. Exactly at the minimum the slope of the potential energy curve will be zero: b is proportional to the slope, so very near the minimum $b = 0$. It then follows that very near the minimum the potential energy can be described by the relation

$$V = cx^2 + dx^3 + ex^4 \cdots$$

With such a relation it is always possible to choose x sufficiently small that x^2 is very much larger than x^3, which is in turn larger than x^4. For example, if x is equal to 0.001, or 10^{-3}, x^2 will be equal to 10^{-6}, and x^3 will be equal to 10^{-9}; so x is very much larger than x^2, x^2 is very much larger than x^3, and so on. No matter what the values of the coefficients c, d, and e may be, sufficiently near the minimum one can always neglect the terms in x^3 and x^4. Therefore, sufficiently near the minimum or equilibrium position we can describe almost any physical situation by the equation that represents the potential energy as being proportional to the square of the displacement,

$$V = cx^2$$

which is the potential-energy relation for simple harmonic motion.

We have shown previously that the force a system exerts on a mass is proportional to the slope of the potential-energy curve.

The force at any position x is equal to the negative rate of change of the potential with respect to x:

$$F = -\frac{dV}{dx}$$

The curve of Figs. 9|4b and 9|4e, which show the force exerted by the system on the mass as a function of the displacement, thus represent the slopes of the curves of Figs. 9|4d and 9|4f, which show the potential energy as a function of the displacement. The ordinates of the upper curves are equal to the negative of the slopes of the lower curves. Since the curve of force versus displacement can always be represented by a straight line over a sufficiently small interval, the force-versus-displacement curve of Fig. 9|4e can be represented by a straight line sufficiently near x_0 and the curve will be identical in character over that small interval with the force-versus-displacement curve of 9|4b, which represents the relation of the force to the displacement required so that the mass moves with simple harmonic motion.

If we then consider either the character of the curve that shows the potential energy of a mass as a function of displacement or the curve that shows the force on the mass as a function of displacement, we see that for sufficiently small displacements the mass will oscillate with simple harmonic motion. For example, if the potential-energy curve of Fig. 9|4f represents a surface in a constant gravitational field—where such a surface represents, itself, the variation of potential energy—and if a cart is allowed to move on the surface with frictionless wheels, the curve will represent the potential energy of the cart. If the cart is placed near any dip in the curve it will roll back and forth, and the motion can be described as simple harmonic motion. If the cart goes very high up on the curve, the motion may be very different from simple harmonic motion; but if the oscillations are small enough— and they can always be made small enough—the cart will oscillate with simple harmonic motion about the equilibrium point.

9|3   *Hooke's law*

We see that the particular character of so many physical situations that makes simple harmonic motion relevant to these situations, and therefore so common, is found in the continuity or smoothness of the variation of forces with displacements. It seems that it is a general character of nature that discontinuities or sharp breaks seldom occur in any phenomena.

A particularly important example of the utility of this continuity of nature is provided by the elastic behavior of substances. Most solids are deformed by small forces in a manner such that the solid returns to its initial position or shape when the force is removed. We call this *elastic* behavior. In order to discuss elastic behavior quantitatively it is convenient to consider the behavior of a particularly simple configuration under stress; we choose to examine the compression and stretching of a thin rod under compressive and extensive forces. Figure 9|5 shows a plot of the extension of such a rod as a function of the force on the rod.

The origin of the graph represents the length of the rod in the x-direction. Now let us consider the character of the situation when we have applied a force to the rod. For the sake of definiteness, let us assume that we hang a weight of mass m on the end of the rod, which is aligned vertically. Then there will be a force on the rod equal to $F_a = mg$, where g is the acceleration of gravity. This force stretches the rod so that the length of the rod corresponds to point d on the graph instead of the origin. As far as any additional forces or additional displacements are concerned, the position of zero force and zero displacement is now moved to the point d on the graph, and we can consider the effects of such further forces or displacements as if the zero of the coordinate system were transferred to the point d. The point d represents the new equilibrium position.

If the curve of force versus displacement for the rod is smooth, we can approximate the curve quite well by a straight line for any sufficiently small section of the curve. This is essentially a definition of smoothness. Then very near the new origin d, the force-

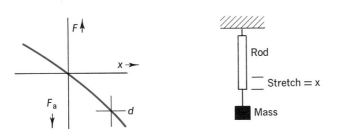

FIG. 9|5
The force-versus-displacement curve for an elastic system. F is the upward force exerted by the rod; F_a is the downward force exerted on the rod by the weight; x is the elongation or stretch of the rod.

versus-displacement curve will be nearly a straight line, just as in Fig. 9|4b, and the force will vary with displacement according to the relation

$$F = -kx$$

where F is the additional force on the mass that results from the additional displacement (from the origin d) equal to x. We assume that additional force will stretch the substance making up the rod, and internal force will oppose this stretching; hence the negative sign. The value of the constant k will depend upon the strength of those forces and will therefore depend upon the dimensions of the rod and upon the character of the material making up the rod.

Since $F = -kx$, we know that the system will oscillate if it is excited by any transient disturbance, such as being stretched slightly and released. Indeed if k, the spring constant, is determined by measuring the slope of the force versus displacement curve of Fig. 9|5, one can calculate the frequency of oscillation from the relations of Eq. (9|5). If the mass is m and if the mass of the rod can be neglected,

$$F = -kx$$

$$ma = -kx$$

$$a = -\left(\frac{k}{m}\right) x$$

$$\omega^2 = \frac{k}{m}$$

$$\omega = \sqrt{\frac{k}{m}}$$

or the frequency

$$f = \frac{\omega}{2\pi}$$

$$= \left(\frac{1}{2\pi}\right) \sqrt{\frac{k}{m}}$$

All elastic substances have force-versus-displacement curves that are smooth. All smooth curves can be approximated over small intervals by straight lines. The straight-line relation between force and displacement is just the relation that results in simple harmonic motion. We call the relation $F = -kx$ *Hooke's law,* after the British scientist of Newton's time who recognized this relation. He did not seem to realize that it followed merely from the smoothness or continuity of the force-versus-displacement curve; he considered it as a fundamental law of nature, perhaps on a footing as fundamental as the law of gravity. Parenthetically, we might add that it is rather surprising in many substances that the linear region of the curve extends over a very large distance; the fact that the curve is linear is trivial, but the fact that it is linear over a large displacement is not trivial and perhaps suggests important things about the character of the forces that hold macroscopic pieces of matter together.

9|4   *The pendulum*

An important example of simple harmonic motion that we will treat separately is the oscillation of a pendulum. A diagram of a pendulum is shown in Fig. 9|6, together with a vector diagram of the forces acting on the pendulum bob. The force downward is equal to the mass times the acceleration of gravity. If the pendulum is inclined at an angle θ with respect to the vertical, there will be a component of the gravitational force in a direction such as to restore the pendulum bob to the vertical. From the dia-

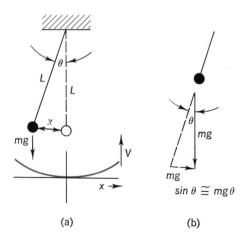

(a)   (b)

FIG. 9|6
The dynamic and kinematic description of the simple pendulum: (a) diagram of the pendulum; (b) diagram of the forces on the bob.

gram of the components of force, we see that this force is equal to

$$F = mg \sin \theta$$

For small angles, where $\sin \theta$ is about equal to θ (in radians),

$$F = mg\theta$$

This can be seen easily in Fig. 9|6b, where the scale of the draw-ing is such that the force triangle is approximately the same size as the figure of the pendulum itself. Since θ is equal to x/L for small angles, where x is the displacement and L is the length of the pendulum,

$$F = -mg\left(\frac{x}{L}\right)$$

where we introduce the minus sign in recognition that the force is directed opposite to the displacement x. It then follows that

$$ma = -mg\left(\frac{x}{L}\right)$$

and

$$a = -\left(\frac{g}{L}\right)x$$

Since

$$a = -\omega^2 x$$

it follows that

$$\omega = \sqrt{\frac{g}{L}} \quad \text{and} \quad f = \frac{1}{2\pi}\sqrt{\frac{g}{L}}$$

These relations hold, and the pendulum oscillates with simple harmonic motion, only for small oscillations such that $\sin \theta \approx \theta$.

The relations developed for simple harmonic motion in general can be used to find the value of the velocity, the acceleration, the kinetic energy, and the potential energy of the pendulum bob as a function of time. These relations do not depend upon any particular characteristics of the pendulum beyond the fact that a mass, the pendulum bob, is moving with simple harmonic motion. Therefore, the following results are valid for all systems in which a mass moves with simple harmonic motion; the relations thus hold for a mass at the end of a light rod or a mass suspended by a light spring, for example.

The amplitude A is, by definition, the maximum value of x, the displacement, and thus is equal to r, the radius of the reference circle used to describe simple harmonic motion in terms of the motion of a point moving on the circumference of a circle (this is *not* the physical circle or arc of the pendulum). It then follows from the results of Section 9|1 that

$$v = -\omega A \sin \omega t \quad \text{and} \quad v_{\max} = \omega A$$

$$a = -\omega^2 A \cos \omega t \quad \text{and} \quad a_{\max} = \omega^2 A$$

The kinetic energy of the mass, equal to $\frac{1}{2}mv^2$, varies with time as

$$T = \tfrac{1}{2}mv^2$$

$$= \tfrac{1}{2}m\omega^2 A^2 \sin^2 \omega t$$

From the results of previous discussions the potential energy is

$$V = \tfrac{1}{2}kx^2$$

where

$$k = -\frac{F}{x}$$

$$= \omega^2 m$$

Since

$$x = A \cos \omega t$$

we can write

$$V = \tfrac{1}{2}m\omega^2 A^2 \cos^2 \omega t$$

Then the total energy E, which is equal to the sum of the kinetic energy T and the potential energy V, will be

$$E = T + V$$

$$= \tfrac{1}{2}m\omega^2 A^2 (\sin^2 \omega t + \cos^2 \omega t)$$

$$= \tfrac{1}{2}m\omega^2 A^2$$

since

$$\sin^2 a + \cos^2 a = 1$$

for any a.

The total energy of the system is therefore independent of time, as it should be. Less striking, but important, the total energy is proportional to the square of the amplitude and to the square of the frequency.

In all of the above calculations we have assumed that we start counting time when the bob is at its maximum displacement, $x = A$. If we use some other starting time, we must replace ωt in the equations by $\omega t - \theta_0$, where $\theta_0 = \omega t_0$, where t_0 is the time elapsed between the time $t = 0$ and the first time the mass reaches the position of maximum displacement.

The diagrams of Fig. 9|7 show the variation of displacement, velocity, acceleration, potential energy, and kinetic energy as a function of time for any body of mass m oscillating with simple harmonic motion with an angular frequency of ω.

The ordinate of the curve showing the variation of v with respect to t is proportional to the slope of the curve showing the variation of x with t; the curve showing the variation of a with t is proportional to the slope of the curve showing v versus t.

The discussion of the role of the arbitrary constants in the solutions of the differential equation were discussed in Section 9|1, where the purely kinematic characteristics of simple harmonic motion were considered. It is interesting to review those results, now that dynamical examples, which lend themselves better to intuitive appreciation, are available. Again, the differential equation that describes the motion of a body when the

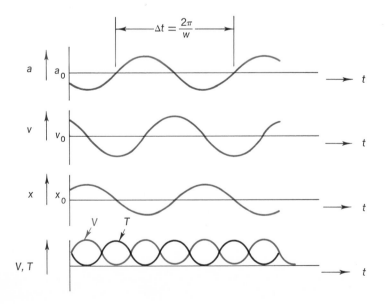

FIG. 9|7
The variation with time of the basic kinematic and dynamic quantities relevant to simple harmonic motion.

force on the body is constant is (DE–CA)

$$\frac{d^2x}{dt^2} = \frac{F}{m}$$

where $F = ma$ and F is the force, m the mass, and a the acceleration of the body. We emphasized that the equation has an infinite number of solutions. The solution that fits a particular physical situation is differentiated from all the possible solutions through two boundary conditions. The usual boundary conditions for uniform accelerated motion consist of the initial position and initial velocity. With $a = -g$, the acceleration of gravity, the differential equation represents the flight of a stone thrown with any velocity from any height. The flight of a particular stone is defined only if the height and initial velocity were stated.

Two different conditions must also be supplied before the motion of an object under simple harmonic motion is defined. For example, a pendulum of length L in a gravitational field of strength g will move with an acceleration defined by the differential equation (DE–SHM)

$$\frac{d^2x}{dt^2} = -\left(\frac{g}{L}\right) x$$

But such a pendulum could be started at time $t = 0$ by giving the bob any particular velocity from a position representing any arbitrary displacement. Again a twofold range of possible initial conditions requires two separate adjustable constants in the final equation to complete the description. In this case the two constants are usually taken to be A and θ_0, the amplitude and a starting time. Then the position of the bob will be described as

$$x = A \cos(\omega t - \theta_0)$$

where

$$\omega = \sqrt{\frac{k}{m}}$$

The relation of the two constants to the initial conditions, as expressed in Section 9|1, is not so direct as was the case for the example of constant accelerated motion. The reader is invited to express the two constants A and θ_0 in terms of an initial velocity v_0 and an initial position x_0; some minor facility in trigonometric manipulation is required.

9|5 *Resonance*

If a ball suspended from a string is disturbed very slightly, perhaps by a brief current of air, the ball will begin to oscillate with a small amplitude like a pendulum, with a frequency determined by the length of the string. If the impulse is repeated exactly one period later so as to reinforce the original impulse, the amplitude will be increased. If impulses are applied with exactly the same frequency as the natural frequency of the system, the amplitude will continue to increase until very large values are reached; indeed, if there is no friction the amplitude will increase until the essential character of the system is changed or the system is destroyed.

In the same way, one builds up a large amplitude of motion for a child in a swing by the application of a large number of gentle pushes applied at the natural frequency of the swing. This production of large amplitudes by the application of small impulses at the natural frequency of the system is described as a resonant behavior or a *resonance;* the natural frequency of the system is the *resonant frequency.*

If the frequency of the impulse is slightly different from the resonant frequency, the reinforcement will not be complete and the amplitude that will be reached will not be so large. It is possible to calculate the variation of the amplitude with respect to the frequency of the driving force in a rather simple manner if we assume an external force acting on the system such that

$$F = F_0 \cos \omega t$$

The system is such that it will oscillate with simple harmonic motion with a characteristic frequency of ω_r. One might think of the system as a pendulum, where the pendulum bob is being pushed or pulled with a force which varies with time sinusoidally with a frequency equal to $\omega/2\pi$. The force on the system in the absence of the external force will be equal to

$$F = -kx$$

since

$$F = ma$$

and

$$a = \frac{d^2x}{dt^2}$$

where a is the acceleration of the system and m the effective mass. Then

$$\frac{d^2x}{dt^2} = -\left(\frac{k}{m}\right) x$$

$$= -\omega_r^2 x$$

When the disturbing force is included,

$$F = -kx + F_0 \cos \omega t$$

and

$$\frac{d^2x}{dt^2} = -\left(\frac{k}{m}\right) x + \left(\frac{F_0}{m}\right) \cos \omega t$$

$$= -\omega_r^2 x + \left(\frac{F_0}{m}\right) \cos \omega t \qquad (9|5a)$$

which is just an expression of the relation that $a = F/m$.

We solve the differential equation by guessing a solution and showing that the solution satisfies the equation. The solution we guess is

$$x = A \cos \omega t$$

where we must still associate the amplitude A with the parameters of the equation. From the results of Section 9|1 we know that

$$\frac{d^2x}{dt^2} = -\omega^2 x$$

$$= -\omega^2 A \cos \omega t$$

Then substituting into equation (9|5a), we have

$$-\omega^2 A \cos \omega t = -\omega_r^2 A \cos \omega t + \left(\frac{F_0}{m}\right) \cos \omega t$$

Then dividing through by $\cos \omega t$ and rearranging the terms,

$$A = \frac{F_0}{m} \frac{1}{\omega_r^2 - \omega^2}$$

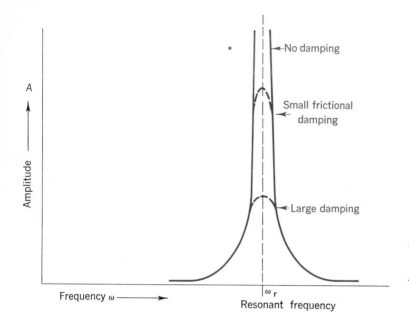

A

Amplitude

←No damping

Small frictional
← damping

←Large damping

Frequency ω ⟶

ω_r
Resonant frequency

FIG. 9 |8
*Amplitude versus
frequency in a resonant
system with various
degrees of damping.*

This variation of A with respect to the driving frequency ω is
shown in the diagram of Fig. 9|8. The amplitude will go to in-
finity when the angular frequency ω is equal to the resonant
frequency ω_r. In most systems a dissipative mechanism such as
friction operates, and the actual variation of amplitude with
frequency follows curves such as those suggested by the dashed
lines in the figure.

The occurrence of resonances is not restricted to mechanical
systems alone: resonant phenomena are important in other systems where some characteristic quantity varies in a manner that
can be described in the same way as mechanical simple harmonic
motion. The emission of radio waves by transmitters at a specific
(resonant) frequency and the reception of waves by a receiver
tuned to a specific (resonant) frequency constitute familiar examples of resonances in electromagnetic phenomena. The reso-
nant curves of Fig. 9|8 are thus representative of the amplitude
of emitted electromagnetic waves as a function of frequency
near the particular central frequency of a radio transmitter;
equally well, they can represent the acceptance of a receiver at
frequencies near a specific frequency to which a resonant circuit
in the receiver is tuned. Neutrons (and other elementary par-

ticles) are scattered by nuclei preferentially for specific energies, or momenta or wavelengths or frequencies, by atomic nuclei. Again this type of behavior can be expressed as a resonant behavior. The amplitude of the scattered beam of neutrons can be expressed as a function of the frequency of the de Broglie wave that describes the neutron beam in a manner that is equivalent to the description of Fig. 9|8.

9|6   *The differential equation* $d^2x/dt^2 = +\omega^2 x$

We have examined the character of the motion of a particle that moves in response to a force that is proportional to the distance from the particle to some equilibrium point and directed toward the equilibrium point. Such a particle moves in a manner that we call simple harmonic motion. We will also be interested in the character of motion of a particle that moves such that the force is proportional to the distance from an equilibrium point, but is directed *away* from the point of equilibrium. A simple physical model that represents examples of the two situations is shown in Fig. 9|9. A cart is shown moving on a surface such that the force on the cart in the x-direction is equal to $F = -kx$ in one case and equal to $F = k'x$ in the other, where k and k' are taken as positive constants. For both situations the magnitude of the force is proportional to the distance from an equilibrium point (taken as $x = 0$); but in one case the force is directed towards the equilibrium point, in the direction opposite to the displacement, and in the other case the force is in the same direction as the

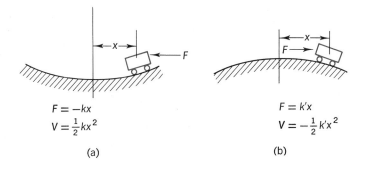

$F = -kx$
$V = \frac{1}{2}kx^2$

(a)

$F = k'x$
$V = -\frac{1}{2}k'x^2$

(b)

FIG. 9|9
Forces on a cart rolling on different potential surfaces.

displacement and directed away from the equilibrium point. The motion of the cart in Fig. 9|9a was shown to follow the relations defined by the differential equation for simple harmonic motion DE-SHM,

$$\frac{d^2x}{dt^2} = -\omega^2 x \qquad \text{where} \quad \omega^2 = \frac{k}{m} \quad \text{and} \quad \omega = \sqrt{\frac{k}{m}} \qquad (9|6)$$

The description of the motion of the cart shown in Fig. 9|9b is, of course, the same except for the sign of k'

$$\frac{d^2x}{dt^2} = +\omega'^2 x \qquad \text{where} \quad \omega'^2 = \frac{k'}{m} \quad \text{and} \quad \omega' = \sqrt{\frac{k'}{m}} \qquad (9|7)$$

The two equations, (9|6) and (9|7), are obviously very closely related. The only formal difference is the sign of k or the sign of ω^2. If we change k to $-k'$ in Eq. (9|6), then $-\omega^2$ goes to $+\omega'^2$ and ω goes to $i\omega'$, where $i = \sqrt{-1}$ is imaginary in a mathematical sense. Even as the solutions of the solutions of the Eq. (9|5) have the form

$$x = a \cos(\omega t + \theta_0)$$

which can be written as

$$x = A' \cos \omega t + B' \sin \omega t \qquad (9|8)$$

where A' and B' are constants determined by the boundary conditions (in this case the initial position and velocity of the cart in Fig. 9|9a), the solutions of Eq. (9|7) can be written as

$$x = A'' \exp(\omega' t) + B'' \exp(-\omega' t) \qquad (9|9)$$

where A'' and B'' are determined by the boundary conditions, which may be the initial position and initial velocity of the cart in Fig. 9|9b. Here $\exp(a)$ is a convenient notation for e^a, where e is the base of the natural logarithms, e = 2.718 . . . The exponential function and the trigonometric functions are closely related mathematically, as demonstrated here. This differential equation (9|7), together with its solution (9|9), is the third and last differential equation we will use in our analysis of the physical universe. We will label it DE-EXP, for Differential Equation of EXPonential decay (or growth). This equation is relevant to the growth of human or bacterial populations as well as the growth of bank accounts; it describes radioactive decay as well as the fading away of a chord struck upon a guitar.

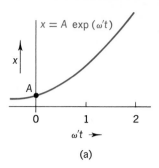

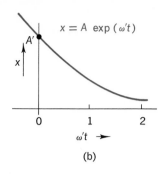

FIG. 9|10
*Solutions of the
differential equation
$d^2x/dt^2 = \omega^2x$.*

Figure 9|10 illustrates the behavior of some particularly simple solutions of Eq. (9|7) as a function of time. Figure 9|10a represents the motion of the cart of Fig. 9|9b, which reaches a point A at time $t = 0$ by rolling away from the origin where it was at rest. It is obviously gaining speed as it rolls downhill. The curve of Fig. 9|10b can be considered to represent the motion of the cart when it is at a position A' at time $t = 0$ and is rolling toward the origin with just enough energy so that it will eventually stop at the peak of the hill.

Although it is important to know the general character of the solutions of the differential equation (9|7), it is not essential to derive the solutions. However, the derivation can be put into a form that is elementary in detail, if a bit tedious, and does provide some physical insight into the necessary character of the solutions.

It is valuable to follow a real physical situation that is familiar to us as an aid to orientation. We choose to consider the compound-interest law—rather than radioactive decay, for example—because most of us are familiar with the general principles of compound interest.

The fundamental equation that describes the variation of monies invested at compound interest is the difference equation

$$\frac{DN}{Dt} = kN \qquad\qquad (9|10)$$

where, typically, N is the amount of money in the account, k is the annual interest rate, and Dt is a time interval of 1 year. This relation describes the change in the account if the interest is compounded annually. After 1 year the amount of money in the account is

$$N = N_0(1 + k)$$

after 2 years

$$N = N_0(1 + k)(1 + k) = N_0(1 + k)^2$$

after t years

$$N = N_0(1 + k)^t$$

Many institutions calculate the interest by compounding the interest semiannually. If the interest rate is again k ($100k$ percent/yr) the sum in the bank is incremented by a factor of $k/2$ every 6 months. At the end of 6 months the account will be

$$N = N_0\left(1 + \frac{k}{2}\right)$$

After a year

$$N = N_0\left(1 + \frac{k}{2}\right)\left(1 + \frac{k}{2}\right)$$

$$= N_0\left(1 + \frac{k}{2}\right)^2$$

After t years

$$N = N_0\left(1 + \frac{k}{2}\right)^{2t}$$

which is larger than the amount accumulated under a system such that the interest is compounded annually.

We might wonder what the situation would be if the interest were compounded 12 times a year, or 365 times a year, or a million times a year. In the limit that we compound the interest every instant, the difference equation (9|10) becomes a differential equation

$$\frac{dN}{dt} = kN \qquad\qquad (9|11)$$

We solve the differential equation by considering it as a difference equation and then making the time intervals over which the relation is considered—the intervals between recalculating the interest—smaller and smaller until the infinitesimal limit.

Then let us assume that we compound the interest M times a year and consider the results for very large M. After t years the account will be equal to

$$N = N_0 \left(1 + \frac{k}{M}\right)^{Mt}$$

where M goes to infinity. To reduce this to a more tractable form, we play a trick and rewrite the relation as

$$N = N_0 \left(1 + \frac{k}{M}\right)^{(M/k)kt}$$

$$= N_0 \left[\left(1 + \frac{k}{M}\right)^{M/k}\right]^{kt} \tag{9|12}$$

For convenience let us write M/k as Q, and then the quantity in the square brackets will be

$$\left(1 + \frac{1}{Q}\right)^Q$$

which, for very large values of Q (and thus large values of M), can be evaluated and is equal to

$$1 + 1 + \frac{1}{2} + \frac{1}{6} + \cdots \frac{1}{R!} \cdots$$

for the $R + 1$ term. This is just $2.718 \ldots$, usually written as e, the base of natural logarithms. Then the relation (9|12) becomes

$$N = N_0 e^{kt}$$

which we prefer to write as

$$N = N_0 \exp(kt) \tag{9|13}$$

If the parameters were named x instead of N and ω instead of k, we would have the differential equation

$$\frac{dx}{dt} = \omega x \tag{9|14}$$

with a solution

$$x = x_0 \exp(\omega t)$$

According to the differential equation (9|14), the rate of change of x with respect to t is proportional to x. We are interested in the second differential; what is the rate of change of x with respect to t? Of course the rate of change of the two sides of the Eq. (9|14) must be the same. Then

$$\frac{d(dx/dt)}{dt} = \frac{d(\omega x)}{dt} \quad \text{or} \quad \frac{d^2x}{dt^2} = \frac{d(\omega x)}{dt}$$

Since ω is a constant,

$$\frac{d(\omega x)}{dt} = \omega \frac{dx}{dt}$$

But

$$\frac{dx}{dt} = \omega x$$

so

$$\frac{d(\omega x)}{dt} = \omega^2 x$$

and

$$\frac{d^2x}{dt^2} = \omega^2 x$$

We have shown that

$$x = x_0 \exp(\omega t)$$

is a solution of the differential equation. Since ω^2 enters into the differential equation,

$$x = x_0 \exp(-\omega t)$$

is also a solution, and the most general solution of the equation is Eq. (9|9), the sum of the two exponential solutions with two arbitrary constants fitted to the boundary conditions.

PROBLEMS

9|1   The bob of a simple pendulum, weighing 1 kg, is pulled back 20 cm from the equilibrium position and released. It returns to the original position after 2 sec.

(*a*) What is the length of the pendulum?

(*b*) What is the maximum kinetic energy of the bob?

(*c*) How much was the bob raised as it was pulled back?

9|2   A 2-kg mass is suspended from a spring. When 100 gm is added, the spring stretches 10 cm. When the added mass is suddenly removed, the 2 kg mass oscillates.

(*a*) What is the frequency of oscillation?

(*b*) What is the maximum velocity of the mass?

(*c*) What is the maximum acceleration?

(*d*) What is the total energy of the system?

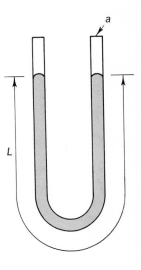

9|3 The tube shown is filled with mercury, whose density is 13.6×10^3 kg/m³. The cross section of the tube, *a*, is 1 cm²; the length, *L*, is 1 m. The level of the mercury is seen to oscillate (the level goes down in one arm, rises in the other). What will the frequency of oscillation be?

9|4 In Problem 9|3, how will the frequency change if:

(*a*) *L* is doubled?

(*b*) *a* is doubled?

(*c*) The mercury is replaced by water, whose density is 1000 kg/m³?

(*d*) With mercury in the tube, the system is transported to the moon, where $g = 1.5$ m/sec²?

9|5 The diagram shows the potential energy of an oxygen atom, which is part of a diatomic oxygen molecule, as a function of distance from the center of gravity of the molecule, which does not move. The units of potential energy are equal to 10^{-20} J; the units of distance are equal to 10^{-10} m (1 Angstrom unit). The molecules will vibrate if they are excited (by collisions with other molecules, for example). From the information on the graph, estimate (within a factor of 3) the vibrational frequency of the molecule. The mass of the oxygen atom is $2.7 \ 10^{-26}$ kg.

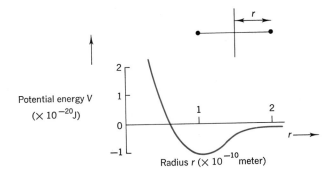

9|6   A space ship is operating in a region where gravity is negligible. A pendulum with a bob having a mass of 1 kg is suspended from a beam in the ship next to another bob of the same mass that is suspended from a light spring. When the ship is accelerating with an acceleration of 5 m/sec², the frequency of oscillation of the two bobs is observed to be the same, though the amplitude of the pendulum bob is double that of the spring bob.

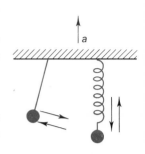

(*a*) What is the relative energy stored in the two systems?

(*b*) What are the relative values of the maximum velocities and the maximum accelerations of the two bobs, as measured by an observer in the ship?

(*c*) The acceleration of the ship is changed to 10 m/sec². How are the frequencies of oscillation of the two systems affected?

9|7   A hydrogen molecule, which is made up of two hydrogen atoms held together by a complex of electrostatic forces, vibrates with a frequency f_h when the atom is struck by other atoms. A deuterium molecule is identical—the spacing between the atoms is the same and the forces are the same—except that the deuterium atom is twice as heavy as the hydrogen atom.

(*a*) What will be the ratio of f_d to f_h, where f_d is the vibrational frequency of the deuterium molecule?

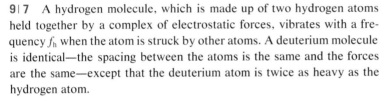

Hydrogen molecule

(*b*) How will the frequencies of vibration change if the atom is excited on another planet where the acceleration of gravity is doubled?

(*c*) If the vibrational energy of the hydrogen molecule is doubled, how will the frequency change? How will the amplitude of vibration change?

9|8   The pan of the scale in the diagram has a mass of 1.0 kg. A weight of 2.0 kg is placed on the scale. This stretches the light spring 10 cm. The 2-kg weight rolls off of the pan, which then oscillates. What is the frequency of oscillation?

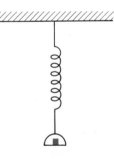

9|9   A cart that has a mass of 20 kg and runs on very small, almost frictionless wheels is at rest at the bottom of a dip in its track. A 1.0-kg weight is attached to the cart through the pulley system shown on the diagram. The cart is pulled 0.1 m from the bottom of the dip by the force of the weight. When the rope breaks or is cut, the cart oscillates back and forth on the track. What is the probable frequency of oscillation?

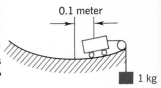

9|10   Suppose you have two equal masses and two identical springs. When one mass is suspended from one spring it will oscillate at a frequency of 1 cycle/sec. What is the oscillation frequency for the three configurations shown? (Neglect the mass of the springs.)

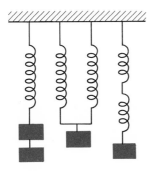

9|11   Show that if $dx/dt = kx$, $d^nx/dt^n = k^nx$ for any integral value of n.

9|12   The equation for simple harmonic motion is $a = -\omega^2x$. For a particular physical situation, the value of ω^2 is 0.1. The initial displacement of the system is $x = 100$, the initial velocity is 0. Continue the table for 20 sec and draw graphs of x, Dx/Dt, and D^2x/Dt^2 as a function of time from $t = 0$ to $t = 20$ sec.

t	x	Dx/Dt	D^2x/Dt^2
0	100	0	−10
$\frac{1}{2}$	—	−5	—
1	95	—	−9.5
$1\frac{1}{2}$	—	−14.5	—
2	80.5	—	—

9 |13   Consider a situation such that the acceleration is in the direction of the displacement and is described by the relation $a = \omega^2 x$, where ω is equal to 0.1. The initial displacement of the system is $x = 100$, the initial velocity is 0. Continue the table for 10 sec and draw graphs of x, Dx/Dt, and D^2x/Dt^2, as a function of time from $t = 0$ to $t = 10$ sec.

t	x	Dx/Dt	D^2x/Dt^2
0	100	0	10
$\frac{1}{2}$	—	5	—
1	105	—	10.5
$1\frac{1}{2}$	—	15.5	—
2	120.5	—	

9 | 14   Pictures are taken of a pendulum swinging from a planetary probe that has landed on the planet Pluto. The frequency of oscillation is desired so as to determine the force of gravity on the surface of Pluto. Because of breakdowns in the transmitting apparatus, only three pictures are transmitted back to earth. These pictures, taken 1 sec apart and show the bob of the pendulum at positions 82.5 cm, 100 cm, and 116.5 cm from the equilibrium point. It is known that the period is much larger than 1 sec. With 10 percent accuracy:

(*a*) What is the period of the pendulum?

(*b*) What is the amplitude of oscillation of the pendulum?

ten Wave motion

10|1 *The wave equation for
waves on a string*

WAVE MOTION IS closely related to simple harmonic motion;
indeed it is essentially an extension of simple harmonic motion.
We find again that many varieties of experience are described
by wave motion: Waves traversing a string, waves traversing a
surface of water, sound, light, and the de Broglie waves involved
in our description of matter itself, all represent phenomena that
we can describe as wave motion. The common factor in all of
these different phenomena is the characteristic that in each there
is a specific relation between the rate of change with time of some
quantity (such as the displacement of the surface of the water in
a water wave) and the rate of change with distance of this same
quantity. Many varieties of phenomena exhibit the same relationships between these rates of change and therefore can be described collectively as wave phenomena. All waves are similar
in many respects, and the study of one particular variety of wave
motion will provide us with information that is relevant to the
others.

We consider the analysis of the behavior of waves in a taut
string as a particularly simple example of wave motion. Our
procedure is directed toward analyzing the motion of a small,
typical segment of string. We will determine the forces on the
segment of string and then calculate the acceleration of the seg-

ment from our knowledge of the forces and the mass of the segment.

The string will be under a tension of T newtons, and the linear density of the string, or the mass per unit length, will be ρ kg/m. Our analysis will be restricted to waves of small amplitude. In particular, we consider only deflections of the string such that the angle any segment of the string makes with the line of the undisturbed string is sufficiently small that the sine and tangent of that angle are sensibly equal to the value of the angle in radians. The typical displacements shown in Fig. 10|1 have the transverse direction magnified so that deflections can be described more easily in the diagrams.

We further consider only those disturbances of the string that are such that the motion of the string is entirely in the direction transverse to the line of the undisturbed string; motion of any segment of the string along the line of the string can be neglected. The tension of the string will then be constant along the length of the string and, if the string is completely flexible, the tensile forces will be directed along the line of the string. A completely flexible string will not support forces that are transverse to the string. In summary: the force on each end of a segment of string will be equal in magnitude to the tension on the string, and the direction of the force will lie along the direction of the string at the end of the segment.

The diagrams of Fig. 10|1 show three configurations of a segment of string in a coordinate system such that the direction along the length of the undisturbed string is labeled x, and the

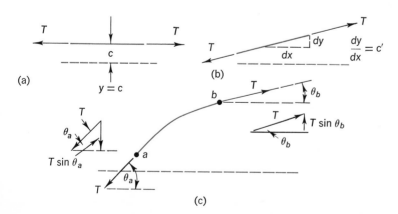

FIG. 10|1
Typical configurations of a section of a string that is under tension.

direction transverse to the string is labeled y. We consider implicitly a displacement in one dimension only, though the results are actually more general. The diagrams show the string at some specific instant or specific time as if the string were photographed.

The piece of string shown in Fig. 10|1a is displaced from the equilibrium position by a constant distance c. This displacement, y, can be expressed by the equation

$$y = c$$

An inspection of the forces on the segment of string shows that the total force is zero: the value of the force on each end of the string is T, and the two forces act in exactly opposite directions. Since there is no net force on the string, the acceleration of the string will be zero. There will be no change in the velocity of that segment of the string.

The section of string shown in Fig. 10|1b is straight but inclined at an angle with respect to the equilibrium position. The slope is therefore constant, which is expressed by the relation

$$\frac{dy}{dx} = c'$$

where c' is a constant. Again the total force on the segment is zero and the acceleration of the segment of string will be zero. In general, if the string is not curved there can be no total force on a section of the string: the forces on each end of a section of string will be equal and oppositely directed and will add to zero.

If the string is curved, as shown in Fig. 10|1c, there will be a resultant force directed toward the center of curvature. This resultant force will induce an acceleration of the section of string toward the center of curvature; the acceleration will be proportional to the resultant force and inversely proportional to the mass of the section of string. There is clearly a total force on the string directed toward the x-axis; the force is in the negative y-direction. The y-component of the force on the left-hand side of the section of string, at the point a, is

$$F_y = -T \sin \theta_a$$

The component of force from the tension on the right-hand end of the section of string is

$$F_y = T \sin \theta_b$$

In the approximation of small amplitudes and small angles of inclination of the string, the sine of any angle of inclination is approximately equal to the tangent of the angle, which is just the slope of the string, dy/dx.

$$\sin \theta_a = \tan \theta_a = \left(\frac{dy}{dx}\right)_a$$

$$\sin \theta_b = \tan \theta_b = \left(\frac{dy}{dx}\right)_b$$

The total force in the y-direction is then equal to

$$F_y = T\left[\left(\frac{dy}{dx}\right)_b - \left(\frac{dy}{dx}\right)_a\right]_t$$

where the subscript t is a reminder that the force is calculated at a specific time. This force must result in an acceleration of the section of string at the position where x is between b and a. The force, F_y, will be equal to the mass of the string times the acceleration. The mass, m, of the section of string will be equal to the linear density ρ kg/m, times the length of the section, dx_{ab}, which is the length between the points b and a. Then $m = \rho\, dx_{ab}$ and $F_y = ma_y$: we write the acceleration in the y-direction, a_y, in the differential form $a_y = d^2y/dt^2$. The relation $F_y = ma_y$ then becomes

$$T\left[\left(\frac{dy}{dx}\right)_a - \left(\frac{dy}{dx}\right)_a\right]_t = \rho\, dx_{ab}\left(\frac{d^2y}{dt^2}\right)_x \tag{10|1}$$

where the subscript x is a reminder that the acceleration refers to the particular part of the string at the point x. In the limit where a very small section of string, dx_{ab}, is considered,

$$\frac{[(dy/dx)_b - (dy/dx)_a]_t}{dx_{ab}} = \left(\frac{d^2y}{dx^2}\right)_t \tag{10|2}$$

from our definition of second differences and then second derivatives. That is, the difference between the slopes of the string at b and a, divided by the distance between b and a, is just the rate of change of the slope with distance, and in the limit of an infinitesimal distance, dx_{ab}, it is just the second derivative of y with respect to x. Then dividing both sides of Eq. (10|1) by dx_{ab}, for very small intervals dx_{ab},

$$T \left(\frac{d^2y}{dx^2}\right)_t = \rho \left(\frac{d^2y}{dt^2}\right)_x \qquad (10|3)$$

which is the *wave equation* for transverse waves in a taut string.

The tension in the string, T, times the rate of change of the rate of change of the displacement of the string with distance, measured at some definite time, is equal to ρ, the linear density of string, times the rate of change of the rate of change of the displacement of the string with time, measured at some particular place on the string.

This is a second-order differential equation dealing with rates of change of rates of change. Since we are dealing with a string along one dimension or direction, labeled here as x, it is a one-dimensional equation, and we call it the one-dimensional wave equation. We will find that this is the basic relation of wave behavior. In this particular situation of a wave in a taut string, the variable we are concerned with is the displacement of the string from its equilibrium position, transverse to the x-direction. We use the symbol y for this displacement. In other wave equations we can be concerned with properties quite different from actual simple spacial displacement. We might be concerned with an electric wave, in which case our parameter of interest will be an electric field. We may be concerned with a temperature wave, in which our variable of interest will be temperature. All these phenomena are related, in that an equation like Eq. (10|3), the wave equation, can be written relating the variation in position of the amplitude of the wave with respect to the variation in time of the amplitude.

10| 2 *Solutions of the wave equation*

We are interested in finding solutions to the wave equation. This equation, like many differential equations or equations relating rates, has many solutions, indeed an infinite number of solutions. This is evident physically even as one sees that waves of quite different shapes can be made to proceed on a string. Figure 10|2 shows typical wave forms that might be seen moving along a string or rope.

It is convenient to consider certain *characteristic* solutions of

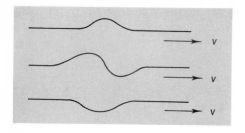

FIG. 10|2
*Waves of different
shapes moving down a
taut string.*

the wave equation which are represented by the class of functions

$$y = A \cos(\omega t + kx + \theta_0) \tag{10|4}$$

where A, ω, k, and θ_0, are constants. Later we will show that all possible waves, such as those shown in Fig. 10|2, can be considered as combinations of characteristic waves. The notation is simpler if we give up some generality and consider, for the moment, the functions or waves

$$y = A \cos(\omega t + kx) \tag{10|5}$$

which is equivalent to setting θ_0 equal to zero in Eq. (10|4), which is equivalent to resetting the clock used to measure time so that the clock is started when $y = \cos kx$.

We will now proceed to show that the function of y expressed in Eq. (10|5) is a solution of the wave equation (10|3) if certain relations hold between the values of ω and k; that is, the function (10|5) fits Eq. (10|3).

We consider the motion in time of a particular point on the string, x. This motion is described by Eq. (10|3) where x is held constant. Then kx is constant and the equation has the form of a solution of the equation of simple harmonic motion: DE-SHM. We can then use the results of our examination of simple harmonic motion (Chapter 9), which is also the result of a more abstract mathematical examination of the equation, and write down immediately some simple relations relating the variation of the value of y in time.

$$\frac{dy}{dt} = -\omega A \sin(\omega t + kx)$$

and

$$\frac{d^2y}{dt^2} = -\omega^2 A \cos(\omega t + kx) \tag{10|6}$$

Now we investigate the variation in x of the wave for a specific time: the *time is held constant* as in a photograph, and x is the variable. Formally the problem of determining the character of the Eq. (10|5), which results, is identical to the problem of determining the character of the equation when x was constant and t was the variable: again we can use the results we developed in the course of our investigation of simple harmonic motion. Then

$$\frac{dy}{dx} = -kA \, \sin(\omega t + kx)$$

and

$$\frac{d^2y}{dx^2} = -k^2A \, \cos(\omega t + kx) \tag{10|7}$$

in parallel with the result (10|6).

Equations (10|6) and (10|7) have very much the same form except for the factors ω^2 and k^2. Multiplying (10|6) by k^2 and (10|7) by ω^2,

$$\omega^2 \left(\frac{d^2y}{dx^2}\right)_t = -k^2\omega^2 A \, \cos(\omega t + kx)$$

$$= k^2 \left(\frac{d^2y}{dt^2}\right)_x$$

or

$$\left(\frac{d^2y}{dx^2}\right)_t = \frac{k^2}{\omega^2} \left(\frac{d^2y}{dt^2}\right)_x \tag{10|8}$$

where the left-hand term represents the second derivative of y with respect to x at a *particular time,* and the right-hand term represents the quantity k^2/ω^2 times the second derivative of y with respect to t as a *particular position.*

Equation (10|8) is the wave equation (10|3) where

$$\frac{k^2}{\omega^2} = \frac{\rho}{T}$$

Thus relation (10|5),

$$y = A \, \cos(\omega t + kx)$$

is a "solution" of the wave equation (10|8) for any set of values of k and ω such that $k^2/\omega^2 = \rho/T$. The value of A is arbitrary: A, the amplitude of the wave, can have any value as long as the amplitude is not so large as to make invalid the approximation that dy/dx is always small, which was used to derive the wave equation.

It is easy to show by the same procedure that Eq. (10|9) is also a solution:

$$y = A \cos(\omega t - kx) \qquad\qquad (10\,|9)$$

The discussion follows the same lines as for (10|5) except that k is replaced by $-k$. It is easy to see that this change does not ·effect the validity of Eq. (10|8). Since the choice of origin of neither the time nor the distance measure is of any importance, the relations that follow are also valid solutions of the wave equation:

$$y = A \cos(\omega t + kx + \theta_0) \qquad y = A \cos(\omega t + kx + \theta_0)$$
$$\qquad\qquad\qquad\qquad\qquad\qquad\qquad\qquad (10\,|10)$$
$$y = A \sin(\omega t + kx + \theta_0) \qquad y = A \sin(\omega t - kx + \theta_0)$$

where θ_0 is any phase angle. Relations (10| 10) represent, again, *characteristic solutions* of the wave equation.

10 |3   *Properties of running waves*

Relations of the type of Eq. (10|10) describe running waves. When one sees a wave traveling in a medium, such as a wave moving along a string or a wave moving across a surface of water, it is the motion of the *shape* of the disturbance that we recognize as the motion of the wave, not the motion of the individual sections of string or individual volumes of water. Although the segments of string move up and down, and the volumes of water—perhaps marked by a floating cork or bottle—move up and down, these elements do not share the rapid motion across the medium of the crests and troughs of the wave, which we call the wave motion.

We can consider the motion of shapes in detail by analyzing a characteristic solution of the wave equation. We consider one solution in particular,

$$y = A \cos(\omega t + kx + \theta) \qquad\qquad (10\,|11)$$

and investigate the situation that results when the argument of the cosine term is zero; that is, $\omega t + kx + \theta = 0$. Then, since

$\cos(0) = 1$, $y = A$, and the displacement is a maximum: this represents the crest of the wave. We can find the position of this crest as time elapses. If the argument is to stay equal to zero at t increases, x must become smaller. The relation

$$\omega t + kx + \theta = 0 \qquad \text{or} \qquad \omega t + kx = -\theta \qquad (10|12)$$

must continue to hold. After a time dt, the value of x must change by an amount dx: then

$$\omega(t + dt) + k(x + dx) = -\theta$$

and subtracting (10|12),

$$\omega \, dt + k \, dx = 0$$

The condition that the argument of the cosine function remain zero and the amplitude of the displacement remain at a crest or maximum is then the condition that

$$\frac{dx}{dt} = -\frac{\omega}{k}$$

The quantity dx/dt is obviously a velocity, and it is a velocity of motion of the condition that the wave be at a maximum: it is therefore a velocity of "shape"; it is the wave velocity. In this particular case the wave velocity is negative; the wave is moving in the negative x-direction as time increases. The relation

$$y = A \cos(\omega t - kx + \theta) \qquad (10|13)$$

represents a wave having positive velocity. In order that the argument remain constant as t increases, x must increase also. Although we have based our discussion on the motion of the crest of the wave, the reasoning concerning the wave velocity is valid if we consider the motion of the position representing *any* constant value of the amplitude.

The reasoning holds for any one-dimensional wave—that is, a wave moving in only one direction. In the particular case of the wave in a taut string, the velocity is equal to

$$v = \pm \frac{\omega}{k}$$

$$= \pm \sqrt{\frac{T}{\rho}}$$

since

$$\frac{T}{\rho} = \frac{\omega^2}{k^2}$$

where T is the tension and ρ the density of the string.

By inspection of relations (10|12) and (10|13) one can define other specific quantities that are of interest for any particular character wave. The *wavelength* of such a wave is defined as the distance between equivalent points on two successive shapes measured at a specific time. For example, if we take a photograph of a wave in a string, we can measure the wavelength from the picture by measuring the distance between crests. That distance will be the distance x such that kx changes by 2π. If we call that distance λ, the wavelength, we have $k\lambda = 2\pi$ or

$$\lambda = \frac{2\pi}{k} \qquad k = \frac{2\pi}{\lambda}$$

We are also interested in the frequency of a characteristic wave. Here we follow an opposite procedure. Instead of taking a particular point in time and looking at the variation in space of the wave, we look at a particular point in space and look at the variation in time of the wave. Now the wave at any particular position x goes from crest to crest in a time such that t changes by 2π. This will be the period of the wave. If we write the period of the wave as P we see that $\omega P = 2\pi$, or

$$P = \frac{2\pi}{\omega}$$

We call ω the *angular frequency* as we did in simple harmonic motion, where ω equals the number of radians per second. We can use these relations to write the basic wave relations in different forms that are more transparently related to measured quantities of frequency, period, and wavelength:

$$y = A \cos(\omega t + kx + \theta_0)$$

$$= A \cos\left[2\pi\left(\frac{t}{P} + \frac{x}{\lambda}\right) + \theta_0\right]$$

The number of complete cycles per second, f, is equal to $1/P$ or $\omega/2\pi$, and is called the *frequency*. (The unit of frequency is the hertz [Hz]; 1 Hz = 1 cycle/sec.) Any single point on the string moves with simple harmonic motion with an amplitude A and a frequency f. We can then express the velocity of the wave in terms of the frequency and wavelength:

$$v = \frac{\omega}{k}$$

$$= (2\pi f)\left(\frac{\lambda}{2\pi}\right)$$

$$= f\lambda$$

The wave contains or holds energy. From the results of the study of simple harmonic motion, the total energy of a small segment of string through which a train of waves is passing is equal to

$$E = \rho \, dx \, \tfrac{1}{2}\omega^2 A^2$$

where dx is the length of the segment and $\rho \, dx$ is then the mass of that segment. The result is particular to waves in a string in the exact dependence upon ρ; the results are quite general in that the energy of most wave forms depends upon the square of the frequency, the square of the amplitude, and the length of the region of concern.

The relations of Eqs. (10|10) represent not just solutions but whole classes of solutions to the wave equation. We note that the constant A can have any value. The frequency f can have any value, and the wavelength λ can have any value constrained by the relation that the frequency times the wavelength is equal to the velocity. For a stretched string the velocity will be equal to $\sqrt{T/\rho}$. For other types of waves the velocity will be another function of physical parameters relevant to the particular situation. In almost all cases that will concern us, however, the velocity will be a specific character of the medium.

10|4   *Combinations of waves—Fourier series*

All of the solutions of the wave equation that we have developed have a characteristic form,

$$y = A \cos(\omega t + kx + \theta) \tag{10|14}$$

where ω, k, and θ are constants that can be arbitrarily chosen subject to the single constraint that $(\omega/k)^2 = v^2$, where v is the wave velocity in the medium and depends upon the character of the medium as expressed by the wave equation that is relevant to the physical situation in question.

Our whole discussion of waves and wave motions would not have much importance if our results were restricted entirely to waves that have the explicit form of the *characteristic* solutions of Eq. (10|14). It is therefore essential to understand the behavior of more general shapes. We will find that the character of the complete set of all possible characteristic solutions (10|14) together with a superposition principle allows us to understand the behavior of a very general class of wave shapes.

Let us assume that we have two different characteristic solutions of the wave equation, y' and y''; we would like to show that the sum of the two solutions, $y = y' + y''$, is also a solution. This demonstration rests on the general result that if

$$y(t) = y'(t) + y''(t) \tag{10|15}$$

for all values of t, then

$$\frac{dy}{dt} = \frac{dy'}{dt} + \frac{dy''}{dt}$$

Although this is very nearly obviously true, we might expand on it somewhat. If t changes by a small amount, the quantities y, y', and y'' will change a small amount, though the equality must still hold. So

$$y + dy = y' + dy' + y'' + dy''$$

Subtracting (10|15) and dividing by dt,

$$\frac{dy}{dt} = \frac{dy'}{dt} + \frac{dy''}{dt}$$

It then follows that

$$\frac{d^2y}{dt^2} = \frac{d^2y'}{dt^2} + \frac{d^2y''}{dt^2} \quad \text{and} \quad \frac{d^2y}{dx^2} = \frac{d^2y'}{dx^2} + \frac{d^2y''}{dx^2}$$

Since both y' and y'' are solutions of the wave equation,

$$\frac{d^2y}{dt^2} = \frac{d^2y'}{dt^2} + \frac{d^2y''}{dt^2} = v^2 \left(\frac{d^2y'}{dx^2} + \frac{d^2y''}{dx^2} \right)$$

$$= v^2 \frac{d^2y}{dx^2}$$

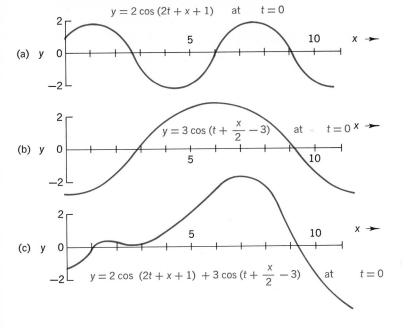

FIG. 10 |3

Two waves, together with their sum, shown at a specific time.

so y is also a solution of the wave equation. This result represents a *superposition* principle. The sum of any set of solutions of a wave equation is also a solution of a wave equation.

In general, the sum of characteristic solutions results in shapes that are very different from the typical sine or cosine wave. Figure 10|3 shows such a sum of two characteristic solutions. Here

$$y = y' + y''$$

where

$$y' + 2 \cos(2t + x + 1)$$

and

$$y'' = 3 \cos(t + \tfrac{1}{2}x - 3)$$

The shape will vary with time; Fig. 10|3 shows the configuration at a time $t = 0$.

The example of Fig. 10|3 suggests immediately that very many different wave shapes might be constructed from the infinite set of characteristic solutions. Indeed, it is both plausible and true, though hardly obvious or trivial, that almost any wave shape can be constructed from an appropriately chosen infinite set of characteristic solutions. Inversely, we might expect that almost any shape can be expressed as a sum—generally an infinite sum—of characteristic solutions. All curves that are continuous and single valued are allowed: if the curve is unbroken, and if for each value of x there is only one value of y, the curve can be expressed as the sum of characteristic solutions such as Eq. (10 | 10).

It is interesting to consider simple examples of the expression of particular shapes in terms of a sum or series of characteristic solutions. Again we will discuss the shapes of waves at a particular time, although a discussion of the time dependence of the amplitude at a particular position would be similar. Figure 10 | 4 shows a repetitive pattern called a *square wave*. This wave can be expressed as an infinite series of characteristic functions, the *Fourier series*, as

$$y = \left(\frac{4a}{\pi}\right)\left(\cos x - \frac{1}{3}\cos 3x + \frac{1}{5}\cos 5x - \frac{1}{7}\cos 7x + \cdots\right)$$

The first few terms are shown graphically in Fig. 10 | 4, together with the sums of these terms. The increasing similarity to the square wave that results as more terms are added is evident.

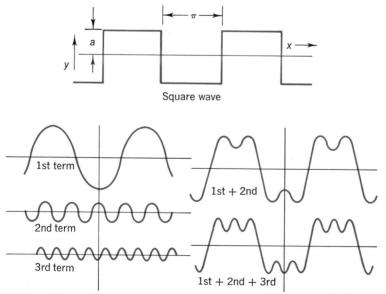

Square wave

1st term

2nd term

3rd term

1st + 2nd

1st + 2nd + 3rd

FIG. 10 | 4
The decomposition of a square wave into characteristic waves.

Nonrepetitive shapes can also be expressed by a set of characteristic functions, though all frequencies generally contribute instead of the discrete set that describes repetitive functions such as the square wave.

10|5 *Longitudinal waves*

We have considered explicitly only one particular variety of wave motion, that is, transverse waves on a taut string, though we have intimated that the general character of those results holds for much larger classes of phenomena. For transverse waves of a string the quantity that changes with time, t, and with distance along the string, x, is the transverse displacement, y, of elements of the string. The parameter of interest equivalent to y in the wave representation of other phenomena will have quite a different character. While the wave equations will have a similar form, the characteristic modes will not appear visibly as a sine or cosine function in so direct a fashion as those for waves of a string. The character of the waves themselves will be necessarily more abstract.

We will be particularly concerned with waves of longitudinal displacement in matter such as sound waves, with electromagnetic waves such as light waves, and with the de Broglie waves pertinent to the descriptions of matter itself. Since the longitudinal elastic waves in material are particularly evident to us as sound waves, we will find it useful to consider this kind of mechanical wave motion in some detail.

The character of such longitudinal waves in an elastic medium can be understood qualitatively by drawing upon our experience concerning the behavior of elastic materials and by considering the extensive similarities between transverse and longitudinal waves. The force on a segment of a string that is vibrating transversely is derived from the tension of the string. Certain types of displacement from equilibrium result in a transverse component of the tension, which tends to restore the segment to the equilibrium position. The forces on a segment of an elastic medium—such as a long rubber band—that is vibrating longitudinally are derived from the elasticity of the medium. Again, certain types of displacement from equilibrium result in a total force on a segment of the material, which tend to restore that

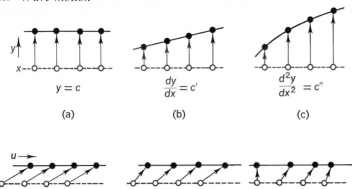

FIG. 10|5

*A comparison of
transverse displacement
(y) and longitudinal
displacement (u) in a
medium.*

segment to the equilibrium position. To exploit these similarities
we will examine the diagrams of Fig. 10|5, which show parallel
configurations of transverse and longitudinal displacements in
a one-dimensional medium. For definiteness it may be useful to
consider that the upper medium is a string or rope under tension,
while the lower medium is a long rubber band, also under tension.
The longitudinal displacements of the rubber band are presented
with a transverse component for simplicity in exposition, but
we will assume that in fact the displacements are solely in the
x-direction, which is the direction of propagation of the wave.
Even as we label the transverse displacement of a point of the
string by the value of the coordinate y, we will label the longitudinal displacement of a point on the rubber band by the coordinate u.

We pointed out in Section 10|1 that the force on a segment
of string displaced uniformly from the equilibrium position, as
shown in Fig. 10|5a, is zero, since the magnitudes of the forces
on the two ends of the segment are equal and the forces are in
opposite directions. Similarly, the total force on the segment of
the rubber band shown in Fig. 10|5a′ will be zero. Since the
lengths of the two segments on either side of the special segment we are considering are not changed by the displacement,
the forces on the ends of the special segment will not be changed
and the total force on the special segment will be zero as it was
at equilibrium.

The total force on the special segment of string shown in Fig.
10|5b will again be zero since the forces on the two ends are

equal but oppositely directed. Similarly, the forces on the special segment of the rubber band shown in Fig. 10｜5b' will be zero, although the rubber is stretched. Since the two segments on either side of the special segment we are examining are stretched the same amount, the forces on the special segment from these pieces will be equal in magnitude and, of course, oppositely directed.

However, there is a total force on the special section of string shown in Fig. 10｜5c, since the slope dy/dx is different at the two ends of the segment. Similarly, there will be a total force on the special part of the rubber band we are considering in Fig. 10｜5c', since the piece to the left is stretched more than the piece to the right. Obviously there is a net force pulling the special section to the left.

From the similarity of the diagrams it can be seen that the force on the segment of rubber band will be proportional to d^2u/dx^2 even as the force on the segment of string was proportional to d^2y/dx^2. The whole wave equation for longitudinal waves is then similar to the wave equation we derived for transverse waves. In place of T, the tension in Eq. (10｜3), we have k, a constant characteristic of the elastic character of the medium. We can define k for the rubber band by considering the force required to stretch a piece of rubber L meters long by an amount dL. The force is proportional to dL (Hooke's law) and inversely proportional to L; or $F = kL/dL$. The definition of k is similar for other elastic materials.

With this definition of k the wave equation takes a form similar to Eq. (10｜3):

$$k \left[\frac{d^2u}{dx^2} \right]_t = \rho \left[\frac{d^2u}{dt^2} \right]_t \qquad \textbf{(10｜16)}$$

The velocity of the wave is such that

$$v^2 = \frac{k}{\rho}$$

and all the relations developed in Sections 10｜2 and 10｜3 hold for these longitudinal waves as well as other wave forms.

The wave equation developed here for elastic materials is especially important in its relation to waves that pass through bulk materials, liquids, solids, and gases, and are generally classified as sound waves. The peaks and valleys we see in the transverse

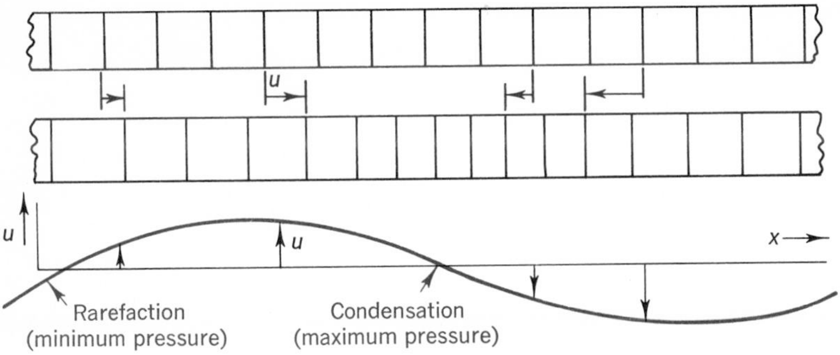

FIG. 10|6
An illustration of the character of the conventional description of the longitudinal displacements corresponding to a longitudinal wave in an elastic medium.

Rarefaction
(minimum pressure)

Condensation
(maximum pressure)

waves on a string or the transverse waves of ripples on the surface of water correspond to peaks of condensation and rarefaction for sound waves. Where the rubber band is stretched there is less rubber, or a rarefaction; where the rubber band is compressed there is more rubber, or a condensation. In a gas a region of condensation represents a region of high pressure and high density of gas, while a region of rarefaction is a region of low pressure and low density. Even as the sound waves be represented as varying amplitudes of displacement from equilibrium they can also be represented in terms of waves of pressure where the amplitude is proportional to the pressure. The diagrams of Fig. 10|6 suggest something of the character of these condensations and rarefactions. Although the diagram ostensibly shows a rubber band with marks for reference printed on it, the general character of the displacements in liquids, gases, and solids is much the same.

10|6   *Elastic waves in media—*
polarization

Transverse vibrations are possible in solid, rigid materials. The restoring forces are again elastic in nature, but now directed transversely as shown in Fig. 10|7. A solid material resists a transverse displacement as shown. Indeed this is essentially the definition of a solid. Fluids (liquids and gases) do not resist such a distortion and thus cannot carry transverse waves. Fluids will resist pressure but not shear or transverse forces. (We are not considering surface waves on a liquid where the gravitational field provides a restoring force.)

In general, the displacement of a section of a solid can take place in any direction. The displacement would thus appear to be a vector. The elastic properties of various media are invariably such that the velocity of propagation of longitudinal waves is different from that for transverse waves; indeed, transverse waves are not transmitted by fluids at all. It is then convenient to divide the general problem of displacements in an elastic medium into the two classes of transverse and longitudinal waves and consider these two waves separately.

The longitudinal displacements of an elastic medium that are induced by a wave traveling in an x-direction can be written as

$$u_x = A_x \cos(\omega_s t - k_s x + \phi)$$

where $\omega_s/k_s = v_s$ is the velocity of the longitudinal wave in the medium. The quantities A_x, ω_s, and k_s have the usual meanings of amplitude, angular frequency, and 2π times the number of waves per meter.

The transverse displacements will be

$$u_y = A_y \cos(\omega_t t - k_t x + \theta_y)$$

and

$$u_z = A_z \cos(\omega_t t - k_t x + \theta_z)$$

where $\omega_t/k_t = v_t$ is the velocity of transverse waves in the medium. This velocity will generally be different from the velocity of the longitudinal wave, v_s. The amplitude, frequency, and wave length can be different for the different directions of displacement. Indeed, in nonhomogeneous materials, such as some crystals, the velocities of propagation of the waves can depend on the direction of the displacement as well as the direction of propagation of the wave.

The only complex situation that will concern us is the description of transverse waves traveling in a homogeneous medium where the frequency of the wave is the same for any transverse direction of the displacement. The amplitudes, A_y

and A_z, and the phases, θ_y and θ_z, can differ, however. The relative amplitudes in the different orthogonal directions together with the phase difference $\theta_y - \theta_z$ define the *polarization* of the wave. The diagrams of Fig. 10|8 show the trajectories of small sections of an elastic material excited by the passage of a polarized wave in a direction out of the paper. Of course, if the character of the medium limits the wave type to longitudinal waves, there can be no polarization. There is therefore no polarization of sound waves.

Some of the most important information concerning the structure of our planet has been obtained through the analysis of the elastic waves produced by natural and artificial disturbances of the earth's crust. In particular, the knowledge of the existence and size of the liquid center of the earth was obtained by noticing that only the longitudinal waves were transmitted through the earth's core.

The general character of the methods used for such deductions is suggested by the schematic drawing of Fig. 10|9, which shows the site of an earthquake and the character of waves received at various seismographic stations. (The Greek word for earthquake is *seismos*, σεισμόσ.) The station at *b* receives only the longitudinal wave from the earthquake at *a* because the transverse vibrations are not carried by the liquid core. The station at *c* receives direct transverse and longitudinal vibrations as well as transverse and longitudinal waves that are reflected from the

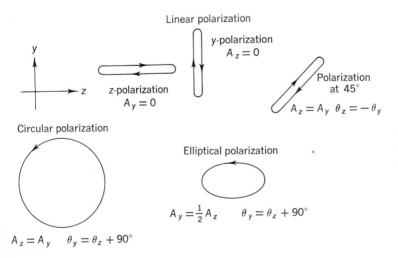

FIG. 10|8
The paths of the displacement of particles of a medium transmitting waves that are polarized in various ways. In each diagram, the direction of propagation is out of the paper.

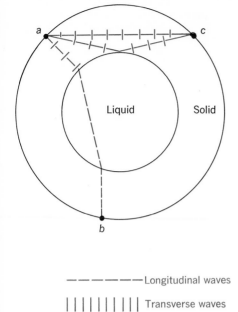

FIG. 10 |9
Typical paths of longitudinal and transverse waves through the earth.

— — — — — —Longitudinal waves

| | | | | | | | | | Transverse waves

discontinuity between the solid crust and the liquid core. The speed of the waves and the amount of the reflection depends upon the character of the media, and an analysis of the intensities and the time sequence of reception of the waves from the many seismographic stations provides a considerable body of information concerning the character of the interior of the earth. We emphasize that the drawing of Fig. 10|9 and the accompanying discussion are meant to be schematic in character. The actual situation is much more complex.

10|7 *Waves in two and three dimensions*

We have concerned ourselves so far primarily with waves that are present either in a one-dimensional medium such as a taut string, or at least proceed in one direction. In nature, as we know, waves travel in all directions available to them. Water waves produced when a stone is thrown in a quiet pool move out in concentric circles on the surface of the water. The sound waves produced by an explosion in the air move out in concentric spheres from the point of disturbance.

The wave equations for two-dimensional and three-dimensional waves have forms such as

$$\frac{d^2u}{dt^2} = v^2 \left(\frac{d^2u}{dx^2} + \frac{d^2u}{dy^2}\right)$$

and

$$\frac{d^2u}{dt^2} = v^2 \left(\frac{d^2u}{dx^2} + \frac{d^2u}{dy^2} + \frac{d^2u}{dz^2}\right)$$

where u may represent a longitudinal displacement or perhaps an electric or magnetic field, or any other physical quantity described by a wave equation. The solution, or wave itself, for any wave in a small region is very much like a wave that is straight or plane, as suggested by Fig. 10|10, where the solid lines represent maxima and the dotted lines minima. Such a wave is represented as

$$u = A \cos(\omega t - \mathbf{k} \cdot \mathbf{r}) \tag{10|17}$$

where

$$(\mathbf{k} \cdot \mathbf{r}) = k_x x + k_y y + k_z z$$

and k_x is equal to 2π times the number of waves per meter in the x-direction. The wave number $\mathbf{k}(k_x, k_y, k_z,)$ is a vector having the same direction as $\mathbf{v}$, the velocity. Equation (10|17) represents a plane wave in the direction of $\mathbf{v}$. We will not use these relations in any very complicated way.

Since a plane wave does not spread out but, in the absence of friction or other damping effects, continues in one direction with no change in the amplitude, the energy density is constant or independent of the distance from the source. A disturbance at a point on a string will disturb the string in a manner that will

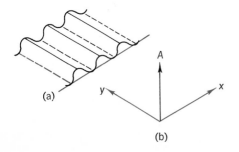

(a)

(b)

FIG. 10|10
*Section of a plane wave
in two dimensions.
Amplitude of the wave is
measured in the A-
direction.*

result in waves propagating along the string. If the string were ideal, and no friction damped the wave, the amplitude of the wave would be constant, or independent of the distance along the string. A wave that passes a point 10 m from the source along the string should have the same amplitude as it had 1 m from the source. Of course, the energy density in the wave is proportional to the square of the amplitude, and this just reflects the conservation of energy.

A disturbance on a two-dimensional surface, such as the surface of a pond, may send out waves such as the ripples in a pond induced by the jump of a fish. Again energy is conserved if we neglect the small frictional losses that tend to damp the wave, but now the energy must be spread over an increasingly wide region as the wave moves out from the source. If the velocity of the wave is v, after a time t the energy that existed at the origin due to the original disturbance—the fish jumping in the water—will be distributed in a circle about the origin of radius r, where $r = vt$. Since the circumference of a circle is proportional to the radius, the energy density will be proportional to $1/r$; since the energy density is proportional to the square of the amplitude of the wave, the amplitude will vary as $\sqrt{1/r}$, where r is the distance from the source of the disturbance.

The energy deposited by a disturbance in a three-dimensional medium will be spread out over a three-dimensional manifold. After a time t the energy will be distributed on the surface of a sphere of radius r, where $r = vt$ and v is the velocity of the wave in the medium. Since the area of the surface of a sphere is proportional to r^2 and the total energy will be conserved in the absence of frictional losses, the energy density will vary as $1/r^2$ and the amplitude will vary as $1/r$, where r is the distance from the source.

PROBLEMS

10|1 A traveling wave is moving in the x-direction along a rope that has a linear density of 1.0 kg/m. All measurements are made from a specific point on the rope taken as $x = 0$, and from a certain time, $t = 0$. The transverse displacement of the rope, y, is found to follow the relation

$$y = 0.1 \cos(2t - 3x + 4)$$

where quantities are measured in meters and seconds.

(*a*) What is the value of the largest displacement of the rope?

(*b*) What is the velocity of the wave?

(*c*) What is the wavelength of the wave?

(*d*) What is the total energy of the wave per meter of rope?

10| 2 A rope having a mass of 0.1 kg/m is held with a tension of 1000 N. As a wave passes along the rope, it seems that at one particular point the rope moves with simple harmonic motion with a frequency of 10 Hz and an amplitude of 0.1 m.

(*a*) What is the velocity of the wave?

(*b*) What is the wavelength of the wave?

(*c*) What is the energy density of the wave in joules per meter?

10| 3 Show that the shape of the wave shown in Fig. 10|3c will persist in time; that is, the shape will move along unchanged at the wave velocity. Will all possible shapes generated by adding any possible set of characteristic solutions of the wave equation keep the same shape with time?

10| 4 The table lists the pressure (in arbitrary units) at various points along the path of a sound wave in a particular medium. The measurements represent the pressures at a time $t = 0$. The wave equation for sound in the medium is known to have the form

$$\frac{d^2 p}{dt^2} = K \frac{d^2 p}{dx^2}$$

where $K = 10^4$ m²/sec². The wavelength is known to be very long. What is the rate of change of the pressure at the 10-meter point? What will the pressure be at this point at the time $t = 0.01$ sec?

Distance (m)	Pressure (arbitrary units)
9	117
10	127
11	138

10| 5 The amplitude of the displacement of a taut string is measured at various points on the string at various times. The distance between the points is known to be small compared to the wavelength of the wave, and the time between measurements is known to be small compared to the period of the wave. The table lists the amplitudes in centimeters, the times are measured in seconds, and the distances along the rope are measured in meters.

(*a*) What are the values of *a*, *b*, *c*, and *d* in the table?

(*b*) What is the velocity and direction of the wave?

	Distance (*m*)		
Time (*sec*)	*11*	*12*	*13*
7	*a*	10	*b*
8	22	17	13
9	*c*	28	*d*

10|6   The diagram represents the variation of the longitudinal displacements, *u*, of elements of a medium as a function of distance, *x*, along the medium in the direction of propagation of the wave.

(*a*) Where are the velocities of the elements largest? Where are they smallest?

(*b*) Where are the accelerations of the elements of the medium largest? Smallest?

(*c*) Where is the density of the medium largest? Smallest?

10|7   If the elastic properties of hydrogen, oxygen, and chlorine are the same (and they are, to a good approximation) and the ratios of the densities are approximately as 1:16:36, how will the velocity of sound differ in these gases?

10|8   A cork is floating in water as a train of waves passes over the water. The amplitude of the waves is 0.10 m, the velocity of the waves is 10 m/sec and the wavelength is 10 m. What is the maximum velocity of the cork as it bobs in the water?

10| 9 A long spring is designed so that it has a mass of 1.0 kg/m. A 1-m length of this spring is stretched to a length of 1.01 m under a force of 10 N. A length of this spring is stretched by a tension of 20 N. Assume that there are no gravitational effects, and ignore the small change in linear density that results from the stretching.

(*a*) What will be the velocity of transverse waves in the spring?

(*b*) What will be the velocity of longitudinal waves in the spring?

11 | 1   *Reflections of waves*

WHEN TWO WAVES moving in different directions cross, the amplitudes measured at any time and at any place are just equal to the sum of the amplitudes of the two waves taken separately. This is a simple consequence of the superposition theorem. When two wave trains, each 5 ft high, cross one another in the ocean, a 10-ft crest will be produced at a point of crossing. Although this addition is exactly correct only as long as the wave equation is an exact description of the physical situation, which is generally the case only if the waves are small in some sense, it is a very good approximation for most situations.

Although we can use this principle of superposition to discuss the reflection of all types of waves, we will consider in detail only the simple case of the reflection of a transverse wave in a taut string. There are two particular special cases of interest: one where the wave is reflected at a restrained end of the string, such as the point where the string is tied to a support; and another where the wave is reflected at an unrestrained or free end of the string. We consider for simplicity a wave form such as might be produced by striking the string with a stick. Figure 11 | 1 shows such a wave moving to the right toward a secured end of the string. This secured end of the string is not free to move at all, so when the wave form reaches this end, there can be no displacement of that point of the string.

241

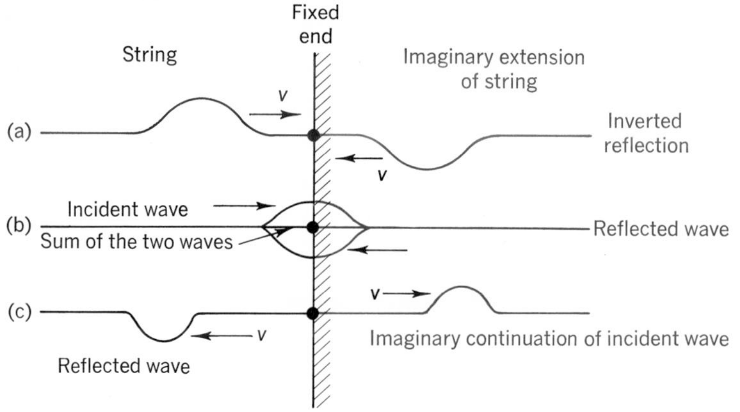

Fixed
end

String

Imaginary extension
of string

(a) ——————— *v* ——— Inverted
reflection

v

(b) Incident wave ———→ ——————— Reflected wave
Sum of the two waves

(c) *v*→ Imaginary continuation of incident wave
v
Reflected wave

FIG. 11|1
*A wave on a string with
a secured end, together
with the reflected wave.*

Any description of the wave that includes the effect of the
boundary must be a solution of the wave equation. Our problem,
therefore, is to find a total wave form that represents a wave
moving toward the boundary at some early time and yet is so
designed that the string at the boundary never moves. An obvious way to do this is to invent a solution that consists of the
wave moving down the string and a reflected wave moving back
up the string so timed that they cancel each other at the boundary.
Figure 11|1a shows such a reflected wave traveling to the left
along an imaginary extension of the string while the real incident
wave moves to the right. Figure 11|1b represents the situation
at the time the incident wave is at the end of the string: the incident wave, the reflected wave, and the sum of the two waves
are shown. Figure 11|1c presents the situation at a later time,
where now the reflected wave is returning from the end and the
incident wave is passing along the imaginary extension of the
string.

If the amplitude at the secured end is always to be zero, it
can be seen that the reflected wave must have exactly the shape
of the incident wave as seen in a mirror, but the opposite sign.

The situation is rather less obvious when the string is free at
an end. Indeed, it is hard to visualize or to set up experimentally
a string that is free at an end and yet under constant tension. A
good approximation to such a condition may be obtained by tying
an extremely light string to the end of a much heavier one and
applying the tension to the heavy cord through the light string.
The end of the heavy cord will now be free in the sense of our

problem, yet the tension can be held constant. For waves of very small amplitude, the free end of the cord will be displaced by the wave action but the slope of the cord will not be effected. If we consider the *x*-direction as the direction along the cord and the *y*-direction as the direction of the displacement of the cord, we can state this precisely: though *y*, the displacement of the end of the cord, will change, dy/dx, the slope of the cord at its end, will remain equal to zero. As long as the force on the end of the cord is directed solely in the *x*-direction by the action of the light string, the cord itself, at that point, must be aligned exactly in the *x*-direction.

This situation can be obtained only by introducing a reflected wave of the same amplitude traveling in the opposite direction. Then, as shown in Fig. 11|2b, the resultant amplitude, derived from the addition of the two waves, will have a slope of zero at the free end. The character of the displacement as a function of time is shown in the Figures 11|2a, b and c.

The two states of the end of the rope we have just investigated are called *boundary conditions*. The conditions for the rope with the end tied such that the displacement is zero can be expressed as

$$y = 0$$

where *y* is the displacement at the end of the rope. There is no restriction on the slope at the tied end of the rope. The boundary

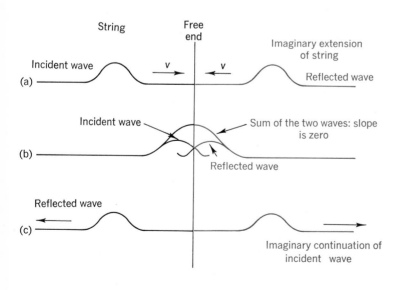

FIG. 11|2
A wave on a string with a free end, together with the reflected wave.

condition on the rope with the free end—though with the tension not relaxed—is that the slope of the rope is zero;

$$\frac{dy}{dx} = 0$$

where dy/dx is the slope of the rope at the end. There is no restriction on the displacement in this case.

There are also boundary conditions for waves in several dimensions; for example, the displacement of a vibrating drumhead is zero at its edge. There are also more complicated boundary conditions. The end of the rope could be attached to a spring, for example. One-dimensional waves in a medium with restrained or unrestrained boundaries are the only cases we shall study in any detail, however. Of course, we have studied the effects of these boundary conditions on waves in a taut string, not because we are so interested in waves on a string, but because the character of the reflections of the waves on a string at such boundaries is typical of the reflections of other kinds of waves at other kinds of boundaries.

In general, waves are reflected at any discontinuity in their medium. If, for example, we arrange a string or a rope of a certain density and change the density abruptly at a point in the rope, there will be a reflected as well as a transmitted component of the wave along the rope, as shown in Fig. 11|3a and b.

Since the velocity of a wave on a taut string is equal to $\sqrt{T/\rho}$ where T is the tension, held constant here, and ρ is the linear density, we see that the velocity will change across the boundary where the heavy cord is tied to the light string: the velocity of the wave in the string is very much greater than that of the wave in the cord. The wave passing from the cord, where the wave velocity is low, to the string, where the velocity is high, will be partially reflected, almost as if the end of the cord were free. The wave

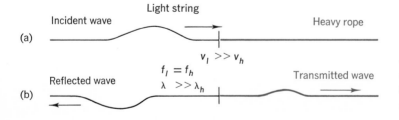

FIG. 11|3
A wave on a light string connected to a heavier string showing reflected and transmitted waves.

passing from the string to the cord—from a region of high velocity to a region of low velocity—will be reflected very much as if the end of the string were a tied end. The waves are partially reflected as a discontinuity where the velocity of the wave changes sharply. It is interesting to note that there will be much less reflection if the medium changes slowly over a region large compared to the length of a wave. If the density of the cord were reduced gradually over a large distance until it matched the density of the string, the reflection would be comparatively weak.

These general principles obtained not only for waves in a taut string but also for sound waves, electric waves, water waves, and de Broglie waves. A discontinuity in the electrical characteristics of a medium, such as a change in the resistance of a wire or cable, will result in reflected electric waves. A discontinuity in the sound-conductive character of a medium will result in reflected sound waves. A boundary in a medium containing water, or even a sharp discontinuity in the depth of the water, will cause reflections of water waves. The de Broglie waves of a neutron will be reflected at the surface of a nucleus. The general character of all of these reflections is quite similar to the character displayed by the reflections of waves in a string. In each of these examples the discontinuity results in a change in the velocity of the wave in the medium and in reflection of the wave. In each of these examples, a reflection from an interface with a medium in which the velocity is lower leads to a reflection with a change in phase; a reflection from an interface with a medium in which the velocity is higher occurs with no change in phase.

11 | 2   *Standing waves*

In the previous section we discussed the reflection of a single discrete disturbance. It is of particular interest to consider a reflection of a whole traveling wave train. We might obtain such a wave train in a rope by tying one end of the rope to an object that oscillates with a circular frequency ω. We can even do this manually by shaking the end of such a rope with constant frequency. A wave train will then propagate from that end toward the other end of the rope with a velocity, v, defined by the tension and linear mass density of the rope. The amplitude of the wave as a function of displacement and time can then be described by a relation of the type we have previously discussed, where the wave is traveling in the x-direction:

$$y = A \cos(\omega t - kx) \tag{11|1}$$

Eventually the wave will reach the end of the rope, where there is a discontinuity; perhaps the rope is tied to a support. The wave will then be reflected from this end with the same amplitude. The reflected wave will travel in the opposite direction with the same velocity and have the form

$$y = A \cos(\omega t + kx) \tag{11|2}$$

If the oscillations keep up indefinitely, there will then be a superposition at any place and any time, of the two wave forms represented by Eqs. (11|1) and (11|2). The total wave will then have the form

$$y = A \cos(\omega t - kx) + A \cos(\omega t + kx) \tag{11|3}$$

The wave represented by this relation has an interesting character. First, the wave represents no obvious motion either to the left or to the right. This must be the case by symmetry. Two equal waves are added, one that goes to the left and one that goes to the right: There can no longer be any preferred direction. The amplitude will reach its maximum value of $2A$ only for specific values of x: where $x = 0$ in Eq. (11|3), or when x is equal to $\frac{1}{2}$ wavelength, or 1 wavelength, or $n/2$ wavelengths, where n is any integer. There are also *nodes* of the *standing wave*, where the amplitude is always zero. If x has a value of $\frac{1}{4}$ wavelength, or $\frac{3}{4}$ or $\frac{5}{4}$ or $\frac{7}{4}$ wavelength, and so on, the value of y will always be equal to zero.

We can see this a little more clearly by using a trigonometric relation and rewriting Eq. (11|3) in the form

$$y = 2A \cos(\omega t) \cos(kx) \tag{11|4}$$

The amplitude of the standing wave A_s is equal to $2A$. This wave form is shown schematically in Fig. 11|4. The black curves represent the amplitude when ωt is equal to zero or π, $\cos \omega t = +1$ or -1, and the amplitudes are maximal. The colored curves represent the amplitudes at different times. We call this wave, which does not move to the left or to the right. and which can be considered as the resultant of two equal waves moving in the opposite direction, a *standing wave*. In general, standing waves

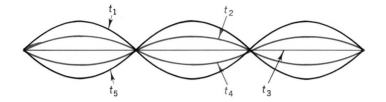

FIG. 11 | 4
*A string secured at both
ends sustaining a
standing wave. The
position of the string is
shown at various times.*

are as natural, as common, and as important, as running waves. The statement we made that we can consider a standing wave as the result of two running waves moving in opposite directions does not mean that standing waves are in some sort of subordinate position. Even as we have discussed standing waves as the sum of two running waves, we could have described running waves as separate parts of a standing wave.

11 | 3   *Characteristic functions and characteristic frequencies*

Usually the medium containing a standing wave is such that specific conditions obtain at every boundary. A string is usually bounded at each end: the real physical situations that are of interest are usually such that the ends of the string are tied down. For any boundary conditions and for waves of any kind, in any medium, only certain standing waves can fit the boundary conditions, and therefore the system will support only waves of specific frequencies. The character of the configurations characteristic to a system will depend upon the character of the system (such as the tension and linear density of a string) and upon the character of the boundary conditions (one end of a string might be free and one end tied down).

A violin string represents a particularly simple and familiar example of such a system. Both ends of a violin string are tied down: any standing wave set up in a violin string by the bow of the violinist must set up waves that fit into the length of the string, so that the amplitudes of the waves are zero at the ends of the string. The set of possible basic configurations of a violin string then represents such a set of waves.

If a violin string is bowed very softly, the wave form of the induced vibration will be similar to that shown in Fig. 11 | 5a, where the figure shows the position of the string at a time such

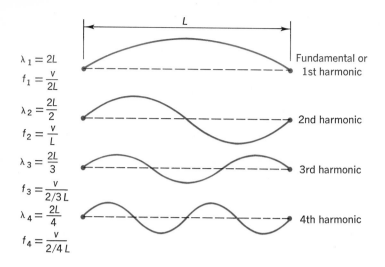

$\lambda_1 = 2L$

$f_1 = \dfrac{v}{2L}$

Fundamental or 1st harmonic

$\lambda_2 = \dfrac{2L}{2}$

$f_2 = \dfrac{v}{L}$

2nd harmonic

$\lambda_3 = \dfrac{2L}{3}$

$f_3 = \dfrac{v}{2/3\,L}$

3rd harmonic

$\lambda_4 = \dfrac{2L}{4}$

$f_4 = \dfrac{v}{2/4\,L}$

4th harmonic

FIG. 11|5
Standing-wave configurations for the vibrations of a string secured at both ends.

that the amplitude is a maximum. The form of the wave is half of a sine wave. If the length of the string is L, the wavelength is $2L$. The frequency times the wavelength equals the velocity of a wave. The velocity is usually a specific of the medium; in the special case of the taut string, $v = \sqrt{T/\rho}$. Then

$$f\lambda = v \qquad \text{or} \qquad f = \frac{v}{\lambda}$$

and

$$f = \frac{v}{2L}$$

since

$$\lambda = 2L$$

This is the expression for the frequency of vibration of a string corresponding to the shape of Fig. 11|5a. This is the lowest possible frequency of vibration of the string even as the configuration represents the longest wavelength of any standing wave that can fit the boundary conditions. This frequency is called the *fundamental frequency* or just the *fundamental*.

Even as other wavelengths can be fitted into the boundary conditions the string can vibrate with other frequencies. The diagrams of Figs. 11|5b, c, and d represent amplitude configura-

tions that correspond to wavelengths shorter than the fundamental wavelength and thus to higher frequencies than the fundamental. We represent the form of the wave shapes by the position
of the string when the amplitude is at a maximum. There is an
infinite number of possible frequencies even as there is an infinite
number of possible wavelengths that fit the boundary conditions.
The values of these frequencies are expressed simply by the
relation

$$f_n = nf_1 \qquad n = 1, 2, 3, \ldots$$

where f_1 is the fundamental or first harmonic and f_n is the frequency of the nth harmonic. We call these frequencies *characteristic frequencies,* and the functions, such as

$$\sin\left(\frac{\pi n x}{L}\right)$$

that describe the displacement for the different oscillations of a
definite frequency, *characteristic functions.* (It is a common, if
pernicious, practice to mix English and German and to use the
terms *eigenfrequency* and *eigenfunction.*) The set of characteristic frequencies $f_1, f_2, f_3, \ldots$, comprises the *spectrum* of frequencies characteristic of the string and its boundary conditions.
Such a spectrum is closely related, in principle, to the optical
spectra of atoms and molecules; the characteristic states of the
vibrating string have an analog in the de Broglie standing waves
that describe the electrons in atoms.

In general, an oscillating string vibrates as a combination of
such characteristic frequencies and characteristic shapes. Consider a string, such as a harp string, plucked at the center, as in
Fig. 11 | 6a, and then released. The orginal shape can be con-
sidered a superposition of characteristic shapes, all with different
amplitudes. The Figures 11 | 6b and c represent an estimate of
the first two important shapes or modes, and 11 | 6d, the sum of
these, is not a bad approximation to 11 | 6a. The sum of an ap-
propriately chosen infinite number of shapes would approach
fitting 11 | 6a exactly. Such a sum or series is, again, called a
Fourier series. In general, any configuration of the string can be
expressed as a sum or series—the Fourier series—of characteristic functions, and the string, deflected in this way, will vibrate
with the various characteristic frequencies.

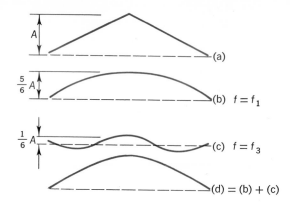

FIG. 11|6
*An initial displacement
of a taut string and the
two most important
characteristic functions
that describe the initial
displacement.*

The string displaced as shown in Fig. 11|6 will vibrate with a frequency of f_1 and f_3 (and also $f_5, f_7, \ldots$). The relative amplitudes can be estimated by constructing the final amplitude as shown in Fig. 11|6. In that figure we have estimated that the amplitude of the fundamental, A_1, would be about five times as large as the amplitude of the third harmonic, A_3. There are techniques for calculating the amplitudes exactly that would make up the sawtooth wave form of 11|6. The exact ratios are

$$A_1:A_3:A_5:A_7: \ldots \qquad \text{as} \qquad 1:\tfrac{1}{9}:\tfrac{1}{25}:\tfrac{1}{49}: \ldots$$

Since the energy is proportional to the square of the amplitude and to the square of the frequency, most of the energy (more than 80 percent) will be found in the fundamental. As a practical or aesthetic matter, the other frequencies—the overtones—are important: they add timbre and richness to the sound generated by a string. The body of a musical instrument, be it a violin, piano, harp, or guitar, contributes in an essential way to the character of the sound because energy is transfered from the strings to the body of the instrument, which is a more efficient radiator of sound. Energy of different frequencies is transferred with different efficiencies, depending upon the detailed construction of the instrument; thus, different instruments of the same genus can vary in the total amount of energy transferred and in the relative amounts transferred from various modes. A good violin, for example, transfers a lot of energy from the string, and hence from the bow, to the body of the instrument over a wide range of frequencies.

If the string is plucked, bowed, or otherwise stroked exactly in the center, as shown in Fig. 11 | 6a, no asymmetric frequency will be excited: $f_2, f_4, f_6 \ldots$, will not occur. This result may appear more evident by considering Fig. 11 | 7, which is meant to represent the mode of f_2 and the same mode excited with a phase difference of $\frac{1}{2}$ beat. Obviously, a disturbance exactly in the center cannot distinguish between the two modes. The two modes must be excited equally; but then they will cancel and not be excited at all. So this frequency is not excited at all. However, if the string is excited asymmetrically, the harmonics $f_2, f_4, f_6, \ldots$, will be excited as well as $f_1, f_3, f_5, \ldots$. Since the overtones are different, the sound will be different when the string is excited in the two different ways.

Similar patterns of characteristic functions and characteristic frequencies result from sound vibrations in tubes of organ pipes, electric waves in cables, wires, and other conductors, and the de Broglie waves of an electron bound to an atom, or a neutron bound in the atomic nucleus. The quantitative character of the standing waves depends upon the character of the medium and its boundaries and is not necessarily very simple. For example, the different characteristic frequencies of the vibrations of a drum head do not vary as integral multiples at all, and the two-dimensional characteristic shapes of the drum head, corresponding to specific frequencies of excitation, are rather complicated.

Even as the phenomenon of resonance occurs in simple mechanical systems, where the motion can be completely described by the equations of simple harmonic motion, resonances are important in systems of standing waves. This is not surprising for standing waves in mechanical systems, since for any particular mode of vibration each region of the medium that supports the standing wave moves with the same frequency in a manner that is just that described by simple harmonic motion. Every part of a violin string excited in a particular mode such as shown in Fig. 11 | 5 oscillates with the same frequency in simple harmonic motion. Then even as the oscillations of a

FIG. 11 | 7
Configurations of a string vibrating in the second harmonic. The two diagrams represent vibrations 180° out of phase.

(a)
(b)

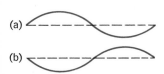

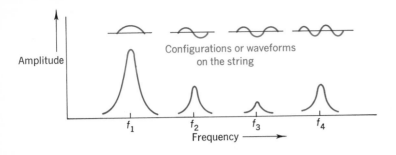

FIG. 11|8
Amplitudes of a taut string secured at both ends as a function of the frequency of the impulses disturbing the string. The relative amplitudes at the different frequencies, depend upon the detailed orientation of the sound waves and string.

ball on the end of a string could be excited by small periodic disturbances, the oscillations of a taut string can be excited by similar recurring impulses. The string has a spectrum of characteristic frequencies, so that a plot of the amplitude of the string as a function of the exciting frequency will look somewhat as Fig. 11|8. The relative maximum amplitude of the string for the different characteristic frequencies will depend in detail upon the character of the excitation as well as the characteristic of the string.

Strings are easily excited by sound vibrations of the appropriate frequency. One can consider the individual condensations and rarefactions of the air as very like small currents of air, and these currents will cause the string to oscillate. The energy thus introduced into the string system must come from the sound: the string absorbs sound of any frequency that is equal to one of the resonant frequencies of the string. In much the same way, light is absorbed by atoms at resonant frequencies of the atoms, and neutrons are absorbed by nuclei at resonant frequencies of the nuclei.

By measuring the absorption spectra—the spectra of resonances of the string—it is possible to deduce from the spacing of the resonances as a function of frequency that the string is tied at both ends rather than tied at one end and free at the other. One can deduce some information about the structure of the string system by analyzing the absorption spectra. In much the same way, one can learn something about the structure of atoms by measuring the absorption spectra of light on the atom, or learn something about the structure of nuclei by examining the neutron-absorption spectra of nuclei.

PROBLEMS

11|1 A violin string 50 cm is tuned to A, $f = 440$ Hz.

(*a*) How much must the string be shortened (by fingering) so that the frequency is raised 25 percent, to 550 Hz?

(*b*) What is the velocity of a wave in the string tuned to 440 Hz?

(*c*) The string is out of tune by 1 percent (4.4 Hz) and vibrates at 435.6 Hz. How much (in percent) must the tension on the string be changed so that it is in tune?

11|2 A cord is tied down at one end and is free at the other (that is, it is tied to a very light string so that the tension is constant throughout the cord). The lowest vibrational frequency of the cord in this configuration is measured to be 10 Hz.

(*a*) What are the frequencies of the next two higher overtones?

(*b*) What are the configurations of the cord as it vibrates at the lowest frequency? At the next lowest frequency?

11|3 A string 4 m long, tied at the ends, is displaced as shown and then released. (The displacement is exaggerated for clarity.) The tension in the string is such that the velocity of waves in the string is 100 m/sec.

(*a*) What is the lowest frequency of vibration?

(*b*) What other frequencies will be excited as the string vibrates? (List four.)

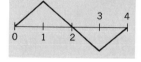

11|4 A string 4 m long, tied at the ends, is displaced as shown and then released. (The displacement is exaggerated for clarity.) The tension in the string is such that the velocity of waves in the string is 100 m/sec.

(*a*) What is the lowest frequency of vibration of the string?

(*b*) List four other frequencies that will be excited.

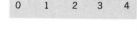

11|5 A string is held in the configuration shown and then released. Then a bow is placed on the string, exactly at the center. The sound diminishes and changes quality.

(*a*) What is the most important or striking difference in the quality of the sound after the string is damped by the bow?

(*b*) Before the bow is applied, *estimate* the relative amplitudes of the fundamental and the second harmonic.

11|6   An analysis of the vibration of a violin string excited under certain conditions shows that the relative amplitudes of the fundamental and the second and third harmonics varies as 9:2:1. What is the relative energy stored in the three modes?

11|7   The speed of sound in steel is about 6000 m/sec. Two steel bars, each 1 m long, are obtained; one is allowed to rest on two knife edges, which hold it without any appreciable constraint; the other is held firmly at the center by a heavy clamp. Then each is struck lightly on the end by a hammer so that it emits a musical sound.

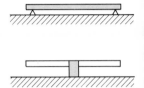

(*a*) What is the fundamental frequency and the frequency of the first overtone emitted by the free bar?

(*b*) What is the fundamental frequency and the frequency of the first overtone emitted by the clamped bar?

11|8   Brass instruments, such as the bugle, are designed so that a resonance is set up in the column of air in the instrument. Both the bell and the mouthpiece can be considered as nonrestrained ends of the air column. The fundamental note or first harmonic of the bugle is of poor quality, and the musical notes consist of the second to the eighth harmonics. The speed of sound in air is about 340 m/sec. What is the length of the air column if the fundamental note is 115 Hz. What are the frequencies of the first four overtones? The speed of sound in hydrogen is about four times the speed in air. What will be the value of the fundamental frequency if the bugle is filled with hydrogen?

twelve *Interference and diffraction*

12 | 1 *The addition of wave amplitudes*

IF THERE ARE two sources of waves in a two-dimensional manifold, such as two sources of ripples on the surface of a body of still
water, or if there are two sources in a three-dimensional manifold,
such as two sources of sound waves in a room, the wave trains
from the two sources will eventually intersect. In the region of
crossing, at any particular time and place, the amplitudes of the
resultant wave will be equal to the algebraic sum of the amplitudes expected from each source taken separately. This is again
a result of the principle of superposition. At a place and time
where the amplitude from each source separately would be a
maximum, we will observe a still larger maximum. At a place
and time where the wave from one source will be a maximum
and the wave from the other source will be a minimum, there
will be some degree of cancellation. If the two amplitudes would
be equal taken separately, they will exactly cancel and there will
be no disturbance at all at that place and at that time. We say
that this general behavior is the result of *interference*, where we
use the term in a technical manner referent to the interaction between two wave trains from different sources.

The most important results of interference relate to the interference of "characteristic" wave trains such that the amplitudes
vary sinusoidally with time with a definite frequency and sinusoidally with distance with a specific wavelength. We will then

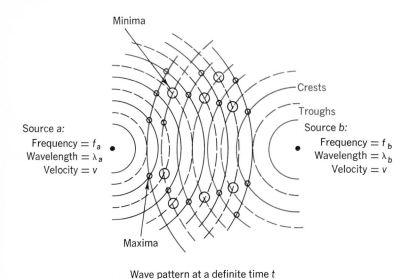

Minima

Crests

Troughs

Source a:
  Frequency = f_a
  Wavelength = λ_a
  Velocity = v

Source b:
  Frequency = f_b
  Wavelength = λ_b
  Velocity = v

Maxima

Wave pattern at a definite time t

FIG. 12|1
Intersection of wave trains from different sources.

limit our specific discussion to the consideration of such waves. Since any wave can be made up from a set of such characteristic waves, we do not lose any fundamental generality by such a simplifying restriction.

Figure 12|1 shows a situation where wave trains from two different sources cross at some particular time. In this diagram the solid lines represent maxima and the dashed line represent the minima or the troughs of the waves, which might be, for example, ripples on a pond. The amplitude at the points indicated by the solid circles represent points at which, at the time the situation is observed, the two amplitudes will *interfere constructively* and produce an exceptionally large amplitude. The dashed circles show points where the maximum from one source is coincident with a minimum or trough in the other source. This is *destructive* interference; the magnitude of the deviation of the water surface from normal will be small. There will neither be a large maximum nor will there be a deep valley. Since the waves in this figure move outwards with a velocity, v, determined by the characteristics of the medium, the positions of these maxima and minima will change with time—a few seconds later they will be in a different position.

It is convenient to describe a wave train by the notation $A(r, t)$, which represents the amplitude of the wave at any point r and time t. Then when two wave trains $A_1(r, t)$ and $A_2(r, t)$, of different character from different sources intersect, the resultant amplitude $A'(r, t)$ is just equal to the sum of the two amplitudes A_1 and A_2 at all times t and all places r.

At any particular point r, we can then describe the variation of amplitude with time of each wave separately (in the absence of the other wave) as

$$A_1 = A_1{}^m \cos(\omega_1 t + \theta_1) \qquad \text{and} \qquad A_2 = A_2{}^m \cos(\omega_2 t + \theta_2)$$

where $A_1{}^m$ and $A_2{}^m$ are the maximum amplitudes at r of the waves from the two sources, ω_1 and ω_2 are the angular frequencies of the two waves, and θ_1 and θ_2 are phases of the waves. The sum of the two waves is simply

$$A' = A_1 + A_2$$
$$= A_1{}^m \cos(\omega_1 t + \theta_1) + A_2{}^m \cos(\omega_2 t + \theta_2)$$

where A' is the observed amplitude at the point r and the time t.

In general, the behavior of A' with time is complicated. The diagrams of Fig. 12|2 show the variation with time of the amplitude for a typical superposition of the two waves A_1 and A_2, where the parameters $A_1{}^m$, $A_2{}^m$, ω_1, ω_2, θ_1, and θ_2 are all different. However, if the frequencies of the two wave trains A_1 and A_2 are the same, $\omega_1 = \omega_2$, the total amplitude A' will change with time in a particularly simple fashion: A' will vary sinusoidally with the angular frequency ω, where ω is the common frequency of the waves from the two sources. Furthermore, the

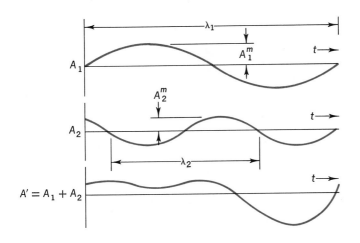

FIG. 12|2
Sum of the amplitudes from different sources as observed at a particular point as a function of time.

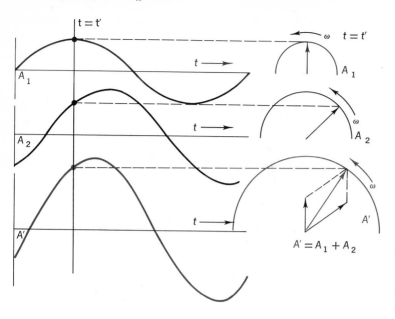

FIG. 12|3

Construction of the sum of the amplitudes from different sources emitting waves at the same frequency. The amplitudes are observed at a particular point.

amplitude of A' is determined in a simple way from the parameters describing the two waves A_1 and A_2. The relations between the original waves A_1 and A_2 and the resultant wave A' can be understood with the help of the diagrams of Fig. 12|3, which show the variation of the total amplitude with respect to time, at some particular place, that results from the various waves.

Figures 12|3a and b show the variation of amplitude with time that results from the waves A_1 and A_2 alone. Since the variation with time of the amplitude at any specific place is similar to the variation described by simple harmonic motion, the amplitude can be described as the projections of points moving with constant velocity ω on the diameters of circles of radii $A_1{}^m$ and $A_2{}^m$. We might consider the distance from the center of the circle to the moving point as a vector; the amplitude is then the component of this vector in the direction of the diameter of the circle. At any time, the amplitude A' is the sum of the amplitudes A_1 and A_2. Since this amplitude also varies sinusoidally, as a particle moving with simple harmonic motion, this amplitude can also be considered as the component of a vector rotating with angular velocity ω. Since $A' = A_1 + A_2$ at any time, the components of the vectors in the diagrams 12|3a and b must equal the component of the vector shown in diagram 12|3c. This will be the case if the vector that generates A' is the vector sum of the vectors that generate A_1 and A_2, a result that is shown in Fig. 12|3c.

We can now summarize these simple but powerful results, which show us that the addition of waves is similar to the addition of vectors and that it is therefore useful to consider a wave as a vector for the purpose of adding amplitudes. If the amplitudes of two waves at a specific point vary with time as

$$A_1 = A_1{}^m \cos(\omega t + \theta_1) \qquad \text{and} \qquad A_2 = A_2{}^m \cos(\omega t + \theta_2)$$

we can represent these two amplitudes as vectors, as shown in Fig. 12|4, with lengths $A_1{}^m$ and $A_2{}^m$ at angles with respect to a reference direction of θ_1 and θ_2. The sum of the amplitudes can be written as

$$\mathbf{A}' = \mathbf{A}_1 + \mathbf{A}_2$$
$$= A'^m \cos(\omega t + \theta')$$

where $\mathbf{A}'$ can also be represented as a vector with a length of A'^m, and the vector $\mathbf{A}'$ is equal to the sum of the vectors $\mathbf{A}_1$ and $\mathbf{A}_2$. Obviously, the sum of many amplitudes can be constructed as the sum of the many vectors that represent these amplitudes.

For completeness we can express A'^m and θ' formally in terms of $A_1{}^m$ and $A_2{}^m$ and θ_1 and θ_2 with a little trignometry:

$$(A'^m)^2 = (A_1{}^m)^2 + (A_2{}^m)^2 + 2(A_1{}^m)(A_2{}^m)\cos(\theta_2 - \theta_1)$$

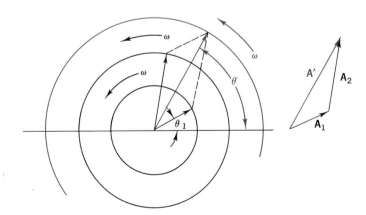

FIG. 12|4
Construction of the sum
of two amplitudes as
the sum of two vectors.

and

$$\tan \theta' = \frac{A_1{}^m \sin \theta_1 + A_2{}^m \sin \theta_2}{A_1{}^m \cos \theta_1 + A_2{}^m \cos \theta_2}$$

Although we have actually shown that the vector that generates the amplitude A' can be constructed as the vector sum of the vectors that generate the amplitudes A_1 and A_2, where $\mathbf{A}' = \mathbf{A}_1 + \mathbf{A}_2$, we consider, as a matter of speech and as a matter of convention, the amplitudes themselves as vectors.

12 | 2   *Interference*

The most striking examples of interference behavior occur when different wave trains of the same frequency, and with a definite phase relation, intersect. In nature there is not likely to be any very particular relation between the frequency and phase relations of waves from independent sources, and interference behavior between the wave trains from such sources is not generally of much importance. The most interesting and important examples of interference result from the interaction of wave trains that originate from the same source but arrive at a region of interaction through different paths. Such waves will have the same frequency, but their relative phase and their amplitudes will differ in general.

The interference patterns produced in the reflection and transmission of light by thin films are particularly interesting in that the existence of the interference effects alone shows that light has a wavelike nature. Figure 12|5 shows two glass plates arranged so that there is a wedge-shaped film of air between the two plates. We consider the situation such that monochromatic light is normally incident upon the plates and that an observer

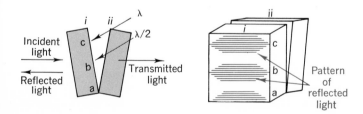

FIG. 12|5
The interference of reflected and transmitted light from a glass–air wedge.

is at first in position to view the reflected light, and then in position to view the transmitted light. Monochromatic light is light of one color or of one particular wavelength. Light will be reflected at all of the glass–air interfaces because such interfaces represent boundaries where the velocity of the wave changes. Light travels more slowly in glass than in air, and light directed toward the air from the glass will be reflected without a change in phase, very much as a wave in a heavy, taut rope is reflected at a free end or at a discontinuity where it is tied to a much lighter string. Light traveling from the air toward the glass will be reflected with a change in phase, very much as the wave in a string is reflected from an end that is tied down, or tied to a very much heavier rope, in which the speed of transmission of the wave is very much slower.

The incident light that reaches the face *i* of the glass plate of Fig. 12 | 5 will be partially reflected backward with no change in phase. The light that reaches the interface *ii* will be partially reflected with a reversal of phase. Since this light was emitted originally from some single source, the two reflected waves are different parts of one original wave, and we can expect them to interfere in a simple way. At every point affected by the two waves, the amplitude can be expressed as the vector sum of the amplitudes *i* and *ii*. These two amplitudes will generally differ in phase and magnitude: the magnitudes will be different because they are reflected with different efficiencies at the different interfaces, and the phases will be different because they travel different distances and because they are reflected with different phase changes. Two waves that are reflected in the same manner but travel distances that differ by $\frac{1}{4}$ wavelength will differ in phase by $360°/4 = 90°$; if they travel distances that differ by $\frac{1}{6}$ wavelength, their phases will differ by $360°/6 = 60°$; and so on.

At point *a*, the air film is negligibly thick and the light reflected from the two surfaces travels the same distance to the observer. The main difference between the two wave trains is the 180° difference in phase: the two vectors that represent the two amplitudes are in opposite directions. The waves will then interfere *destructively*; they will tend to cancel each other, and the region of reflection will appear dark, as shown. At point *b*, the width of the air film is $\frac{1}{2}$ wavelength. The wave reflected from surface *ii* then travels a full wavelength farther than the wave reflected at *i*. This alone would put the two waves in phase, but the different phase changes upon reflection put them out of phase by 180° and there is another dark band at *b*. At *c*, the film is a full wavelength thick and the two reflected waves travel a distance that differs by 2 wavelengths; again, destructive interference occurs. Half way between *a* and *b* the thickness of the air film is $\frac{1}{4}$ wavelength, and the two waves travel distances that differ by $\frac{1}{2}$ wavelength. If they were reflected in the same fashion they, would then be 180° out of phase and interfere destructively. Since the reflection process is different for the two waves and introduces another 180° phase difference, the resultant waves are in phase, add constructively, and create a bright band of reflected light.

If the amplitude of the light reflected from surface *i* is written as A_i and that of the light reflected from the surface *ii* is written as A_{ii}, the resultant amplitude reflected from the darker portions will be $A_i - A_{ii}$, and the amplitude reflected from the bright portion will be $A_i + A_{ii}$. The intensities will be proportional to the square of the resultant amplitudes. If A_i and A_{ii} are about equal, as will be the case, the reflected intensity from the darkest part will be very near zero, while the intensity from the brightest sections will be about four times as bright as the reflection from a single surface.

Since the reflected intensity at bands *a*, *b*, and *c* is very small, the transmitted intensity must be correspondingly larger. At the intermediate regions where the reflected intensity is greatest, the transmitted intensity must be reduced. Therefore, the transmitted light will exhibit a band structure of light and dark that is the reverse of the reflected pattern. Since most of the light is transmitted anyway, the effect on the transmitted light is relatively small, however.

Lenses are often coated with a thin film so designed that the reflected light is largely eliminated through destructive interference in a manner very much like that described here, so that almost all the light is transmitted.

Circular patterns of very much the same nature as the linear patterns produced by the air wedge are produced when a plano-convex lens of large radius of curvature is placed against a flat piece of glass as in Fig. 12|6. These circles are called *Newton's rings* after Newton, who first mentioned this effect. Newton believed that most of the phenomena associated with light were easily explained if light were corpuscular in nature; and though he may have recognized the simplicity of an interference explana-

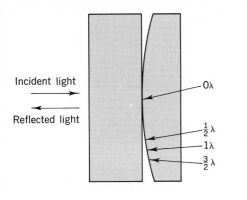

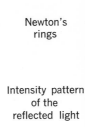

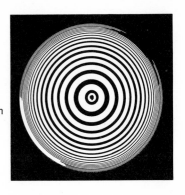

Incident light

Reflected light

Newton's rings

Intensity pattern
of the
reflected light

FIG. 12|6
*Interference from the
surfaces of a plane and
a sphere showing the
Newton's-rings
phenomenon.*

tion of the ring patterns, which would require that light have
wave properties, he attempted (with no particular success) to
understand the Newton's-rings phenomenon using his cor-
puscular model of light.

"White" light is a mixture of light of various colors or of various
wavelengths. The wavelength of visible light ranges from 0.4
microns (violet) to 0.7 microns (red) (a micron, abbreviated μ, is
one millionth of a meter). In a situation like that of Fig. 12|5 or
Fig. 12|6, the interference patterns of light of different colors or
of different wavelengths do not fall in the same place. Where there
is a destructive-interference minimum for red light, there may
be a constructive-interference maximum for violet light intensity,
or vice versa. It is this effect that gives us the rainbow patterns
from light reflected by an oil film on water or by the film of water
that makes up a soap bubble. If the film of a soap bubble is extremely thin, there will be destructive interference for all wavelengths of light. When a black spot appears on a soap bubble, this
is then an indication it is about ready to burst.

Interference patterns of much the same nature can be constructed with sound waves and with the de Broglie waves that
represent the behavior of small elements of matter.

12|3 *Huygens' principle*

The propagation of a wave must result causally: the configuration
at a particular instant must result as the consequence of the conditions at any previous time—for example, a second before. If we
know the positions and velocity of every point of a string at some

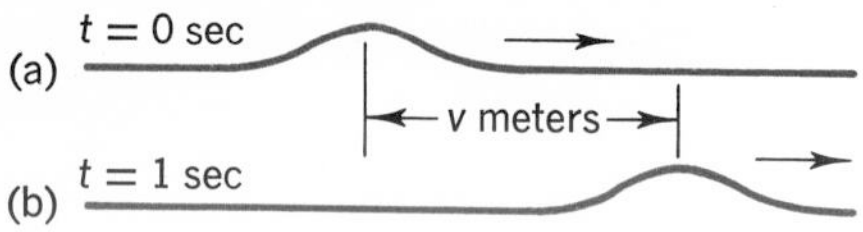

(a) t = 0 sec

←— v meters —→

(b) t = 1 sec

FIG. 12|7

*A wave form at two
different times.*

instant, such as shown on Fig. 12|7a we should, in principle, be able to calculate or predict the velocity and position of every point on the string at any later time, such as shown on Fig. 12|7b. Although the details of such calculations may not interest us, a particular aspect of the considerations involved is important. From the principle of superposition we should be able to consider each point of the string of Fig. 12|6a separately: each point will generate further waves by virtue of its displacement and velocity and its connection to the rest of the string. From considerations of symmetry the motion, up and down, of a point on the string must send equal waves out in both directions, left and right. We can calculate the waves generated by each point on the string and add the contributions by the vectorial technique we have discussed; we would find that all the wavelets moving to the left interfere in such a way that they exactly cancel, and the contributions from all the wavelengths moving to the right, taken after 1 sec, interfere so that they add up to just the configuration of 12|7b.

The general arguments used here are equally valid for more abstract and more general situations than waves in a taut string. Each point in a disturbed medium can be considered as a source of wavelets, be they sound waves, electromagnetic waves, or any other kind of waves, in one, two, or three dimensions. The displacement and motion of any point of a ripple in a pond, or the magnitude and rate of change of the electric field at any point in an electromagnetic wave, can be considered to be the source of concentric circular ripples, or concentric spherical electromagnetic waves. The whole wave pattern on the pond, or the whole electromagnetic wave pattern in space, can be considered to result from the addition of such concentric wave patterns from each point at some previous time. The principle of superposition allows us to consider any complex wave phenomenon as the sum of an infinite number of small wavelets: the principle of causality requires us to conclude that the future behavior of the complex wave pattern can be described as the result of the original pattern and thus as the result of the set of small wavelets. This concept is useful because we have only to understand the propagation of the effects of such simple singular disturbances in order to understand, in principle, the effects of complex patterns of disturbances.

The fundamental concept that we can consider each point of a wave as an individual further source of waves is so useful that it is dignified by a particular name: *Huygens' Principle*, after Christian Huygens (1629–1695) a Dutch physicist and astronomer who made extraordinary contributions to optics as well as other areas of physics. A most obvious and important use of Huygens' principle lies in the insights it presents into the understanding of *diffraction*, a general term relevant to the effects of barriers on waves.

12｜4   *Diffraction*

In considering the diffraction of waves it is convenient to examine qualitatively an elementary case of diffraction at a small aperture. We will consider explicitly small water waves or ripples because the results are quite general, the behavior of such ripples is very close to our immediate experiences, and we can easily visualize the results.

The diagram of Fig. 12｜8a represents a wave train of parallel waves, for example, ripples on a water surface, striking an ab-

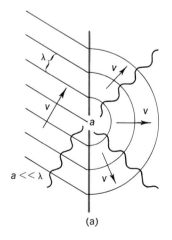

(a)

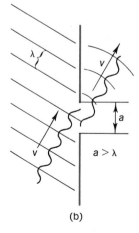

(b)

FIG. 12｜8
Transmission of a wave (a) through a small slit and (b) a large slit.

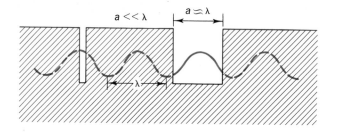

FIG. 12|9
*The amplitude of water
waves incident upon a
wall near a narrow
aperture and near a
wide aperture.*

sorbing barrier. The solid lines represent the crests of the waves. The barrier has a small hole, the diameter of the hole being small compared to the wavelength of the ripples. The water in the opening will rise and fall as the wave train passes by. If the hole is narrow, all the water in the hole will act very much the same, as suggested by the left-hand part of Fig. 12|9, which represents a narrow slit (narrow compared to the wavelength) in a barrier. Beyond the barrier a wave train is evident. The water in that opening will rise and fall with the characteristic frequency of the wave (in this case determined by the density of the water and the surface tension of the water). It is the effects of this motion that are transmitted to the surface at the right of the barrier in Fig. 12|8a. Since the opening is small compared to the length of a wave, essentially all of the water at the opening will rise and fall together. This perturbation will then initiate, as usual, a circular wave, which will proceed as shown on the right-hand side of the barrier.

If the aperture is larger, as shown at the right of Fig. 12|9, there will generally be a difference in phase or timing between the rise and fall of the water at various parts of the aperture. The wavelets from different parts of the aperture will proceed differently: they will travel sensibly different distances toward any particular point and arrive such that the timing is different. All of this will result in a pattern like that of Fig. 12|8b. A pattern of waves emitted from the aperture will proceed in the same general direction as the original parallel or plane wave. There will be a spread in direction, however; the waves will have spread out over a larger interval than the size of the aperture. As a result, part of the wave will be traveling in a direction different from that of the original plane wave.

These behaviors can be understood quantitatively rather simply by considering the propagation of wavelets from small sections, *da*, of the aperture, *a*, separately. We choose sections such that *da* ≪ λ, determine the contributions of the wave at any point from each section *da*, and then add these contributions vectorially to account for their differences in phase. The diagram of Fig. 12 | 10 shows a plane wave normally incident upon an absorbing barrier of aperture *a*, which is divided into ten parts. We choose to discuss a normally incident wave for simplicity; quite similar results obtain for other angles of incidence.

We consider in detail the amplitude of the wave in the region of a screen or line shown in Fig. 12 | 10. The amplitude of the waves at the position of the screen is shown by the curve at the right of the screen. Straight in front of the aperture, at point *b* on the screen, the partial amplitudes from the ten sectors all travel about the same distance. Since the waves were in phase at the aperture and they all travel the same distance, they will still be in phase at point *b*. They interfere constructively, and we can add up the vectors to get a total amplitude as shown. Since the individual amplitudes have very nearly the same phase, they add almost as if they all lie on a straight line. Since the wavelets from the first and tenth segment of the aperture travel slightly farther than the wavelets from the center segments, there is a small deviation from the straight line, as suggested by the vector diagram. Because this is a small effect, the final amplitude, A_b, is almost equal to the algebraic sum of the ten partial amplitudes. If we write the magnitude of the partial amplitudes as dA, then

FIG. 12 | 10
Construction of the wave amplitudes resulting from the diffraction of a wave by a narrow slit.

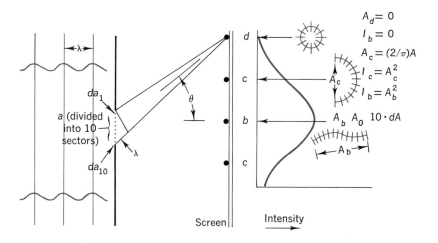

$A_d = 0$

$I_b = 0$

$A_c = (2/\pi)A$

$I_c = A_c^2$

$I_b = A_b^2$

$A_b \quad A_0 \quad 10 \cdot dA$

$A_b = 10 \, dA$ and $I_b = 100 \, dI$

where $dI = dA^2$.

At point d the wavelet from segment 10 travels a full wavelength farther than the wavelet from segment 1, and the phase of A_{10} differs from the phase of A_1 by about 360°. The wavelet from segment 5 travels half a wavelength farther than the wave from segment 1, and the phase of A_5 differs from A_1 by about 180°. All the other amplitudes are proportionally out of phase with A_1. The graphical addition of the partial amplitudes then has the form of a circle. The circle is closed—A_1 and A_{10}, differing by 360° in phase, are in phase again—and the resultant amplitude, the vector sum of the partial amplitudes, is equal to zero. Of course the intensity at this point is also zero. We neglect here the small differences in the magnitude of the partial amplitudes that result from the slight differences in path lengths from the various segments of the aperture.

At point c the wavelets from the extreme segments travel a distance that differs by half a wavelength, and the amplitudes A_1 and A_{10} differ in phase by about 180°. The sum of all of the partial amplitudes then takes the form of a half circle. The circumference of such a circle would be equal to 20 dA or $2A_b$. The resultant amplitude, A_c, is equal to the diameter of the circle, so

$$A_c = \frac{20 \, dA}{\pi} = \frac{2A_b}{\pi} \quad \text{and} \quad I_c = \frac{4I_b}{\pi^2}$$

The intensity along a longer section of the screen is shown in Fig. 12|11, together with some other vector configurations.

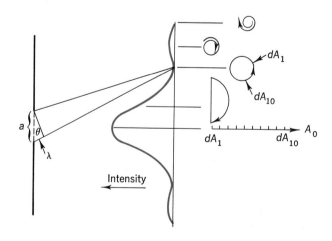

FIG. 12|11

Diffraction pattern produced by incident plane waves and a narrow slit.

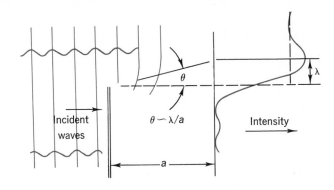

FIG. 12|12
Diffraction of waves at the edge of a barrier.

It can be seen from an inspection of the diagram shown in Fig. 12|10 that the angle between the direction of the maximum from the slit and the direction of the first minimum is almost exactly equal to θ where

$$\sin \theta = \frac{\lambda}{a}$$

For small angles,

$$\theta = \frac{\lambda}{a}$$

in radians. If the aperture a is narrow, the spread of the transmitted waves, which is measured by $\sin \theta$, is large; if the aperture is wide, the spread of the transmitted waves is small.

Diffraction also occurs at a single edge. The character of this diffraction can be considered in a fashion similar to that used to analyze diffraction from an aperture, except now one must add wavelets from very far away from the edge and it is necessary to consider the reduction in the amplitude that results from the increased distance the wavelets travel. We will not consider the analysis of this phenomenon in detail. However, Fig. 12|12 shows the intensity pattern at a screen near the position of the edge of a barrier that absorbs a plane wave. The solid line shows the intensity as we should expect from the wave theory of light, which is in accord with observations; the dashed line shows the amplitude if all of the energy from the source traveled in a straight line. The waves "curve" around a corner to a distance of the order of a wavelength.

Waves are refracted by a narrow rod or disk in a manner very similar to the way waves are refracted by a slit or hole. From

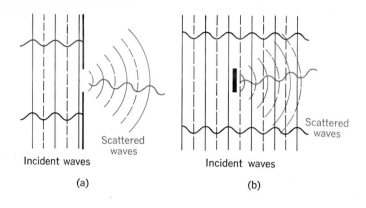

FIG. 12|13

Diffraction of waves by a hole in a barrier and by a disk the same size as the hole.

Huygen's principle, that all parts of the wave act separately, we can deduce that what is subtracted from the plane wave by the disk is just equal to what gets through a hole in a barrier if the hole is just the same size as the disc.

The curved wavelets in Fig. 12|13b, which represent the diffraction effect of the disk, are equal in amplitude but opposite in sign to the wavelets of Fig. 12|13a. Where there is a peak in the pattern of 12|13a there is a valley in the pattern of 12|13b. If we add the apertures of the two situations, we have no barrier at all and the plane wave will proceed unimpeded. Therefore, if we add the patterns of 12|13a and 12|13b they *must* add up to the plane wave. This can be the case only if the disturbance that results from each is exactly the same as that from the other, except for a change in sign. From each system, the hole or the disk, waves are scattered in the same pattern with a pattern of $\theta \approx \lambda/a$.

The difference between the "straight line" character of light transmission and the comparatively diffuse transmission of sound waves now appears to be a quantitative difference and not a difference in basic quality. The wavelength of visible light ranges from 0.4 to 0.7 $\times$ 10^{-6} m, while audible sound ranges from 10 m to less than 10 cm in wavelength. The wavelength corresponding to the standard note *A* is about 75 cm. We can therefore expect sound to pass around corners, especially the lower notes with their long wavelengths. A great deal of the diffused sound results from reflection as well as diffraction, so that some care must be made in considering effects in general.

The finite wavelengths of light and sound place important limitations on the operation of optical and accoustical instruments. The aperture of the eye varies according to the intensity of the incident light, but we may consider a mean aperture of about 0.5 cm. As a result of diffraction of light by the aperture of the iris of the eye, the angular resolution of the eye is limited to about $\lambda/a \approx 10^{-4}$ radians, where λ represents the wavelength of light, taken as about 5×10^{-7} m, and a is the diameter of the aperture, 5×10^{-3} m. A point observed by a perfect eye is effectively blurred, or spread out, by the diffraction effect over an angular interval of 10^{-4} rad. A point 100 m away will appear to be at least as large as 100 m $\times 10^{-4} = 1$ cm in diameter. Two points 1 cm apart will appear to blend into one another. A camera having an aperture of 0.5 cm will do no better, no matter how high the quality of film or degree of enlargement. A binocular with an objective aperture of 50 mm will have a maximum resolution of 10^{-5} rad and can resolve points a cm apart at a distance of 1000 m if the binocular is perfect and if the magnifying power of the binocular is sufficient so that the aperture of the eyepiece or the aperture of the iris of the observer's eye does not limit the resolution. The resolution cannot be better.

Something of the character of the effects of the finite resolution of optical systems is suggested by the diagrams of Fig. 12|14, which shows the images of two points that are very close, as two stars, where the stars are photographed (or seen) with a telescope of large aperture (a) and a telescope of small aperture (b). Below the images the brightness (or perhaps the density on the photographic plate) is plotted as it varies along a line through the centers of the images. We see how the two points might not be resolved by the smaller telescope because the large diffraction patterns overlap too much.

The designer of audio systems is faced with the inverse problem. The highest notes ordinarily written into music range to

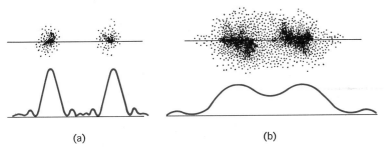

(a)   (b)

FIG. 12|14
The intensity of light from two point objects viewed by optical systems with different apertures.

about 4 octaves about middle A, the frequency of such notes being about 440×16, a little less than 8000 Hz. The wavelength at 440 Hz is about 75 cm, at 440×16 Hz it is about 4 cm. Overtones, which give character to the tones, run even higher; the clash of cymbals involves important intensities up to the audio limit. This audio limit is a function of the age of the listener: the limit is near 25,000 Hz for small children (and dogs); it is about 18,000 Hz, on the average, at the age of 20, about 13,000 Hz at age 40, and so on. The emitter of the sound must be smaller than a wavelength or else diffraction patterns will be set up so that the intensity will vary sharply with angle in front of the speaker. On the other hand, it is difficult to design a speaker that will inject much power into sound at frequencies such that the wavelength of the sound is very much larger than the speaker. As a result of these considerations, high-fidelity speakers are designed in two (or more) parts, which are essentially separate speakers. A large speaker, the woofer, generates the low-frequency, long-wavelength sounds, and a very small speaker, the tweeter, generates the short-wavelength, high-frequency sounds.

12 | 5 *Diffraction from a double slit*

The diffraction of a plane wave by several apertures is particularly important. We consider, first, the transmission of waves through two slits, a problem that contains all the principles of more complex situations. The diagram of Fig. 12 | 15 illustrates the diffraction of a wave train incident upon two apertures. The apertures are assumed to be sufficiently small compared to the wavelength so that the waves from each aperture proceed in circular arcs. An inspection of the pattern of interference between the waves from the two apertures shows that far from the apertures there are regions where the two sets of waves are always in phase and reinforce each other. In the diagram of Fig. 12 | 15 this constructive interference between the waves from the two apertures takes place along the solid lines marked on the diagram; along these lines the crests of the waves from the two sources coincide and the troughs coincide. Waves that procede in these directions have the largest possible amplitudes and the largest possible intensities. Along the dashed lines the crests of the waves from one source coincide with the troughs from the

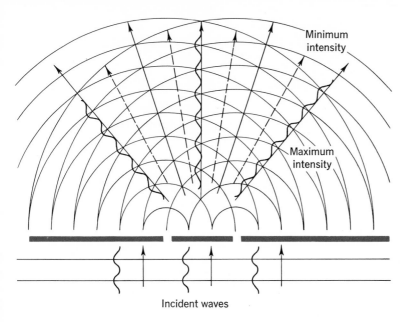

FIG. 12|15
A construction showing the formation of maxima and minima in the amplitude of waves transmitted through a pair of slits.

other source, cancellation takes place, and the amplitudes and intensities along these lines are zero.

Diffraction patterns of the type just discussed also result when the scattering elements are bars rather than slits. Similar patterns result from diffraction by sets of holes, or from diffraction by sets of regularly spaced objects, such as the atoms in a crystal or in a molecule. The scattered waves may be light waves, sound waves, X-rays, or the de Broglie waves representing the density of electrons or neutrons. Not only is the principle the same as that for the scattering by slits, but the detailed calculations are often hardly more complicated.

The diagram of Fig. 12|16 shows the same type of pattern in a slightly different way in order to develop a quantitative relation between the wavelength of the light, the distance between the apertures, and the angular deviations of the different maxima. Again plane waves are incident normally on a barrier provided with two slits. The aperture, a, of each slit is sufficiently small that the plane wave is diffracted appreciably, and the wave is emitted from each slit over an angle $\phi = \lambda/a$. The diffraction patterns from the two slits overlap on the screen, which is far away from the slits. That is, over an appreciable area the screen is illuminated by waves from both slits. At point i the waves from

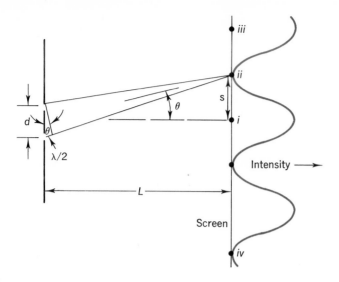

FIG. 12|16
*Construction showing
the character of a
double-slit diffraction
pattern.*

each slit travel the same distance and are therefore in phase. The amplitude at that point is thus twice as great as that contributed from each slit alone. At point *ii* the two waves have traveled distances that differ by half a wavelength. Here there is destructive interference and the amplitude is zero. If the wavelength, λ, is much smaller than the spacing between the slits, d, the angle θ is just the ratio of the side of the small triangle opposite the angle, $\lambda/2$, divided by one of the sides, d. Then

$$\theta = \frac{\frac{1}{2}\lambda}{d}$$

$$= \frac{\lambda}{2d}$$

If the distance between the two apertures, d, is very small compared to the distance to the screen where the intensities are measured, the triangle with sides s and L is similar to the triangle with sides $\lambda/2$ and d. Therefore,

$$\theta = \frac{\lambda}{2d}$$

$$= \frac{s}{L}$$

At point *iii* the difference is a full wavelength and the amplitude is again a maximum: the angle of deviation here is $\theta = \lambda/d$, which is the angular distance between bright bands on the screen. At point *iv* the difference in distance is $3\lambda/2$; the angle is $\theta = 3\lambda/2d$, and the amplitude is again zero. These bands will continue as long as $\theta \ll \phi$; for angles such that $\theta > \phi$ there will be no diffracted light to interfere. In general, the angle between any two neighboring maxima or neighboring minima will be

$$\theta = \frac{\lambda}{d}$$

and the distance between the two adjacent maxima or minima will be

$$s = L\theta$$
$$= \frac{L\lambda}{d}$$

The results are not modified very much if there are more than two slits—for example, *n* slits. The maxima are still separated by the angle $\theta = \lambda/d$, but the amplitudes are now equal to *n* times the amplitude from one slit. Since intensities are proportional to the square of amplitudes, the intensities at the maxima are equal to n^2 times the intensity from a single slit. For waves of a given frequency, the energy of the wave is proportional to the intensity or square of the amplitude. It is nearly obvious that *n* slits will admit $\frac{1}{2}n$ times as much energy as two slits. If the maxima are $\frac{1}{4}n^2$ times as bright it follows that they must be $\frac{1}{2}n$ times narrower. The multislit pattern is similar to the two-slit pattern, but the maxima are $\frac{1}{4}n^2$ times as bright and $\frac{1}{2}n$ times as narrow as for the two-slit pattern.

12 |6   *Coherence and incoherence*

In the interference situations we have discussed, the phase differences between the two or more sources is a result of the geometry of the problem and is constant in time. This results, always, because there is but one individual cause of the phenomena. Since there is but one discrete cause, all subsequent effects are related in a definite way. The diffraction from two slits presents an illuminating example of this. Although the diffraction pattern from the two slits results from the interference of waves from two sources—the two slits—these two sources oscillate with a specific and constant relative phase because their oscillation, in turn, results from one particular source, the source of the plane wave incident upon the slits. The difference in phase between the waves that pass through the two slits results solely from any difference in total path length between the source and the final position. We give a special name to sources, such as the two slits, that are so connected causally that the phase difference between the two sources is constant in time. We say that the sources are *coherent*. The interference behaviors we have discussed all refer to situations such that the individual sources are coherent.

When the sources are not connected causally the phase difference between two sources will be determined essentially by accident; the value of the phase difference can be any value at random. Any two sources will have a definite phase relationship, but many situations that are of interest actually involve millions of individual sources. If the double-slit diffraction pattern of light is considered, the source of light is only nominally one particular filament. Actually there are enormous numbers of separate, infinitesimal, incoherent sources with no particular phase relation between them. But the light passing through the two slits onto the screen has a definite interference pattern because the difference for the two paths from each infinitesimal source is always the same. However, if we replace the single source, as in Fig. 12|17a, by two separate sources, as Fig. 12|17b, we will get no interference patterns. The two sources are now *incoherent*. Although the phase difference between any two infinitesimal sources of S_1 and S_2 will have a definite value, this value will be randomly distributed for many pairs of sources. The amplitude A' representing the sum of representative amplitudes from infinitesimal sources A_1 and A_2 will have the form

$$A' = \sqrt{A_1{}^2 + A_2{}^2 + 2A_1 A_2 \cos \theta}$$

where θ is the phase angle between the two amplitudes. If we take the average of very many pairs of amplitudes such as $\mathbf{A_1}$ and $\mathbf{A_2}$, the phase angle θ between the amplitudes will vary randomly between 0 and 180°. The average value of $\cos \theta$ will then be equal to zero; this is evident from an examination of a graph of the values of $\cos \theta$ plotted against θ; $\cos \theta$ is negative as much as it is positive, so the average value is zero. Constructive interference, where the two vectors make an angle θ greater than 90°, and destructive interference, where the angle is less than 90°, are equally

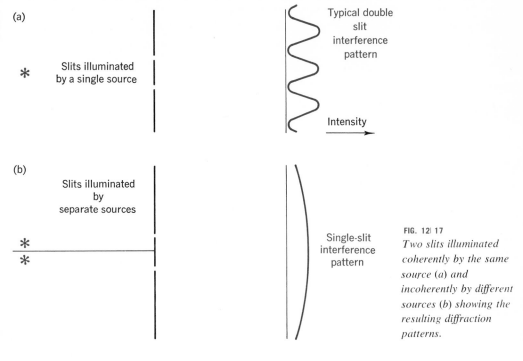

FIG. 12| 17
*Two slits illuminated
coherently by the same
source (a) and
incoherently by different
sources (b) showing the
resulting diffraction
patterns.*

common. Then, on the average,

$$A' = \sqrt{A_1^2 + A_2^2}$$

or

$$A'^2 = A_1^2 + A_2^2$$

Since the intensity is proportional to the square of the amplitude for any wave phenomenon,

$$I' = I_1 + I_2$$

Where I is the average intensity. When the sources are incoherent, the total *intensity* is the sum of the individual intensities. When the sources are coherent the total *amplitude* is equal to the sum of the vector amplitudes.

12| 7   *The classical uncertainty principle*

Information is lost when a wave passes through an aperture. This is evident when we consider the limitations of optical instruments that result from diffraction. If the aperture of a telescope or

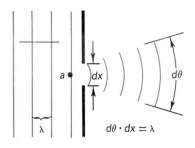

FIG. 12I18
*Diffraction pattern
produced by a plane
wave incident on a
narrow slit.*

camera is no larger than that of the human eye, it will be impossible to determine the character of the mountains of the moon no matter what the magnifying power of the telescope or the enlargement ratio of the camera film; it will be impossible to show that the planet Jupiter is a round disk in the sky rather than a point. Information about the mountains and the shape of the planet is lost as a result of the diffractive effects of the telescope aperture or camera aperture, and this information cannot be regained by any program of magnification. The knowledge of the position of a ray of light from the object—we know that the ray passes through the aperture of the telescope or camera—places a restriction on the accuracy with which the direction can be known. Figure 12I18 shows a plane wave incident upon a very small aperture. The direction of the plane wave is precisely defined before the barrier; after the barrier this information is lost—the wave moves out in all directions, independent of the original direction. An observer to the right of the barrier cannot deduce the direction of the original wave: information is lost.

The character of the uncertainty involved is further suggested by the following problem: determine the direction of motion of a point a of a wave. We must answer this in some operational way, and we can do so by isolating this point and following the resultant effects. We can isolate the point by allowing that part of the wave to pass through a barrier that stops the rest of the wave. This procedure is illustrated in Fig. 12I18. Of course, the aperture in the barrier will have a finite width dx which will encompass the position of a. After the wave passes through the barrier it will be spread out by diffraction over an angular interval

$$d\theta = \frac{\lambda}{dx} \qquad\qquad (12I1)$$

and we will not known the direction point *a* took within this error. We know the position of *a* within an amount *dx* and the direction it took within the amount *d*θ. If we had relaxed the accuracy we required of our knowledge of the position of *a* by increasing *dx*, we would have decreased our uncertainty in the direction *d*θ. But the product $dx\, d\theta = \lambda$ cannot be improved; there is a fundamental uncertainty principle: we cannot know both the position of a wave, *x*, and its direction, θ, better than a product $dx\, d\theta = \lambda$.

It is desirable to examine the impossibility of simultaneously measuring these two *complimentary* quantities—the direction and the position of a portion of a wave—in a more complete manner. If a wave travels in an arbitrary direction as shown in Fig. 12|19, there will be a wave form traveling along any other direction such as the *x*-direction shown in the diagram. Indeed, the velocity of the wave along that line will be greater than the velocity of the wave in the direction of the wave propagation even as the wavelength of the wave form along the *x*-direction line will be longer than the normal wavelength. Most of us have observed this pattern as ocean waves traveling at an angle with the shore strike a breakwater. The position of the impact of the crest of the wave with the breakwater moves along the breakwater at a very high speed—a speed greater than the normal speed of the waves. Also, the distance between the breaking waves along the breakwater will be greater than the normal distance between crests.

The pattern of crests and troughs along the breakwater will have a normal wave form, and we can therefore write an equation that represents such a wave form in an arbitrary direction such as the *x*-direction as

$$A = A_0 \cos(\omega t - k_x x)$$

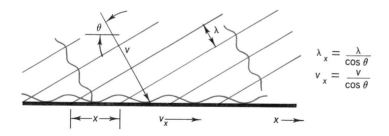

$$\lambda_x = \frac{\lambda}{\cos\theta}$$
$$v_x = \frac{v}{\cos\theta}$$

FIG. 12 |19

A plane wave incident on a barrier at an angle.

where k_x is equal to 2π times the number of waves per meter in the x-direction; also $k_x = 2\pi/\lambda_x$ where λ_x is the wavelength in the x-direction, in this case along the breakwater.

If θ is the angle between the direction of propagation of the wave and the reference direction, such as the x-direction along the breakwater in Fig. 12|19, the following relations are seen to hold:

$$\lambda_x = \frac{\lambda}{\cos\theta} \quad \text{and} \quad v_x = \frac{v}{\cos\theta}$$

where λ is the normal wavelength of the wave and v is the velocity of the wave; v_x is the velocity of the wave along the x-direction or the direction of the breakwater.

When the wave passes through a slit of width dx, which defines the position in the x direction of a part of the wave, the wave will be diffracted by the slit (see Fig. 12|20). Notice that a part of the wave of width of a will pass through the slit so that the spread in angle after the slit will be equal to

$$d\theta = \frac{\lambda}{a} \tag{12|2}$$

and some of the information concerning the direction of the incident wave will be lost.

We can express a in terms of dx:

$$a = dx \sin\theta$$

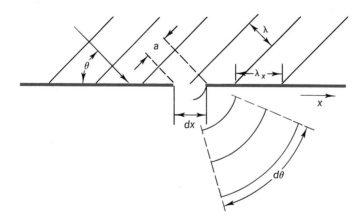

FIG. 12|20
The diffraction pattern resulting from the incidence of a plane wave at an angle on a barrier with an aperture.

Then

$$d\theta = \frac{\lambda}{dx \sin \theta}$$

Also

$$\cos \theta = \frac{\lambda}{\lambda_x}$$

$$= \lambda \frac{k_x}{2\pi}$$

or

$$k_x = \frac{2\pi}{\lambda} \cos \theta$$

In our study of simple harmonic motion we showed that if

$$x = A \cos \omega t$$

Then

$$\frac{dx}{dt} = -A\omega \sin \omega t$$

Of course this is a general relation no matter what the meaning of the symbols. Setting

$$\omega = 1$$
$$t = \theta$$
$$x = k_x$$
$$A = \frac{2\pi}{\lambda}$$

we have

$$\frac{dk_x}{d\theta} = -\left(\frac{2\pi}{\lambda}\right) \sin \theta$$

Then using Eq. (12 | 2) for $d\theta$ and simplifying,

$$dk_x = -\frac{2\pi}{dx}$$

and

$$dk_x \, dx = 2\pi \tag{12 | 3}$$

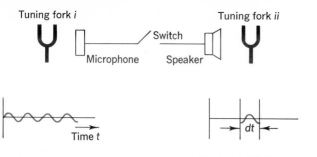

Time t

Amplitude A of emitted wave

dt

Amplitude A of transmitted wave

FIG. 12|21
*A schematic system
designed to transmit a
wave for a short time.*

We drop the minus sign as being irrelevant for our purpose, which is to relate the uncertainty in k_x, the wave number, with the uncertainty in dx. This form is not particularly more useful than relation (12|2) in expressing the relation between the constraints in position and the uncertainties in direction of a wave, but it lends itself more clearly to an understanding of the parallel uncertainty relation that connects the complementary quantities time and frequency, and finally to an understanding of the Heisenberg uncertainty principle of quantum mechanics.

Since the quantities ωt and $k_x x$ have mathematically equivalent positions in the equation $A = A_0 \cos(\omega t - k_x x)$, which describes the projection of the wave in the x-direction, and since the results of the last paragraphs, though they were derived from a specific physical model, must apply to the mathematically abstract description itself, independent of that physical picture, a similar diffraction effect must exist relating time, t, and angular frequency, ω. Therefore it follows that

$$d\omega\, dt = 2\pi \qquad\qquad (12|4)$$

If a wave is constrained to a short period of time, dt, we must lose information concerning the angular frequency, ω. What does this mean?

It is especially useful as an illustration to consider the diffraction in time of sound waves. For that purpose we construct a special situation as shown in Fig. 12|21. We have on the left a tuning fork, i, emitting into a microphone a continuous sound of a definite frequency; for example, A at 440 Hz. The sound is transmitted electrically, through a circuit that contains a switch, to a speaker on the right and another tuning fork, ii. If the switch is kept closed, the second tuning fork will begin to vibrate in resonance with the first tuning fork if its natural frequency is also 440 Hz. If the natural frequency of the second tuning fork is different, it will not vibrate with any appreciable amplitude. If the second fork has a natural frequency of 450 Hz, it will start moving when the switch is thrown closed under the small buffeting of the sound waves, but soon the fork will be out of phase with the waves and the sound waves will damp the small motion of the fork. The first few sound waves will reinforce the vibration of the fork—they will push the prongs of the fork approximately in phase. But after a short time the motion of the fork will be out of phase with the impulses from the speaker, and those impulses will actually slow down the motion of the fork. As a result, after some time the transient motion of the fork at its natural frequency of 450 Hz will be damped out and disappear and the fork will vibrate with a very small amplitude at the frequency of 440 Hz of the impulses from the speaker. The amplitude developed in any tuning fork exposed to the speaker will be very small except for those forks which have very nearly the same natural frequency of 440 Hz as the tuning fork at the microphone and are then in resonance with the impulses from the speaker. (See Section 9 | 6 on resonance.)

Figure 12 | 22a represents a plot of the amplitude of vibration of such tuning forks plotted against the natural frequency of the fork where the broadcast frequency is 440 Hz. This is a typical resonance curve where the width of the resonance peak depends upon the friction generated by the vibration of the forks. If there is very little friction, and the fork will vibrate for a very long time after the excitation is stopped, the width of the peak will

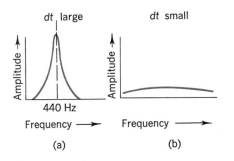

FIG. 12 | 22
The amplitude of the oscillations of tuning forks as a function of the natural frequency of the forks. The forks are disturbed by waves of a definite frequency of different durations.

be very small; if the friction is considerable, damping the vibration quickly, the width of the peak will be larger.

Quite a different result will occur if the switch is thrown on and off very quickly, allowing the note through for a very short time *dt*. On the left-hand side of Fig. 12|21 we see the wave emitted by fork *i* into the microphone; on the right-hand side we see a similar schematic representation of the wave transmitted by the system when the switch is closed only for the short time *dt*. Only one pulse will now pass through the speaker, and it will set all tuning forks in motion equally. Each gets "hit" once—there is no question of reinforcement, in or out of phase. The resulting amplitudes are shown as Fig. 12|22b. All frequencies are equally excited. From an operational view—from a view that has meaning only in measurement—the time-constrained wave contains all frequencies equally, and all knowledge of the original frequency is lost. This is analogous to diffraction through a narrow slit in space. The space-constrained, diffracted wave contains all directions, and all knowledge of the original direction is lost through the constraint. The time duration and the frequency of a wave are then complementary quantities as position and direction.

If the switch is thrown closed a longer time, but still not extremely long, there will be some selection of tuning forks excited. A typical situation is suggested by the graph of Fig. 12|23, where the switch is thrown closed for $\frac{1}{10}$ sec. Again the amplitude of the tuning forks at the speaker end of the system is plotted against their natural frequency. The width of the peak in the curve, *df*, will be described approximately by the relation

$$d\omega \, dt = 2\pi \qquad \text{or} \qquad df \, dt = 1 \qquad \text{or} \qquad df = \frac{1}{dt} \qquad (12\,|\,5)$$

The uncertainty in direction of the waves emitted from a source does not depend on whether the source is secondary, such as a

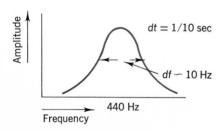

FIG. 12 |23

The amplitude induced in similar tuning forks plotted as a function of frequency when the forks are excited by a wave at a frequency of 440 hz for a time of $\frac{1}{10}$ sec.

slit passing waves originating elsewhere, or a primary source, such as an atom. In either case, $d\theta = \lambda/a$, where a is the dimension of the effective source. In the same way, the uncertainty in frequency need not result from a constraint in the time of transmission of the waves; the constraint will more likely result from the character of the source. This condition has definite musical consequences. If the note A is played briefly, as a short note on a piano where the felt damps the note very quickly, the note will be slightly blurred. If the note sounds for only $\frac{1}{10}$ sec, the note will not represent a sharp frequency of 440 Hz; the frequency will have a spread of about 10 Hz: there will be an appreciable intensity at a frequency as low as 430 Hz and as high as 450 Hz.

Indeed, precise frequencies are operationally impossible. A tuning fork cannot have a completely definite frequency unless all friction is eliminated and it continues to vibrate forever. If the sound dies out in 100 sec, there must be a spread in frequency of about 1 Hz. The time of emission of a typical light wave from an atom is of the order of 10^{-8} sec; there is thus an uncertainty or spread in the frequency the atom emits of about 10^8 Hz. If the atom collides with another atom very quickly, extinguishing the radiation, the spread in frequency is increased. Measurements of such spreads in frequency make it possible to determine how often atoms collide, which is in turn proportional to the density of material around the atoms. By using these principles it is then possible to measure the spreads of frequencies in the atoms that make up the atmospheres of stars and therefore determine the densities of the surfaces of the stars.

PROBLEMS

12| 1 Wave trains from two different sources overlap near a particular point. The amplitude at that point is equal to A when either of the wave trains is blocked by some obstacle. The frequency of the two waves is the same.

(a) If the two waves are in phase, what is the value of the resultant amplitude? If one of the waves is blocked how much will the intensity be reduced?

(b) What will the intensity be if the waves are 90° out of phase? If the waves are 180° out of phase?

12|2   Waves from six different sources reach a point such that the second lags the first by 60°, the third lags the second by 60°, and so on. The amplitudes of each individual wave at the point is equal to A; the frequencies are the same. What is the resultant amplitude?

12|3   Three identical small audio speakers are driven in phase from the same oscillator in such a way that the wavelength of the sound they emit is 6 m. The speakers are placed 2 m apart in a straight line. A detector (microphone) is placed far from the speakers in the same line. If the intensity at the detector is equal to I when only one of the speakers is connected, what will the intensity be when speakers 1 and 2 are connected? When 1, 2, and 3 are connected?

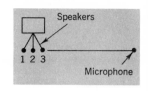

12|4   Each of two radio antennas is designed to radiate radio waves (electromagnetic waves) having a wavelength of 20 m. Each antenna, alone, radiates energy isotropically. The two antennas are placed 10 m apart on a turntable as shown. When each transmits alone, an observer far away records an intensity of I.

(*a*) When both antennas are transmitting and the turntable is rotating slowly, what are the maximum and minimum intensities recorded by the observer?

(*b*) If the intensity emitted by one of the antennas is increased by a factor of 4, what will be the maximum and minimum intensities recorded by the observer in terms of I?

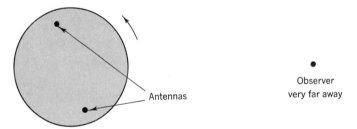

12|5   (*a*) A human hair is set between two microscope slides as shown in the diagram. The slides are illuminated at normal incidence with yellow light that has a wavelength of 0.5×10^{-6} m. From the edge of the slides to the position of the hair one can see 25 black bands by reflected light. What is the diameter of the hair?

   (*b*) When the system is viewed with white light, the pattern near the edge of the slides shows a rainbow-like pattern. Describe the procession of colors one would expect to see. (White light contains all colors: violet $= 0.4 \times 10^{-6}$ m, green $= 0.5 \times 10^{-6}$ m, yellow $= 0.6 \times 10^{-6}$, red $= 0.7 \times 10^{-6}$ m.)

12 | 6 A large box with thin plastic walls is placed between a source of sound and an observer. The wavelength of the sound in air is 2 m. The box is filled with a helium–neon mixture in which the speed of sound is twice the speed of sound in air. The box is designed so that the thickness, t, of the box can be changed continuously. As the thickness of the box changes, the observer hears maxima and minima of intensity. What are two values of t at which the transmitted intensity is a maximum?

12 | 7 Two parallel slits 0.1 mm apart are illuminated normally, from far away, by a single light of wavelength 5.0×10^{-7} m. A viewing screen is 0.8 m from the slits.

(a) How far from the central bright line is the next bright line?

(b) How far from the central bright line is the third dark line?

12 | 8 A continuous sound wave is emitted by a horn at a frequency such that the wavelength is 1 m. Five-hundred meters from the source is a high barrier with a gap in the barrier 5 m wide. Five-hundred meters on the other side of the wall an observer walks laterally and finds that the sound changes from zero to maximum and back to zero as he walks along. How far is it from minimum to minimum?

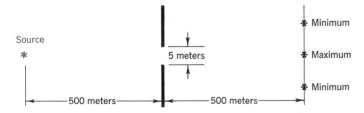

12 | 9 A continuous sound wave is emitted by a device at a frequency such that the wavelength is 1 m. One-hundred meters from the source is a high barrier with two slits 10 m apart (from center to center) and 1 m wide. One-hundred meters on the other side of the wall an observer finds a particular position at which he hears the sound at a maximum. What distance, *s*, must he move laterally so that the sound disappears?

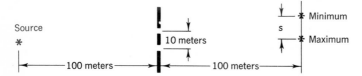

12 | 10   What must be the diameter of a radio telescope to achieve the resolution of the human eye? (The telescope is designed for 20-cm waves, the eye for a wavelength of 0.5×10^{-6} m.)

12 | 11   Light of wavelength 5×10^{-7} m is scattered from a suspension of opaque small particles in water. The light is scattered in such a way that the scattered intensity varies with angle as shown in the figure. It is known that all of the particles are the same size. Approximately how big are the particles?

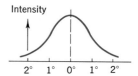

12 | 12   The intensity of fast neutrons scattered from atomic nuclei varies with angle according to the figure. If the de Broglie wavelength of the neutrons is 10^{-16} m, approximately how big is the nucleus?

12 | 13   A large telescope having an aperture of 1 m cannot quite resolve a distant double star, though the system is quite bright. The director of the observatory covers up the center of the telescope as shown, and the two stars are then found to be resolved on the photographic plates used to photograph the stars. Use a one-dimensional model to explain how the improvement was achieved.

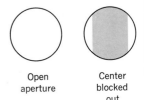

Open aperture

Center blocked out

12 | 14   Ten audio speakers are set in a line so that the speakers are 1 m apart. They are connected to the same electronic system so that

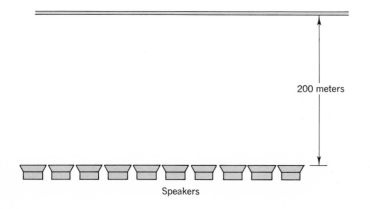

200 meters

Speakers

they emit sound at a frequency such that the wavelength is 2 m and the ten speakers are in phase. Draw a graph showing the relative variation in intensity across a line 200 m in front of the line of speakers. Only moderate accuracy is required.

12|15   An experimenter constructs an instrument that is very much like a large stethoscope. Two horns, acting as receivers of the sound, are placed 5 m apart, and the sound is directed from the horns along tubes that are each 5 m long to a single outlet, which is pressed to the ear of an observer. An object, that emits a steady sound whose wavelength is 1 m moves in a straight line parallel to, and 100 m in front of, the horns. The observer notes that the recorded intensity varies sharply as the source of the sound moves slowly, in a straight line, in front of the line of the horns. Draw a graph of the intensity the observer hears as a function of the position of the object along its path. Only moderate accuracy is required. How will the pattern be changed if the length of the tube leading from one of the horns is decreased $\frac{1}{2}$m?

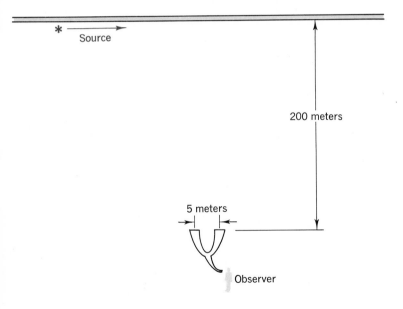

12|16   (*a*) Two tuning forks that emit sound with a wavelength of 10 cm are placed in absorbing boxes with narrow slits as shown. Discuss qualitatively the intensity patterns at the position of the distant screen.

(*b*) Two lamps that emit light with a wavelength of 0.5×10^{-6}

m are placed in black boxes with slits as in the figure. Discuss qualitatively the intensity patterns at the position of the distant screen.

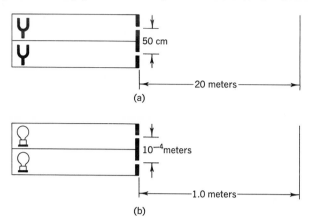

(a)

(b)

12|17 Soldiers marching in step are sometimes told to break step when crossing a bridge. Very rarely this practice may be sensible. Discuss the source of the possible danger and the characteristics of a bridge that might make it completely safe for men out of step but dangerous if they are in step. How would you measure the *two* important characteristics of the bridge that are relevant to your inquiry?

12|18 Assume that the index of refraction of the glass from which a lens is ground is equal to 1.60. Assume that you have a wide variety of transparent substances with different indices of refraction and that you have methods of coating these substances onto glass in a controlled fashion. If you wish to coat the lens so that a minimum amount of light is reflected from the face of the lens, approximately what index of refraction and what thickness would you choose? (The velocity of light in a medium is equal to the velocity in air divided by the index of refraction.)

12|19 The reflected light from a coated lens appears to be purple; a careful analysis shows that it is actually a mixture of red and violet. Why is this the case?

12|20 The light from certain atom in a gas is known to consist of just one almost discrete wavelength, $\lambda = 0.5 \times 10^{-6}$ m, when the gas is at low pressure and collisions are infrequent. At a certain high pressure it is noted that the wavelength is spread out to 0.5×10^{-6} m ± 0.1 percent. About how often do collisions occur at this pressure? ($f\lambda = c = 3 \cdot 10^{8}$ m/sec. Consider that each collision interrupts the emission of the light.)

THE STUDY of the behavior of waves in situations such that the wave length is very small compared to the magnitudes of all the relevant apertures and obstructions is called *geometric optics*. When all of the angles of diffraction, $\theta = \lambda/a$, where a is the magnitude of the objects and apertures, are sufficiently small, it is useful to make the approximation that we can neglect these diffraction effects and treat waves moving in a homogeneous medium as traveling in straight lines. The error or deviation from a straight line will be about equal to θ. In particular, we introduce and use the concept of a ray. A *ray* is defined as the path of a small portion of a wave front, such as that which might be determined by the position of a very small source and the position of a very small aperture, all taken in the limit of vanishing wavelength or vanishing diffraction.

The term *geometric* results from the use of straight lines and hence geometric constructions in the development of conclusions concerning such waves. The most common situation such that the wavelength is very much smaller than magnitudes of relevant apertures and obstructions is found in the observation of light on a macroscopic scale; hence our use of the term *optics*. Specifically, we will generally talk about light in this section. However, our conclusions will be valid for any wave system in an environment such that diffraction is not important. The conclusions that follow, then, hold for sound waves, all electromagnetic waves (including light), and the de Broglie waves that describe the behavior of matter.

Although we will finally consider geometric optics in a manner such that the wave nature of the light will be irrelevant, we will develop the theorems that express the behavior of rays at an interface through consideration of the wave nature of light. We noted in our study of one-dimensional waves that waves are reflected at any discontinuity of the physical medium that results in a change in wave velocity. Waves in a string are reflected with a change of phase if the end of the string is secured and immovable. If the end of the string is free to move laterally, the wave will be reflected without a change of phase. If there is a discontinuity in the physical character of the medium—for example, if the mass per unit length of the string changes abruptly at a particular point—the wave will be reflected at this point. If the wave moves from a region where the string is less massive to a region where the string is more massive, a portion of the wave will be reflected with a change in phase and a portion will be transmitted. Equally, if the wave moves from the massive region to a region less massive, a portion will be transmitted and a portion will be reflected. In any case, a wave is reflected at any discontinuity in the physical character of the medium that results in a change in velocity of the wave. Indeed, the magnitude of the reflection is dependent solely upon the change in velocity and therefore describes the discontinuity. We have shown that the velocity of a wave in a string is equal to $\sqrt{T/d}$, where T is the tension and d the mass per unit length. The tension will necessarily be the same throughout a taut string, and the velocity will change at the point that d changes.

Very much the same situation obtains for a wave in two or three dimensions. Such a wave is also reflected at a line or surface representing the boundary between regions in which the velocity of the wave differs. Again a wave traveling from a region of high velocity to a region of low velocity will be reflected with a change in phase at the boundary. A wave traveling from a region of low velocity to a region of high velocity will be reflected without a change in phase. There is no question of the direction of reflection of the one-dimensional wave: the wave is simply reflected backward. The situation is more complicated when we consider wave fronts in two or three dimensions. In an isotropic medium the

direction of a wave is the direction perpendicular to the wave
front: this direction will in general be changed upon reflection.
We can understand this change in direction of propagation by
considering directly the change in direction of the wave front.

First let us review the meaning and importance of the wave
front by studying its propagation. Consider the wave front of
a plane wave at a particular time, $t = 0$. In order to be concrete
we might consider, for example, an essentially linear ripple on a
surface of water. Each point of the ripple constitutes a disturbance that sends out circular wavelets of its own according to
Huygens' principle. At a certain later time, $t = t'$, as in Fig. 13 | 1,
the wave will be recreated on a line that is tangent to all the
individual circles at a distance vt', where v is the velocity of the
wave and t' is the elapsed time. The wavelets from each point of
the previous position of the wave front will add coherently to
produce the new wave front on the line of this tangent. At any
other position the contributions from the individual wavelets will

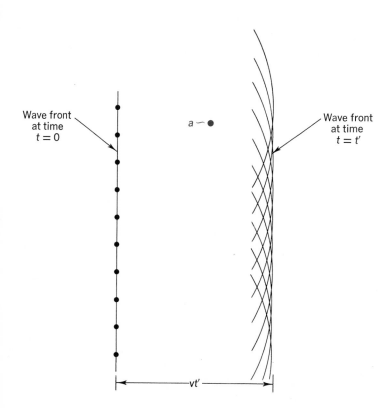

Wave front
at time
$t = 0$

a

Wave front
at time
$t = t'$

vt'

FIG. 13 | 1

*The construction of a
wave front as the
tangent to a set of
Huygens' wavelets.
The wave front at time
$t = t'$ is the tangent
common to all the
circular wavelets. The
sum of the amplitudes of
all the wavelets is zero
at any point behind the
line of tangents, such as
point a in the diagram.*

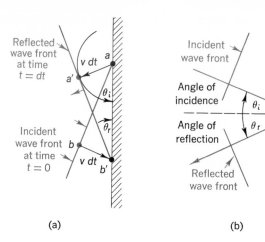

FIG. 13 |2
Diagram showing that the angle of incidence is equal to the angle of reflection.

exactly cancel out so there will be no disturbance behind the wave. We may consider that the wave propagates in this way.

We see such a wave front in Fig. 13|2a moving toward a discontinuity in a medium. We pick two particular points on this wave front—point a, which is already at the discontinuity, and point b, which is some distance away—and construct Huygens' wavelets such that after a time dt the wavelet from point b moving in the direction perpendicular to the wave front will have struck the barrier. The wavelet from point a will already have been deflected; its position is shown by the tangent $a'b'$ drawn in the diagram. The Huygens' wavelets from intermediate points are reflected from the barrier so that they are tangent again to the line $a'b'$, the front of the reflected wave. The direction of motion of a wave is perpendicular to the wave front, as shown by the colored arrows in Fig. 13|2a.

To determine the relationships between these directions we first consider the relationships between the triangle $bb'a$ and $ab'a$. There are similar right triangles sharing the same hypotenuse, the distance from a to b'. Therefore the angles θ_i and θ_r are equal. These angles are in turn equal to the angle of incidence and the angle of reflection as shown in diagram 13|2b. The angle of incidence, θ_i, is defined as the angle between the direction of the incoming plane wave and the perpendicular to the reflecting surface. The angle of reflection, θ_r, is the angle between the direction of the reflected wave and the perpendicular to the surface. Our conclusion is that these two angles are equal.

$$\theta_i = \theta_r \qquad\qquad\qquad\qquad\qquad\qquad (13|1)$$

Although we have discussed plane waves and plane surfaces, the results are quite general, since most varieties of waves and most varieties of surfaces can be approximated adequately by plane surfaces over sufficiently small intervals.

13|2   *Refracted rays*

Again, in a one-dimensional situation the direction of the transmitted wave is completely defined. It is simply the forward direction. In a two- or three-dimensional situation the direction of a wave front may be, and generally is, changed as the wave moves from a region characterized by one velocity to a region characterized by another velocity. We can study this *refraction* of waves using essentially the same ideas and principles we encountered in the discussion of the reflection of waves. Figure 13|3a shows a wave front impinging upon the boundary between two media: the velocity of the wave is v in one medium; it is v' in the other medium, where v' is taken, for definiteness in this particular case, as being smaller than v. Again we construct Huygens' wavelets from point a and point b, where the wavelets represent the situation after a time dt. The wavelet from point a will be moving in the medium with velocity v', and therefore the radius of this wavelet will be equal to $v'\, dt$. The radius of the wavelet from point b will be equal to $v\, dt$. Again the tangent constructed to the wavelets from points a and b will determine the position of the wave front $a'b'$ propagated from the wave front ab after a time dt. In the diagram of Fig. 13|3a there are now two right triangles, abb' and $b'a'a$. These two right triangles share a common hypotenuse, $h = ab'$ then:

$$\sin\theta = \frac{v\, dt}{h} \qquad \text{and} \qquad \sin\theta' = \frac{v'\, dt}{h}$$

Dividing the first relation by the second,

$$\frac{\sin\theta}{\sin\theta'} = \frac{v}{v'} \qquad\qquad\qquad\qquad\qquad (13|2)$$

The direction of the wave is perpendicular to the line of the wave front. From diagram 13|3b it may be seen that the angle of incidence is the angle θ, and the angle of the transmitted or refracted

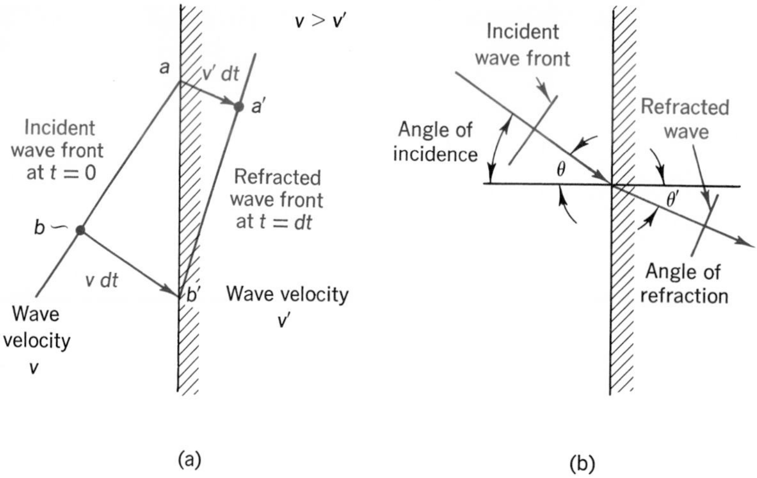

FIG. 13|3
Diagram showing the relation between the angle of incidence and the angle of refraction.

ray, known as the angle of refraction, is θ'. Equation (13|2) is then a relation between the angle of incidence of the wave and the angle of refraction.

In optics it is common practice to describe the characteristics of the medium not by the value of the velocity of light in the medium but by the value of a quantity called the *index of refraction*. The value of n is defined by the relation $n = c/v$, where c is the velocity of light in a vacuum and v is the velocity of light in the medium. The equation representing the relation between the angle of incidence and the angle of refraction then takes the form

$$\frac{\sin \theta}{\sin \theta'} = \frac{n'}{n} \qquad (13|3)$$

where n and n' and the indices of refraction of the two media. This relation was first noticed by a Dutch physicist named Snell, about three hundred years ago, and is called Snell's law.

13|3   *Total internal reflection*

In general, both reflection and refracted transmission will occur when a wave strikes the interface between regions such that different physical properties of the regions result in different indices of refraction. The particular character of refraction results in the interesting phenomenon of *total internal reflection*. Consider a wave passing from a medium where the wave velocity is small (a high index of refraction) to a medium where the wave velocity is large (a low index of refraction) as shown in Fig. 13 | 4a. The angle if incidence, θ, will now be smaller than the angle of refraction, θ'; if the value of sin θ is large, the value of sin θ' may be required to be larger than 1.0 according to the relation of Snell's law. However, according to our ordinary understanding of the function sin θ, this function cannot have a value greater than 1.0. Such a situation, where equations derived to represent certain physical phenomena cease to have any meaning, very often reflects a physical situation such that the premises originally used are no longer valid. If we produce experimentally the situation we have discussed, as shown in Fig. 13 | 4b, we will find that all of the light is reflected at the surface, and there is no transmission at all. We call this *total internal reflection.* One hundred percent of the energy is reflected at the barrier. This is to be compared with the figure of about 95 percent for reflection from a silvered surface.

We are interested in gaining some insight into the cause of

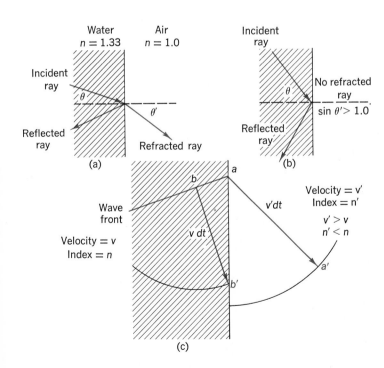

FIG. 13 | 4
Diagrams showing the absence of a refracted ray if the incident angle is greater than the critical angle: (a) reflection and refraction; (b) total internal reflection; (c) analysis of total internal reflection.

the breakdown of our formula. In Fig. 13|4c we show the plane wave as it reaches a barrier and construct Huygen wavelets from point a at the barrier and from point b. We construct the wavelets so that after a time dt the wavelet from point b traveling in the direction of the plane wave will have struck the surface between the two media at b'. The wavelet from point a will have traveled farther, since the velocity v' is greater than the velocity v. The arc labeled a' represents the position of this wavelet. We now see that it is impossible to construct a tangent from point b' to the wavelet a' to the right of the interface. This means that no wave front can be set up: there is no set of loci for a front where wavelets from the wave ab interfere constructively to form a new front on the right-hand side of the intermediate surface. In detail, we will find almost wholly destructive interference in such a way that there is no disturbance at all on most of the right-hand side of the interface.

Very close to the interface on the right-hand side, there will be some total contribution from the different wavelets on the left-hand side of the division. The incoming wave will not be stopped totally at the interface, but will penetrate into the second medium, only to be damped out over a space of about a wavelength. Some energy will pass about one wavelength beyond the interface, but this energy will not penetrate much farther, and no light will be completely transmitted to an observer distant from the interface.

This can be understood in more detail in a reasonably simple fashion. The diagrams of Fig. 13|5 show an incident wave and a refracted wave at an interface, where the incident wave is traveling in a medium of high index of refraction and the region to the right of the interface represents a region of much lower index of refraction. Diagram 13|5a represents a configuration at a particular instant where the angle of incidence is not large and the wave is transmitted; diagram 13|5b represents a similar configuration where the angle of incidence is larger; no transmitted wave exists, and the condition of total internal reflection holds. (The reflected wave is not shown in either case so as to simplify the drawing.)

It is useful to consider the wave along the direction perpendicular to the interface; this is the x-direction in the diagram. In general, the amplitude at any particular time will have a form such as

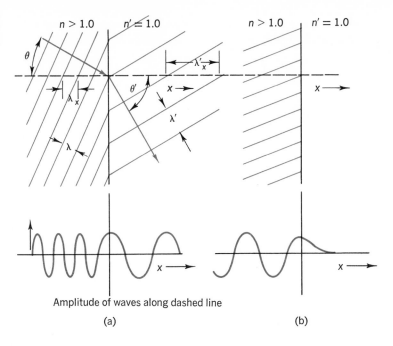

Amplitude of waves along dashed line

(a)   (b)

FIG. 13|5
*The variation of the
amplitude of a wave
along a normal to the
interface (a) when the
angle of incidence is less
than the critical angle
and (b) when the angle
of incidence is greater
than the critical angle.*

$$A(x) = A_0 \sin\left(\frac{2\pi x}{\lambda_x}\right)$$

where A_0 is a constant and λ_x is the wavelength along the x-direction. From the diagram of Fig. 13|5a we see that

$$\lambda'_x = \frac{\lambda'}{\cos\theta'}$$

From the Pythagorean theorem

$$\cos\theta' = \sqrt{1 - \sin^2\theta'}$$

and

$$\lambda'_x = \frac{\lambda'}{\sqrt{1 - \sin^2\theta'}}$$

Taking $n' = 1.0$ (as it would be in air) for convenience and simplicity, noting that $\lambda' = n\lambda$, and from Snell's law that $\sin\theta' = n \sin\theta$,

$$\lambda'_x = \frac{n\lambda}{\sqrt{1 - n^2 \sin^2\theta}}$$

The form of the wave on the right-hand side of the interface can be written as

$$A(x)' = A_0 \sin \left(\frac{2\pi x}{n\lambda} \sqrt{1 - n^2 \sin^2 \theta} \right) \tag{13|4}$$

thus expressing the wave form on the right in terms of the quantities determined by the incident wave on the left of the interface.

Although Eq. (13|4) expresses the relations between the waves in the x-direction on the two sides of the interface in a well-defined manner when transmission occurs, it is also relevant when the angle θ is so large that

$$n \sin \theta > 1.0$$

and total internal reflection occurs. Then the quantity under the square root sign in Eq. (13|4) is negative and the argument of the sine function is imaginary. Here we can use the general rule we developed in Section 9|7 when we considered the solutions of the harmonic-oscillator equation when the frequency was imaginary: we replace the trigonometric function by an exponential, and the form of the wave on the right-hand side of the interface is

$$A(x)' = A_0 \exp \left(-\frac{2\pi x}{n\lambda} \sqrt{n^2 \sin^2 \theta - 1} \right)$$

where the argument was made real by changing the sign of the quantity under the square-root sign. The lower diagrams of Fig. 13|5 show the shapes of the waves on the two sides of the interface when examined at some particular instant.

The phenomenon of total internal reflection has some practical importance in that it allows us to "pipe" light from one point to another. Light that enters a rod of transparent material at a sufficiently small angle that it is totally internally reflected at the boundaries will continue along this rod of material for a very long distance without appreciable attenuation. The reflection in the boundary will be almost perfect, and almost no energy will be lost in each reflection. If the rod is silvered, however, we will find that the transmission of light down the rod will be very much impeded. We have noted that only about 95 percent of the energy is reflected at a silvered surface. Now the energy that passes beyond the surface shown in Fig. 13|5b will be somewhat absorbed by the silvering. The reflection will no longer be near 100 percent, and the energy or light will not be transmitted down the rod as effectively.

13 |4   *Fermat's principle— a variational principle*

There are a number of interesting principles in physics that can be compactly described as *minimal* or *variational* principles. Certain phenomena take place invariably in such a way that some property representative of the phenomena is always a minimum. We find a particularly interesting example of such a minimal principle, and the only one we will discuss in any detail, in *Fermat's principle* of optics. According to Fermat's principle, the path of a ray from one point to another, in any environment described by reflecting and refracting materials, will be such that the ray takes less time along this path than along any nearby path. We illustrate this by considering particular cases of reflection and refraction. In Fig. 13 | 6a three possible paths from a point x to a point x' are shown. Path a is that path such that the angle of reflection is equal to the angle of incidence. Paths b and c are different nearby paths. It can be shown that light will take less time along path a than along either path b or path c, or, for that matter, any other nearby path. Although we will not attempt to prove this rigorously, it is easy enough to show it on a trial-and-error basis by simply constructing the different paths and measuring them with a ruler.

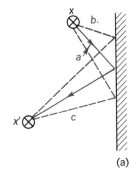

(a)

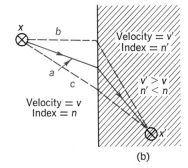

(b)

FIG. 13 |6
Paths of least time for reflected and refracted rays.

The significance and subtlety that result from Fermat's principle might be made more evident by considering the tactics in a possible race. Let us consider two or more runners at a point in a race such that the rule is that one must run to the wall represented by the barrier in Fig. 13⏐6a and from the wall to x', the goal. There is, then, a question of tactics. What route should one take, assuming that one runs at equal speed throughout the race? Again one can show by trial and error, and of course by more elegant means, that the best route is the route a, such that the angle of incidence is equal to the angle of reflection.

In Fig. 13⏐6b we show a similar situation, where now points x and x' lie in regions having different indices of refraction, so that velocity of the wave is different in the two regions. Again we have a choice of different paths. Path a is the path defined by Snell's law, where the ratio of the sine of the angle of incidence to the sine of the angle of refraction is equal to the ratio of the velocities in the two media. Paths b and c are other nearby paths. It is possible to show by trial and error, as well as by more elegant methods, that the path of least time is the path defined by Snell's law. Again it is interesting to discuss this result in terms of a race. Let us consider that the region to the left of the barrier is a region of plowed ground in which it is difficult to run very fast and that a contestant calculates that his velocity will be v over this plowed ground, perhaps 10 mph, and that the region to the right of the barrier is paved in such a manner that he can run with a higher velocity, v', perhaps 15 mph. Again there is a question of tactics. Should one run straight toward the interface between the two media to reduce the amount of time spent in running over the rough ground, as in path b, or run straight toward the mark x' to reduce the total distance traveled to a minimum, as in path c? Over much of this second route one would be running over rough ground and make slower progress. Intuitively, one would probably arrive at some sort of compromise. With a map and measuring instruments one might, by trial and error, determine the best possible path, or the best possible tactics. If we should do so we would find that the best path would be defined by the relation we call Snell's law.

These discussions of reflection and refraction are limited, inasmuch as we have studied only simple plane surfaces and interfaces. If the surfaces are more complicated, there may be many rays traveling along many different paths from point to point. However, for each such ray traveling along its path, the time required if the path be changed infinitesimally will be greater—or, rarely, the same. No infinitesimal variation of the path will result in a quicker route. Fermat's principle is thus a *variational principle*.

This particular variational principle, Fermat's principle of least time, contains both the law of reflection and the law of refraction, which we have derived using Huygens' principle. Although Fermat's principle must be, and is, equivalent to Huygens' principle, it remains an elegant, concise, and powerful statement of the principles of geometric optics.

Other laws of nature can be expressed as variational principles also. The law of mechanics—essentially Newton's laws of motion —are contained in the statement that the path in space and time of a body moving with kinetic energy T and potential energy V must be such that the sum (or integral) of the quantities $(T - V)$ dt, over all the segments of time dt that make up some total time, must be a variational minimum. For example, we might consider the path in space and time of a body falling for 1 sec: in the earth's gravity, the body will fall 5 m. Here, of course, the quantities T and V, and therefore $T - V$, will change as the body falls. If we divide the second up into a thousand parts, dt, and calculate the value of the quantity $T - V$ for each time and multiply that quantity by $\frac{1}{1000}$ sec, the sum of the thousand quantities will be smaller if the body falls 5 m in 1 sec according to the familiar prescription

$$s = \tfrac{1}{2}gt^2$$

where g is the acceleration of gravity, than if any other prescription were tried. Of course, in general, we should make up an infinite number of infinitesimal segments of time and add all of them together. The sum of all of the quantities $(T - V)\,dt$ is called the *action*, and the variation principle is called the *principle of least action*.

The idea that the universe is so designed that one can express important aspects of it in terms of such minimum principles is aesthetically attractive—a sort of economy of nature—and at one time these principles were considered to have a theological importance.

13|5   *The formation of images*

Any set of optical elements that act so as to transfer a variety of rays, starting out in somewhat different directions, from one point to another, is an image-forming system. We call the point from which the rays emerge the *object point* and the point to which the rays converge the *image point*. An extended image of an extended object is formed as a result of the point-to-point correspondence of image points and object points. We say that the object is "mapped" into the image. The mapping may preserve the proportions of the image, changing only the size, or the mapping may result in an image that is distorted, having quite a different aspect than the object. Or the optical system may not produce an image at all; rays that proceed from a particular point on the object may not be returned to any common image point. Of course we are usually most interested in image forming systems.

The use of Fermat's principle allows us to draw some simple qualitative conclusions regarding the simplest of elementary optical systems, a converging lens, and a concave mirror. From Fermat's principle we understand that rays traveling from one point to another travel a path such that light takes a minimum time to make the journey compared to nearby paths. If rays emitted from an object point in slightly different directions are to converge to the same image point, the different paths must be such that light takes the same time along each path. The de-

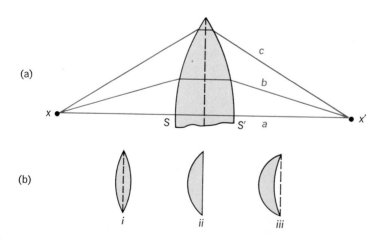

FIG. 13|7
Paths of equal time through a lens. The three lenses shown in (b) are almost equivalent.

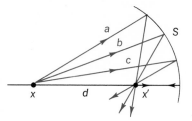

FIG. 13|8

*Paths of equal time for
rays reflected at a
surface.*

sign of an optical element that forms an image is thus reduced
to the design of an element that has the property that all paths,
or at least a large variety of paths, from the object point to the
image point are such that light takes the same time to travel each
path. Such an element is shown in Fig. 13|7a; various rays, *a*,
b, and *c*, are emitted from a point *x* in a medium where the velocity of light is *v*. A section of a medium in which the velocity
of light is smaller, $v' = v/n$, where the index of refraction in the
material is *n*, is then interposed between the object and image
points. The first medium might be air, the second glass. Ray *a*
is slowed in passing through the glass; ray *b* is also slowed in
the glass, but since it passes through less glass it loses less time
in the glass; on the other hand, it has to travel farther in total
distance to the object point, *x'*. The thickness of the glass evi-
dently must be such that these effects just cancel so that rays *a*
and *b* take the same time to go from *x* to *x'*. Ray *c* has the greatest
distance to travel, but it passes almost no time in the slow
medium, and therefore takes just as long to go from *x* to *x'* as
the others.

The condition that all rays, over some angular interval, travel
the same time defines the thickness and shape of the slow
medium, the glass. In general this will not be a simple shape. If
the angles the rays make with each other and the straight line
connecting the points *x* and *x'* are very small, the surfaces *s* and
s' will be nearly parts of circles in two dimensions, or parts of
spheres in three dimensions. As long as the thickness varies
with radius correctly, the lens will refract light in a manner independent of other aspects of the shape. Lenses shaped like *i*,
ii, or *iii*, of Fig. 13|7b will refract light in the same way if the
angles of deviation of the rays are small.

We use the same ideas to determine the shape of a reflector
designed to focus rays from point *x* to point *x'*. The reflector
surface shown in Fig. 13|8 must be designed so that rays *a*, *b*,

and *c* travel for the same time in going from *x* to *x'*. The shape of the surface, *S*, is determined by this requirement. Again the shape is not necessarily simple: however, if the rays make very small angles with respect to the line between *x* and *x'*, the shape of the mirror will be very close to the surface of a sphere.

13|6   *Images formed by a lens*

In general, a lens that will focus rays from an object point, *a*, to converge on an image point, *b*, will also focus rays from a point *a'* near *a* to a point *b'* near *b*. Then light from a set of points making up an object, *O*, will be focused to a conjugate set of points, *I*, which we call the image. The image may be larger or smaller than the object (magnification) and the image may be shaped differently than the object (distortion). However, for any image-forming system, such as a lens, each point on an object will correspond to one particular point on the image. The path of any light ray is unchanged if the direction of the light is reversed, so the object and image positions can be interchanged: any system that will form an image at a point *b* of an object at a point *a* will also form an image at *a* of an object at *b*.

If the angles rays make with the line connecting object and image are not too great, single lenses can be made that will take rays from various object points at different distances from the lens and focus these rays almost exactly at different corresponding image points. We will discuss such practical lenses briefly.

Figure 13|9 shows a lens that brings to focus rays from an object point, *O*, that is very far away—at infinity—to a point *F*. Point *O* is so far away that the rays can be considered to be parallel at the position of the lens. All of these rays are then refracted by the lens to pass through the point *F*, which is called the *focus* of the lens. The distance from this focal point to the

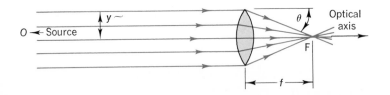

FIG. 13|9
Parallel rays passing through a lens.

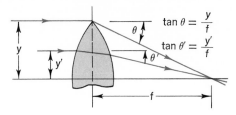

FIG. 13|10
Geometric relations for parallel rays on a lens.

lens is defined as the *focal length, f*, of the lens. This focal length, the distance from the lens to the focus when the object is at infinity, is as much a property of the lens as its aperture and thickness are. We note that for simplicity we consider here "thin" lenses whose physical thickness is small compared to the focal length. Since the position of the rays is not changed if the direction of the light is reversed, light rays emitted from a point source at the focus and passing through the lens will emerge from the lens as a beam of rays parallel to the optical axis.

Rays that are parallel to the optical axis and at a distance y from the axis are deflected in passing through the lens by an angle θ, where $\tan \theta = y/f$. For small angles of deflection, the angle of deflection is proportional to y for all angles of incidence of the ray on the lens: for such a "thin lens" the deflection of all rays is expressed by

$$\theta = \frac{y}{f}$$

and therefore a ray passing through the center of a thin lens (where $y = 0$) is undeflected. These relations are shown graphically by the diagram of Fig. 13|10. The description of a thick lens, where the deflections of the rays are large and the approximation $\theta = \tan \theta$ is not valid, is somewhat more complicated, but not very different in principle.

We are now prepared to discuss the formation of the image, I, of an extended object, O. The arrow marked O in Fig. 13|11 is considered an extended object. On the diagram, the object distance (the distance between the object and the lens) is labeled p and the corresponding image distance is labeled q. The focal length of the lens is f. The rays A and B are especially chosen rays from the head of the arrow O, which is the object: the ray A is defined to be parallel to the optical axis and thus is refracted so as to pass through the focal point of the lens even as all rays

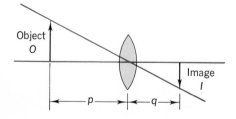

FIG. 13|11
A geometric construction showing the formation of an image by a lens.

parallel to the axis are refracted so as to pass through the focus. The ray B follows a related path, passing through the near focus of the lens and then emerging from the lens parallel to the optical axis just as all rays from a focus that pass through a lens are refracted so as to emerge parallel to the axis. The image distance can now be determined from the object distance and the focal length of the lens as a matter of geometry. No more physics is necessary.

The triangle abc of Fig. 13|11 is similar to the triangle Fdc. And then, from the relations between the corresponding sides of similar triangles

$$\frac{bc}{ab} = \frac{dc}{Fd} \qquad \text{or} \qquad \frac{I+O}{p} = \frac{I}{f}$$

even as the length bc is equal to the sum of the lengths of the object O and the image I, and ab is equal to p, the object distance. Also dc is equal to the image size, I, and Fd is equal to the focal length of the lens, f.

Similarly, the triangle ebc and the triangle Fdb are similar triangles, and

$$\frac{bc}{ce} = \frac{bd}{dF} \qquad \text{or} \qquad \frac{I+O}{q} = \frac{O}{f}$$

FIG. 13|12
The geometric relation between image size and object size.

Adding the two equations,

$$\frac{I+O}{p} + \frac{I+O}{q} = \frac{I}{f} + \frac{O}{f}$$

$$= \frac{I+O}{f}$$

and dividing both sides by $I + O$, we obtain

$$\frac{1}{p} + \frac{1}{q} = \frac{1}{f}$$

This relation between the object and image distances and the focal length of the lens does not depend upon the size of the object or upon the position of the head of the arrow. The position of the head of the arrow is therefore an arbitrary point on the plane perpendicular to the optical axis that contains the arrow, and the relations must hold for any arbitrary point on that plane. It then follows that a complete image of the arrow (or any other plane figure that might be substituted for it) will be formed at the image position; each point on the image corresponds to a particular point on the object.

It is easy to see that the two right triangles with the image and object arrows as sides, shown in Fig. 13|12, are similar and thus that

$$\frac{I}{O} = \frac{q}{p}$$

where I is the size of the image and O is the size of the object. The ratio I/O is called the magnification. Since the ratio does not depend upon the size of the object or the position of the arrowhead, all lengths in the object plane will be magnified by the same ratio and the image will not be distorted.

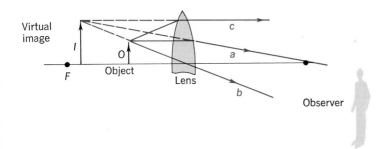

FIG. 13|13
The construction of a virtual image by a lens.

In certain situations, an observer will see light *appear* to come from certain points when in fact it does not. We say then that a *virtual image* is formed. Your reflection as seen in a plane mirror comprises such a virtual image. The light that seems to come from your figure a few feet on the other side of the glass does not in fact come from any region behind the mirror. Virtual images are also produced by lens systems under certain conditions, as shown in Fig. 13|13. Again the object is represented as O. From the view of an observer far to the right of the lens, the light appears to come from the *virtual image, I*.

13|7   *Images formed by a concave mirror*

A perfectly designed concave mirror, like a perfect lens, will focus rays only from some particular point to another particular point. However, if the angles the rays make with the surface of the mirror are sufficiently near 90°, the mirror will reflect rays from any point taken from a wide range of points to a very small region near some conjugate point. This region may be sufficiently small so that for practical purposes we might consider these conjugate regions as points. To the extent that this approximation is justified, there will exist a point-to-point correspondence between an object region and an image region for objects at various positions with respect to the mirror, and the mirror will be a flexible and useful image-forming device.

We can analyze the optical properties of such a small-aperture mirror in a manner that is directly analogous to our analysis of the optical properties of the thin lens. Figure 13|14 shows such

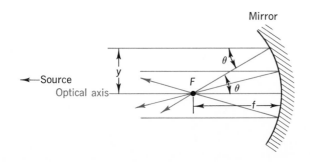

FIG. 13|14
Parallel rays brought to a focus by a concave mirror.

a mirror, which brings into focus rays from an object point, O, at infinity to an image point, F. The point O is so far away that the rays from O can be considered to be parallel as they approach the mirror. Then all the rays are reflected by the mirror so as to pass through the point F, which is called the focus. The distance from the focal point F to the mirror is the focal length of the mirror. This focal length is a property of the mirror and is independent of the position of any object or image. Even as the rays parallel to the optical axis converge to the focal point and are reflected by the mirror, rays that emanate from the focal point and are reflected by the mirror are reflected so that they are then parallel to the optical axis.

The angular deflection of the rays that strike the mirror in Fig. 13 | 14 is defined by the relation

$$\tan \theta = \frac{y}{f}$$

where y is the distance from the ray to the optical axis and f is the focal length of the mirror. For small values of the angle θ,

$$\theta = \frac{y}{f}$$

The mirror will focus a wide range of object points to image points only if this approximation is valid. Even as any incident ray parallel to the optical axis will be reflected through the focus, any incident ray that passes through the focus will be reflected such that the reflected ray is parallel to the axis. One further ray is of particular interest: a ray that strikes the center of the mirror at an angle ϕ with respect to the optical axis will be reflected such that the ray makes an angle ϕ with the axis. Since the surface of the mirror is perpendicular to the optical axis at the center of the mirror, this result follows simply from the equivalence of the angles of incidence and reflection.

We are now prepared to discuss the formation of the image, I, of an extended object, O. In Fig. 13 | 15 the arrow that represents the object is labeled O, and the arrow I represents the image. The object distance is p, the image distance is q, and the focal length is f. The rays A and B are emitted from the head of the object arrow. The relation between the distance from the object to the mirror (the object distance) and the distance from the mirror to the image (the image distance) and the focal length

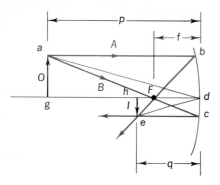

FIG. 13|15
A geometric representation showing the formation of an image by a concave mirror.

of the mirror can be determined geometrically in a manner analogous to the argument used to determine similar relations for images formed by a thin lens. The triangle abc is similar to the triangle Fdc and then from the relations between the corresponding sides of similar triangles

$$\frac{bc}{ab} = \frac{dc}{Fd} \qquad \text{or} \qquad \frac{I+O}{p} = \frac{I}{f}$$

even as the length bc is equal to the sum of the lengths of the object and the image, and ab is equal to p, the object distance. Also dc is equal to the image size, I, and Fd is equal to the focal length of the mirror, f.

Further, the triangles ebc and Fdb are similar triangles and

$$\frac{bc}{ce} = \frac{bd}{dF} \qquad \text{or} \qquad \frac{I+O}{q} = \frac{O}{f}$$

Adding the two equations,

$$\frac{I+O}{p} + \frac{I+O}{q} = \frac{I}{f} + \frac{O}{f}$$

$$= \frac{I+O}{f}$$

Dividing both sides by $I + O$ we have

$$\frac{1}{p} + \frac{1}{q} = \frac{1}{f}$$

which is the same relation that was derived for the thin lens.

Remembering that the ray that strikes the center of the mirror is reflected such that the angle of reflection is equal to the angle incidence—and therefore that the angle the incident ray makes with the optical axis is equal to the angle the reflected ray makes with the axis—we see that the triangles *agd* and *hed* are similar triangles, so that

$$\frac{he}{ag} = \frac{hd}{gd} \qquad \text{or} \qquad \frac{I}{O} = \frac{q}{p}$$

which is the magnification of the system.

PROBLEMS

13|1 An object is 1 m in front of a plane mirror. Show by tracing rays that the virtual image is 1 m in back of the mirror. Note that the image will be in the same place for observers in different positions. Trace rays for different observers.

13|2 The Greeks constructed ellipses by placing two pegs at the foci and running a stylus about a perimeter where the stylus is constrained by a string about the stylus and the two pegs as shown in the diagram. Show that the ellipse is the locus of a reflector that takes the light emitted from one focus and reflects it to the second focus. Use Fermat's theorem, not geometry.

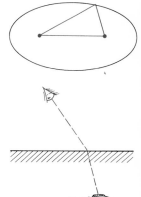

13|3 I look directly down into the water and see a fish that appears to be 1.0 m below the surface. The index of refraction of the water is 1.33; the index of refraction of air is 1.0. How deep is the fish actually swimming? Note that I actually see an image of the fish, and that the image will be in the same place if I move slightly. Draw rays and use Snell's law and the relation that for small angles $\sin \theta = \theta$ in radians.

13|4 The diagram shows a configuration of sound absorbers together with a triangular box filled with sulfur hexafluoride, SF_6. The walls of the box are constructed of very thin plastic sheet that has a negligible effect on the transmission of sound. The speed of sound in SF_6 is about half as great as in the air that fills the rest of the space in the diagram. The box is 5 m wide on the smaller sides, and the wavelength of sound emitted by the whistle in the distance is 10 cm.

(a) Assume that the configuration of the box can be changed so that θ can be varied. What is the largest value of θ such that an observer at *a* can hear the whistle?

(b) Assume that the observer in the region *a* cannot hear the whistle when he stands far behind the box. Can he hear the whistle if he gets very close? How close?

(*c*) Observer *a* cannot hear the whistle, but *b* hears it clearly. What can *a* do to stop *b* from hearing the whistle (at least very loudly) without leaving his area or touching the box? He has only a piece of sound-absorbing felt as equipment.

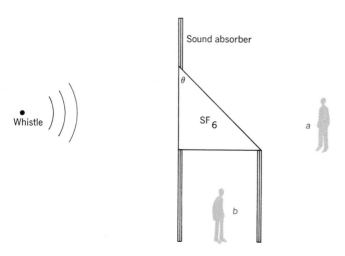

13 | 5   Light from a source that is very far away to the left in the diagram passes through a glass lens such as that shown in the diagram. The diameter of the lens is 10 cm, the thickness is 2 cm. The index of refraction of the glass is 1.5. Show that the light will be focused at a point about 12 cm beyond the lens. Fermat's principle should be used.

13 | 6   Sound of a wavelength of 25 cm is emitted from a device very far from a balloon filled with sulfur hexafluoride, SF_6. The balloon is shaped as in the diagram (the surfaces are sections of spheres). The velocity of sound in SF_6 is about half the velocity in air. Show that the sound is focused to a point about 50 m from the balloon. (Use Fermat's principle.)

13 |7 A camera is designed to use a lens that has a focal length of 50 mm.

(*a*) What will be the value of the distance between the optical center of the lens and the film if the film is to take clear pictures of objects that are very far from the camera?

(*b*) What will the correct distance be if the camera is to be used to take picture from a distance of 50 cm?

13 |8 The ratio of the focal length of a lens to the diameter of the aperture of the lens is called the *f-number*. A camera with a lens of focal length of 50 mm is focused at infinity. The aperture stop is set at $f:2.5$.

(*a*) A point 1.0 m from the camera will be photographed as a blurred circle. What will be the size of the blur (the size of the circle of confusion)?

(*b*) If the aperture is set to $f:50$, how big will the blur be?

13 |9 The diagram represents the two lenses of a compound microscope. Trace appropriate rays from the object through the objective lens to form an image; then trace rays from that image (used as an object) through the eyepiece and form the virtual image seen by the user of the microscope.

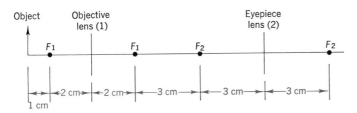

14 | 1   *The diffraction of "particles"*

WE HAVE stated that entities we usually call particles, and regard as the fundamental pieces of matter, exhibit properties that are very similar to properties we consider as specific to waves. We must be careful to consider all statements concerning the character of such particles as statements concerning experimental results. The names we assign to the collection of experimental results and to the general relations we use to correlate these results are important—we need to use common names such as *waves* or *particles* in order to communicate. But we must not make the error of confusing specific results of experiments and the specific character of the theoretical models used to correlate these results—be they right or wrong—with verbal or semantic properties of the names themselves. Certain properties of the entity we call an electron are very much like the properties we attribute to primitive particles—stones or balls. Other properties of electrons are like those of waves. It is not necessary, however, to make a decision as to whether an electron is a wave or a particle. It is an entity to which we give the name electron, with properties, which are well understood and lead to no contradictions, that are somewhat like those evident in a ripple and somewhat like those of a stone.

The description we have of the entities we commonly call *particles* is based on experiment and designed to fit the results of experiments. The totality of all the experiments that define the description we use, and thus confirm in great detail and with great precision the salient points of this description, is very large. Furthermore, some of these results are complicated, and the conclusions require some subtlety of thought. Rather than recreate the historic experiments, we prefer to discuss the experimental results in terms of model experiments, similar to actual experiments in principle, but simpler in detail. We will study two such experiments in particular.

First, beams of electrons, protons, neutrons, and other "particles" behave in a manner similar to that which we have considered as characteristic to waves; effects that suggest interference and diffraction are observed. Figure 14|1 shows a double-slit-diffraction–like pattern showing the intensity of electrons incident upon a photographic plate. Here a monoenergetic beam of electrons passes through the two slits and then onto a photographic plate. At the point an electron hits the plate it activates or "exposes" the film. At point *a* the intensity is at a maximum; a large number of electrons have struck the plate at this point. At point *b* the intensity is small, indicating that amost no electrons have struck the screen at point *b*. If we double the velocity of the electrons the distance between the maxima decreases by a factor of 2. If we perform the same kind of experiment with heavier particles moving at the same velocity, we find that the diffractionlike maxima are closer together by the ratio of the particle mass to the mass of the electron. In general, the spacing of the diffraction minima is inversely proportional to the momentum of the particles, and we can express the relation, for any particle, as

$$\theta = \frac{(h/mv)}{d} \qquad\qquad (14|1)$$

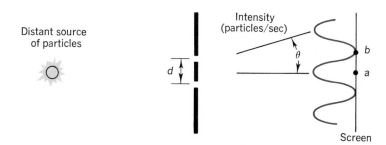

Distant source
of particles

Intensity
(particles/sec)

d

θ

b

a

Screen

where θ is the angle between the maxima. d is the spacing between the slits, and h is a proportionality constant.

Relation (14|1) has very much the same form as the relation
for the diffraction of a wave by the two slits,

$$\theta = \frac{\lambda}{d}$$

where λ is the wavelength of the wave. This suggests that we
ascribe a wave property to the particle where the wavelength
of the particle is

$$\lambda = \frac{h}{mv} \qquad (14|2)$$

where the constant h is found to be a constant of nature, the
same for all particles, and is equal to 6.5×10^{-34} J-sec. The
constant was first noticed by Max Planck in a different context,
and is called Planck's constant.

The wavelike character of the electron beam is illustrated
further by examining the effect of the closing of one of the slits
as in Fig. 14|2. The pattern of sharp maxima and minima no
longer appears. The intensity, or number of electrons per second,
at a is reduced by a factor of 4. The intensity of electrons at b
is increased! The number of electrons going from the source to
point b is greater with one slit open than with two! It is of course
most difficult, really impossible, to understand this behavior if
the electron behaves like a classical particle. It is easy to understand if the electron behaves, in some respects, like a simple
sound wave or water wave.

The second of the model experiments is conducted by passing
the monoenergetic electron beam, with incident energy equal to
E, through a shutter that passes the beam for a very short time,

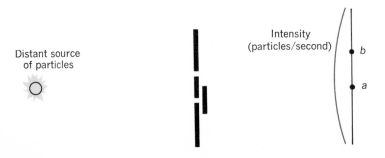

Distant source
of particles

Intensity
(particles/second)

b

a

FIG. 14|2
*The double-slit intensity
pattern when one slit is
blocked.*

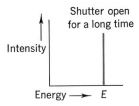

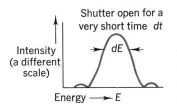

FIG. 14|3
*The spread in energy of
electrons that pass
through a shutter.*

dt, and measuring the energy of the electrons that pass through
the shutter. The energy distributions before and after the shutter
are suggested by the graphs of Fig. 14|3. The transmitted elec-
trons show a spread of energy equal to *dE* where

$$dE = \frac{h}{dt} \qquad (14|3)$$

The shorter the time the shutter is open, the larger the spread
in electron energy. Relation (14|3) is very much like the relation

$$df = \frac{1}{dt}$$

developed in Section 12|7 to express the spread in frequency
of waves that were observed for a short time *t*. The electron
beam then has properties very much like those of a wave where
the frequency of the wave is such that

$$f = \frac{E}{h} \qquad \text{or} \qquad \omega = 2\pi f = \frac{2\pi E}{h}$$

where ω is the circular frequency of the wave and *E* is the energy
of the particle.

   The results of the two experiments we have described are a
normal consequence of a description of the electron beam as a
wave:

$$U(x, t) = u_0 \cos (\omega t - kx) \qquad (14|4)$$

where

$$\omega = \frac{2\pi E}{h} \qquad \text{and} \qquad k = \frac{2\pi}{\lambda} = \frac{2\pi p}{h}$$

and *p* is the momentum of the particles and *E* is the energy. In
analogy with the results of other wave equations, we expect
that the intensity, which is the square of the amplitude, $u(x, t)^2$,
is proportional to the density of electrons at the point *x* and time

t; the density will be expressed in terms of the number of electrons per unit volume or the number per cubic meter in the mks system. We call this kind of wave a *de Broglie wave* after Louis de Broglie, who proposed such a relation in 1924.

Experiments precisely like the diffraction experiment suggested here are quite difficult, but results that are similar in principle were obtained thirty years ago by Davisson and Germer, and by Thomson, who scattered electrons from the ordered arrays of atoms in a crystal. The crystal acted like a grating. Very nearly the same sort of results have been obtained for neutrons, and closely related experiments have been performed showing similar results for other particles.

The time-diffraction experiment, as described above, is even more difficult. Again, analogous measurements have been made, generally on the energy spread of particles emitted from sources that have naturally short lifetimes, and the results are in accord with the wave description. The model experiments discussed here should be considered as condensed and simplified versions of the actual experiments that have been conducted.

Equation (14 | 4) is a concise statement of these experimentally observed results concerning the diffractive effects that have been observed in the scattering of particle beams and the energy spread of such beams that has been observed when the beams are limited in time. These observations are not consistent with a classical description of particles nor with classical mechanics. It is therefore necessary to construct a new description of these entities we have called particles in order to encompass the newly observed experimental results. This new description is called *quantum mechanics*. The wavelike equation (14 | 4) that describes the behavior of a beam of particles represents one way of expressing an important part of quantum mechanics.

Of course the discovery that classical mechanics does not correctly describe the small-scale events of nature does not and cannot mean that classical mechanics is inadequate to describe the macroscopic observations of nature—after all, we invented classical mechanics to describe the large-scale observations of nature and constructed this system to fit these observations within our errors of observation. Must we, then, have two unrelated systems of mechanics; one for the macroscopic world and one for the microscopic world? Certainly that is an unaesthetic hypothesis. The dichotomy must be reduced, and the obvious reduction is to be found in the character of quantum mechanics: the quantum mechanical description of nature must *correspond* to the classical description of nature when the value of *h* is negligible compared to the magnitudes of the relevant dynamic quantities. Or, in other words, quantum mechanics must correspond to classical mechanics in the limit where the de Broglie wavelength is small compared to the magnitudes of all measured quantities. There is, then, only one system of mechanics: quantum mechanics. Classical mechanics is a limiting case of quantum mechanics, valid when *h* is negligible. This is a statement of the *correspondence principle*.

Quantum mechanics corresponds to classical mechanics very much as physical optics, where the wave properties of light are considered, corresponds to geometric optics, where the wave properties of light can be neglected and light can be considered to travel in rays. If the apertures of Fig. 14|1 are very large compared to the wavelength, there will be no diffractive effects, and the electrons will travel through one or the other slit just as ordinary classical particles.

14|2 *The probability interpretation of the intensity*

The results of the experiments discussed in the last section can be understood in terms of a model of a beam of particles that describes the beam very much as a plane wave, where the intensity of the wave is interpreted as the density of particles. We will find that a detailed examination of the experimental results will require us to adopt a modification of this interpretation.

The large difference between the density of particles at point *a* and point *b* in Fig. 14|1 represents the large difference between the intensity of the wave at *a* and *b*. It is possible to reduce the intensity of the electron source in experiments such as this to such an extent that one can change the recording film so rapidly that most of the film has no track at all on it. If the negative film is quite transparent we might hold all of the separate films together in a stack and look through the many layers as in Fig. 14|4. We would then see just the intensity pattern shown on Fig. 14|1. However, if we analyze the distribution of electrons on the separate films and count how many have no tracks, one

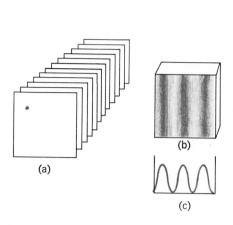

FIG. 14|4

The distribution of hits of single electrons that pass through a double slit onto emulsions: (a) individual transparencies with an average of one electron spot per photograph; (b) transparencies stacked together showing intensity pattern; (c) plot of density across the stack.

(b)

(a)

(c)

track, two tracks, and so on, we will find that the distribution is precisely that determined by the laws of probability for random events.

For example, if one spins a roulette wheel 37 times (a Monte Carlo wheel with 36 numbers and one zero, not a Las Vegas wheel with 0, 00, and 000) the probability is that 7 will come up once. If one conducts this sequence of 37 spins a thousand times, 7 will come up very nearly a thousand times. Not one number 7 will turn up during about 370 of such sequences; one 7 will show up in about 370 sequences, or 37 percent of the time; 7 will come up twice in about 185 sequences; 7 will come up three times in about 60 sequences, or about 6 percent of the time; there will be four sevens in 37 spins, or about 1.5 percent of the time; and similar probabilities will ensue for other combinations. If we select a region of the diffraction pattern such that there will be one electron per 37 transparencies, on the average, for a very large number of transparencies, we will find that the probability of getting zero electrons, one electron, two electrons, and so on in a set of 37 films is just the same as the probabilities found at the roulette wheel.

We must therefore interpret the intensity of the de Broglie wave, $u(x, t)^2$, as a measure of the probability that a particle is at the position x at the time t. In the mks system of units the numerical value of $u(x, t)^2$ is equal to the probable number of particles per cubic meter at the point x and time t. This definition extends, rather than contradicts, the definition of u^2 that was introduced previously; that is, u^2 is proportional to the density of particles or number per cubic meter. Indeed, when very large numbers of particles are involved, the two definitions are nearly identical; if the probable number of particles in a certain region is 1,000,000, the actual number is not likely to be very different if the distribution follows the laws of probability.

It is desirable to emphasize again that this description of events concerning particles in terms of probability, a description we have presented simplified and only in part, is determined by experiment and is just sufficient to fit all the experiments that have been conducted. It is not certain that this description is unique or that it is correct, in the sense that a new and different description might also fit every observation that has been made equally well. Any such alternative description of nature can be really new, and not just a restatement of the conventional description, only if it predicts a different result for some kind of possible observation than the conventional description. Attempts to construct such an alternative description of reality have not been successful.

14|3   *The Heisenberg uncertainty principle*

The description of nature we have adopted to include the results of observations of the type introduced in Section 14|1 leads immediately to a most interesting restriction on the character of the information we can obtain concerning the physical universe. If quantum mechanics represents a correct and complete (in principle) description of mechanics, pairs of *complementary quantities* exist such that it is not possible to know, or measure, the values of both quantities simultaneously to an unlimited precision. Classical mechanics has always admitted the possibility of measuring the quantities of mechanics, such as position and momentum, or energy and time, to any degree of accuracy; it is therefore permissible to ascribe an exact momentum and an exact position to a particle, since it is implicitly assumed that exact measurements could be made of these quantities. If the description of nature implied by quantum mechanics is correct, and we proceed on the assumption that it is, such measurements cannot be conducted in *principle* with unlimited accuracy: then, from an operational view, such as we adopt in physics, a particle does not have an exact position and momentum. The resulting uncertainty in the values of complementary quantities, such as position and momentum, was particularly evident in Werner Heisenberg's formulation of quantum mechanics, hence the *Heisenberg uncertainty principle.*

It is useful to examine the constraints the nature of the universe appears to impose upon the position and momentum of a particle by analyzing the results of an attempt to identify a particle with a well-defined position and momentum in some direction. We first examine the character of this problem as if the classical description of nature is valid. We assume that we are able to produce a beam of monoenergetic particles that travels approximately in the x-direction of Fig. 14|5. Two slits are set up as shown with the object of determining the position in the y-direction of any particle that passes through the second slit to an accuracy of a, the width of the slit. The component of momentum of the particle in the y-direction will nominally be equal to zero, but since the slits have a finite width the, measuring apparatus will admit particles that have small components of momentum in the y-direction. A particle that grazes the lower edge of the first slit and the upper edge of the second will have a component of momentum in the y-direction such that

$$p_y = \frac{p(a+b)}{L}$$

where p is the momentum of the particle, b and a are the widths of the first and second slits, and L is the distance between the slits. The deviation of the possible momentum from zero can be reduced indefinitely, from a classical view, by decreasing the size of a and b and increasing L. If a and b are constructed so that they are very small, and L is large, both the position y and the transverse momentum p_y of a particle that passes through the system will be very well known. From a classical view there is no limit on the accuracy that can be obtained.

However, the description of nature we have used in this anal-

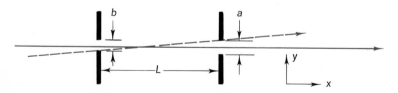

ysis is not valid! This description is inadequate to explain the diffraction-like results discussed in Section 14|1. We know, through our observations of such phenomena, that the particles will be diffracted as they pass through the slit a and deflected through angles of the order of θ, where

$$\theta = \frac{\lambda}{a}$$

and since

$$\lambda = \frac{h}{p}$$

then

$$\theta = \frac{h}{pa}$$

If the angle θ is small, the momentum component of the particle in the y-direction will be

$$dp_y = p\theta$$

or

$$dp_y = p\left(\frac{h}{pa}\right)$$

$$= \frac{h}{a}$$

Using dy for a, the uncertainty in the y-coordinate of the particle as it passes through the slit,

$$dp_y\, dy = h \tag{14|5}$$

The equation, $dp_y\, dy = h$, relates a specific probability distribution in y with a specific distribution in p_y. In our formulation of the problem, the probability of the particle having a position y is the same for any value of y in the interval dy and zero outside of that interval. The probability of the particle having a momentum p_y is expressed by the single slit diffraction pattern, where dp_y is the difference between the values of p_y such that the probability is $4/\pi^2$ of the maximum probability. If we should choose to define the uncertainties, dp_y and dy, as the intervals from the central value to the extreme (half of the whole interval) the product of the uncertainties would be equal to $\frac{1}{4}h$. If it is possible to choose the two probabilities such that they have the same form (gaussian), then the product of the half-widths is $h/2\pi$. This is the usual *conventional* statement of the uncertainty principle. For qualitative discussions of uncertainties, any of the formulations is adequate.

If a very large number of particles pass through the slit system and strike the screen of Fig. 14|6, the curve that describes the intensity of particles can be considered to represent the variation of the density of particle hits over the surface of the screen. The density will be at a maximum near *i*, a little less near *iii*, and a minimum near *ii*. For one particle, the curve can be considered a probability curve; the probability of a particle striking the screen near *ii* will be very small; the probability of the particle near *iii* will be larger, and the probability will be still larger that the particle will strike near *i*. For example: the probability of the single particle hitting anywhere on the screen is 1.0; the probability of the particle hitting between *i* and *iii* will be about 0.30; the probability of hitting between *iii* and *ii* will be about equal to 0.11. Furthermore, it seems that this is an "honest" gambling device. The distribution of hits and misses follows the laws of probability like an honest set of dice or an honest roulette wheel.

Although we have described only one specific method of determining the position and momentum of a particle, the general results obtained by analyzing that method also hold for any other technique; it is impossible to determine both the position and momentum of a particle at any particular time with unlimited accuracy: the product of the uncertainty of position of the particle dy at some particular time, multiplied by the uncertainty in the component of momentum in that direction dp_y, cannot be less

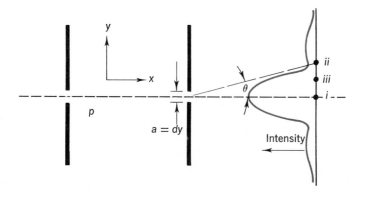

FIG. 14|6
The spreads in trajectories of particles passing through a double-slit system when quantum effects are important. The intensity curve represents the distribution of particles on the screen.

than h, as expressed in relation (14|5). We say that a pair of quantities that are related by the uncertainty principle, such as dp_y and dy, are *complementary quantities*. One can learn the value of y only at the expense of knowledge of p_y; as the slit is closed down, the determination of the value of y of the particles that pass through is improved, but the angle of diffraction, and therefore the spread in the values of p_y, is increased. Contrariwise, the diffraction and spread in p_x can be reduced by increasing the size of the slit. But this represents a loss in the accuracy of knowledge of y.

Energy and time are another set of complementary quantities: we cannot measure the energy of a particle, or any other system, at a specific time. We cannot say that the energy of a particle is exactly E at a time that is precisely t: we cannot say that the energy of a particle is exactly 1.0 J at the exact time 12:00 m., Greenwich time. There will be an uncertainty in the measurement of the energy dE and time dt such that

$$dE\ dt = h$$

Although this uncertainty is extremely small on the macroscopic scale, it is quite important on the microscopic scale of elementary particles.

The uncertainty in energy that results from a limitation of the time of observation does not depend upon whether the time limitation is imposed externally by obvious actions of an observer (who might activate a shutter) or whether the time limitations are intrinsic in that the state has a definite lifetime. Therefore, particles that are unstable and decay with some well-defined lifetime that is a property of the particle do not have a definite energy or, therefore, a definite mass, since the mass, m, and energy, E, of the state are related by Einstein's mass–energy relation, $E = mc^2$, where c is the velocity of light. If the lifetime of the state is T,

$$dE\ T = h$$

or

$$d(mc^2)\ T = h$$

or

$$dm\ T = \frac{h}{c^2}$$

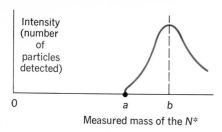

Intensity (number of particles detected)

0

a   *b*

Measured mass of the N*

FIG. 14|7
The distribution of the measured masses of a short-lived particle.

where *dm* is the uncertainty of the mass of the particle. For example, the neutron decays into a proton, an electron, and a neutrino after a mean time of about 1000 sec. There is thus an intrinsic undertainty or spread in the energy of about 10^{-37} J; the uncertainty in the mass of a neutron is then about $10^{-37}/c^2$ kg, or about 10^{-54} kg. This is only about 1 part in 10^{27} of the mass of a neutron and is not detectable by any techniques we have available now.

Some of the more exotic particles have very short lives, and the spread in mass is considerable. A particle labeled the N^*, discovered by Enrico Fermi, decays into a proton and another particle called a *pion* in an average time of about 5×10^{-24} sec. The mass spread or uncertainty that results from this short lifetime is about 10 percent of the average mass of the particle. The diagram of Fig. 14|7 shows the distribution of the measured masses of many of these particles. The mass represented is the mass of the proton plus the mass of the pion plus the kinetic energies of these two decay particles divided by c^2. According to Einstein's mass–energy relation, $E = mc^2$ or $m = E/c^2$. This sum will represent the original mass of the particle that decayed. The ordinate of Fig. 14|7 is proportional to the number of events, and the abscissa is proportional to the mass. Point *a* represents the sum of the masses of the proton and pion; point *b* represents the average mass. Note how much this curve is like the curve of the amplitude of the pendulum near resonance in Fig. 9|8, or the amplitudes of the vibrating string as a function of exciting frequency shown in Fig. 11|8. This behavior also represents a kind of resonance.

The difference between the classical description of nature, which is so near to our intuition, but is incorrect, and the quantum description can be expressed in a number of ways. In the classical model of the universe, particles are discrete and all dynamical quantities such as time, velocity, momentum, and so on are continuous. There is a granularity of particles but no granularity of the dynamic quantities. These distinctions are blurred in quantum mechanics. The dynamic quantity "action," equal to momentum times distance, or energy times time, is quantized into integral multiples of h, while particles have continuous properties like a water wave.

14|4   *The interaction of the observer with measurements*

It has always been recognized that there are uncertainties in measurement, and it has always been recognized that an exactly precise measurement of any quantity is impossible in practice. Before the discovery of the uncertainty principles, or the wave nature of particle behavior, it was always assumed that there was no limitation *in principle* to the accuracy of such measurements. Now we have a description of nature that strongly suggests that there are very definite limits on the accuracy with which quantities can be known. The act of measurement itself disturbs the quantity being measured. The determination of the position of a particle to an accuracy dy results in a random diffractive impulse to the particle, giving it an uncertainty in momentum dp_y, where $dp_y = h/dy$. The act of measurement always involves an interaction between the measurer, or his apparatus, and the system that is measured. If we want to know the position of a particle in a y-direction, we must somehow detect that it holds that position to a certain accuracy dy—perhaps by seeing that it passes through a slit of width dy—but this determination gives the particle an uncertainty in momentum at least as great as h/dy. If we wish to determine the energy of a particle, we must perform some measurement in a time, dt; the measurement itself will induce a spread or uncertainty in the energy, dE, such that $dE = h/dt$.

An interesting illustration of the interaction of the observer and his apparatus is provided by an examination of a modification of the double-slit experiment shown in Fig. 14|1. Let us assume that the observer wishes to determine the identity of the slit through which each electron passes. He might then construct a counter and place it in front of one of the slits; presumably the counter would be designed to make a minimum interaction with the electron. If an electron strikes the screen and the counter registers a count, we know that the electron passes through the slit guarded by the counter; if the counter did not register a count, the electron must have passed through the other slit. If this is done, the observer will find that the typical double-slit pattern shown in Fig. 14 | 1, which was observed before the counter was installed, has now disappeared, and the pattern formed by each set of electrons—those that are counted by the counter and those that are not registered—will look like the single-slit pattern shown in Fig. 14 | 2. Indeed, unless the counter is made with great ingenuity, the pattern made by the electrons that interact with the counter will be even broader.

We can understand this to some extent by considering the minimum interaction possible of an electron with the counter. Certainly there must be some interaction, since the counter is to register the passage of the electron. The electron must at least interact with some particle inside the counter. But any particle localized by the counter in the region that is as wide as the slit da must have a momentum at least as large as $p = h/da$ that can be transferred to the electron in the collision. Of course, this is just the uncertainty in momentum that the electron acquires in passing through a single slit of width da, so the electron will be diffracted as if it passed through a single slit. Of course, the counter might not be that well designed, and the particle in the counter might well have more momentum.

Since the electron passing through the counter will receive a statistically indeterminate amount of momentum upon interacting with the counter, it will no longer be coherent with the electron beam passing through the other slit, and such electrons will form a single-slit diffraction pattern with a width determined by the width of the slit.

If quantum mechanics is to be a consistent description of nature, it is not possible to reduce the interaction of the observer below a certain amount expressed by the uncertainty principle: the disturbance that results from the act of observation or measurement by the experimenter cannot be reduced indefinitely by the use of more and more subtle techniques. The influence of the observer and his apparatus cannot be reduced beyond the minimum set by Planck's constant. This conclusion is important to philosophers interested in epistemology, the study of the origin and limits of knowledge.

According to the classical description of nature, if one knows the positions and the velocities of a set of objects and has an understanding of the forces between them, in the absence of any outside interaction one can predict or calculate the configuration of positions and velocities at any later time. Since this set could be the complete set of all particles in the universe, this result suggests that the future could be predicted in principle and, more important, that a specific and unique future exists. The whole course of the universe, including the whole course of our lives, would be predetermined, or predestined. If this argument were valid, free will could not exist.

Now we believe that we cannot know the exact positions and momenta of all particles. We are limited, *in principle,* in our measurements of complementary quantities by the uncertainty principle. If we perform a set of measurements on the assembly of objects, we can determine their positions and moment only up to a certain limit. According to the operational view of reality used in practice by most physicists, a particle does not have a definite position and definite momentum. No operational meaning can be attributed to such a concept if it cannot be measured in principle. If the particle does not have a definite position and momentum, it is not possible to predict where the particle will be later. However, one could, in principle, conduct a series of mea- surements that would determine the probability distribution of the particles in the future exactly. One could then predict, exactly, the probability of the particles being in any particular configuration in the future. And this probability depends only upon the initial situation as determined by our instruments. Of course, we have no more free will this way than in our classical argument. Instead of having the future exactly determined, inde- pendent of our volition, now we are at the mercy of chance, of the cut of the cards, again independent of our volition.

From an operational view none of this can be taken at all seriously until it can be shown that it is possible in principle to obtain all the information required. It seems most unlikely that this is possible, so we will have to leave predestination with the theologians, who originated the idea.

We should not leave the subject of the uncertainty principle without pointing out that a small, but respectable group of physicists do not accept the probability interpretation of quantum mechanics as representing the ultimate reality. This was Einstein's position—he is supposed to have said that he cannot believe that "God plays dice with the world."

14|5 *Standing waves*

De Broglie waves undergo reflection at any interface where the physical situation results in a change in the velocity of the wave in just the same manner as other waves are reflected. Since the velocity of the wave is closely related to the velocity of the particles represented by the wave, we can expect reflections in situations where we would expect the classical velocity of a particle to be changed as a result of the influence of forces on the particle. Even as we can consider that the nucleus exerts a force on a neutron that strikes the surface of the nucleus, we can consider that the de Broglie wave of the neutron will be reflected at the surface. A quantum-mechanical treatment of the scattering of neutrons by a spherical nucleus is thus very much like the calculation of sound scattering from a spherical object, or of light scattering from a spherical drop of water. The mathematical, or logical, treatments are almost identical.

The reflection of such particle waves at the boundaries of a medium can therefore result in standing waves. Since states described by standing waves do not change their character with time, we call these states *stationary states*—stationary in time. The statement that the states do not change with time implies that our observations extend implicitly over a very long time and thus that the states have very well-defined energies. A neutron or proton inside a nucleus can be considered to be reflected at the surface of the nucleus as a result of the forces that hold the nucleus together and keep the neutron or proton from escaping. Such a neutron or proton will be represented by a standing wave. In the same spirit we must consider the electron bound to an atom by the electrostatic force as a standing wave. Indeed, any static piece of matter must be described as a standing wave.

Later we will consider atomic and nuclear structure in detail. More nearly artificial models can be constructed to exhibit the character of particle standing waves in detail. In particular, we may consider the character of the wave description of a particle in a "box." The box has completely rigid walls so the particle cannot penetrate the walls at all. The probability must then go to zero at the wall and a standing wave will be set up so that the amplitude goes to zero at the wall. The wave—and particle—is reflected at the wall just as a wave in a rope is reflected at a tied end where the amplitude is zero.

Because of the mathematical simplicity, it is convenient to discuss the stationary states of a particle in a one-dimensional box. A three-dimensional box that is very large in the y-direction and z-direction and comparatively short in the x-direction will act very much as a theoretical one-dimensional box. If the y and z dimensions are very large, the particle will be relatively un-constrained in these directions and only the constraint in one dimension—the x-dimension—will be important. Figure 14|8 shows, schematically, a one-dimensional box of length L, together with a characteristic set of possible standing waves similar to the set of standing waves of a violin string.

Since p, the momentum of the particle in the box, is equal to h/λ, the possible momenta of the particle are restricted to the values

$$\frac{h}{2L}, \quad \frac{2h}{2L}, \quad \frac{3h}{2L}, \quad \frac{4h}{2L}, \quad \cdots$$

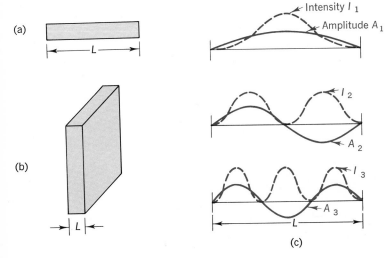

(a)

(b)

(c)

FIG. 14|8
De Broglie standing waves in a one-dimensional box: (a) schematic representation of the box, (b) realistic approximation of the box; (c) the de Broglie waves.

even as the wavelengths are limited to the values of $2L$, $2L/2$, $2L/3$, $2L/4$, . . . Since the kinetic energy of the particle is $p^2/2m$, the least possible kinetic energy a particle can have is not zero but

$$T_1 = \frac{h^2}{8L^2m}$$

where m is the mass of the particle. The other kinetic energies are

$$T_2 = \frac{h^2}{2L^2m} = 4T_1$$

$$T_3 = \frac{9h^2}{8L^2m} = 9T_1$$

and in general

$$T_n = \frac{n^2h^2}{8L^2m} = n^2T_1$$

This set of possible energies is the energy-level *spectrum* of the static system consisting of a particle of mass m in a one-dimensional box of length L. The system can have no other energies; in particular, the energy cannot be zero!

If the energy, and thus the wavelength or momentum, of the particle is well known, the position must be indeterminate because the momentum and position of the particle are complementary quantities. The probability distribution of the position of the particle is represented by the intensity of the standing wave shown in Fig. 14|8, along with the amplitude; it is this intensity that has a direct operational meaning inasmuch as it is the intensity that is directly observable. If there is a very large number of particles in the box occupying the same state, the intensity of the wave at any point will be proportional to the number of particles per unit length at that point; if there is just one particle in the box and the particle has an energy corresponding to the state n, the intensity, $I_n(x)$, multiplied by an increment of distance, dx, represents the probability that the particle will be found between x and $x + dx$.

We can give an operational meaning to this intensity by considering the probability that an appropriate probe will find the particle at a particular position within the box. Figure 14|9 represents a rather fanciful probe, which nevertheless illustrates the principles of our description. We assume that a gunner is attempting to hit a ball that is occupying a certain state in the one-

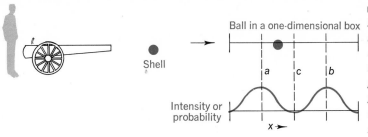

FIG. 14|9

*Probability distributions
in a one-dimensional
box. The curve
represents the
probability of the
presence of the ball as it
depends upon the
position of the ball in
the box.*

dimensional box. The shell from the gun is assumed to be sufficiently heavy and moving sufficiently fast so that it has a very high momentum and thus a very short wavelength itself. If this is true, we can neglect the uncertainty in position of the shell with respect to the uncertainty in position of the ball in the box. Now the shell may strike the ball as it passes through the box, but we cannot know whether the shell will strike, even though the gun is well aimed, since the position of the ball is not well defined. The plot of the intensity in Fig. 14|9 represents a plot of the probability of the ball being hit as a function of x even as it represents a plot of the probability of the ball being at a position x. The shell will have a relatively high probability of striking the ball near points a and b, and almost no probability of hitting the ball near c. If, somehow, the gun were moved so that it fired into the paper, at the side of the box, the gunner should aim at point a or b to maximize his probability of a hit. If he aimed accurately at the exact center of the box, he could shoot all day and never hit anything. Though the ball is to be found often either side of the center, it will never be found in the center of the box. Of course if the ball occupies other states having other kinetic energies and wavelengths, the appropriate strategy will be different even as the probability distributions will be different.

We note that in the limit of very high energy, where the wavelength of the particle is very small compared to the length of the box, the ball has an equal probability of being at any place in the box. This is just what we would expect in the classical limit where the ball moves from wall to wall, bouncing elastically off the walls. The quantum-mechanical description *corresponds* to the classical description in the limit of small wavelength.

The states of the particle in the box that we have discussed are states for which the energy is known precisely: these states correspond to the characteristic standing waves of a vibrating string, where the frequencies are known exactly. But we might have a different kind of information; for example, we might know the position of the particle at some initial time—perhaps the particle was located by hitting it with the shell from the gun. Then we know the initial configuration or state of the particle in the box: the particle is at the position of the shell and at no other place. This corresponds to the state of the string where the initial position of the string is in some particular configuration—perhaps as a result of the application of a bow. Even as the string then vibrates with different frequencies where the amplitudes and intensities of the different frequencies are determined by the particular character of the initial state, the particle in the box has a set of probable energies where the probabilities of these different energies are determined by the particular character of the original state—or original information.

Although the problem of describing the system of a particle in a one-dimensional box in terms of standing waves is the only example of this kind that we can easily treat rigorously, it is interesting to examine qualitatively the standing-wave representation of a particle acting under forces such that it moves classically as a simple harmonic oscillator in one dimension. The character of the problem is particularly clear, and no less general, if we choose to discuss the motion of a particle sliding on a surface in a gravitational field, since the surface itself represents the potential

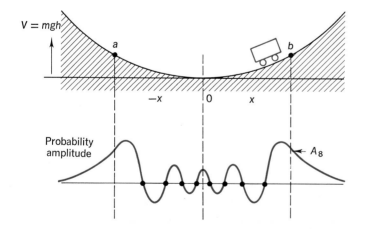

FIG. 14|10

Typical de Broglie amplitudes for a simple harmonic oscillator.

energy as a function of position. The particular system is shown in Fig. 14|10: a cart is sliding on a surface that is so shaped that the force acts on the cart toward the center of the slope, the force being proportional to the distance from the center, x. The force is then equal to

$$F = -kx \quad \text{and} \quad F = ma$$

where m is the mass of the cart and a is the acceleration of the cart. Then since $a = d^2x/dt^2$

$$\frac{d^2x}{dt^2} = -\omega^2 x$$

where

$$\omega = \sqrt{\frac{k}{m}}$$

is the classical description of the motion of the cart.

We assume that this is a microscopic cart indeed and that the momentum of the cart is so small that the appropriate de Broglie wavelength is of the same magnitude as the classical amplitude of the cart's oscillation. The lower curve of Fig. 14|10 shows the de Broglie amplitude for a particular stationary quantum state of the system consisting of the cart and its track. Points a and b mark the extent of the amplitude of the cart's classical motion. Classically, at these points the total energy of the cart, E, is equal to the potential energy, mgh_a; the kinetic energy, T, is zero. Then

$$T = E - mgh_a$$

and the cart will go no farther: classically the cart will never be found outside the region bounded by a and b. Since the potential energy of the cart will be greater than the total energy in these regions, the kinetic energy will be negative, and a negative kinetic energy has no meaning in a classical situation.

The de Broglie-wave description of the particle amplitude has the form

$$A = A_0 \cos\left(\frac{2\pi\, px}{h}\right)$$

where $p = \sqrt{2mT}$. When the kinetic energy is negative, the momentum, p, is (mathematically) imaginary and the de Broglie amplitude takes a form such as

$$A = A_0 \exp\left(\frac{-2\pi\, px}{h}\right)$$

where we use the absolute value of p: this is discussed more fully in Section 9|7. The wave curves away from the origin as shown in the diagram of the amplitude of Fig. 14|10. The cart has a finite probability of being beyond the classical limit. The amplitude decreases by about a factor of 3 over a characteristic distance equal to $h/\sqrt{2mT}$, where T is the absolute value of the kinetic energy of the cart. For macroscopic situations this characteristic length is very small, a result that is comforting in that we can then rely on the fences at the zoo to keep the animals safely in their enclosures. If h were larger—enormously larger— there would be an appreciable probability of the polar bear leaking out of his pen.

The mass, in a classical oscillator, moves most quickly when the amplitude is small, and correspondingly moves most slowly, and spends most of its time, where the amplitude is large. If you shoot at the bob of a pendulum in a shooting gallery, your best tactic is to shoot when it is at an extreme of its amplitude. These results are reflected in the wave-mechanics description of the oscillator shown in Fig. 14|10; the amplitude of the de Broglie wave is largest where the classical system would be found with the highest probability, and the wavelength is shortest where the mass would have the largest momentum in the classical system. Again, in the limit of very small wavelength, where the correspondence principle is valid, the quantum description is indistinguishable from the classical description.

The amplitude of the system shown in Fig. 14|10 represents one of an infinite, but discrete, number of possible stationary states even as a particle in a box can occupy any of an infinite number of possible states. This amplitude corresponds to a state such that the total energy of the system is equal to $8\frac{1}{2}hf$, where $2\pi f$ has the value of $\sqrt{k/m}$, just as for the classical harmonic oscillator. In general, the energies of the various possible states or standing waves of a harmonic oscillator are such that

$$E_n = (n + \tfrac{1}{2})hf$$

where n is the number of nodes in the standing wave. The eight nodes in the standing-wave description of the state shown in Fig. 14|10 are marked by small solid circles.

14|6   *The quantization of*
angular momentum

Quantum mechanics places certain interesting restrictions on the properties of particles moving in orbits. Perhaps this is best said in another way: The description of particles moving in orbits is consistent with the experimental results that suggest the wave nature of particles only if there exist certain restrictions on the character of possible orbits. Quantum mechanics is a logically consistent description of nature. Although it is customary to speak of a property of nature—such as the properties of orbits, which we will discuss—as required by the axioms of quantum mechanics, we should not forget that it is properties of nature that fix the axioms.

The diagram of Fig. 14|11a shows a particle of mass m moving in a circular orbit with a velocity, v, and a momentum, p, equal to mv. Such a description is valid only if the wavelength of the particle, $\lambda = h/p$, is very much smaller than the diameter of the orbit, in which case classical expressions are an adequate approximation of reality. If the wavelength of the particle is so very small compared to the natural dimensions of the orbit, it is possible to determine the position of the particle at any time without

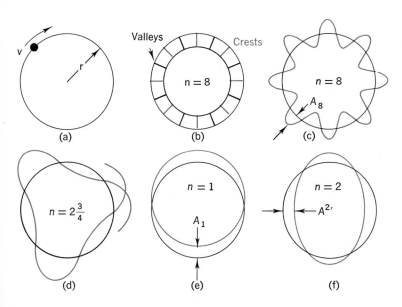

FIG. 14|11
Schematic representations for de Broglie amplitudes for particles moving in a circle.

seriously disturbing the orbit. We can know the position of Mars by measuring the light from the sun that is reflected to us from the planet. Although the light—which is part of our measuring apparatus—does disturb the orbit, the disturbance is extremely small compared to the parameters that characterize the orbit, and we can neglect such effects.

In order to account for the properties of microscopic systems of particles in orbit, it is necessary to introduce the wave character of the particles. Even as a beam of particles is represented by a plane wave, the beam of one particle in an orbit must be described by a running de Broglie wave about the orbit. However, information that defines the orbit occupied by the particle is complementary to information concerning the position of the particle in the orbit. Any consideration that the particle holds a particular position in the orbit can have an operational meaning only if we are able, by some operation, to actually determine this position. This might be done by scattering another particle off the orbiting particle or by shining light that scatters off the orbiting particle. In either case, the measurement will affect the particle so that in general it will be knocked into a new orbit— indeed, any measurement of the particle's position thus destroys the information we might have concerning the exact orbit of the particle. If we wish to know the position of the particle in the orbit, we cannot know the exact orbit—or state—of the particle; if we wish to know the exact orbit, we cannot know the position of the particle in the orbit. When the wavelength is very small compared to the dimensions of the orbit—and this is certainly the case for the orbit of Mars about the sun—the different quantum-mechanical states or orbits are very close together and the exact orbit, to the accuracy of a wavelength, is hardly relevent. But for an electron, in an orbit in an atom, orbits that differ by one wavelength may be quite different and we cannot sensibly talk about both the orbit and the position of the electron in the orbit at the same time.

The diagram of Fig. 14|11b represents an attempt to suggest the character of a running wave about a circular orbit. We might compare this with a model where a circular channel is filled with water and waves on the surface run around in circles. We consider a situation that is constant or stationary in time where the particle in the orbit then has a definite energy. The particle in the circular orbit will then have a finite kinetic energy and a definite momentum and wavelength, all of which will not change with time. This is possible only if the orbit contains an integral number of wavelengths. If there is not an even number of wavelengths, there will be some place in the wave train where the amplitude will vary with a different effective momentum and energy, contrary to the specifications of the system we are trying to describe.

The running wave about an orbit of radius a can then be described approximately by the expression

$$A = A_0 \cos(kr - \omega t) \quad \text{or} \quad A = A_0 \cos\left(\frac{2\pi r}{\lambda} - \omega t\right)$$

where r represents distance around the circumference of the circle. The condition that an integral number of wavelengths be equal to the circumference of the orbit can be expressed as

$$n\lambda = 2\pi a$$

where $n = 1, 2, 3, \ldots$ It is often useful to express the system as a standing wave if the direction of motion of the particle in the orbit is not known. The standing-wave form is, as in Section 11 |2, the sum of equal running waves moving in opposite directions. Thus the expression for the standing wave is

$$A = A_0 \cos\left(\frac{2\pi r}{\lambda}\right)$$

where again $n\lambda = 2\pi a$.

It is always difficult to represent particle waves without risk of being misleading in some way. Figure 14 | 11c shows a representation of a standing wave that corresponds to a particle in an orbit. The distance between the wavelike line and the circular line that is meant to represent the position of the classical orbit is supposed to be proportional to the amplitude of the wave. *The particle itself does not move in a snakelike path.*

The diagram of Fig. 14 | 11d shows a situation such that the number of waves around the orbit is not an integer. Although it is difficult to interpret this nonexistent form, it would seem that the effective wavelength where the beginning and end of the wave appear to merge at the top of the figure corresponds to a shorter wavelength, and thus a higher momentum, than the rest of the wave.

The diagram of Fig. 14 | 11c represents an orbit where there are seven wavelengths about the orbit; Fig. 14 | 11e shows an orbit with only one wavelength about the circumference, while Fig. 14|11f shows an orbit where two wavelengths span the circumference.

If the radius of the circle is a, we have emphasized that

$$2\pi a = n\lambda$$

where $n = 1, 2, 3, \ldots$, so that n wavelengths is equal to the circumference of the classical orbit. Since

$$\lambda = \frac{h}{mv}$$

we see that

$$mva = \frac{nh}{2\pi}$$

where mva is the angular momentum. In general, the orbital angular momentum of any particle about any point in space must be equal to an integer times Planck's constant divided 2π.

The comparison between the orbiting particle and the wave moving around in a circle is clumsy and is indeed only an approximation to a more precise description, which takes the form of a three-dimensional wave that depends upon the details of the interaction that keeps the particle in orbit. The specific conclusions we have reached here, using a simple model, are valid, however.

PROBLEMS

14|1   In a universe such that $h = 10^{-6}$ J-sec a rifleman is shooting at a target 100 m away. If the bullet has a mass of 100 gm and travels at a speed of 1000 m/sec, and if the bullet is centered in the barrel of the gun as it is fired with an accuracy of 10^{-4} m, what is the maximum accuracy that can be expected from the marksman? You can express the result in your own way.

14|2   In a universe such that $h = 10^{-6}$ J-sec (instead of 6×10^{-34} J-sec) a ping pong ball is dropped from a height of 1 m onto a flat round table 20 cm in diameter. The mass of the ball is 10 gm and the ball bounces elastically on the table. Assume the initial aim (or position) of the ball is such as to maximize the probable number of bounces before the ball misses the table; about how many bounces (within a factor of 5) can one expect before the ball misses the table?

14|3 An intensity pattern, such as shown in Fig. 14|1, is generated by the passage of electrons through a pair of slits. How will the pattern change if

(*a*) The velocity of the electrons is doubled?

(*b*) The spacing between the slits is doubled?

(*c*) The spacing between the slits is kept the same but four slits are cut in the barrier instead of two?

(*d*) Protons, having a mass 2000 times as great as the elections, are used, the energy of the protons being the same as the energy of the electrons?

(*e*) Before the electrons reach the double slit they pass through a shutter that is open for a very short time? (That is, how will the observed pattern vary with respect to the time the shutter is open?)

14|4 In a convenient universe where the value of h is 1 J-sec (instead of 6×10^{-34} J-sec) a scientist is measuring the properties of particles that are emitted from a very small source 1000 m away having a momentum of 10 kg-m/sec. He passes the particles through a counter 1 m wide so as to register the number of particles he is working with, but finds that this counter scatters the particles. Though he works very hard to design the counter so that the effect on the particles is minimized, he does not succeed in eliminating the scattering.

(*a*) Why is it impossible for him to eliminate the scattering?

(*b*) What is the smallest (approximate) average scattering angle from the counter that he can possibly expect?

14|5 In a universe such that $h = 10^{-2}$ J-sec a small ball weighing 10 gm is enclosed in a box that measures $1 \times 1.5 \times 3$ m in size. What are the values of the lowest two energies the ball can have? (Remember that $p^2 = p_x{}^2 + p_y{}^2 + p_z{}^2$.) We did not postulate that the ball moved and bounced without energy being lost to friction. How do you think the introduction of friction could modify the character of the system of the ball and box?

14|6 In a universe such that $h = 10^{-2}$ J-sec a particle having a mass of 1 gm is in a one-dimensional box that is 1 m long. The particle has the least possible energy. The box is squeezed down to half its original size with the ball still inside. The only resistance to the change in dimension results from the force of the ball on the sides. What is the minimum amount of energy required to change the size of the box? (The result of this problem should suggest the origin of the "hardness" of atoms and nuclei.)

14|7   In a universe such that $h = 10^{-2}$ J-sec, a particle having a mass of 1 gm is in a one-dimensional box 1 m long. The particle is in the second-lowest energy state. A rifle bullet having a mass of 40 gm and a velocity of 1000 m/sec passes through the box (along the length of the box in this one-dimensional situation). Draw a sketch showing the relative probabilities of collision between the particle and bullet as a function of distance along the box.

14|8   Show that the velocity of a de Broglie wave is one-half the classical velocity of the particles the wave describes. (This does not mean that we are incorrect in our measurement of particle velocity—the particle velocity is the "group velocity" of the wave, which is a slightly subtle concept that we will not take up further.)

14|9   In a quantum universe ($h = 10^{-3}$ J-sec) a hunter is selecting a gun with which he will hunt deer. If the nominal size of deer is 1 m, and the bullet, which has a mass of 0.01 kg, is held in the barrel to an accuracy of 1 cm, what is the least muzzle velocity required so that it is reasonably probable that the hunter can hit a deer at a distance of 100 m?

14|10   In a quantum universe ($h = 1$ J-sec) a baseball pitcher throws three consecutive balls a distance of 20 m over a plate 50 cm across. From the rules of the game in this universe, he is required to throw the balls from a region no greater than 100 cm across. Estimate the minimum speed at which he could have thrown the balls. The mass of a ball is 1 kg.

14|11   A rifleman is firing bullets at a house that has two narrow windows 5 m apart. In this universe the value of h is 1 J sec. Men lined against the back wall of the room, 12 m behind the windows, find that the most dangerous position is at a between the windows, whereas they are completely safe just behind the windows at points b. If each bullet has a mass of 10 gm, what is the lowest possible velocity of the bullets?

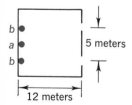

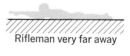

Rifleman very far away

14|12   In a universe where the value of h is 1 J-sec, a mass of 1 kg is swung about on the end of a string 1 m long. What are the values of the three lowest frequencies of rotation that are possible and the three lowest kinetic energies of the system that are allowed?

14|13 In a quantum land, where $h = 100$ J-sec, a dog weighing 10 kg, sick with rabies, is held in a pen 6 m wide. The dog is running back and forth in the cage. It is decided that it is necessary to shoot the dog because it cannot be cured. The keeper takes a gun that fires a heavy shell with a very high muzzle velocity and fires at a point 1 m from the edge of the cage; the dog drops dead. The keeper says, "I didn't know where to aim exactly; but I knew how fast the dog was running, and then I knew that the point at which I aimed was as good a place to aim as any." How fast was the dog running? (Treat this as a one-dimensional problem. There are many correct answers: you might well choose the lowest velocity.)

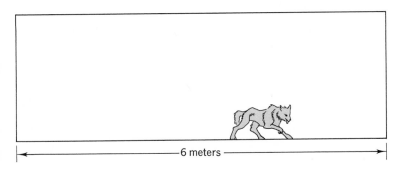

— 6 meters —

14|14 Two gamblers are inspecting a game in a quantum-land shooting gallery. They are to shoot at a ball constrained to a (one-dimensional) box. From the width of the box and the value of h in this universe, they know that the lowest possible energy of the ball in the box will be 1 J. One of the men fires at the exact center of the box and hits the ball (which remains in the box). He then turns to his companion and says, "Without doing more calculation than I want, I don't know the probable energy of the ball now, but I will bet that the energy in joules can be expressed as the square of an odd integer." Will he win the bet? Why?

14|15 In the quantum universe where the value of h is 1.0 J-sec, a pendulum is swinging. The length of the pendulum is 10 m; the mass of the bob is 1 kg; the acceleration of gravity is 10 m/sec².

(*a*) What are the values of the three lowest energies the pendulum can have?

(*b*) If you have a gun that shoots a heavy bullet with a very high muzzle velocity, where should you aim in order to have the maximum likelihood of hitting the bob when the pendulum is in the lowest energy of excitation? When the pendulum is in the second-lowest energy of excitation?

14|16   In a quantum land, where $h = 100$ J-sec, it is a practice to hunt turtles (which are used for soup) by digging pits into which the turtles fall and are trapped. A hunter digs a pit 5 m deep and 5 m across. A second hunter says that "This is a good pit, as it will hold turtles weighing over 1 kg, but of course it won't hold smaller turtles." Why won't the pit hold smaller turtles? (Take g, the acceleration of gravity as 10 m/sec², and assume that one may consider only one dimension of constraint by the walls of the pit.)

fifteen *The theory*
of relativity

15|1   *Measurements of space*
and time

DURING THE LAST DECADES of the nineteenth century it became evident that some aspects of nature could not be understood using the intuitive or classical meanings of space and time. In particular, evidence that the speed of light was the same for all observers, independent of the character of their motion, seemed to demand a review of the classical concepts of space and time. These problems were largely resolved by the formulation of a new description of nature by Albert Einstein in 1905, which is called the Special Theory of Relativity.

In order to appreciate the character of the Special Theory of Relativity and the difference between the relativistic and classical attempts to map nature, it is desirable to analyze the meaning of *space* and *time*. Space and time are best defined, for our purposes, according to the procedures used to measure these quantities. In the role of physicists we can only discuss operations. We will eschew elegance in our attempt to provide satisfactory operational definitions of space and time by examining the measurements of space and time conducted by actors in an appropriate scene.

We consider a scene in which there are two men in different environments who wish to measure the distance between two events and the time that elapses between the two events. Man

O' is in a railroad car traveling in a definite direction with a velocity v. Man O is on the platform at a station through which the train passes. For the sake of definiteness (we could make other reasonable choices without altering the arguments in any fundamental manner) we choose the two events as flashes from two electric sparks that occur upon the contact of electrodes from the car, i' and ii', with similar electrodes mounted on the platform, i and ii. The two observers are provided with appropriate measuring instruments—in particular, a clock and a meter stick. At some previous time, when the train was stopped at the station, the two meter sticks were compared and seen to be identical and the two clocks were compared and seen to run at identical rates. We assume that both observers have access to other apparatus sufficient to their needs, but that the calibrated clock and measuring rod are then fundamental measures of elapsed time and distance.

Figure 15|1 shows the system of car and platform at some particular time. Notice the coordinate systems attached to the car and the platform. The system labeled x', y', z' is the coordinate system of the space S', which is the railroad car; the system labeled x, y, z is the coordinate system of the platform, S. The car is moving with velocity v with respect to the platform; the

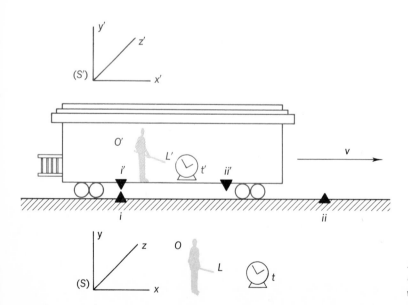

FIG. 15|1
Observers in reference frames moving with different relative velocities.

platform is moving with respect to the car with velocity $-v$. We continue to assume that velocity has only a relative meaning—and none of our observations will contradict this hypothesis.

We now consider that a flash is emitted when the two electrodes i and i' come into contact: this is event i. Another flash, event ii occurs when electrode ii comes into contact with ii'. Now we can examine the procedures used by the two observers to determine the time elapsed between the two events and the distance between the two events. Observer O' can measure the distance between the two events by laying off his meter stick between the electrodes i' and ii' on the railroad car and recording the distance (which is the number of times he laid down the meter stick) in his notebook. This will be the distance between the two events in the system S' of the railroad car. We can write the distance as dx', where

$$dx' = x'_{ii} - x'_i$$

where x'_{ii} and x'_i are the positions of the electrodes according to the coordinate system established in the system of the railroad car, S'.

Observer O on the platform S makes the same kind of measurements; in his system the distance between the two events is just the distance between the two electrodes on the platform, which he can measure by laying off his standard meter stick. He will find that the distance is

$$dx = x_{ii} - x_i$$

where x_{ii} and x_i are the coordinates O measured with his meter stick on the platform S. He will write down the results in his notebook.

The measurement of elapsed time is a little less trivial. Let us suppose an instantaneous signal is possible from the flash to the observer. The observer, in either space, need then simply read his clock when the signals come in. The recorded intervals will then be

$$dt = t_{ii} - t_i \qquad \text{and} \qquad dt' = t'_{ii} - t'_i$$

in system S and S' respectively.

Perhaps, for either practical or fundamental reasons, no instantaneous signal is available. Then a signal moving at a finite rate of speed must be used. This might be the light of the spark itself, which travels at a speed of about 3×10^8 m/sec, or it might be a pet turtle moving at a pace of 0.1 m/sec. In either case, the times recorded by the clock must be corrected for the time it takes a signal to travel to the observer. If the observer is 10 m closer to one signal than the other, the correction will be about 100 sec if the turtle is used, about 3×10^{-7} sec if light is used as the signal. Of course careful calibration measurements must be made of the velocity of light or the velocity of the turtle. However the results are obtained, by turtle or light beam, the results on the time difference between the two signals are definite numbers, which the observers write down in their notebooks.

If the relative velocity of the two observers—here the velocity of the train—is not too great, the two observers will record nearly the same time interval between the two events. Indeed, even now, unless the most advanced techniques of measurement are used, for the modest velocities that can separate different human observers, the times will be identical within the errors of measurement:

$$dt = dt'$$

If instantaneous signals exist, they could be used by the two observers to continually compare their clocks. If velocity is relative, the two reference systems must be disposed symmetrically with respect to one another and one clock cannot run slower than another. Therefore, the clocks must agree and the observers must agree on the time interval which has elapsed between signals. The possibility of such instantaneous signals, and then the equality of time intervals, was an implicity precept of classical physics. In this case the number of seconds elapsed between the two events shown in Fig. 15|1, as measured and recorded by the two observers occupying the different reference systems moving with respect to one another, must be unique: each observer must record the same number. The elapsed time between two events must be invariant with respect to the motion of the observer.

To the extent that this hypothesis is valid the observers O and O', observing each other's actions, will each agree that his opposite number is proceeding competently and correctly in making his respective measurements. The distances dx and dx' recorded in the notebooks of the two observers will differ in a simple manner. The electrode ii' will have moved a distance $v\,dt'$ in the time

dt' between flashes, so $dx = dx' + v\,dt'$. Altogether, we have two sets of equations relating the results of measurements in one system to the results of measurements in another system.
From the view of observer O' on S':

$$dx = dx' + v\,dt'$$
$$dt = dt'$$

From the view of observer O on S:

$$dx' = dx - v\,dt$$
$$dt' = dt$$

These are the equations of the Galilean transformation, which we discussed previously. They are relations between the recorded measurements of the two observers, O and O'.

We now use these relations, the equations of the Galilean transformation, to consider some results of measurements when instantaneous signals are not available to the observers. It is convenient to discuss the particularly simple case such that $dx = dx'$ and $dt = dt' = 0$; that is, the two signals are simultaneous as noted by the observer O on the platform, who has available to him instantaneous signals. The relative configuration of the two systems, the platform and the railroad car, are shown in Fig. 15 | 2a.

Observer O' is located, for convenience, exactly between the

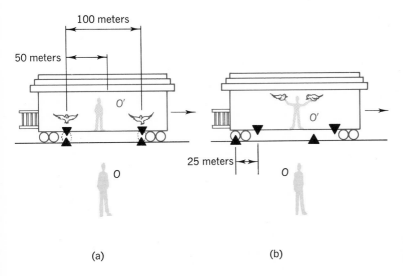

(a)   (b)

FIG. 15 | 2
Observers in different inertial systems watching the flight of pigeons: (a) the pigeons are released at the time of the sparks; (b) O' receives the pigeons.

two electrodes on the car, which he has measured to be 100 m apart. He uses a coordinate system such that the origin of the coordinate system is at the first electrode; then $x_{i'} = 0$ and $x_{ii'} = 100$ m. Of course we are primarily interested in discussing measurements such that the signals are carried by light. However, in order to emphasize both the generality of our results and the problems concerning the media in which the signal travels in a manner that is close to our intuitive understanding, we will consider another familiar carrier of signals, the pigeon. The man O' on the car will then receive his signals from the two electrodes by two calibrated pigeons, which fly at a speed u of 10 m/sec. The velocity of the railroad car, with respect to the platform is $v = 5$ m/sec. The car is an enclosed car carrying its atmosphere along with it. From the view of O', the two birds reach him simultaneously. Since each bird has a speed of 10 m/sec and has traveled 50 m, he knows that the events took place simultaneously and 5 sec before the birds reached him.

The observer O on the platform sees a different, though simply related picture. He sees (we will use "see" to represent the reception of the instantaneous signals) the two birds leave promptly at the time of the two sparks, and he sees the birds reach O' simultaneously 5 sec later. However, according to O, observer O' will have moved with respect to the coordinate system of the platform during the 5 sec. At the time of the sparks, the coordinates on the platform system of the first spark, the observer O', and the second spark are

$$x_i = 0 \qquad O' = 50 \text{ m} \qquad x_{ii} = 100 \text{ m}$$

At the time the pigeons reach O', observer O' has moved a distance equal to 5 m/sec times 5 sec, or 25 m down the track. Bird i, which started from electrode i has traveled 75 m, and bird ii from electrode ii has traveled 25 m in the 5 sec in the platform system. Clearly the velocity of bird i is 15 m/sec, and that of bird ii is 5 m/sec, according to the measurements of O in the platform system.

In general, we can express these velocities as

$$u = u' + v$$

where u is the velocity of the pigeon as determined in the S system (and recorded in the notebook of observer O) and u' is the velocity of the pigeon in the S' system as measured and recorded by O'. The velocity, u, of the bird in system S is equal to the velocity, u', in system S' plus the velocity, v, of system S' with respect to S: velocities are additive. This result follows, in an essential manner, from the relations of the Galilean transformation.

We might as easily discuss the inverse of the previous situation. Perhaps observer O on the platform, S, has only pigeons to carry signals. Again we would come to the conclusion that $u = u' + v$, and from the view of O' observing O on the platform, S,

$$u' = u - v$$

The minus sign is used because the platform is going backward from the view of O' in the car, S'.

In the preceding example the signal was carried by a bird in a closed car. It is certainly plausible that the velocity at which the bird will fly will be the same in a closed car, relative to the car, as it would be on the platform, relative to the platform. We assume that no wind is blowing. If we used sound as our signal we again find it reasonable that the velocity of sound is a velocity with respect to the mass of air through which the sound is transmitted. This follows naturally from Huygens' principle, which considers a wave as a propagation of disturbances in a medium: in this case the medium is air. If the railroad car is closed and carries the air along with it, the sound in the car will have its natural velocity, U, with respect to the car, where by *natural velocity* we mean the velocity with respect to the medium. If there is no wind on the platform and the sound is traveling through the air of the platform, the velocity of that sound with respect to the platform will again be equal to U.

If the sound is traveling in the positive x-direction on the car, the velocity in the car, as measured by O', is

$$u' = U$$

The velocity measured and recorded by O on the platform will be

$$u = u' + v = U + v$$

If the sound is traveling in the x-direction through the still air on the platform, O' will record the velocity as

$$u' = u - v$$
$$= U - v$$

and O will measure the velocity as

$$u = U$$

These relations are exactly the same in form as the relations that pertain to the flight of pigeons, where the pigeons fly with a standard speed, U, with respect to the medium they traverse.

In preparation for an examination of the velocity of light, we should consider a variation of the conditions analyzed above. It is possible that the car on the train is an open flatcar and does not carry the air with it. In this case observer O' will note that a pigeon flies 50 m in the positive x-direction in 10 sec, so his average velocity is only 5 m/sec. The pigeon flying in the negative x-direction will cover the 50 m in 3.33 sec for a velocity of 15 m/sec. Whether O' concludes that there is a wind, or that the flatcar is moving, or merely that pigeons perversely like to fly faster in one direction than the other, is of no practical relevance in the analysis of the observations.

Birds i and ii will not reach the observer at the same time in this case. Bird i, which carried the message from spark i, will arrive 6.67 sec after bird ii, which carried the message from spark ii. Knowing that the distance each flies is 50 m, O' deduces that the events i and ii occurred simultaneously.

Observer O will view the efforts of his colleague O' from a different viewpoint. He would say that the two birds traveled at the same speed of 10 m/sec, but that the movement of the car changed the position of the observer. His position was at the point $x = 50$ m, according to the platform coordinate system, at the moment the sparks were emitted. Since observer O' was moving at a rate of 5 m/sec in the positive x-direction, the bird from i had to fly farther to overtake the observer, and it took him 10 sec. Observer O' was moving toward bird ii, so that bird had a shorter distance to travel and reached the observer after only 3.33 sec.

15│2   *The velocities of signals carried by a moving medium*

If light is used to propagate signals and if the relations of Galilean relativity are correct—that is, if they really describe reality—we must expect to have to consider the detailed character of the propagation of light. It is necessary to ask two questions: (a) What is the medium that transmits light; and (b) does the earth pass freely through the medium like an open flatcar through the atmosphere, or does the earth carry the medium with it like the enclosed railroad car? We give the hypothetical medium the name *ether*: of course this does not result in any increase in knowledge of the medium. Our classical concept of space and time, as coded in the relations of the Galilean transformation equations, allows no fundamental alternatives to those listed in (b).

The problem of determining which of the alternatives is valid (and we shall find, paradoxically, that neither is valid) differs from the analyses of the observers on the car and platform inasmuch as we have no platform; we are resident only on the train—our earth. Then, in order to illuminate the problem of measuring the ether drift, and answering the question (b), we consider in detail the similar problem where the observer on the railroad car must measure the velocity of wind past the car. How can observer O' in car S' measure the velocity of the car with respect to the air that carries the pigeon? The simplest thing he can do is simply measure the velocity of the pigeon in the direction of suspected motion of the car and in the opposite direction. If the car is moving with velocity v and the pigeons are known to fly, with respect to the air, with velocity c, the pigeon flying in the direction of the car's motion will have a velocity

$$c_+ = c - v$$

The pigeon flying in the direction opposite to the motion of the car will have a velocity

$$c_- = c + v$$

Half of the difference between these velocities is the velocity of the car:

$$\tfrac{1}{2}(c_- - c_+) = v$$

This is the same result we would obtain if the car were stationary and a wind was blowing from the $+x$ direction with velocity v.

Before we establish this method as a basic procedure for measuring the relative velocity of the flatcar and the air, we must decide how we are going to measure the velocity of the pigeon. In practice we might establish a specific flight distance, perhaps

100 m, station ourselves with a stop watch at the finish line, and observe and time the start and finish of the flight. This procedure presupposes the use of a signal that is instantaneous, or at least very much faster than the pigeon and independent of air flow. In practice we would see the pigeon start its journey. We would use the light as our signal.

If no such instantaneous signal were available, or no signal we could be certain was unaffected by the air flow, this simple procedure would not be at all simple. How could we tell when the pigeon started? When would we start our stop watch? Certainly it would be ridiculous to use another pigeon to bring a message that the racing pigeon had left the starting line. We must therefore use a more subtle scheme.

A method of measuring a pigeon's velocity that does not require instantaneous signals is to measure the time it takes the bird to fly back and forth—from the observer to some goal at a distance L, and back again. We don't have to know when he reached the far point, and therefore incur signaling problems; we need know only that the bird did get there, which is easy to check in various ways. If there is no wind from the motion of the car, the time elapsed between the departure and return of the bird will be

$$t = \frac{L}{c} + \frac{L}{c}$$

$$= \frac{2L}{c}$$

If the car is moving with velocity v, the elapsed time will be

$$t' = \frac{L}{c+v} + \frac{L}{c-v}$$

A little algebraic manipulation puts this in the form

$$t_1' = \frac{2Lc}{c^2 - v^2}$$

and finally

$$t_1' = \frac{2L}{c} \left(\frac{1}{1 - v^2/c^2} \right) \tag{15|1}$$

If the car is moving, the pigeon will take longer for his journey: the nominal time for the journey, $2L/c$, will be increased by a factor $1/(1 - v^2/c^2)$. If we know the value, c, of the pigeon's velocity relative to the air, we can use the measured values of L and t_1' to determine the wind velocity v. But we may not know the value of c: if we have spent our lives on the flatcar, we may never have had the opportunity to race the pigeon in still air and calibrate the pigeon.

We solve this problem of determining c, the air speed of the pigeon, by sending the pigeon back and forth along a course transverse to the motion of the flatcar—or motion of the wind. An analysis of the pigeon's behavior on this course will show that the pigeon is still affected by the wind; his times will be again a little longer because of the wind, but the effect will be less, and by an analysis of the different slowing-down factors we will be able to deduce both the velocity of the wind, v, and the air speed of the pigeon, c.

If the pigeon aims at a goal transverse to the motion of the car, closes his eyes, and starts flying toward the goal, he will miss the goal by a large margin. From the view of the man on the platform, the goal was carried upstream by the motion of the car while the pigeon was in flight: from the view of the man on the car, the wind swept the pigeon downstream. The diagram of Fig. 15|3a shows the intended and actual path of the pigeon as inscribed on the map of the man on the car. If the pigeon is to actually reach the goal, the bird must aim at a point upstream before closing its eyes and beginning the flight. How far upstream must the bird

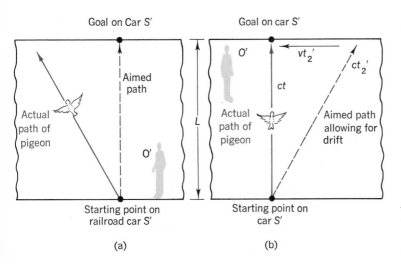

(a)   (b)

FIG. 15|3

The paths of pigeons as seen from a moving flatcar. In (a) the pigeon is blown off course from the view of observer O' on the car.

aim? And, then, how far must the bird fly and how long will it take for the bird to fly to the target? It is most simple to consider this from the view of an observer who is stationary with respect to the medium in which the pigeon flies—that is, the air—and the man on the platform will represent such an observer.

From the view of the man on the platform, both the pigeon and goal are in motion. If the pigeon's course is correct, the pigeon will reach the goal after a flight of t_2' sec. During this time the goal will have moved upstream a distance of vt_2' m, where v is the velocity of the car. If the bird's flight speed is c m/sec, the bird will have flown a distance of ct_2' m, and this distance will represent the hypotenuse of a triangle where L, the transverse distance from the starting point to the goal, is the base, and vt_2' is the altitude. This is suggested by the drawing of Fig. 15 | 3b. From the Pythagorean theorem,

$$L^2 = (ct_2')^2 + (vt_2')^2$$

Then

$$(t_2')^2 = \frac{L^2}{c^2 - v^2}$$

or

$$t_2' = \frac{L}{c} \frac{1}{\sqrt{1 - v^2/c^2}}$$

and the round trip takes twice as long. The pigeon's round-trip flight takes longer than the time it would take if the car were stationary—or the wind were not blowing—by the factor

$$\frac{1}{\sqrt{1 - v^2/c^2}}$$

Both of the pigeon round trips, the trip around the course parallel to the direction of motion of the car and the trip transverse to the direction of motion, take longer when the car is moving or the wind is blowing. The parallel trip takes longer than the transverse trip. If we start one pigeon on the parallel course and one on the transverse course simultaneously (we presumably choose identical twins—an interesting problem for biologists—so that the pigeons have identical airspeeds) the pigeon on the transverse course will return before the pigeon flying the parallel course, and the time difference, dt, will depend upon the velocity of the wind (or from the view of the man on the platform, where the air is still, on the velocity of the railroad car):

$$dt = t_1' - t_2' = \frac{2L}{c} \left[\frac{1}{1 - v^2/c^2} - \frac{1}{\sqrt{1 - v^2/c^2}} \right]$$

If v is very much smaller than c, $v^2/c^2 \ll 1$, and we can use the results of the binomial theorem to express dt in a simple fashion.

The binomial theorem gives

$$(1 + x)^a = 1 + ax \qquad \text{if} \qquad x \ll 1$$

Then for $v^2/c^2 \ll 1$

$$\left(1 - \frac{v^2}{c}\right)^{-1} \approx 1 + \frac{v^2}{c^2}$$

and

$$\left(1 - \frac{v^2}{c^2}\right)^{1/2} \approx 1 + \frac{1}{2}\frac{v^2}{c^2}$$

Using these approximations,

$$dt = \frac{2L}{c}\left(1 + \frac{v^2}{c^2} - 1 - \frac{1}{2}\frac{v^2}{c^2}\right)$$

$$= \frac{2L}{c}\left(\frac{1}{2}\frac{v^2}{c^2}\right) \tag{15|2}$$

Thus, from the time difference between the two pigeons observer O' can determine the ratio of v to c.

At first glance it might seem that the observer on the railroad car has not improved his knowledge of the velocity of the car much, since he must still know c in order to find v. But now he is measuring the ratio v^2/c^2 instead of the difference between c^2 and $v^2 - c^2$ [Eq. (15|1)] which he would have to measure if he timed only the parallel round trip. If v is very much smaller than c, and if c is known only approximately, the comparison of the two flights will give the value of v rather accurately, while the measurement of the time of one flight is almost useless. It is useful to consider a particular example for illustration.

Let us assume that the value of c, the speed of the bird, is actually 100 m/sec, the value of v is only 1 m/sec, and the length of the two courses is set at 5000 m (10,000 m for the round trip). Then for the round trip parallel to the direction of motion of the train, the elapsed time will be 100.01 sec from Eq. (15|1). But this does not really tell us what the velocity of the car is: we might just as well conclude that the bird flies at a speed of 100.01 m/sec. However, if we let the two equal birds fly the two courses simultaneously, the birds' flight times will differ by $\frac{1}{200}$ sec, according to Eq. (15|2). And this difference is solely due to the motion of the car. At this time differential one bird will be leading the other by 0.5 meters, which is easy to measure rather accurately—perhaps by measuring the distance on a photograph taken at the finish line—and the value of v can be calculated to the same relative accuracy to which c is known. For example, c might be taken as 100.01 m/sec from the first measurement instead of 100 m/sec. This approximation would introduce an error of only 0.01 percent in the value of v.

Of course, these measurements allow the man on the flatcar to measure the absolute velocity of the flatcar (with respect to the air). The velocity of the flatcar is not truly relative: the earth and its atmosphere is a priviliged reference system. Is there such a *universal* priviliged reference system? We will examine this question by measuring the velocity of light rather than pigeons.

15|3   *The Michelson–Morley experiment*

The procedures used in the last section to determine the velocity of a flatcar through still air by measuring the flight times of pigeons can be used to detect the motion of the earth through the ether—to detect the ether wind expected by most physicists of a century ago. The railroad car is now the earth; the signal is now not a pigeon or sound, but light; the wind we try to detect is not air but the supposed carrier of light, the ether; and the observers are ourselves in the persons of Albert Michelson and Edward Morley at the Case Institute and Western Reserve University in the Cleveland of 1886–7. Since the velocity of the earth about the sun is only about 10^{-4} times the velocity of light, $v^2/c^2 \approx 10^{-8}$ and a very sensitive experiment must be designed. Of course, since the sun is moving through the galaxy and the galaxy itself may be moving, the effective velocity might be somewhat larger, but we cannot be sure what that relevant velocity will be.

A schematic and simplified diagram of the apparatus of Michelson and Morley is shown in Fig. 15|4. A beam of light from a

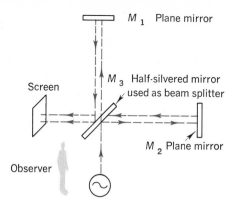

FIG. 15 | 4

*A schematic diagram
showing the paths of the
light beams in the
Michelson–Morley
experiment.*

source designed to provide light that is nearly monochromatic
is incident upon a half-silvered mirror, M_3, which splits the
beam; about half the light is transmitted and about half reflected.
The transmitted beam passes to mirror M_1 and is reflected back
to M_3, where it is reflected again to a screen viewed by an observer. The reflected beam from M_3 passes to a mirror M_2, which
reflects it back to, and through, M_3 so that it is also incident on
the screen. If the total distance the two beams travel is the same,
and if the velocity of light is the same for the two beams, the light
waves from the two beams will be in phase at the position of the
observer and he will see a bright spot on the screen. If the waves
are out of phase by half a wavelength, the two beams will tend to
cancel and there will be, at best, only a very dim spot on the
screen. By carefully moving one of the mirrors a very short
distance and observing the shifts in brightness, Michelson and
Morley convinced themselves that they could detect a shift of
$\frac{1}{100}$ wavelength. (Their exact procedures were somewhat more
complicated, but the same in principle as that described here.)

The experiment was performed by setting mirrors M_1 and M_2
in a specific position—let us say so that the beams are in phase—
and then observing the interference as the apparatus was rotated.
Let us assume that the apparatus was set so that the times required for the two beams to traverse their respective courses
were the same. This would be done by adjusting the mirrors
until the brightness of the spot was a maximum. Then, when the
apparatus is rotated 90°, the rays will take different times to
traverse the apparatus if there is an ether wind. The light beams

are analogous to the pigeons even as the ether corresponds to the air through which the flatcar passes.

The number of waves per second in each light beam is equal to the frequency of the light, f. If the traversal time of the two beams differs by an amount dt, the number of wavelengths in the two rays will differ by an amount $d\lambda$, where

$$d\lambda = f\,dt$$

The wavelength shift would represent a difference in phase of the two beams at the screen and thus a difference in the intensity of the spot viewed by the observer.

The Michelson–Morley apparatus was designed to detect a velocity of $\frac{1}{30}$ the velocity of the earth about the sun. No wavelength shift was noted at all! The experiment was repeated at different times of the year, and with other variations, but no effect was ever observed. There was no ether wind!

15|4   *Aberration*

Though it seemed, a priori, improbable, it might still be possible that the earth swept the ether with it even as the closed railroad car swept the air along with it. If this were the case the Michelson–Morley experiment would give a null result; even as pigeons in a closed railroad car will fly at the same velocity in the longitudinal and transverse directions, light will travel at the same velocity, independent of direction, if the ether is pulled along with the earth. However, an astronomical observation made long before, in 1827 by Bradley, then the Astronomer Royal of England, was a serious obstacle to such a view. Bradley noticed that he had to orient his telescope at a slightly different angle, depending on the time of year, in order to align the telescope on the various fixed stars. The positions of the stars appeared to vary slightly in a regular fashion during the year. The character of this *aberration* is suggested by the diagram of Fig. 15|5. The angle at which the telescope is oriented to view any fixed star changes by an angle equal to 2θ over a period of six months; the angular position of each fixed star appears then to change by an amount equal to 2θ during that period. The apparent position of the stars moves about in a circle during the year such that the radius of the circle subtends an angle equal to θ.

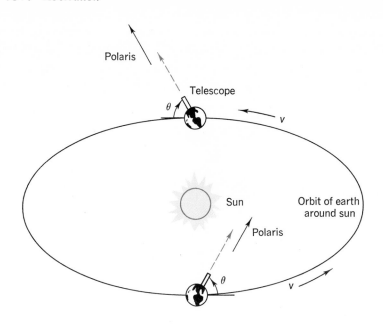

FIG. 15|5
*The orientation of a
telescope viewing
Polaris at different times
of the year.*

Upon careful analysis of his measurements Bradley found that a particularly simple explanation fit all his observations of the aberrations. The telescope moved slightly, as a result of the earth's motion, as the light passed down the tube. This is illustrated schematically in Fig. 15|6, where the earth and telescope are moving to the left with velocity v. The light enters the telescope at a and takes a time equal to $dt = L/c$ to travel to the bottom of the telescope, where L is the length of the tube. During this time the telescope moves a distance $v\,dt$. If the light is to strike the center of the telescope, the telescope must be tilted

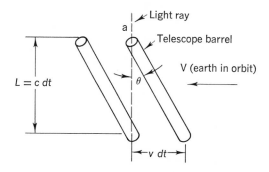

FIG. 15|6
*Light passing through a
moving telescope.*

as shown in the figure. The angle of the tilt, θ, of the telescope with respect to the true direction of the star is such that

$$\tan \theta = \frac{v}{c}$$

and for $v/c \ll 1$,

$$\theta = \frac{v}{c}$$

where v is the velocity of the earth about the sun and c is the velocity of light. The telescope must be inclined toward the direction of motion of the earth.

If the ether were dragged along with the earth, the phenomenon of aberration would not be observed. A plane wave of light from a far-off star would produce a plane wave in the region of the earth that would travel in the same direction as the original wave if the medium carrying the wave were carried along with the earth. This result is suggested by examining a hypothetical situation illustrated in Fig. 15|7, where, for conceptual simplicity, the ether is considered to be undisturbed above the heavy solid line and completely carried along with the earth and its atmosphere below the line. The light waves from the star, shown in the diagram such that the surfaces of equal phase are shown as solid lines, will strike the interface and excite waves in the moving ether. Since the wave fronts from the star will strike the whole length of the interface at the same time, the Huygens' waves set up at the interface will all originate at the same time, and the propagation in the moving system will proceed such that

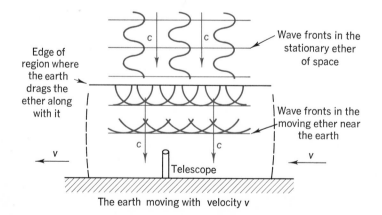

The earth moving with velocity v

FIG. 15 | 7
The passage of light waves to a moving earth that carries the ether along with it.

the wave fronts are parallel to the wave fronts in the stationary system, and hence the direction of the light will be the same in the moving system as in the stationary system. Although the whole earth system, complete with waves, is swept to the left with the velocity of the earth v, the wave direction is still determined by the perpendicular to the lines of equal phase (which may represent the amplitude peaks) and the direction of the light incident on the telescope will be the same as the direction that would be observed if there were no motion at all. The measured direction is therefore unaffected by the motion of the earth. The light in Fig. 15|6 would be carried along with the telescope, and no effect would be observed.

The general form of the argument is not restricted to light waves in the ether. The moving system might have been a railroad car, the stationary system the surrounding countryside, and the interface the window of the car. If a bell sounds far from the car, at right angles with respect to the track, an observer in the car will hear the sound as if it came from the bell, independent of the velocity of the railroad car. If the observer were on a flatcar, the sound of the bell would appear to come from a point ahead of the actual bell: aberration would occur.

The observation of aberration shows that the ether (if there is an ether) is not carried along with the earth like the air in the enclosed railroad car. But the Michelson–Morley experiment showed that the ether is carried along with the earth. We have a paradox.

For completeness we should also examine the "projectile" theory of light. Can we resolve the paradox by such a model of light? If light had properties such as those of a classical particle, and the wave nature was somehow not important, we might expect that the relevant velocity of light would be always measured relative to its source. Such a theory is consistent with both the Michelson–Morley and the aberration results. There would be no Michelson–Morley effect if their experiment had been performed with machine-gun bullets. There would be an aberration effect if light traveled like bullets.

This rather unattractive particle model of light is excluded by direct measurements on the velocity of light emitted by elementary particles that are themselves moving with high velocities, as well as by observations on the light emitted by binary stars. Certain of the elementary particles, in particular, the π^0 and the

Σ^0, particles undergo transitions such that they emit very-high-energy gamma rays: gamma rays are similar to light, but of extremely high frequency. These elementary particles are produced by the interactions of protons accelerated by very-high-energy accelerators—cyclotrons, synchrotrons, linear accelerators, and so on—and they are produced in such a manner that they are usually traveling at very high speeds, speeds very near the velocity of light, with respect to the experimental apparatus in the laboratory. While traveling at these high velocities, they emit light in the course of their decays. Typically, the particles will be moving forward at a speed of 90 percent or more of the speed of light and then emit light (or gamma rays) in the forward direction. If the projectile theory of the addition of light velocities were valid, the total speed of this light would be nearly twice the speed of light emitted from a stationary source. Instead, the velocity has been measured quite accurately to be equal to 3×10^8 m/sec, the same as light from a stationary source; the velocities do not add.

Measurements of binary stars are interesting historically, as these measurements comprise the first demonstration of the independence of the velocity of light with respect to the velocity of the source, and they are also interesting as they concern measurements on light of the same character—or same frequency—as the light used in the Michelson–Morley experiment. A binary star system often consists of a very heavy star and a lighter star; the lighter star can be considered to rotate about its heavier sibling as suggested by the sketch of Fig. 15|8. Let us examine a particular (and imaginary) system 100 light-years (lt-yr) from

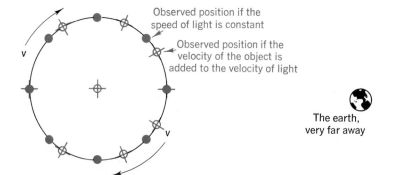

Observed position if the speed of light is constant

Observed position if the velocity of the object is added to the velocity of light

v

v

The earth, very far away

FIG. 15|8
Real and observed positions of the lighter member of a binary star system if the speed of light depends upon the speed of the object that emits the light.

the earth where the plane of the orbit lies edge-on to the earth. (A light-year is a convenient astronomical distance—the distance light travels in 1 year.) Let us assume that the smaller star revolves about the larger in a circular orbit with a period of 0.10 yr, the velocity of the small star being 30 km/sec, which is just $10^{-4}c$.

The solid circles in Fig. 15|8 represent the position of the smaller star as it would be observed if the speed of light were constant. If the velocity of the object is added to the speed of light, the light from the star at point a will be about $1.0001c$, and the speed from point b will be about $0.9999c$. If the system is 100 lt-yr from the earth, light will take 100 yr to reach the earth ordinarily, but the light from a will reach the earth about $\frac{1}{100}$ yr ahead of time, and the light from b will be about $\frac{1}{100}$ yr late. As a result, the observer on earth will see the star at the position of the empty circles instead of the correct positions of the solid circles. The star will appear to speed up from b to a and slow down from a to b. Although actual double star systems are not so tractable as this imaginary one, it is nevertheless clear that binary stars move in their orbits in a normal manner and that the speed of light is independent of the motion of the source as it appears to be independent of the motion of the receiver. The projectile model is thus inconsistent with observations and cannot be used to resolve the paradox posed by the Michelson–Morley experiment and the observation of aberration.

The existence of this paradox contradicts our classical beliefs as to the relations of time and space itself. The Michelson–Morley experiment shows that the velocity of light is not dependent upon the motion of the earth—our metaphorical pigeon representing light flies at a constant velocity with respect to observer O' on car S'. On the other hand, the aberration results show that the ether, or air on our car, is not swept along, and therefore the pigeon must fly with its standard velocity with respect to the observer. If the pigeon—or light—travels with velocity c as measured by O', and the same velocity c as measured by O, and if O' is moving at velocity v with respect to O, we can use the theorem of the addition of velocities to show that

$$c = c + v$$

which is obviously nonsense.

Our logic is impeccable; our result, that the velocity of light is the same for all observers in inertial reference frames, that velocity is truly *relative* inasmuch as an observer cannot detect his absolute motion by measuring the speed of light, is in contradiction to the conclusions derived from our logical constructions; therefore some basic assumption we have made must be wrong. We will find that our implicit assumptions concerning the character of space and time must be revised and a new description of nature must be constructed, a description that must include the absolute character of the speed of light and the relative character of the velocity of inertial reference systems. This description is, of course, the Special Theory of Relativity.

15|5 *The Lorentz–Fitzgerald hypothesis*

The basic result of all our observations on the speed of light shows that the speed of light has the same constant value for all observers in inertial systems, independent of their velocities. How can we understand this result—an experimental result—and retain the description of nature that works so well in correlating so many other observations? This was an essential problem of physics at the end of the nineteenth century.

If an ether wind exists, a classical view of space and time measurements leads to the conclusion that light will take a time equal to

$$t_L = \frac{2L/c}{1 - v^2/c^2}$$

to complete a journey back and forth over a distance L parallel to the direction of the wind. A path of the same length, transverse to the wind, will be covered in a time

$$t_T = \frac{2L/c}{\sqrt{1 - v^2/c^2}}$$

The results of the Michelson–Morley experiment showed that $t_L = t_T$ on earth, though we know that the earth is in motion.

Perhaps the ether wind distorts the measuring instruments. Hendrik Lorentz, professor at Utrecht, and independently, George Fitzgerald at Trinity College, Dublin, pointed out that if the ether wind compressed matter in the direction of the wind such that any length, dx, would be shortened by the wind to a value dx' given by

$$dx' = dx \sqrt{1 - v^2/c^2} \qquad (15\,|\,3)$$

where v is the velocity of the wind, the meter stick used to measure the distance L parallel to the wind, and thus the distance L itself, would be shortened just enough that the light traveling back and forth on the parallel course would take exactly as long as the light traveling the transverse course. The times would be

$$t_L = t_T = \frac{2L/c}{\sqrt{1 - v^2/c^2}}$$

The particular recipe of (15 | 3) appears to have been selected by Fitzgerald on a purely *ad hoc* basis—that is, the relation was selected solely because it would solve the paradox. On the other hand, Lorentz derived the relation from his incorrect—but very perceptive—theory of electricity.

If such a contraction took place it would still be possible to determine the existence of the wind by performing very precise, and very difficult, experiments to measure the time elapsed for trips under conditions such that the velocity v would be different. Light would still take longer on either path if the system were moving through the ether than if the system were stationary. For a stationary system, $t_T = t_L = 2L/c$. The value of t should differ (by about 1 part in 10^8) from summer to winter, or fall to spring, as the earth's velocity adds to or subtracts from the velocity of the sun moving through the galaxy.

However, Lorentz pointed out that if the wind made the clock run slow, such that a second, dt', on the moving system was greater than a second, dt, on the stationary system by an amount

$$dt' = dt \frac{1}{\sqrt{1 - v^2/c^2}} \qquad (15\,|\,4)$$

the wind could not even be detected by a measurement of the elapsed time. Although the time would "actually" be greater by a factor of

$$\frac{1}{\sqrt{1 - v^2/c^2}}$$

if an ether wind of velocity v were blowing, the seconds on the clock would be "incorrectly" longer by the same factor,

$$\frac{1}{\sqrt{1 - v^2/c^2}}$$

and the effect would not be noticed. Lorentz further showed that no possible experiment could then detect the wind if the wind caused the clock to run more slowly and shortened the meter stick according to the Lorentz–Fitzgerald prescription. These hypotheses also suggested that nothing can exceed the speed of light—the ether wind will have already squeezed any material body to zero thickness at that velocity.

15 | 6   *The relative character of different observers*

Explanations of the Michelson–Morley results that demand such particular distortions of the measuring instruments are unsatisfactory inasmuch as they are specially designed to fit one particular experimental result and thus have an artificial character. The ether wind is undetectable because it affects the measuring instruments in precisely the way needed to fool the measurements. Logic like this is all right as a beginning hypothesis, but carried further is very close to the reasoning of a witch-doctor. If the ether cannot be detected, it is simpler to assume that it does not exist—what meaning can it have if it is, in principle, undetectable? This was the view taken by Einstein.

In much the same spirit we must disregard the idea that the clock is incorrect or that the meter stick is incorrect because of this external agency, the ether, if the ether is undetectable in principle. The clock measures time; the meter stick measures distance; if the clock on the railroad car runs slowly from the view of the man on the platform, it must be time itself that is seen to pass slowly; if the meter stick is observed to be shortened, it must be space itself that is seen to be compressed. Time and space have meaning only in measurement.

The rejection of the concept of a stationary ether through which all bodies move without friction leads to a further conclusion—there is no longer any basis for absolute motion. The existence of an ether demanded the reality of absolute velocity: the velocity of any object could always be defined, and in principle measured, in terms of the velocity relative to the ether. If there is no ether, velocity need not have any absolute meaning: only relative velocities are defined.

In 1904 Henri Poincaré stated that a new dynamics must be developed such that the laws of the dynamics did not differentiate between observers in different inertial frames (relativity) and that the speed of light was the same for all such observers. In 1905 Einstein published his Special Theory of Relativity, which accomplished that aim. The basic equations of Einstein's theory were the equations of Lorentz and Fitzgerald. But Einstein gave them a new meaning.

If only relative velocity is meaningful, there can be no intrinsic difference between the view of S', the car, by O, the observer on the platform, and the view of the platform, S, by O', the observer on the car. Furthermore, the speed of light must be the same as measured by each observer. The particular distortion of space and time suggested by Lorentz is uniquely determined by these requirements. A system, S', moving in the x-direction, as seen by a stationary observer, O, will appear to be shortened in the x-direction, and time will appear to pass more slowly. According to O the clocks on S' will appear to run slowly and the meter

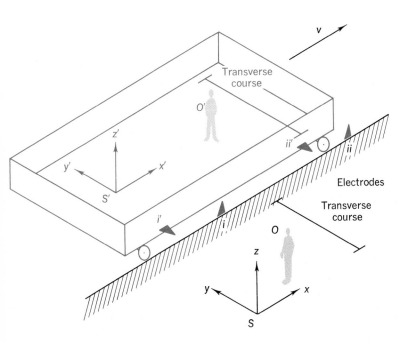

FIG. 15|9

Observers in different inertial reference systems timing the sparks of electrodes.

sticks on S' will appear to be less than a meter long when the sticks lie parallel to the direction of motion of the car, S'. From the view of O', the observer on the railroad car, the platform system, S, will appear to be moving backward—in the negative x-direction. If there is no absolute velocity, either view, that of O or O', is correct, and any description of nature must be symmetric with respect to O and O'. Then from the view of O' the clocks on the platform appear to be running slowly and the meter sticks on the platform appear to be shortened.

There must be no contradiction between these views. In order to illuminate these conclusions, we discuss in detail a particular sequence of events, using the scene and equipment of Fig. 15|9. We require both O and O' to set their respective electrodes 100 m apart. They measure this distance using their meter sticks. Each stands exactly between the two electrodes and receives signals from the sparks that allow him to decide which spark occurred first, i or ii. Furthermore, each measures the velocity of light by measuring the time a ray takes to go a certain distance in the transverse y-direction and return. We consider their results in the form of a dialogue between O and O'.

O: I measured the speed of light by timing light on the transverse, to-and-fro, course and got the correct handbook answer for the velocity of light. I noted that the electrodes on the car, S', which was moving in the positive x-direction with velocity v, were not so far apart as mine; therefore, spark i occurred before ii.

O':   I also measured the velocity of light by timing the transverse course and got the correct handbook value. The electrodes on the platform, S, which was moving by in the negative x-direction with velocity v, were less than 100 m apart, not so far apart as mine, and therefore ii occurred before i.

O: As for the measurements of O', I know that he measured his electrode distance as 100 m, but his meter stick is short. The reason he saw ii before i is that he was moving toward it, so naturally the light did not take as long to reach him from ii as from i; it didn't have as far to go. As to his measurement of the velocity of light, actually the light took longer to go back and forth, since the car was moving, but his clock was wrong; it was just slow enough so that he got the usual result for c.

O': It was *O* who measured his electrode distance incorrectly.
His electrodes were less far apart than mine because his
meter stick was too short. Since he was moving in the −*x*-
direction, the light from *i* reached him before the light from
ii, while, as I have noted, the spark *ii* came first. Since he
was moving, the time the light took to run his transverse
course was longer than it should have been. He got the right
answer only because his clock was slow.

Notice that for each observer, *O* and *O'*, both their measurements and their views of the other's measurements are symmetric. As a third observer or judge we might ask, "Who really
was right? Which spark occurred first? Which electrode-spacing
measurement was correct? Which electrode spacing was the
greater?" The answer is that each observer was correct and that
neither the length of the meter sticks nor the timing of clocks is
an invariant independent of the observer. They have no more
absolute meaning than has the distance between *x*-coordinates
of two points. Different observers, with different coordinate
systems, will give different answers. We will find that the distance
between two events, and the time between two events, are not
invariants, independent of the observer, but are more like components of a vector, dependent on the disposition of the observer.

15|7   *The Lorentz transformation*

We now can use the information we have about short meter
sticks and slow clocks to consider the relations between the
values of measurements in the two systems *S* and *S'*. The time
between two events and the distance between two events in
classical physics are expressed by our equations of the Galilean
transformation:

$$x = x' + vt' \quad \text{and} \quad x' = x - vt$$

$$t = t' \quad \text{and} \quad t' = t$$

Let us review the meaning of these relations. Two events have
occurred, such as the sparks between railroad car and platform
discussed in Section 15|1, and are considered by observers *O*
and *O'* who inhabit different coordinates systems *S* and *S'*: *S'*
is moving with a velocity *v* in the *x*-direction with respect to *S*.

For convenience we arrange that event *i* occurs at the origin of the two coordinate systems as they pass one another, and that each clock is started at the time of the event. Then event *i* is characterized by the numbers

$$x_i = 0 \qquad t_i = 0 \qquad x'_i = 0 \qquad t'_i = 0$$

Later another event, *ii*, takes place and is measured by each observer, who then records his measurements in his notebook. (These are definite numbers of course; the distances are measured in meters, the time in seconds.) These values are

$$x_{ii} = x \qquad t_{ii} = t \qquad x'_{ii} = x' \qquad t'_{ii} = t'$$

So observer *O* in system *S* notes that event *i* takes place at time 0 sec and place 0 meters. Later another event, *ii*, takes place, which he records as happening at a time of *t* sec and a place at *x* meters. Observer *O'* in system *S'* observes the same events taking place at times of 0 sec and *t'* sec and at positions of 0 meters and *x'* meters as measured in his system. The distance between the two events is *x* and *x'* in the two systems, while the time that elapses between the events is equal to *t* and *t'*. The values measured in the two systems *S* and *S'*, and recorded in the respective notebooks, are related to one another by the equations of the Galilean transformation in the framework of non-relativistic theory. If observer *O* has lost his measurements, *x* and *t*, he can deduce them from the measurements of *O'* if he knows or can measure the relative velocity, *v*.

The result of the Michelson–Morley experiment, interpreted as indicating that the velocity of light is the same in all inertial reference frames, and the accompanying Lorentz–Fitzgerald contraction of meter sticks and dilation of time scales, is inconsistent with the equations of the Galilean transformation. If observer *O* uses the Galilean transformation to predict the results of *O'*, he will get the wrong answer; the results of his calculations simply will not agree with the actual numbers *O'* wrote down in his notebook if the measurements are made with sufficient accuracy. We can develop correct transformation equations by carefully considering the measurements made by *O'* from the view of *O'*.

We consider first the relations between the distances measured between the two events; *O* measures the distance as *x* meters in his system, *S*; *O'* measures the distance as *x'* meters in his system, S'. The quantities x and x' are numbers written down in their respective notebooks and represent, for example, the number of times they have laid down their meter sticks in laying off the distance between two points.

We take the view of O first: O says that the distance x he measures is equal to the distance between the electrodes on the car S' (which O' measured as x' meters) plus the distance the car moved during the elapsed time, t: that distance is vt. Although O' says the distance is x' meters—that is, he laid down his meter stick x' times along the distance—his meter stick was too short by a factor of

$$\sqrt{1 - \frac{v^2}{c^2}}$$

and the correct distance is not so great as x' meters. (If his meter stick were the correct length he would need to lay down the meter stick fewer times along the distance.) The "correct" distance would be

$$x' \sqrt{1 - \frac{v^2}{c^2}}$$

and

$$x = x' \sqrt{1 - \frac{v^2}{c^2}} + vt$$

or

$$x' = \frac{x - vt}{\sqrt{1 - v^2/c^2}} \tag{15 | 5}$$

It is desirable to emphasize that the equation relates the results of measurements in the two systems.

If we carry through the same analysis from the view of O', we arrive at the relation between the measurement of length made by O and the measurements of length and time made by O': the relation has the same form as Eq. (15 | 5):

$$x = \frac{x' + ct'}{\sqrt{1 - v^2/c^2}} \tag{15 | 6}$$

except that the sign of v is reversed, since the platform is traveling backwards with respect to the railroad car.

We have implied that the measurements of the times between the two events by the different observers will not necessarily result in the same values: t will not necessarily be equal to t'. This difference is established by the Eqs. (15|5) and (15|6): not only are the equations inconsistent if $t = t'$, but they determine the relation between t and t'. Only minor algebraic manipulation is required to deduce this relation. First we rewrite (15|5) in the form

$$vt = x - x' \sqrt{1 - \frac{v^2}{c^2}}$$

Then we use (15|6) to express x in terms of x' and t':

$$vt = \frac{x' + vt'}{\sqrt{1 - v^2/c^2}} - x' \sqrt{1 - v^2/c^2}$$

Putting the right-hand side of the equation over a common denominator,

$$vt = \frac{vt' + x' - x'(1 - v^2/c^2)}{\sqrt{1 - v^2/c^2}}$$

Simplifying and dividing through by v,

$$t = \frac{t' + x'v/c^2}{\sqrt{1 - v^2/c^2}} \tag{15|7}$$

If we carry out the operations in the same way but solve for t',

$$t' = \frac{t - xv/c^2}{\sqrt{1 - v^2/c^2}} \tag{15|8}$$

and t and t' are each expressed in terms of the measurements made in the other reference system: t in terms of x' and t', and t' in terms of x and t.

These four equations, (15|5), (15|6), (15|7), and (15|8), are the equations of the *Lorentz transformation*. These equations relate the numerical results of the operations of measuring the distance, x, between two events and the time, t, that elapses between the two events in one system, S, with similar measurements of x' and t' made in another system, S', where the relative velocity of the two systems is v. Do the equations demand that time and distance, such as the time between two events or the distance between two events, be actually different as seen from two different systems, or merely that they be measured differently? As physicists we can accept no meaning to time and space independent of measurements and the operations involved in measurement; as physicists we cannot accept a difference between the time between two events and the measurement of the time between two events: time and space intervals are defined only in terms of the operations measuring time and space intervals.

There are some aesthetic advantages to arranging these equations so that the fundamental variables are x and ct rather than x and t. The symmetry of the resulting equations emphasizes the close relation between space and time in relativistic kinematics. As a further simplifying convention we use the symbol β for v/c: β is then the relative velocity of the systems in the natural units where the velocity of light is equal to 1. Then

$$x = \frac{x' + \beta ct'}{\sqrt{1 - \beta^2}} \qquad x' = \frac{x - \beta ct}{\sqrt{1 - \beta^2}}$$

$$ct = \frac{ct' + \beta x'}{\sqrt{1 - \beta^2}} \qquad ct' = \frac{ct - \beta x}{\sqrt{1 - \beta^2}}$$

$$(15\,|\,9)$$

We have limited our discussions to displacements in the direction of motion. It is rather easy to see that distance measured perpendicular to the direction of relative motion of two observers is the same for both. In our picture of platform and railroad car, shown in Fig. 15 | 10 distance measured in the y- and z-directions must be the same for both observers. This follows from the symmetry of the two observers. Let us consider the contradiction that occurs when we assume that when the moving object expands in the y-direction. Then observer O on the platform concludes that when the train passes at high speed it will strike a low bridge, since the train will expand in height. The engineer,

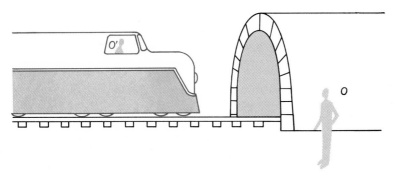

FIG. 15 |10
Observers in different inertial reference systems comparing the height of a tunnel transverse to their relative direction of motion.

knowing velocity is relative, says, "I'm standing still and the bridge will increase in height and I'll clear it very easily." They must both see the same thing—either the train will hit the bridge or it won't—this is possible only if the bridge and train are measured to be the same size by either observer. We then add to the description of a space–time event information about the components in the y- and z-direction. Our space–time vector is then: (x, y, z, t) and to the transformation equations we already have discussed, we add

$$y' = y \quad \text{and} \quad z' = z$$

and our previous discussions are valid with obvious minor changes. Since the description of a space–time event requires, now, four numbers, we call that description a *four-vector*. Vectors in three dimensions, which are still useful when the velocities are low, we call *three-vectors*.

Even as the transformation equations developed for the archetypical three-vector, displacement, hold also for other vector quantities such as momentum, electric field, and so on, the transformation equations developed to describe the relations between measurements of space and time intervals—which are the components of the space-time four-vector—by observers in different inertial frames are valid for other four-vectors. That is, other sets of four quantities are known such that the relations between measurements of these quantities by observers in different inertial frames can be described by the equations of the Lorentz transformation. These sets of quantities are thus also four-vectors. The equations that relate the measurement of the components A_x, A_y, A_z, and A_4 of a general four-vector $\mathbf{A}$ in two inertial systems, S and S', such that S' is moving with velocity $\beta = v/c$ in the x-direction relative to S, are

$$A_x = \frac{A_{x'} + \beta A_{4'}}{\sqrt{1 - \beta^2}} \qquad A_{x'} = \frac{A_x - \beta A_4}{\sqrt{1 - \beta^2}}$$

$$A_y = A_{y'} \qquad A_{y'} = A_y$$

$$A_z = A_{z'} \qquad A_{z'} = A_z \tag{15|10}$$

$$A_4 = \frac{A_{4'} + \beta A_{x'}}{\sqrt{1 - \beta^2}} \qquad A_{4'} = \frac{A_4 - \beta A_x}{\sqrt{1 - \beta^2}}$$

15|8   *The geometric description of space and time*

Previously we classified physical quantities in terms of their properties (transformation properties) under a rotation of the coordinate system. In particular, there was a class of invariants or
scalars, such as work or energy, in general represented quantitatively by one number; and their was a class of vectors, which were
quantities represented by two numbers in a two-dimensional
space, or three numbers in a three-dimensional space. These numbers varied, in a prescribed manner, as the physical situation was
viewed from, or described in terms of, different coordinate systems. For example, we consider a vector quantity, **a**, which would
represent a displacement, a velocity, a momentum, or a force,
for example, under two different coordinate systems in a two-
dimensional space. If the components of **a** are (a_x, a_y) in a coordinate system, S, in another coordinate system, S', the components of **a** are $(a_{x'}, a_{y'})$. The components in the two coordinate
systems are related as

$$a_{x'} = a_x \cos\theta + a_y \sin\theta \qquad a_x = a_{x'} \cos\theta - a_{y'} \sin\theta$$

$$a_{y'} = -a_x \sin\theta + a_y \cos\theta \qquad a_y = a_{x'} \sin\theta + a_{y'} \cos\theta \tag{15|11}$$

As shown in Fig. 15|11 the (x', y') coordinate system, S', is
rotated from the (x, y) system, S, by an angle θ. Or the (x, y) system can be considered as a rotation of the (x', y') system by an
angle $-\theta$. The transformation equations relate the numerical

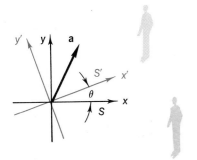

FIG. 15 |11

*Observers using
differently oriented
coordinate systems
writing down the
components of a vector.*

results of measurements of components of the vector **a** by an observer O using the (x, y) system and measurements of an observer O' using the (x', y') system.

We have emphasized that if certain symmetries or invariances exist in nature, certain observers must be equivalent in that their descriptions of nature will be essentially the same. Thus any general equation purporting to be a part of the general description of nature must be covariant with respect to the transformations that take us from the reference frame of one of these observers to another: the relation must be the same in the two reference frames. Descriptions valid only in a special coordinate system can be very useful, such as the statement "Boston is north of New York." But such statements are not a satisfactory basis for the construction of a simple set of generally valid relations. We have concerned ourselves with the construction of relations that are covariant with respect to the transformation between the systems of observers who are oriented in different directions; we are now interested in examining the problems in the construction of relations that are covariant with respect to the transformations between the systems of observers who are moving with different velocities.

We can describe the relations between measurements of kinematic quantities, such as the time and distance between two events, made by observers moving at different velocities in a manner analogous to the methods used to describe the relations between the measurements of the components of a spatial vector made by observers using different coordinate systems. For simplicity we restrict our space–time events so that the space difference lies in the x-direction, which is the direction of the relative velocities of the various inertial systems inhabited by the observers. The space difference is therefore written as x, and the

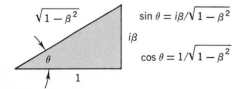

$$\sin \theta = i\beta/\sqrt{1-\beta^2}$$

$$\cos \theta = 1/\sqrt{1-\beta^2}$$

FIG. 15|12
A geometric representation of the transformation coefficients for the Lorentz transformation.

time difference between the two events is t: It is covenient to use ict as the parameter, where $i = \sqrt{-1}$. The space–time difference between the two events, **s**, is then specified in time and space by the values of the components x and ict even as a vector, such as a displacement, **a**, in a two-dimensional space manifold, is specified by the values of the components a_x and a_y. An angle, θ, can be defined as shown by Fig. 15|12. We use here the abbreviation $\beta = v/c$.

The equations of the Lorentz transformation then take the form

$$x' = x \cos \theta + ict \sin \theta$$

$$x = x' \cos(-\theta) + ict' \sin(-\theta)$$

$$\qquad\qquad (15|12)$$

$$ict' = -x \sin \theta + ict \cos \theta$$

$$ict = -x' \sin(-\theta) + ict' \cos(-\theta)$$

where

$$\sin \theta = \frac{i\beta}{\sqrt{1 - \beta^2}} = -\sin(-\theta)$$

and

$$\cos \theta = \frac{1}{\sqrt{1 - \beta^2}} = \cos(-\theta)$$

Here x and ict, or x' and ict', are the components of a space–time vector that represents the space–time interval between two events. The "angle" θ is not an angle in the ordinary sense, but represents a parameter that is a measure of the velocity difference between the two systems S and S'. Notice the formal similarity between the Eqs. (15|11), which are the transformation equations relating the measurements of two observers using coordinate systems that are aligned at different angles, and Eqs. (15|12), which are the transformation equations relating the measurements of two observers using coordinate systems that are moving at different velocities.

The quantity $a_x{}^2 + a_y{}^2$ is equal to the square of the length of the vector **a** shown in Fig. 15|11. This is equal to $a_{y'}^2 + a_{y'}^2$ since the length of the vector, or the square of the length of the vector, is a scalar, invariant with respect to the orientation of the coordinate system. Likewise, the quantity

$$x^2 + (ict)^2 = x'^2 + (ict')^2$$

as can be seen from Eqs. (15|9) or Eqs. (15|11) by direct substitution. This quantity, invariant under a Lorentz transformation, can be considered as the square of the length of a vector, **s**, in space–time. Commonly we use

$$s^2 = -\frac{1}{c^2}\left[(ict)^2 + x^2\right]$$

where the factor $-(1/c^2)$ is introduced as a matter of convention so that the quantity s has the dimensions of time. When two events take place at the same position ($x = 0$) in a space, s is just equal to the time between the events in that system and is known as the *proper time*. Since the proper time is an invariant or scalar in space–time, the proper time between two events will be the same for all observers in inertial frames, independent of the velocities of those frames.

Even as there are interesting similarities between the equations of the Lorentz transformation and the equations that describe the transformation of quantities under rotation, and therefore interesting similarities between time and space, there are essential differences also. The invariant length of a vector in a two-dimensional space is

$$a = \sqrt{a_x^2 + a_y^2}$$

where a_x and a_y are the two components of the space vector. The corresponding invariant proper time is

$$s = \sqrt{t^2 - \frac{x^2}{c^2}}$$

which is the square root of the *difference* of the squares of the components, rather than the sum. The minus sign represents an important difference between the two transformations even as the $\sqrt{-1}$ represents an important difference. There is a limit on the length to which we can carry the analogy. If time is to be regarded as a fourth dimension, it is a very different kind of dimension—a conclusion that is hardly surprising to us intuitively.

For convenience, we have neglected carrying along the transverse space directions in our discussions because they transform so simply. If we include these dimensions, the proper-time interval has the form

$$ds = \frac{1}{c} (c^2\, dt^2 - dx^2 - dy^2 - dz^2)^{1/2}$$

where dx, dy, dz are the spatial distances between the two events in an inertial frame and dt is the time difference.

15|9 *The separation between past and future*

Although different observers see the space–time interval between two events as composed of different intervals of space and time taken separately, even as observers using different coordinate systems assign different values to the x- and y-components of a vector, space and time are not completely interchangeable as are x and y. If we rotate a coordinate system by 90°, we interchange x and y: $x \rightarrow y$, $y \rightarrow -x$. By rotating the coordinate system 180°, a half circle, we change x to $-x$ and y to $-y$. If we could perform the same kind of transformation on the (x, ct) coordinate system, we would be interchanging past and future. Of course we cannot do this—time travel is not in this scheme. Even as we can classically divide time into past and future, we can divide space–time into a part that is absolutely in the past, and a part that is absolutely in the future. But we have a third region of space–time—a part that is neither past or future but may seem to be in either the past or future depending upon the state of the observer.

As a pragmatic definition of future, let us tentatively use the concept that "If event A can effect or initiate event B, B is the future with respect to A, and A is in the past with respect to B." We say "tentatively," because it is conceivable, though unattractive, that this concept has no operational meaning, leads to paradoxes, or can be contradicted in some way. We will investigate how the equations of the Lorentz transformation, and therefore the concepts of special relativity, effect this definition of past and future.

In a system, S, we consider a situation such that two events take place: One event, A, occurs at a point $x = 0$ and a time $t = 0$ (we ensure this by starting our clock when the event takes place, and measuring distance from the point of the event); the other event, B, takes place at a point x and a time t. First we investigate relations between a pair of events such that $x < ct$: a ray of light can then start at $x = 0$, $t = 0$, from event A, and reach point x at a time t_c that is before t, when event B takes place. Event B might be the closing of a relay initiated by the reception of light from A by a photocell. Event A could initiate or cause event B. How will the distance x' and the time interval t' measured in the system S' compare with the distance between the events x and the time between the events t as measured in the system S? From the invariant relation

$$s^2 = t^2 - \frac{x^2}{c^2}$$
$$= t'^2 - \frac{x'^2}{c^2}$$

$(15 | 13)$

we see that if the distance between the two events x is less than ct, where t is the time interval between the events in one system S, x' will be less than ct' in any other system. Then if A can be the cause of B in one system it can be the cause of B from the view of an observer in any system. The invariant relation $(15 | 13)$ insures that past and future are invariant with respect to the observer if they can be causally connected. For any observer, event B is in the future of A and A is in the past of B. This situation will obtain if s^2 is positive. If this is the case, we say that the space–time interval, **s**, is *timelike*. No observer will see the events reversed in time, and there is no conflict with our simple ideas of the relations between past, future, and the principle of causality.

If the distance between the events, x, is larger than the value of ct, no light signal can pass from event A to the position of event B before B occurs. Since we postulate that no signal can travel faster than light, event A cannot be the cause of event B. With $x > ct$, s^2 is negative. We then say that the space–time interval, **s**, is *spacelike*. From the equations of the Lorentz transformation $(15 | 9)$,

$$ct' = \frac{ct - \beta x}{\sqrt{1 - \beta^2}}$$

it can be seen that t' will have a different sign than t if βx is smaller than ct. This means that observer O' will see the events in a different time order than observer O: If O observes event A

before event B, O' will see B before A. Since event A cannot cause event B, and vice versa, there is no conflict with causality and the precisely defined definition of past and future we adopted.

If the space-time interval, $\mathbf{s}$, is timelike, different observers may see the positions of A and B reversed along the x-axis. If the interval is spacelike, all observers will see them disposed in the same order. This is suggested from the results on the elapsed time between the two events and can be shown in detail from the invariance relations and the equations of the Lorentz transformations in a fashion similar to the preceding arguments.

15|10 *The addition of velocities*

If an object, A, is moving with velocity u' with respect to observer O' in system S', what will be the value of the velocity, u, of object A with respect to observer O in the S system? The S' system is moving with respect to the S system with a velocity v, and as usual we limit our discussion to one dimension—the velocities are collinear. As a concrete example, shown in Fig. 15|13, O' might be an observer in an airplane, S', moving with respect to observer O on the earth, S, and u' is the muzzle velocity of a bullet, A, fired forward from the gun on the plane. We are interested in the velocity of the bullet with respect to the ground.

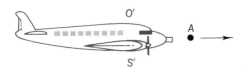

O'

S'

A
→

S

O

FIG. 15|13
Observers in different coordinate systems observing the flight of an object.

It is again important to express the velocity in terms of the operations involved in the measurement of velocity. Observer S' measures the velocity of object A (the bullet) by measuring the length of a course, dx', and measuring the time it takes for the bullet to pass over the course, dt'. The velocity, u', is simply the ratio of these two numbers,

$$u' = \frac{dx'}{dt'}$$

Observer S can measure the length of the same course and time the bullet himself with his instruments. He will find that the length of the course is dx and the time that elapses while the bullet is moving through the course is dt. His value of the velocity is then

$$u = \frac{dx}{dt}$$

The equations of the Lorentz transformation determine the values of dx and dt in terms of dx' and dt':

$$dx = \frac{dx' + \beta c \, dt'}{\sqrt{1 - \beta^2}}$$

$$dt = \frac{dt' + (\beta/c) \, dx'}{\sqrt{1 - \beta^2}}$$

Therefore

$$\frac{dx}{dt} = \frac{dx' + \beta c \, dt'}{dt' + (\beta/c) \, dx'}$$

Dividing both numerator and denominator by dt' and using the relation $u' = dx'/dt'$,

$$u = \frac{dx}{dt} = \frac{u' + \beta c}{1 + \beta u'/c}$$

Since $\beta c = v$,

$$u = \frac{u' + v}{1 + u'v/c^2} \tag{15|14}$$

which is the formula for the addition of velocities. This is to be contrasted with the formula for the addition of velocities under the classical Galilean transformation:

$$u = u' + v$$

It is particularly interesting to use the relativistic formula to consider the velocity of light in the two coordinate systems S and S' when the light is emitted by a source in S'. Then $u' = c$ and

$$u = \frac{c + v}{1 + v/c}$$

$$= c\,\frac{1 + v/c}{1 + v/c}$$

$$= c$$

As we expect, the speed of light is the same in both systems. This is of course information that was used to deduce the formulas we have developed, and the result $u = c$ is a check on our chain of reasoning.

15|11   *Time dilation and the twins paradox*

Although the slowing of clocks follows directly from a relativistic interpretation of the Michelson–Morley experiment and is therefore a startling point, rather than a conclusion, of our detailed logical discussions, this time dilation leads to such intriguing results that we consider some of these results in detail. Further, there is ample experimental evidence concerning most aspects of time dilation.

Nature is well supplied with minute natural clocks. The vibrations of atoms or molecules or the rates of decay of unstable nuclei or unstable elementary particles allow these atoms, nuclei, and particles to serve as clocks themselves. We can easily accelerate these clocks to high velocities and detect the time dilation by a factor of

$$\sqrt{1 - \beta^2}$$

from the view of a stationary observer, O. Here $\beta = v/c$ and v is the velocity of the clock with respect to the observer. From the view of the observer, 1 second of time in the system of the clock will be equal to

$$\frac{1}{\sqrt{1 - \beta^2}}$$

seconds in the system of the observer. If $\beta = \sqrt{\tfrac{3}{4}} = 0.866$, 1 second of the moving clock will be equivalent to 2 seconds of the stationary clock as both are read by the stationary observer.

Time dilation, as such, was first detected about 1938 by Herbert Ives, an American physicist, who used radiating atoms as his clock. When he accelerated the atoms to high velocities, he noticed that their frequency of vibration, as determined by the frequency of light they emitted, was slightly reduced to the degree predicted by the Lorentz equations. The velocity of the atoms was not large compared to the velocity of light; therefore the effect was not very large. More recently it has been possible to make measurements on unstable elementary particles such as pions, muons, and so on, which have velocities almost equal to c, so that the time dilation factor is very large. Time dilation factors exceeding 100 have been measured.

We can illustrate some of the results of time dilation and length contraction in a somewhat gaudy manner by considering a fanciful trip from the earth to a near star—perhaps Alpha Centauri, which is about 4 lt-yr from the earth. Light from Alpha Centauri thus takes about 4 yr to reach the earth. Since we are interested in time dilation and space foreshortening, we can use a poetic license to disregard restraints on our journey that result from our physiological limits on tolerable acceleration and even the limitations, resulting from the conservation of energy, on the velocities attainable by a vehicle that carries its own fuel. We consider two records of the trip, one from the view of an observer on the earth, and the other from an observer on the ship.

From the view of the observer on the ground, the ship left earth January 1, 1990, and accelerated quickly to a velocity very near the velocity of light. After 4 yr the ship (must have) reached Alpha Centauri. The crew explored that system for a year (according to the plan, we have no direct communication) then returned to earth, landing January 1, 1999. From the television shots of the debarkation, the crew seemed hardly to have aged.

The crew's journal reads as follows: "As we begin our journey, Alpha Centauri is 4 lt-yr away, according to our Captain. We quickly accelerate to a velocity $v = 0.866c$. Though this takes only a few days, the Captain announces that our destination is now 2 lt-yr away. We are already halfway there! [Though the ship has covered very little distance, and is still very near the earth, the space-contraction factor is now $\tfrac{1}{2}$. From the view of the ship the distance has become shortened to 2 lt-yr.] A few days later we reach a velocity $v = 0.99c$. The Captain says we are about 0.4 lt-yr away. [They have still not traveled very far relative to the earth, in the earth's system, but the foreshortening has increased.] After a few days more the Captain announces that our velocity is $0.9999c$, that we are 20 light-days from Alpha Centauri, and will therefore be there in 20 days."

The observer on earth knows, from the flight plans, that they have barely left earth, have reached a maximum velocity of $0.9999c$, and now will travel for 4 yr to reach Alpha Centauri. From his view, the men on the ship think they have only a little way to go, about $\frac{1}{70}$ of the actual distance, because of the contraction of length. They think the trip takes about 20 days because of the time dilation. Their clocks, and of course all physical and physiological processes, are slowed by a factor of 70.

The same processes take place on the trip back. So the travelers, who feel they have been gone one year and two months—a year exploring and two months traveling—find that 9 yr have elapsed on earth. If two men were twins and one remained on earth and one went on the voyage, the man who stayed home would be physiologically 8 yr older than his brother. Of course, he has eaten 8 more years' meals, slept more nights, and so on.

There is a seeming defect in this result. Can't we consider that it was the earth that moved away from the ship, then traveled with a velocity of $0.9999c$ away from the ship, and then returned? Why did not time pass more slowly on the earth? Do we not have a postulate that velocity is relative? Are the relations not symmetric between the twin brothers?

This is the famous twins paradox. The paradox, that the twins age differently as a result of the velocity of one of the twins when we have postulated that velocity has only a relative meaning, is removed when we observe that one of the twins undergoes an acceleration while the other does not. The situations are not symmetric. Let us put both twins in enclosed rooms without access to the outside. The traveling twin will notice accelerations as the ship starts out, turns around, and finally stops upon returning to earth; the stationary twin will notice no such accelerations. There is an asymmetry.

We can understand the difference in elapsed time, which must be related to the fact that an acceleration exists, by using the results of the discussion of Section 4|6, where we calculated the time dilation in an accelerating reference system. We showed that if you stand in an accelerating system time passes slower below you. As 1 sec elapses on your watch, only a time equal to

$$\frac{1}{1 + ah/c^2} \quad \text{sec}$$

elapses below you, where a is the acceleration and h is the distance of the clock below you. During the 1 sec that passes at your level, a time equal to

$$1 + \frac{ah'}{c^2} \quad \text{sec}$$

is ticked off by a clock mounted h' m above you.

The traveling twin is in an accelerating system as the ship leaves the earth (Fig. 15|14a), as it slows down near Alpha

FIG. 15|14
Periods of acceleration of the twin who travels to Alpha Centauri.

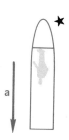 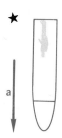

★ Alpha
Centauri

a

a

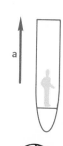

a

a

Earth

(a)　　　　(b)　　　　(c)　　　　(d)

Centauri (b), as it leaves Alpha Centauri for earth (c), and as the ship slows down to land on the earth (d). The direction of the acceleration is shown in an obvious way by the direction in which the man stands.

If this traveling twin is a well-informed physicist, he should be able to calculate the difference in age between his brother and himself from his viewpoint—from the reference system of the ship. Let us assume, then, that the twin in the ship knows the character of the theory of relativity and records his musing about the relative age of his brother and himself. As he is accelerating upon leaving the earth he knows that his brother is "below" him and is aging comparatively slowly. But his brother is not very far below him, and the acceleration does not take very long, so the age difference is not changed very much. As he travels, after the acceleration, as a thorough-going relativist, he says "My brother is traveling away from me at high speed so he is hardly aging at all because of the time dilation." Upon decelerating at Alpha Centauri, he notes that his brother is very far "above" him and that time must be passing much faster at his brother's position, so that his brother is aging considerably even though very little time is passing on the ship. The same effect occurs as they accelerate to leave Alpha Centauri; again his brother ages greatly as time passes very quickly on earth so far "above" him in the accelerating system. During the trip back he knows that his brother is traveling very fast compared to the ship and so very little time will pass for the brother; and during the deceleration before landing on earth the brother ages very little, but the damage is done; his brother aged eight years during the turnaround at Alpha Centauri.

All of this is not to say that the "cause" of the age discrepancy is to be found solely in the act of turning around—there is no operational significance to such a statement. The only observations made are the comparison of clocks by the twins at the beginning and end of the journey. If the traveling twin does not turn around, he will never come back; the clocks can never be correlated, and the ages of the twins can never be compared.

The time dilation of "twins" has been seen and measured experimentally, though the twins were twin nuclear clocks rather than men. It has been found that the nucleus of an atom in a hot material will decay more slowly than a similar nucleus in cold material. The atom containing the nucleus vibrates back and forth with an average velocity that is proportional to the square root of the absolute temperature, so the nucleus in the hot material is traveling back and forth at a higher velocity than the nucleus in the cold material. The difference in lifetime is extremely small, but it has been detected and is in accord with our calculations.

15 | 12   *The energy–momentum four-vector: $E = mc^2$*

Only covariant descriptions in terms of four-vectors and invariants (and the higher forms called *tensors*) can serve as general laws holding for all observers. All of our classical three-vector concepts, such as velocity, acceleration, force, momentum, and so on, and the laws of behavior that we have discussed in terms of these three-vectors can be valid approximations to reality only when all the relevant velocities are small. Even as no fundamental relation in classical physics can depend upon one component of a three-vector, no fundamental relativistically valid relation can depend upon the values of the components of a four-vector. Even as no fundamental classical relation can depend upon the directions up, down, or north, no relation that is valid for observers moving at different velocities can depend upon time, a component of the four-vector space–time, or displacement, the other three components, except as they take part as the four components of the four-vector. Therefore, the classical laws that describe nature in terms of three-vectors must be replaced by covariant laws that describe nature in terms of four-vectors. Although we will not concern ourselves with developing a complete relativistic kinematics and dynamics, we will discuss the conservation of momentum and energy.

The law of conservation of momentum, as it is understood in nonrelativistic situations where all velocities are small compared to c, is a rule concerning three-vectors. Since displacement itself transforms as a Lorentz four-vector, we immediately suspect that our rules concerning three-vectors are not valid, and are probably seriously wrong when high velocities are encountered. The thesis of the covariance of the laws of nature suggest to us that the classical law of the conservation of momentum, which states that the components of a three-vector are conserved, must be replaced by some law concerning the conservation of the components of a four-vector. Of course it is possible that there is no conservation law at all; it is possible that the classical law represents an approximation that is good only at low velocities. Conservation laws are summaries of experience and are not derivable from pure logic. We cannot, then, expect to derive a relativistic counterpart to the classical law of the conservation of momentum purely from the Theory of Relativity. The Theory of Relativity only tells us that no description of reality in terms of three-vectors can be truly general and valid for all observers, and if the law of the conservation of the three-vector momentum is to be extended to high energies, and if the law is to be valid for all observers in inertial frames of reference, the law must concern the conservation of the components of a quantity with appropriate transformation properties in four-dimensional space–time. It is a reasonable guess that the components of some four-vector will be conserved and that for small velocities the components that are similar to the space components of the space–time vector will correspond to the components of the classical momentum vector. If this is the case, the resultant four-vector will transform in the same pattern as displacement and time under the observations of different observers.

We might therefore proceed on an intuitive basis to construct a four-vector that has reasonable transformation properties and reduces to the familiar three-vector momentum for small relative velocities. We cannot deduce from first principles any conservation laws concerning the components of the four-vector; we must, in principle, examine that question by experiment.

First let us demonstrate what we may well suspect—that the conservation of momentum, as momentum is described classically, is not valid if we consider velocities that are not very small compared with the velocity of light. On the train shown in Fig. 15|15, two masses, each equal to m_0, which are initially at rest on the train, are pushed apart by the pressure of a light spring placed between them. An observer on the train, O', measures their velocities in the x-direction as u_x and $-u_x$. Before the spring was activated, the total momentum of the system of the two weights was zero in the train system; they were not moving. After the interaction, the total momentum was

$$p'_x = m_0 u_x + m_0(-u_x) = 0$$

and momentum was certainly conserved.

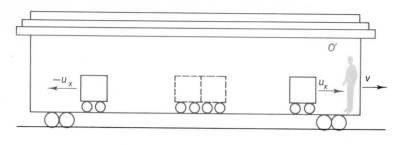

FIG. 15I15
*Observers in different
inertial systems
observing the motions
of two carts.*

From the view of observer O on the platform, the momentum of the two masses was originally

$$p_x = 2m_0v$$

where v is the velocity of the train. After the spring sends the two masses apart, we can use the equations for the addition of velocity to determine their final velocity and thus their final momentum, as momentum is defined classically:

$$p_x = m_0 \frac{v + u_x}{1 + u_xv/c^2} + m_0 \frac{v - u_x}{1 - u_xv/c^2}$$

Let us assume, for convenience, that $u_x = \tfrac{1}{2}c$ and that $v = \tfrac{1}{2}c$. Then before the collision

$$p_x = m_0c$$

and after the collision

$$p_x = \tfrac{4}{5}m_0c$$

Momentum, as it is defined classically as mass times velocity, is not conserved.

The classical momentum three-vector is written as

$$\mathbf{p}' = m \frac{d\mathbf{r}}{dt}$$

where $\mathbf{dr}$ is the displacement three-vector with components dx, dy, and dz. The mass, m, and the time interval, dt, are scalars.

We can procede to construct a quantity that will be very much the
same at small velocities by replacing the elements that are vectors
and scalars in the classical three-dimensional manifold by related
quantities that transform as four-vectors and four-scalars. We
replace, or redefine, m by m_0 where m_0 is the rest mass, the mass
measured by any observer when the object is at rest in his system
of reference; this mass is clearly the same for any observer and
therefore is a four-scalar. The displacement **dr** is replaced by the
four-vector **ds** having components dx, dy, dz, and $c\,dt$, and the
three-scalar dt is replaced by the four-scalar proper-time, ds.
Then

$$\mathbf{p} = m_0 \frac{\mathbf{ds}}{ds}$$

where **p** will certainly transform as a four-vector. (Whether it
corresponds to anything useful has not been established.)

The form of the components of the four-vector **p** can be expressed in a simple form. We examine p_x explicitly:

$$p_x = m_0 \frac{dx}{ds}$$

where

$$ds = \frac{1}{c} \sqrt{c^2\,dt^2 - dx^2 - dy^2 - dz^2}$$

dividing both the numerator and denominator by dt,

$$p_x = m_0 \frac{dx/dt}{ds/dt}$$

$$= m_0 \frac{dx/dt}{(1/c)\,\sqrt{c^2 - (dx/dt)^2 - (dy/dt)^2 - (dz/dt)^2}}$$

Writing

$$v_x = \frac{dx}{dt} \qquad v_y = \frac{dy}{dt} \qquad v_z = \frac{dz}{dt}$$

and

$$v^2 = v_x^2 + v_y^2 + v_z^2$$

we have

$$p_x = \frac{m_0 v_x}{\sqrt{1 - \beta^2}}$$

where $\beta^2 = v^2/c^2$. Similarly

$$p_y = \frac{m_0 v_y}{\sqrt{1 - \beta^2}} \qquad p_z = \frac{m_0 v_z}{\sqrt{1 - \beta^2}} \qquad p_4 = \frac{m_0 c}{\sqrt{1 - \beta^2}}$$

By direct calculation the length of the invariant four vector is

$$\sqrt{p_4^2 - p_x^2 - p_y^2 - p_z^2} = m_0 c$$

justifying our use of m_0 as a scalar.

Although we have implied that the spacelike components of the four-vector **p** are related closely to the components of the classical three-vector momentum, we have not established the precise character of the relation. It would seem that they might *correspond* in the limit of small values of v/c. The reduction of relativistic equations in the limit of small v/c is facilitated by the use of the binominal theorem. For the sake of our limited use of the binominal theorem, we can express it as

$$(1 + b)^n = 1 + nb + \text{terms in } b^2, b^3, \text{ etc.}$$

For very small values of b, where b is very much smaller than 1, only the first two terms will be important and

$$(1 + b)_n \approx 1 + nb$$

Then for very small values of v^2/c^2,

$$\frac{1}{\sqrt{1 - v^2/c^2}} = \left(1 - \frac{v^2}{c^2}\right)^{-1/2}$$

$$= 1 + \frac{1}{2}\frac{v^2}{c^2}$$

Using this relation, in the limit of small values of v^2/c^2, where we neglect quantities which approach zero for large values of c,

$$p_x = m_0 v_x \left(1 + \frac{1}{2}\frac{v^2}{c^2}\right) = m_0 v_x$$

$$p_y = m_0 v_y \left(1 + \frac{1}{2}\frac{v^2}{c^2}\right) = m_0 v_y$$

$$p_z = m_0 v_z \left(1 + \frac{1}{2}\frac{v^2}{c^2}\right) = m_0 v_z$$

$$cp_4 = m_0 c^2 \left(1 + \frac{1}{2}\frac{v^2}{c^2}\right) = m_0 c^2 + \frac{1}{2} m_0 v^2$$

In the nonrelativistic limit the three spacelike components of the four-vector correspond to the three components of the classical momentum vector, and the fourth component, when multiplied by c, is equal to the classical kinetic energy plus a term, m_0c^2, that has the dimensions of energy. This suggests that it is sensible to name the four-vector the *energy–momentum* vector, where the three spacelike components are the components of the *relativistic momentum* of a particle and the fourth component, multiplied by the velocity of light cp_4, is the *total energy* of the particle. The quantity m_0c^2 is the rest energy; the difference between the total energy and the rest energy is called the *kinetic energy*.

Different observers, inhabiting different inertial systems moving with respect to each other in an x-direction, will record different values for the components of momentum and the total energy of a particle, but their measurements and records will be related by the equations of the Lorentz transformation (15|10). Furthermore, our observations of the character of the universe suggest that the sum of the values of each component of the energy–momentum four vector, for a system of interacting particles, will be conserved from the view of any observer. In the nonrelativistic limit, the difference between these quantities, $cp_4 - m_0c^2$, was shown to have the familiar value of $\frac{1}{2}m_0v^2$ and corresponds to the classical kinetic energy.

Even as momentum and energy, as they are defined classically, were shown to be conserved to the limit of experimental observations under classical conditions, the extended definitions of momentum and energy as components of a relativistic four-vector appear to result in conserved quantities. Within the accuracy of our observations it appears that the components of the energy–momentum four-vector are conserved.

It is important to examine the concepts of mass and rest mass. Everywhere that mass is considered in classical physics the quantity

$$\frac{m_0}{\sqrt{1 - \beta^2}}$$

appears in relativistic mechanics. We can well lump the whole term as mass and say that *mass increases with velocity.*

Does mass really increase with velocity, or is it just a convenient way of expressing the results of the Theory of Relativity? To put this question in context it is necessary to review our original definition of mass in Chapter 5. Mass was introduced and defined in such a way that a particular simple pattern, which we called the conservation of momentum, emerged in our observations of the interactions between bodies. If we extend our observations to higher velocities, our simple pattern will remain simple, and correct, only if we adopt this augmented definition of mass.

Does the relation between energy and rest mass, $E = m_0c^2$, have a meaning other than as a convenient naming of quantities? Certainly we can name the fourth term of the energy–momentum four-vector total energy. We can divide the quantity

$$\frac{m_0c^2}{\sqrt{1 - \beta^2}}$$

into two parts, one of which is m_0c^2, and call this an energy. But is this important, or merely a new use of old words? It seems that the identification of the quantity as an energy is really meaningful. We support this by two kinds of examples. For one thing we have experimentally observed that an electron and a positron, both of which are particles having a definite rest mass, m, can annihilate each other to produce an amount of energy equal to $2mc^2$. There are other examples of change from mass to energy and, inversely, changes from energy to mass.

Furthermore, energy demonstrably has a mass according to our original definition of mass. We outline a calculation that will result in a demonstration of the meaning of this statement. Consider a box that holds a ball of mass m_0, which is bouncing around elastically in the box with velocity v. Further assume, for convenience, that the box is of negligible mass. Now if a force, F, is applied to the box, the acceleration of the box will be irregular as the ball bounces around. But on the average, if we calculate this using Newtonian mechanics, the acceleration will be equal to $a = F/m_0$. If we calculate the result correctly, using relativistic mechanics, we will find that the acceleration will be

$$a = \frac{F}{m + T/c^2}$$

Where T is the kinetic energy of the ball, approximately equal to $\frac{1}{2}m_0v^2$. But our definition of mass is founded on the relation $m = F/a$.

The mass of the box is thus equal to m, where

$$m = m_0 + \frac{T}{c^2}$$

$$= m_0 + \tfrac{1}{2}m_0\beta^2$$

and the kinetic energy, T, contributes to the mass as T/c^2.

We find, in general, that all energy has an inertia of the sort we have associated with mass—all energy has mass. We might therefore consider that all mass in the ordinary sense, as the mass of a particle, is the mass associated with a condensation of energy. Perhaps particles are essentially "boxes" that hold energy. Indeed, modern views of the origin of the mass of elementary particles have very much this character. Perhaps there is no meaning to the concept of mass separate from energy!

Of course the preceding comments refer to all kinds of energy; a hot cube of uranium is heavier than a cold cube by an amount

$$dm_h = \frac{dE_h}{c^2}$$

where E_h is the difference in the heat energy in joules. If the uranium cube is burned in oxygen to form uranium dioxide, the mass of the uranium dioxide will be less than the original mass of the uranium plus the oxygen used in combustion by an amount

$$dm_c = \frac{dE_c}{c^2}$$

where dE_c is the chemical energy of combustion. If the uranium is used as a fuel in a reactor, it will undergo fission to lighter nuclei plus a few neutrons and give off energy. The products of this nuclear reaction will be lighter than the original uranium by an amount

$$dm_n = \frac{dE_n}{c^2}$$

where dE_n is the energy given off in the fission process.

The mass change in the nuclear reaction, dm_n, is about equal to 1 percent of the original mass of the uranium, the proportional values of dm_h and dm_c are very much smaller—too small to measure directly. Nevertheless, the basic relations are the same; the equation $E = mc^2$ is as relevant to the burning of coal as it is to the fission of uranium. As much mass is changed to energy in a conventional electric power station, burning coal for its power source, as in a nuclear plant of the same capacity.

15|13 *The general theory of relativity*

Special Relativity is derived from the necessity of finding a conceptual framework in which one can fit the experimental information concerning the impossibility of defining an absolute coordinate system. The results of the Michelson–Morley experiment, together with the results of the classical experiments on electromagnetism, requires us to adopt a description of the universe in terms of a new geometry—a geometry in which time and space are considered together.

The success of this use of a new geometry to solve serious problems, or to classify otherwise unrelated phenomena, suggested to many physicists, Einstein in particular, that other fundamental problems of physics might also be understood through further extensions of a geometric description of space–time. In particular, the existence of the equivalence principle, the exact equivalence of gravitational and inertial mass and the exact equivalence of acceleration and a gravitational field, suggested that gravitation might be only another aspect of acceleration and therefore be accountable as a kinematic effect of the character of space–time. Further, it might then be possible to include it in the geometry of space–time. Einstein's General Theory of Relativity encompasses this aim; gravitation is expressed as a part of the geometry of space–time.

The gravitational force is unique at present in that we have been able to construct a view of the universe in which gravity does not exist as a force, but only as a geometric consequence. The General Theory of Relativity has the result of reducing the problem of the description of the motion of several bodies from dynamics to kinematics, where dynamics is the study of the effects of forces on bodies and kinematics is the study of the motion of bodies without reference to forces. If we consider only gravitational effects, all bodies always travel in straight lines. The presence of other bodies distorts the shape of space in such a way as to change the character of a straight line.

We construct two loose analogies to provide an intuitional

framework for a qualitative understanding of the effects of curvatures of space. In particular, we consider two-dimensional
spacelike manifolds rather than the four-dimensional universe
we live in (three space dimensions plus one time dimension).

We first consider the description of motion on the surface of a
globe, or on any other curved surface? We use an extension of
the definition of a straight line on a flat surface: a straight line
is the path of shortest distance between two points. Or more
properly, a path such that no nearby path is shorter. Using this
definition, a straight line on the surface of a globe is an arc of a
great circle.

Let us consider two objects, *a* and *a'*, moving in parallel
straight lines, at some time, on the surface of a globe, as in Fig.
15|16. They will draw closer together as time passes and eventu-
ally collide at point *c*. A two-dimensional inhabitant of this universe, who found it difficult to conceive of a third dimension,
might construct a dynamics to explain such phenomena. He could
assume that space is flat and invent a force that he might call
"gravity" that would act on the two bodies. Of course the bodies
a and *a'* would not "feel" a force, but this is also true of a planet
or a man in free fall in our universe.

A good geometer of the two-dimensional universe could, however, determine that the space was not flat and describe the
"gravitational" forces as simple consequences of the curvature
of space.

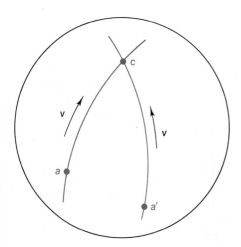

FIG. 15|16
*Paths of objects moving
in straight lines on a
spherical surface.*

The "force" on a' and the path of a' are independent of the presence of a in the global system as we have described it, and the analogy is still distant from our experience. We approach the character of our own universe by considering a two-dimensional space such that the space is flat if no bodies (no matter) exists at all, but the presence of matter distorts the space. The space might have a certain curvature near matter, the curvature being greater as the quantity of matter was greater. Then the path of a' would depend on the presence of a, because the geometry at the position of a' would be determined by the presence and size of a, and in general would depend upon the distribution of matter in the universe.

Einstein's General Theory of Relativity is just such a geometric description of our four-dimensional universe. According to this view, gravity does not exist as a force at a distance but a manifestation of geometry. A body falls toward the earth in a path that is a "straight line" in space–time near the earth. We examine the meaning of this a little further using the diagrams of Fig. 15|17. Figure 15|17a shows the path in space–time of a particle at rest in the system of reference. Figure 15|17b shows the path of a particle moving with constant velocity in the x-direction. Figure 15|17c shows the path of a particle moving under acceleration, in the x-direction, under the influence of gravity. If we construct an appropriate geometry, as Einstein did, we can consider the path of 15|17c as a straight line in a curved space. The curvature of the space is caused by the presence of the body we normally consider as the source of the gravitational force. According to the General Theory, the path of Fig. 15|17c appears curved for much the same reason that the path of an airplane flying in a straight line (or great-circle route) on the surface of the earth appears as a curved line on a

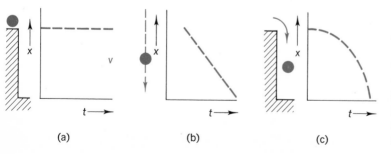

(a)   (b)   (c)

FIG. 15|17

Paths in space-time of an object under different conditions (a) a stationary object and its path in space-time; (b) the path in space–time of an object moving in a straight line with constant velocity; (c) the path in space–time of an object falling in a gravitational field.

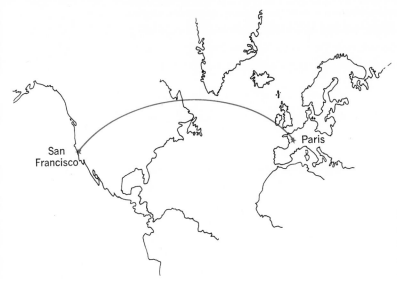

San
Francisco

Paris

FIG. 15|18
*A straight line on a
curved spherical
surface shown on a flat
map of the surface.*

Mercator projection, as in Fig. 15|18. The Mercator projection
is not an adequate representation of the curved spaces even as
it is not an adequate map of the curved surface of the earth.
Newton's first law, which can be stated as, "A body that is not
under the influence of an unbalanced force will move in a straight
line in space–time," is thus extended so that the effects of gravity
are considered not as a force but as the result of the curvature
of space–time induced by the presence of a perturbing mass,
and therefore a change in the character of the "straight line."
Dynamics is changed to geometry.

   The equivalence principle is an axiom of any general theory
of relativity rather than a result, so that the equivalence of acceleration and gravity and any consequences of this equivalence
are not tests of a particular theory. In that sense the change in
flow of time in a gravitation field, which has been observed, is
not a strong test of general relativity.

   There are, however, two consequences of Einstein's geometric theory that do not arise simply from the equivalence
principle. The exact value of the curvature of light by the sun
is one; and the rate of precession of the orbit of an object in a
gravitational field is the second.

   Although the curvature of light in a gravitational field measured by an observer in that gravitational field must be the same
as if the reference system and observer were accelerating, the

magnitude of the curvature of light by a gravitational field as measured by an observer who is in another frame of reference does not follow uniquely from the equivalence principle. The relation between observers in different accelerating reference systems is determined uniquely by Einstein's geometric theory, however, and the curvature of light passing near the edge of the sun, as measured by an observer in the earth's reference frame, is calculated to be 1.75 seconds of arc (the symbol for seconds of arc is "). It is difficult to make precise measurements of the deflection, but the results of many measurements, all made during total eclipses of the sun, are in agreement with the geometric theory with an accuracy of about 10 percent.

The other striking consequence of the General Theory that does not arise immediately from the equivalence principle and differs from the classical theory of gravitation is found in the prediction of the rate of precession of the orbit of an object in a central gravitational field. Classically, the orbit of an object in the gravitational field of another object, such as the orbit of a planet in the field of the sun, will take the form of a conic section. Stable orbits will have the form of ellipses such as that in Fig. 15 | 19a, where the planet will be moving faster at the perihelion, *a*, and slower at the aphelion, *c*. If we include the effects of the Special Theory of Relativity, the planet will be heavier at the perihelion than at the aphelion and will move as in Fig. 15 | 19b (where the effect is shown very much exaggerated) and change the orientation of the ellipse. This change in the position of the ellipse is called a *precession*; for Mercury, the innermost planet, the precession can be observed and measured with some ac-

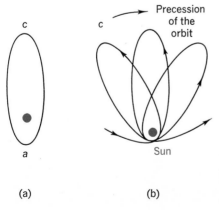

(a)   (b)

FIG. 15 | 19
An elliptical orbit of a planet about the sun, showing the relativistic precession of the orbit.

curacy. This shift is 574"/century, about 1°/600 yr! The shift from the perturbations of other planets is 513", leaving 43" unaccounted for classically. The Special Theory of Relativity alone accounts for about 7"/century, but the General Theory of Relativity, which considers all motion under gravity as motion in a straight line in a curved space, predicts 42.9"/century—almost exactly what is observed.

The unacceptable idea of action at a distance is thus supplanted by two different hypothesis. Electromagnetism (and the nuclear interactions) can be considered to act through the exchange of particles or quanta, while gravity is the result of a distortion of space—a change in geometry. This is rather an embarrassment of success: two entirely different hypothesis to explain two quite similar characteristics of nature. We generally believe that these two ideas represent different faces of some more generally valid description. There has been considerable effort devoted to including electromagnetism in the geometry of space–time, and to quantizing the gravitational field (the particles are called gravitons). But no remarkable success has been achieved in either endeavor.

PROBLEMS

15|1 (*a*) How would you synchronize two clocks 1 mi apart, one directly north of the other, if you are limited to transmission of signals by sound, and a 36 mph (0.01 mpsec) wind is blowing from the north? Take the speed of sound as 0.2 mpsec in still air. You may have assistants and a reasonable set of apparatus such as clocks and measuring tapes. You know the direction of the wind, but not the velocity.

(*b*) How would you synchronize the clocks if the wind were from the east?

15|2 (*a*) As an observer on the platform you watch an experimenter on an open flatcar, moving by with a velocity of 10 m/sec, conduct flights of a pigeon back and forth along two courses on the flatcar. One course is 100 m long parallel to the track; the other course is 100 m long transverse to the track. There is no wind. If the pigeon flies at a rate of 20 m/sec, how long will a round-trip flight take on the parallel course? On the transverse course?

(*b*) We watch a different experimenter lay out courses on the flatcar and measure the time of flight of the pigeons. He lays out a course that he considers to be 100 m long in the parallel direction and another course 100 m long in the transverse direction. Using the same pigeon as was used in part (*a*), he finds that the pigeons fly each course in 10 sec. Upon investigation it turns out that the meter stick he used for laying out the course parallel to the track was too short. He used another accurate meter stick to lay out the transverse course. However, his clock was also slow: it lost many minutes per hour. What was the length of the meter stick? How many minutes per hour did the clock lose?

(*c*) Using the bad meter stick and poor clock of part (*b*), the man on the train measures the velocity of the train by measuring the time a particular point on the platform takes to pass the 100-m distance he has laid out on the flatcar. What value does he find for the velocity?

15|3 Assume that you are an observer in a universe that has the property that the speed of light is 1 m/sec for all observers, independent of their relative velocities. Another observer is on a train passing you at a velocity of 0.6 m/sec. He has constructed a clock designed to send a beam of light along a path 1 m long, at the end of which it is reflected to the origin, where it is reflected again, and so on. A mechanism counts the round trips, giving 1 count per 2 sec. This clock is aligned with the light path transverse to the direction of motion of the train. The observer on the platform agrees that the length of the clock is 1 m, but he claims that the clock runs slow. From the view of the man on the platform, how long does the light take to make one back-and-forth circuit in the clock? How many minutes will the clock lose per hour from his view? (Calculate the answers from elementary principles. Do not merely substitute numbers in transformation equations.)

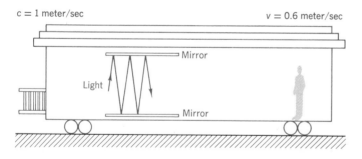

15 | 4   An observer, O', is on a long railroad car, S', on a fast train going 75,000 km/sec. He has a clock and a lamp, and a mirror is placed 150,000 km away according to his calibrated meter stick. He will measure the time it takes light to travel from his lamp to the mirror and back again.

Another observer, O, on the platform, S, has identical equipment and will perform the same experiment. Previously, before O' boarded the train, they had compared their clocks and meter sticks and know them to be alike.

The lamps flash at the instant they pass one another, at which time each clock reads 0.0 sec.

Answer the following questions twice, first from the viewpoint of O, then of O':

(*a*) Which mirror does the light strike first?

(*b*) What does the clock on the train read when the light ray on the train returns?

(*c*) What does the clock on the platform read when the light ray on the platform returns?

(*d*) To which observer did the signal first return?

(S')

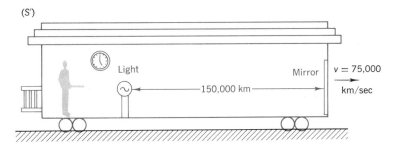

(S)

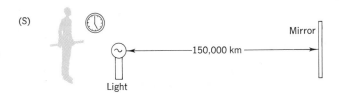

15 | 5   A man on a train that is moving past the platform has pigeons flying back and forth on a path 40 m long that is transverse to the train track. Both the man on the train, using the clock on the train (which may be incorrect), and the man on the platform, using the clock on the platform (which is certified to be correct), find that the pigeons fly at a velocity of 50 m/sec. According to the man on the platform, the train is moving with a velocity of 30 m/sec. When 100 sec have passed on the clock on the platform, how much time has elapsed according to the clock on the train?

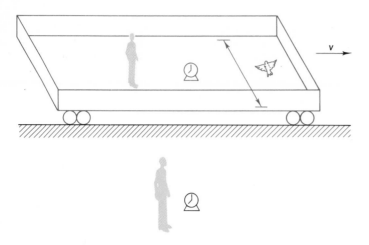

15|6   Assume that you are in a universe such that the velocity of light is equal to 10 m/sec *with respect to its source* (like the velocity of bullets from a gun). You are watching toy cars travel around a 1-m-radius track with a constant velocity of 1.0 m/sec. Discuss qualitatively how the apparent motion of the car will differ from the real motion if you are watching the cars from a distance. Show that a car starting at *s* will appear to get to *b* before *a* from a viewpoint far enough distant from the track.

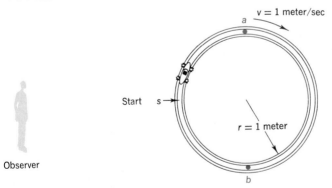

15|7   *O'*, in a moving coordinate system, *S'*, notes that meter stick *m* is shorter than meter stick *m'*. In turn, *O*, in a stationary system, *S*, notes that stick *m'* is shorter than *m*. Explain why these observations are not necessarily contradictory. (Do not just refer to equations.)

15|8 Two lamps set 10 m apart along a track in a railroad station are flashed simultaneously by a man on the platform. From the view of a man in a train passing the station at a velocity of $\frac{1}{2}c$, how much time elapses between flashes? (Assume that he makes corrections for the time it takes for the light to reach him.)

15|9 A lamp beside a track in a station is flashed twice, with a 1-sec interval, by the station master. From the view of a man in a train passing the station at a velocity of $\frac{1}{2}c$, how much time elapses between the flashes of light? (Assume that the man on the train corrects for the time it takes the light to reach him from the lamp.)

15|10 Starting with the equations of the Lorentz transformation, show that the *proper time* interval between two events,

$$ds = \frac{1}{c}\,(c^2\,dt^2 - dx^2 - dy^2 - dz^2)^{1/2}$$

$$= ds' = \frac{1}{c}\,(c^2\,dt'^2 - dx'^2 - dy'^2 - dz'^2)^{1/2}$$

for two inertial systems moving with a relative velocity v in the x-direction where dt, dx, dy, and dz are the time and space differences between the two events in one system and dt', dx', dy', and dz' are the differences in the other system.

15|11 A traveler in an interstellar vehicle notes that he is traveling at velocity v and that he will reach his destination, a planet of the star Deneb, in 1 yr. An observer on earth agrees that his velocity is v, but determines that he will not reach Deneb for about 10 yr.

(a) About how far is the ship from Deneb from the view of the traveler? About how far is it from Deneb according to the observer on earth?

(b) Why do they disagree?

(c) Who is right?

15|12 A traveler in an interstellar vehicle notes that he is traveling at a velocity v and that his destination, a planet of the star Deneb, is 1 lt-yr away. An observer on earth agrees that the velocity of the ship is v, but determines that Deneb is 10 lt-yr from the ship.

(a) About how long will the trip take from the view of the traveler? How long will it take from the view of the observer on earth?

(b) Why do they disagree?

(c) Who is right?

15|13   Professor *A* says that it is possible that mechanical clocks are affected by velocity so that they run slowly, but that physiological processes may be unaffected so that both twins of the twins paradox actually age the same amount. Professor *B* says that if that were to be true one could determine absolute velocity by comparing physical and physiological time scales, and this would be a most interesting violation of the thesis that only relative velocity has any meaning. Explain in more detail the meaning of Professor *B*'s statement.

15|14   A particular observer measures the distance between two events, *i* and *ii*, as *L* and notes that *ii* took place a time *T* after *i*. Another observer states that according to his measurements *i* took place after *ii*. What conclusions obtain concerning the relation of *L* and *T*?

15|15   A light on a passing train is blinking once a second. The speed of light in this universe is 10 m/sec. An observer on the platform takes a time exposure of the passing train and finds that the light flashes are 10 m apart. How often does the light blink according to the observer on the platform?

15|16   A red light and a blue light fastened to the edge of the platform blink as two trains pass the platform going in opposite directions. An observer on one train says that the blue light blinks first; an observer on the second trains say the red light blinks first. According to measurements made on the platform, the lights are 100 m apart. The speed of light in this universe is 100 m/sec. What is the longest possible interval between flashes as measured on the platform, and why must this restriction obtain?

15|17   An elementary particle called the *muon* has a rest mass of 1.8×10^{-28} kg. The muon is unstable; about 50 percent of all muons live more than 1.7×10^{-6} sec before decaying. Assume that a muon is produced through the interaction of cosmic rays 30 km above the earth and that the muon has a high velocity directly toward the earth.

   (*a*) What is the least energy the particle must have in order that it will have at least a 50-percent chance of striking this earth?

   (*b*) From the view of a microscopic observer riding on the muon, how far is the earth from the point of production of the muon?

15|18   The energy of an electron emitted from the Stanford Linear Accelerator is equal to $40{,}000mc^2$, where *m* is the rest mass of the electron. (In considering these problems remember the binomial theorem!)

(*a*) How much slower is the electron traveling than the speed of light?

(*b*) The linear accelerator is about 3 km long. From the view of an observer sitting on an electron, how long does the accelerator appear to be as the electron leaves it?

(*c*) From the view of the observer on the emitted electron, how long will it take to go another 3 km?

(*d*) Two such electrons pass each other going in opposite directions with the same velocity. What is their relative velocity—that is, what is the velocity of one electron as measured by an observer riding on the other electron?

15|19 Classically force, $\mathbf{F}$, is a three-vector defined as $\mathbf{F} = d\mathbf{p}/dt$, where $\mathbf{p}$ is the three-vector momentum and t is the time. Construct a four-vector such that the spacelike components of the vector reduce to the nonrelativistic force. Show that the fourth component times the velocity of light, cf_4, is equal to power in the nonrelativistic limit. (You should follow a procedure similar to that used to develop the four-vector momentum.)

15|20 Two particles are traveling in the x-direction with momenta equal to p_1 and p_2 and total energies equal to E_1 and E_2. Show that $p_1p_2 - E_1E_2/c^2$ is a Lorentz invariant by showing that the value of the quantity is the same for another observer moving with a velocity v is the x-direction.

15|21 A train, S' is traveling in the x-direction with a velocity of $v = \frac{1}{2}c$ with respect to the platform, S. An object that is at rest on the train breaks up into equal pieces. The two pieces fly off in opposite directions with velocities of w and $-w$ in the x-direction as measured by the observer on the train. The mass of each piece is found to be equal to m_0, and the value of w is $\frac{1}{2}c$.

(*a*) Find the momentum and total energy of each piece in the train system.

(*b*) Find the velocity of each piece in the platform system, using the relations concerning the addition of velocities.

(*c*) Find the momentum of each of the two pieces in the platform system.

(*d*) Find the energy of each of the two pieces in the platform system.

(*e*) Show that momentum and energy are not conserved in the platform system if the mass of the original object is taken as $2m$.

but that momentum and energy are conserved if the mass of the object is taken as

$$\frac{2m_0}{\sqrt{1 - w^2/c^2}}$$

15 |22 A group of 100 particles, each having a mass that has been measured with a scale to be equal to 10 gm, is placed in a box that has a mass of 1 kg. The particles are excited so that each particle bounces around elastically in the box with a velocity equal to $\frac{2}{3}$ the velocity of light. An external force of 1 N is exerted on the box containing the moving particles. What will be the value of the average acceleration of the box?

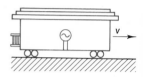

15 |23 A railroad car is moving past a platform with a velocity of 40 m/sec in a universe where the velocity of light is 50 m/sec. Just as a light on the car passes an observer on the platform, the light flashes. It flashes again 1 sec later, according to the time on the railroad car. If the observer on the platform starts his stop watch when he *sees* the first flash and stops his watch when he *sees* the second flash, what will be the reading on the watch? (The answer is *not* $\frac{5}{3}$ sec.)

15 |24 An electric-power station using nuclear fuel produces about 6×10^{15} J of energy per year. Assuming an overall efficiency of 60 percent, what is the difference in mass between the original uranium fuel and the final fission products in a year's operation? A steam plant of the same capacity uses coal as a fuel; assuming the efficiency is the same, 60 percent, what is the difference in mass between the coal and oxygen used to burn the coal and the combustion products (mainly carbon dioxide) for one year of operation?

16| 1 *Temperature scales*

WE HAVE BEEN endowed through our physiological senses with a perception of temperature. Using only our senses we can arrange an order of temperatures. We can perceive that solid carbon dioxide, or dry ice, is colder than a melting ice cube, which is in turn colder than ordinary room temperature, which is in turn colder than boiling water, which is in turn colder than a flame. It is possible to construct more complex orders where each quantity in order is perceived, physiologically and subjectively, as warmer than the next. An appropriate set of such temperatures can be selected and numbered, perhaps from 1 to 10. Such a scale is called an ordinal scale and can be very useful. Moh's scale of scratch hardness is such a scale: on this scale diamond is rated 10, corundum 9, topaz 8, quartz 7, feldspar 6, apatite 5, and so on. The higher numbered mineral can scratch the lower numbered mineral; diamond can scratch corundum but corundum cannot scratch diamond.

The numbers of an ordinal scale are assigned arbitrarily and represent only an order. The ratio of two hardnesses as defined by the Moh scale has no meaning; diamond is not 10 percent harder than corundum or twice as hard as apatite; we know only that diamond will scratch corundum and that diamond and corundum as well as other materials will scratch apatite. Nevertheless, the scale is very useful; the scratch hardness of any material can be classified according to the scale in a meaningful way. The

413

information that ordinary steel has a scratch hardness of about 5, while carbide steels have scratch hardnesses as high as 8.5, is relevant and technically interesting.

One could also arrange the weights of 10 men according to an ordinal scale. An equal-arm balance or seesaw could be used to arrange an arbitrarily selected group of men in order of how they overbalance their comrades. The heaviest could be numbered 10, the next heaviest 9, and so forth down to the lightest who is numbered 1. This scale could be useful—we can assign all men to divisions of size using such a scale. Ratios are meaningless, however: consider the statement "The ratio of the measure of man 10 to man 5 is the same as the ratio of man 4 to man 2." This is not so much wrong as it is nonsense. The result is useless.

It is necessary to have a continuous measure of an attribute defined in terms of some operation if ratios are to have any meaning. We can call such a scale a ratio scale. The scale of the weights of men, as measured on a standard balance or spring scale, is a ratio scale. The statement that man a, who weighs 220 lb according to the scale, weighs twice as much as man b, who weighs 110 lb on the scale, is well defined. Indeed, the ratio is well defined even if the scales are incorrect in that the readings are not proportional to the mass as defined by precise physical measurements and the definition of mass we adopted in Chapter 5. It may be that we are actually measuring something like the square root of the mass or something equally wild: we may not know just what quantity we are measuring, but the ratio will be relevant to that quantity and to that method of measurement, whatever the procedures. Of course an eccentric choice of measurement operation will leave us with a definition and scale that is so narrow as to be nearly useless, and it is very desirable to adopt a scale that is simply and broadly related to other areas of experience: we would rather that the scale actually measured the mass of the men.

We thus need a ratio scale of temperature if we are going to attempt to discuss temperature quantitatively, and we prefer a scale that is established in some way so that temperature might be meaningfully related to other characteristic measurements and thus to other attributes of the universe—the attributes of mechanics, for example.

Such a quantitative scale can be established in an empirical manner, using the properties of materials. A typical ratio scale of temperature is a scale based on the expansion of mercury. If we place a quantity of mercury in a bulb with a capillary tube, we find that as a result of the differential expansion of the mercury and the glass that the level of mercury in the capillary changes in correspondence with the ordinal physiological scale we have previously established. At a very low temperature, the temperature of a cold winter night in Maine, the level of the mercury is low in the capillary. If the bulb is placed in contact with a melting ice cube, the level of the mercury is higher; at room temperature the level is higher yet. When the system is immersed in boiling water, the level is still higher; and when it is brought near a flame, the mercury will reach levels that are higher yet.

It is conceivable that instead of the mercury–glass system we might have chosen some physical phenomenon that is not even in accord with the order of our physiological sense results. We might have found something that gives a low value at the temperature of dry ice and a low value at a flame temperature, but a high value at a physiologically defined intermediate temperature. Certain thermocouple arrangements, for example, do just that. Such a choice would be less satisfactory.

The definition of temperature in terms of the expansion of a mercury column still requires a scale. There are many possible scales: Fahrenheit chose the zero of his scale as the temperature of a salt–ice mixture, and he chose the temperature of a cow as a 100° point; perhaps the cow was sick, as we now know that a cow with a temperature of 100°F is a rather sick cow (actually his measurements were probably not very accurate). This is a rather arbitrary scale—salted ice for the 0°F point and a sick cow for the 100°F point—but it is nevertheless quite serviceable.

The *centigrade* scale is somewhat more fundamental in that the 0°C point is defined as the temperature of melting ice and the 100°C point is the temperature of boiling water at a standard atmospheric pressure. Water is universally available, cheap, and easily purified.

On either scale, we can find any intermediate temperature by the proportional rise of the mercury in the capillary. When the mercury is halfway between the 0° point and the 100° point we arbitrarily call that temperature 50°; when it is $\frac{3}{4}$ of the way up, we call it 75°; when it is $\frac{1}{4}$ of the way up, we call it 25°. This establishes a quantitative, useful, and quite convenient scale of temperature. This is a ratio scale; the statement that the difference between 20 and 40° is twice as large as the difference between 0 and 10° is well defined; the length of the mercury column in a thermometer will change twice as much when the temperature changes from 20 to 40° as it does when the temperature goes from 0 to 10°. The scale depends upon the properties of mercury, and through the definition of the calibration points, 0 and 100°, upon the properties of the standards used for calibration—the melting and boiling points of water in the case of the centigrade scale.

The dependence of the centigrade scale on the properties of mercury is of more serious concern than the dependence of the scale factor on the properties of water. Only the size of the degree and the choice of the origin of the scale are affected by the selection of the 0 and 100° points, but the meaning of temperature itself is made very special by the dependence on the properties of mercury. We might well expect that the expansion of mercury is a very complex phenomenon dependent upon detailed characteristics of the mercury atom, and that it will be difficult to connect temperature, as defined by the properties of mercury, with the fundamentals of mechanics, for example.

We can further understand something of the problem of a choice of measuring element by analyzing the readings of another thermometer—a thermometer based on the expansion of another material, such as solid metal, for example. The bimetalic strip, used as the element of most dial thermometers, acts from the differential expansion of two metals. We can set the 0° point of such a thermometer in very much the same way as we set the 0° point on a mercury thermometer. We can immerse this thermometer in water in which ice is melting and number that reading arbitrarily as 0°; we can set the 100° point by immersing the thermometer in boiling water or in condensing steam. The two thermometers, the mercury thermometer and the bimetallic-strip thermometer, must agree at 0° and 100°. They will not necessarily agree at any intermediate point. If we plot the readings of one thermometer versus the other, as in Fig. 16|1, we will find in general that the graph will not be a straight line. If we choose a third way to measure temperature, again the 0° point and 100° point will be equivalent by definition or by the way we set the scale, but the intermediate points will not be the same. For many choices of thermometers the intermediate points will be very

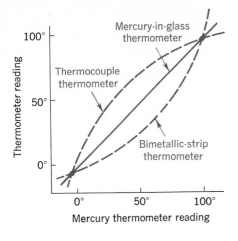

FIG. 16 | 1

A schematic representation of the comparative readings of different natural thermometers. The differences are exaggerated.

nearly the same, but this is essentially an accident; 50° read on a mercury thermometer, constructed as we have suggested, will represent very nearly the same temperature as 50° measured on a bimetalic-strip thermometer. The difference is not very important for physiological purposes, but the difference, which can be on the order of a degree or two, will be important for scientific purposes and emphasizes that we really do not know quite what we are talking about when we are talking about temperature.

We must therefore attempt to find some type of thermometer that appears to us to be less dependent upon the particular material involved. A gas thermometer appears to have these qualities. In Fig. 16 | 2 we show, schematically, a gas thermometer. This ideal gas thermometer consists of a large bulb and a very small capillary that holds some liquid. As the temperature rises or falls about the bulb, the level of liquid in the capillary will rise and fall corresponding to a change in the volume of the gas in the bulb. The gas thermometer thus measures the volume of the gas as a function of temperature when the pressure of the gas is held constant. The pressure—that is, the force per unit area—is often conveniently measured in atmospheres (atm), where 1 atm is near the average atmospheric pressure at sea level. If we make such thermometers with different gases we will have very nearly equivalent temperature scales. They will not be quite the same, but as we produce such a thermometer under lower pressure, by artifically decreasing the pressure below atmospheric pressure, we'll find the difference between the temperature scales of the different thermometers

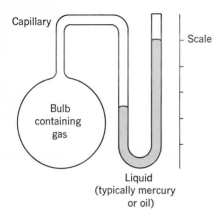

Capillary

Scale

Bulb
containing
gas

Liquid
(typically mercury
or oil)

FIG. 16|2
*A constant-pressure gas
thermometer.*

using different gases becomes smaller and smaller. At the limit
of very small pressure, or at the extrapolated limit of zero pressure, we'll find the difference between the reading of the different
gas thermometers will fall to zero. All gas thermometers that
measure temperature by the variation of the volume of a gas held
at constant pressure thus read exactly the same in the limit of
zero pressure. We can then define temperature as being proportional to the volume of a constant-pressure gas thermometer
at zero pressure.

We can construct another type of gas thermometer by putting
a definite mass of gas in the bulb, holding the volume constant,
and using the pressure as an indication of temperature. The pressure will be higher at the steam point, 100°, than at the ice point,
0°. At an intermediate point this constant-volume gas thermometer will not read exactly the same as the ideal constant-pressure
thermometer: at 50° as determined by the constant-pressure thermometer, the constant-volume thermometer will not read quite
50°. Furthermore, the reading will depend to some extent upon
the particular gas used in the bulb. However, if we reduce the
mass of gas used in the bulb to a small amount, the readings will
be very nearly the same as the ideal constant-pressure thermometer, and in the limit of extrapolation to zero mass of gas in the
bulb, the reading of the two kinds of thermometer will be exactly
the same and independent of the gas used.

This suggests to us that the gas-thermometer scales may be
intrinsically more fundamental than the mercury scale, or the
bimetallic-strip scale, or other scales. We will find upon investigation of the kinetic character of gases that this is indeed so, and

we will therefore consider that the gas thermometer scales are the fundamental scales of temperature.

It is still necessary to define the size of a degree. We choose this arbitrarily as $\frac{1}{100}$ of the temperature change between the temperature of melting ice and the temperature of boiling water. We will call this increment of temperature a degree. The natural placement of the 0° point on the gas thermometer scale will be the point at which the volume of the gas is zero when the pressure is held constant or when the pressure is zero when the volume is held constant. Of course the volume and pressure never actually go to zero, but we can extrapolate from points at finite temperature to find the zero of the temperature scale. With the use of this zero, we find that the temperature of melting ice is 273° and the temperature of boiling water is then 373°. This temperature scale is called the Kelvin scale or the *absolute temperature scale.* If we use the same scale, but for convenience, use the traditional zero as the temperature of melting ice—so that the temperature of boiling water is 100°—we have the *centigrade scale.* The size of the degree is the same in the two scales, obviously: one *Kelvin* (or *absolute*) degree is equal to one centigrade degree. Other simple relations follow from the definitions: 0°C = 273°K; 100°C = 373°K. We might note here that it is useful to remember that almost always, when temperature, T, enters into a relation in physics, it is absolute or Kelvin temperature that is meant: absolute temperature is more nearly fundamental than the arbitrarily defined centigrade temperature.

If we measure temperature in degrees Kelvin, then, partially as a definition and partially as an experimental result, we find that (1) if the volume is held constant, the pressure of a gas is proportional to the absolute temperature, and (2) if the pressure is held constant, the volume is proportional to the temperature.

$$P \propto T \quad (V \text{ held constant}) \quad \text{and} \quad V \propto T \quad (P \text{ held constant})$$

These relations are known as the laws of Charles and Gay-Lussac, and Boyles Law, respectively.

16|2   *Heat*

The existence of temperature differences implies the existence of a quantity that we call heat. Colloquially, heat and temperature are to some extent used interchangeably. Here we use the word *heat* in a technical fashion, and define qualitatively what we mean by considering simple experiments. Let us take a quantity of water at 0°C, the temperature of melting ice, and place it over an efficient burner so designed that all of the heat from the flame is used to heat the water. We can measure the amount of fuel it takes to heat 1 kg of water from the ice point up to the boiling point. If we place 2 kg of water in the container, we will find that we need to use more fuel to change the temperature of the water by the same amount. If we conducted the experiment carefully we would find that it requires twice as much fuel to heat 2 kg of water from 0° to 100°C as it does to heat 1 kg of water through the same temperature range. Furthermore, we would find that it takes only half as much fuel to heat 1 kg of water to 50°C as to 100°C. All of this implies that we might usefully define a quantity that we call heat, where heat has properties such that the amount of heat introduced into a substance is equal to some constant times the mass of the substance times the change in temperature (if the temperature change is small).

It is convenient to use water as the standard substance. We define the unit of heat as the amount of heat required to raise the temperature of 1 kg of water 1°C (or 1°K). We call this unit a Calorie (the Calorie, defined in the mks system, is sometimes called a kilocalorie to differentiate it from the calorie, a thousand times smaller, used in the cgs system of units). A Calorie is thus the amount of heat that raises 1 kg of water 1°C or 1°K. This definition of the Calorie implies that the same amount of heat will be required to change the temperature of water 1°, independent of the temperature of the water. Although this relation holds true to a fair degree of precision, it is not exactly correct; therefore, a Calorie is defined precisely as the amount of heat required to raise a kilogram of water from $14\frac{1}{2}$ to $15\frac{1}{2}$°C.

16 | 3   *Specific heat and the conservation of heat*

The quantitative definition of heat is primarily useful because with this definition there exists a conservation law. Under circumstances such that no mechanical energy is introduced, or produced and then lost, by the thermal system, and under circumstances such that no heat is lost from the system through the boundaries of the system, heat can be considered a conserved quantity. This is part of a more general conservation law—the first law of thermodynamics.

In order to make use of this conservation law we must introduce a further concept, the concept of *heat capacity*, which we define numerically, and give the name *specific heat*. By definition, 1 Cal of heat will raise the temperature of 1 kg of water 1°C. We define the *specific heat* of a material as the amount of heat, measured in Calories, required to raise 1 kg of the material 1°C: the specific heat of water is thus 1.0. All other quantities have well-defined specific heats, though the specific heat will vary with temperature. This variation is often not important, and we will usually neglect it. For example, at normal temperatures the specific heat of copper is about 0.10. This means it requires 0.10 Cal of heat to raise 1 kg of copper 1°C. A large specific heat, then, represents a large heat capacity. We might consider that 1 kg of water holds 10 times as much heat as 1 kg of copper. This treatment of heat as a quantity to be held by the material is reminiscent of the spirit of the caloric theory of heat, the prevalent view in the eighteenth century, when heat was considered a fluid permeating a material. Some materials were thought to have the capacity to hold a large amount of fluid, some a small amount of the fluid.

We use a particular example to illustrate the utility of the concept of the conservation of heat together with the concept of specific heat. One kilogram of water, at 100°C is poured on 100 kg of copper shot, which is at a temperature of 0°C. The specific heat of water is 1.0; the specific heat of copper is 0.10. We wish to know the final temperature, T. If heat is conserved, the heat gained by the copper must be equal to the heat lost by the water. The heat gained by the copper is equal to the mass of the copper times the specific heat of the copper times the increase in temperature of the copper. The heat lost by the water is equal to the mass of the water times the specific heat of the water times the temperature decrease of the water. The law concerning the conservation of heat can be written as

$$dQ_a + dQ_b + dQ_c + \cdots = 0$$

where dQ_i represents the change in heat content of some quantity of one particular material

$$dQ_i = C_i M_i \, dT_i$$

where C_i is the specific heat of the substance, M_i is the mass of the quantity, and dT_i is the change in temperature of the quantity.

The conservation law states that the total change in heat is zero for a closed system. Then for the water–copper system we have $dQ_a + dQ_b = 0$:

$$\text{copper } (a) \qquad\qquad \text{water } (b)$$

$$C_a \times M_a \times \quad dT_a \;+ C_b \times M_b \times \quad dT_b \quad = 0$$
$$0.10 \times 100 \times (T - 0) + 1.0 \times 1.0 \times (T - 100) = 0$$
$$dQ_a \qquad\qquad + \qquad dQ_b \qquad\qquad = 0$$

The heat gained by the copper plus the negative heat gained by the water equals zero. Solving for T, we find $T = 90.9°C$, which will be the final temperature of the copper–water mixture. We assume implicitly in this problem that the mixing of the hot water and copper takes place in an insulated container of negligible heat capacity so that no heat is lost or gained from the system by interaction with the contained.

Certain processes, such as the change of state of material from solid to liquid and from liquid to gas, require a specific amount of energy in the form of heat. To change 1 kg of ice at 0°C to 1 kg of water at 0°C requires 80 Cal of heat. On the other hand, when water freezes to ice 80 cal/kg are given off. This is called the *heat of fusion* of water. The change of liquid water at 100°C to gaseous water or steam also requires an input of energy. At normal atmospheric pressure, 540 Cal of heat are required to change 1 kg of water to vapor: the condensation of 1 kg of vapor releases 540 Cal/kg. This is the *heat of condensation* of the water.

Incidently, this latent heat accounts for the danger of steam. If air is heated to a temperature of over 100°C and directed upon the skin, no more than slight discomfort occurs. On the other hand, if water vapor at a temperature of a little over 100° is directed on the skin, the skin will be severely scalded. The difference in tissue destruction is due to the different amount of energy supplied to the tissue. The steam condenses to water on the tissue, giving off heat of condensation, which is extremely large.

The graph of Fig. 16|3 suggests something of the character of the heats of fusion and vaporization as well as specific heat. The plot indicates the temperature of 1 kg of water as a func-

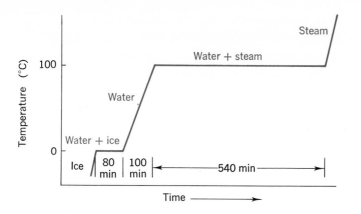

FIG. 16|3
The state of 1 kg of
water as a function of
time under a heat input
of 1 cal/min.

tion of time when heat is introduced into the water at a rate of 1 Cal/min. The water, originally in the form of a very cold piece of ice, changes to liquid and then to gas or steam as the temperature increases. Even as the specific heat of water is different in the solid, liquid, and gaseous phases the rate of change of the temperature differs with the phase.

At first the ice warms up under the influence of the added heat: since the specific heat of the ice is about 0.5 Cal/kg-°C, the temperature of the ice increases at a rate of about 2°/min; that is, 1 Cal of heat raises the temperature of the ice about 2°C. When the ice reaches a temperature of 0°C, the temperature will stop rising. Instead, the ice will slowly turn to liquid water. A total of 80 Cal will be required to change the kilogram of ice at 0°C to a kilogram of liquid water at 0°C; therefore, for 80 min the temperature will remain constant while the water changes from the solid phase to the liquid phase: the heat of fusion of water is 80 Cal/kg.

As soon as the ice is completely gone, the temperature of the water will begin to rise. Since the specific heat of water is 1.0, the temperature will now rise for 100 min at the rate of 1°/min. When the water reaches a temperature of 100°C, the temperature will again remain constant while the heat induces another phase change, this time from the liquid to gaseous state. Since the heat of vaporization of water is 540 Cal/kg this change will take 540 min. After all the water is changed to steam, the specific heat of the steam is about 0.48 at temperatures near 100° so the temperature will now increase at a rate slightly greater than 2°/min.

All of these factors, the specific heats and the heats involved in the phase changes, depend somewhat on the atmospheric pressure. The numbers used here correspond to a pressure of about 1 atm.

16|4   *The mechanical equivalent of heat and the first law of thermodynamics*

Until the nineteenth century, the study of heat and temperature followed a pattern almost completely independent of the study of other physical phenomena. Although Newton considered that heat was probably related to mechanical motion, this view was not generally accepted. The consensus of physicists or natural philosophers was rather that heat was some form of fluid, the "caloric fluid," that permeated a material. The heat produced in friction, for example, was believed to be the result of fluid being squeezed out of the material upon being rubbed. There are inherent contradictions in such an idea. If heat is squeezed out of a material, there should be less left in the material and presumably the temperature of the material should drop or alternatively the material should have lost capacity to hold heat. Although no such effects were observed, the programs of measuring the capacity to hold heat, the specific heat, which now seem rather obvious and comparatively trivial, were beyond the techniques and even the concepts of that day.

Early in the nineteenth century a number of men made investigations that seemed to show a connection between heat and mechanical energy. The work of Count Rumford, born Benjamin Thompson in Connecticut, is particularly well documented and particularly interesting. Rumford, at a time when he was Minister of War for the Bavarian government, made semiquantitative measurements concerning the amount of heat developed in boring a cannon that were clearly inconsistent with the caloric theory of heat and suggested strongly that heat is a form of mechanical energy. In particular, Rumford was able to show that the amount of heat developed by the boring mill was proportional to the amount of work put into the mill. Boring mills of that size were then driven by oxen yoked to a shaft, which they pulled in a circle about a track. The shaft drove the mill through a simple set of gears. When the oxen drove the mill by pulling the shaft several revolutions about a full circle, the cannon was heated about the same amount whether the boring tool was sharp and cut away a lot of material or was dull and cut away almost no material at all. On the other hand, if the oxen were restrained so that they moved slowly and drove the bar half as many revolutions in a given time, the amount of heat produced was reduced by about a factor of 2, independent of the sharpness of the tool. Rumford then concluded correctly that the heat was wholly the result of the work done and could therefore be regarded as a form of mechanical energy.

Rumford also measured the heat capacity, or specific heat, of the turnings from the cannon and an equal amount of material cut from the same kind of metal with a small, sharp hack saw where little heat was developed and found that the specific heats of the samples was the same: certainly caloric fluid has not been extracted from the turnings.

Later in the nineteenth century a variety of experimenters, of whom the most successful was Bernard Joule, an English brewer with a deep interest in science, made quantitative measurements of the relationship between mechanical energy and heat energy. We describe schematically a particular experiment —one of the many experiments conducted by Joule. Joule arranged a paddle wheel inside a container of water such that the

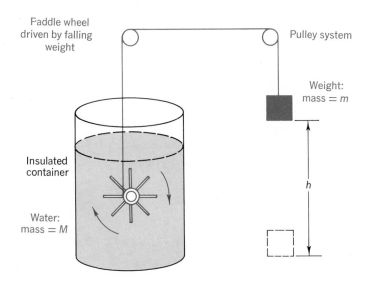

FIG. 16|4
A schematic diagram of an apparatus used by Joule to measure the mechanical equivalent of heat.

paddle wheel was driven by falling weights on a chain, as suggested by the sketch of Fig. 16|4. He could measure the temperature of the water before beginning the experiment, measure the amount of energy conducted to the water by measuring the mass of the weights and the distance they fell, and from this deduce the ratio of the heat introduced to the water to the mechanical energy put into the water. The energy introduced to the water would be equal to mgh, the change in potential energy of the weight, where m is the mass of the weight, g is the acceleration of gravity, and h is the distance the weight fell. The change in heat is $CM\,dT$, where C is the specific heat of water, M is the mass of the water, and dT is the temperature change of the water. The relation

$$mgh = jCM\,dT$$

follows, where j is a proportionality constant called the mechanical equivalent of heat. By refinements of these techniques he found that a Calorie is equal to 4,180 J. He used other units, of course, and we have translated his results into our units of Calories and joules: The joule as a quantity of energy is named after Joule himself.

It is now possible to formulate a concept of the energy contained in a material. We call this internal energy and use the symbol U. When heat is added to a system, the internal energy increases; when heat is extracted from the system, the internal energy decreases. When work is done on the system (as was the case with the water stirred by Joule's paddle wheel), the energy of the system is increased; when the system does work, the internal energy of the system is decreased. We express this formally by the relation

$$dU = dQ - dW \tag{16|1}$$

where dU is the change in internal energy of the system, dQ is the heat introduced into the system, and dW is the work done *by* the system on some external environment. Relation (16|1) is called the *first law of thermodynamics*. It is clearly an expression of the law of conservation of energy extended to include heat as energy.

As Newton suggested, heat is a mode of motion, and the insights of men like Rumford and Joule have provided us with quantitative relationships between heat and mechanical energy.

The hypothesis we must inevitably come to is then that heat and mechanical energy are not just related or similar, but that they are identical. We hypothesize, then, that heat is a macroscopic manifestation of the ordinary kinetic motion of microscopic particles. Such a hypothesis is only useful and only in any real sense true if from it we can derive quantitative results concerning other phenomena. The quantitative consequences of this hypothesis and their experimental verification is therefore a subject for further discussions.

16|5 *The transfer of heat*

Although the transfer of heat from one object to another can take place in many ways, most of the modes of transfer can be classified sensibly into three classes labeled convection, conduction, and radiation. The transfer of heat through the macroscopic movement of material is called *convection*. The transfer of heat from the Gulf of Mexico to northwestern Europe through the physical movement of warm water from the Gulf to the coasts of Europe represents an example of convection. The warmth carried by a wind from the south as well as cold carried by a north wind are also examples of convection. Convective transfers are usually complex and special: although the broad pattern of winds on the planet is understood to some extent, for example, the reasons for the behavior of the Gulf Stream have not yet been clearly established.

The transfer of heat through materials, where there is no macroscopic motion of the material, is called *conduction*. Although the differences in the thermal conductivities of materials cannot be understood without some detailed knowledge of the microscopic structure of the materials, it is possible to describe much of the character of conduction in a manner almost independent of detailed mechanisms.

Elementary experiments confirm the following intuitively plausible description of the condition of heat through most media. For simplicity we consider in detail the conduction of heat through a rectangular section of material as shown in Fig. 16|5: the results will still be general; the section might be a part of a more complicated structure. The rate of heat transfer from one side of the section to the other, dQ/dt, in Calories per second, is

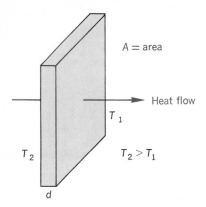

A = area

Heat flow

T_1

T_2

$T_2 > T_1$

d

FIG. 16|5
*A diagram used to
illustrate the character
of heat flow.*

proportional to the area of the section, A, inversely proportional to the thickness, d, and proportional to the temperature difference across the section, $T_2 - T_1$. Then

$$\frac{dQ}{dt} = \frac{KA(T_2 - T_1)}{d}$$

where K, the constant of proportionality, is called (or defined as) the thermal conductivity of the material.

Radiation is the name given to the transfer of energy through the agency of electromagnetic radiation like light. When the transfer of heat by radiation is considered, the inference is usually made that we restrict ourselves to the consideration of radiation given off by bodies in consequence of their temperature. We do not consider radiation emitted by a radar station in this context, but the energy transmitted to the earth by the sun constitutes a definite example of the radiative transfer of heat.

Since the general pattern of radiative transfers is not strongly dependent upon the particular material of the radiator, it is possible to establish rather general relations that describe the radiative transfer of heat for all materials.

All bodies, at any temperature, emit radiant energy even as all bodies absorb some proportion of the radiant energy incident on them. We define the emittance of a surface, E, as the energy emitted per unit area per unit time; in the mks system emittance is measured in joules per square meter per second. Emittance is a function both of the material of the surface and the temperature of the surface.

All surfaces absorb radiation: the absorption power, A, is the ratio of the amount of energy absorbed by a surface to the total amount of energy incident on the surface; the remaining energy is reflected. Of course the maximum possible absorption occurs at a hole where the radiation goes into the hole and nothing comes out. A hole in a box serves as a very good approximation to the ideal hole: the radiation that passes through the hole into the box will be absorbed as it is reflected from wall to wall, and very little radiation will find its way out through the hole in ordinary circumstances. The *absorption power, A*, is therefore equal to 1 for a hole: the hole is an ideal *black body*.

The box with the hole will also emit radiant energy; this is particularly evident if the box is heated. In particular, the hole will radiate—radiation will be emitted from the hole. Measurements of this radiation have established that the energy density from the hole—or black body—can be expressed as

$$E_b = \sigma T^4$$

where E_b is the energy radiated per second per square meter, T is the absolute temperature, and σ is a constant of proportionality, the Stefan–Boltzmann constant: σ is equal to 5.7×10^{-8} J/m²-°C⁴-sec.

The energy radiated per second per unit area by any other surface will be less than that radiated by the black body by a factor A', which is thus less than one, which we will call the *emissivity*. An interesting relation exists between the absorbing power, A, and the emissivity, A': for any surface, $A = A'$; the absorbing power is equal to the emissivity. This relation, called *Kirchhoff's law*, follows from the second law of thermodynamics (discussed in Chapter 18), as does the dependence of the emission on the fourth power of the temperature. We will not attempt to prove this, however.

PROBLEMS

16|1   A body and a hot filament are placed in a vacuum chamber where the walls of the chamber are black and very cold—near absolute zero. Show that the equilibrium temperature of the body will vary inversely as the square root of the distance from the filament. (At equilibrium the body loses as much heat as it gains.)

16|2   One kilogram of boiling water is poured into an insulated container of negligible heat capacity, containing 10 kg of metal immersed in 1 kg of water in which is floating 1 kg of melting ice. The final temperature is 5°C. What is the specific heat of the metal?

16|3   A lead bullet (specific heat 0.05 Cal/°C-kg) traveling 500 m/sec strikes a hardened steel plate, flattens out, and drops a few feet to the ground. Assuming the moving bullet was at a temperature of 20°C, what is its approximate final temperature?

16|4   The velocity of escape from the earth's gravitational field is about 11 km/sec, which is also the velocity of an object that falls to the earth from very far away. If the mean specific heat of the constituents of the earth is 0.2, and if the earth was produced by the gravitational attraction and condensation of cosmic dust, about how hot (within a factor of three) would the earth be at formation?

16|5   The Victoria Falls is about 130 m high. Estimate the difference in temperature of the water at the top of the falls and at the bottom.

16|6   The right-hand side of the section of material shown is at a temperature of 0°C. The thermal conductivity of the material, K, is equal to 1 Cal/m-sec-°C. If the thermal transmission is equal to 1 Cal/sec, what is the temperature at the left-hand end of the section? At the center point, a?

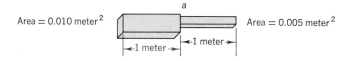

16|7   Assume that the center of the earth has a density 5 times that of water, 5000 kg/m³; the temperature as the center is 8000°C; the specific heat of the core material is 0.1; and the molten core is 4000 km in radius. If the solid mantle, 2000 km thick, has a thermal conductivity of 10^{-3} Cal/m-sec, how long will it take for the core to cool? (None of the input data are very accurate, so it is foolish to attempt a precise calculation; one might estimate the time required for the core to cool to half its present temperature with an accuracy of a factor of 2. But such an estimate is not foolish, since it can be compared with the age of the earth, $\approx 5 \times 10^9$ yr.)

16| 8   A container with a volume of 20 l. holds a quantity of an ideal gas at a temperature of 27°C and a pressure of 1 atm.

(*a*) What is the pressure when the temperature is increased to 100°C?

(*b*) What is the pressure if the gas is compressed to 10 l., the temperature remaining at 27°C?

(*c*) What volume does the gas occupy when the temperature is raised to 100°C, the pressure remaining at 1 atm?

17 | 1 *The ideal-gas law*

IN THE STUDY OF mechanics it was shown that it is possible to divide all collisions or interactions between two bodies into two specific classes: a class of elastic collisions, and a class of inelastic collisions. Although momentum is conserved for both elastic and inelastic collisions, the kinetic energy of macroscopic bodies is not conserved for inelastic collisions. Since it is attractive to consider that all collisions are intrinsically elastic and intrinsically conserve energy, we might attempt to understand the energy defect in inelastic collisions in terms of a lack of experimental perception or completeness. The missing kinetic energy might well be found if one could investigate the motion of the microscopic particles making up the macroscopic bodies.

Under certain conditions, using our own sensory perceptions, we can notice that what we subjectively call temperature has increased in the case of inelastic collisions. The colliding bodies will be warm to the touch. This might lead us to suspect that the quantities we call casually heat and temperature are manifestations of the kinetic energy and thus the motion of such microscopic bodies. Indeed this view was first suggested by Newton. However, in spite of Newton's enormous and well-deserved reputation, the view that heat is a mode of motion was not generally accepted in Newton's time. This is hardly surprising, nor is this lack of acceptance attributable to any blind ignorance on the part of scientists or natural philosophers of the time. There was then no quantitative indication that heat could be microscopic motion, and the well-known qualitative characteristics of heat appeared to be explained as well or as badly by competitive theories. In particular, the idea that heat was some kind of fluid that permeated macroscopic bodies and could be transfered under certain conditions from one body to another was popular. This "caloric theory of heat" was the generally accepted view until nearly the middle of the nineteenth century.

During the nineteenth century the view that heat is a mode of motion—that heat is a macroscopic, collective description of microscopic motion—was firmly established. First the establishment of the equivalence of heat and energy through the work of men such as Rumford and Joule made it appear very likely that heat and mechanics were closely related. The most striking and conclusive evidence in favor of this hypothesis was found in the results of the kinetic theory of gases. Many properties of gases, including the thermal properties, were explained in detail by the application of elementary principles of mechanics to a model of gas that considered these properties as a consequence of the motion and collisions of microscopic particles. Later, these considerations were extended to the more complex structures of solids and liquids.

The object of this section is to deduce important properties of gases by the application of the laws of elementary mechanics to a simple model of a gas. The model represents a gas as consisting of a very large number of very small, identical, individual, particles, which are called molecules, moving to and fro with high velocity. We consider at first that they do not interact with each other and that they interact with the walls of any container only by elastic collisions. We might state now that we can relax these conditions considerably and retain the results of this specific elementary calculation. The calculation to be discussed is of particular importance in that it is probably the first excursion of man intellectually into the region of the universe that is imperceptible to him directly because of its smallness. Newton, and before him others, projected man's insights into the large, into the planetary system and into cosmology itself. The kinetic theory of gases was the first intellectual excursion into the minute.

We will analyze the properties of a gas in a box, as in Fig.

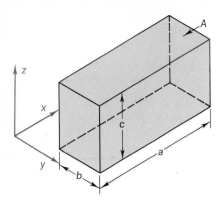

FIG. 17|1

A box containing gas molecules.

17|1, where the box is laid out on a rectangular coordinate system where the dimensions of the box in the x-, y-, and z-directions are a, b, and c, respectively. The volume of the box is thus equal to abc. In this box are n particles, or molecules, moving in random directions, presumably at high speed. There is no preferred direction in the box as the effects of gravity are almost completely negligible. Since there is no preferred direction, we can expect that the distribution of the components of velocity of the molecules in the x-direction is about equal to the distribution of velocity components in the y- or z-direction.

Of course any particular molecule will travel in a particular direction with some component of velocity in each direction. These components of velocity can be considered separately. Since

$$v^2 = v_x^2 + v_y^2 + v_z^2$$

where v is the magnitude of the velocity of the particle, and since all directions are equivalent,

$$\overline{v_x^2} = \overline{v_y^2} = \overline{v_z^2} = \frac{\overline{v^2}}{3}$$

where the overline indicates the average taken over all the molecules.

For definiteness we now consider only collisions with the far wall bc. We need only be concerned then with the x-component of velocity of the molecules. A molecule will make N' collisions per second with that wall, where N' will be equal to the velocity of the molecule in the x-direction divided by the distance between collisions with the wall. That distance will be equal to $2a$, and the x-component of the velocity is v_x. Then

$$N' = \frac{v_x}{2a}$$

These are elastic collisions, so the molecules rebound from the wall with the same velocity with which they struck the wall. The x-component of momentum of the molecule before the collision is

$$p_x = mv_x$$

where v_x is the x-component of the velocity of the molecule before the collision and m is the mass of the molecule. Since the collision is elastic—and we assume that the box is very heavy compared to the mass of the molecule so the box does not move as a result of the collision—the x-component of the velocity will be reversed and the x-component of the momentum of the molecule leaving the wall will be reversed.

$$p_x' = -mv_x$$

The difference in momentum will be

$$dp_x = p_x - p_x'$$
$$= 2mv_x$$

which, by the law of conservation of momentum, is equal to the momentum transfer to the wall. The total momentum transfer to the wall per second is equal to the product of the number of collisions per second and the momentum transfer per collision. For each molecule, the momentum transfer per second to the wall will be

$$dp_x \text{ (in 1 sec)} = (2mv_x)\left(\frac{v_x}{2a}\right)$$
$$= \frac{mv_x^2}{a}$$

For all n molecules the momentum transfer per second will be equal to n times the momentum transfer from the collision with the wall of a molecule which transmits an average force to the wall through collisions. The value of v_x^2 for such a molecule will be equal to $\overline{v_x^2}$, which is the average value of v_x^2 for the n molecules in the box. Then the total momentum transfer per second will be

$$dp_x \text{ (total)} = \frac{nm\overline{v_x^2}}{a}$$

$$= F_{bc}$$

Since the change in momentum per unit time is essentially the definition of force, dp_x (total) is equal to F_{bc}, the force on wall bc. Since

$$\overline{v_x^2} = \frac{\overline{v^2}}{3}$$

then

$$F_{bc} = \frac{nm\overline{v^2}}{3a}$$

Pressure is defined as force per unit area: the pressure of the atmosphere at sea level is about 10^5 N/m². The pressure on the face of the box, bc, is then equal to the force on the face divided by the area of the face of the box A_{bc}, which is equal to bc.

$$P = \frac{F_{bc}}{A_{bc}}$$

$$= \frac{F_{bc}}{bc}$$

$$= \frac{nm\overline{v^2}}{3abc}$$

Since abc is equal to V, the volume of the box,

$$P = \frac{nm\overline{v^2}}{3V} \quad \text{or} \quad PV = \frac{nm\overline{v^2}}{3} \tag{17|1}$$

The kinetic energy of an average molecule is

$$\bar{E} = \tfrac{1}{2}m\overline{v^2}$$

and the total kinetic energy of all n molecules is

$$E = n\bar{E}$$

$$= \tfrac{1}{2}nm\overline{v^2} \tag{17|2}$$

where we use the symbol E for the total kinetic energy of all of the molecules in the box. Combining (17|1) and (17|2) we have a relation connecting the pressure, volume, and total kinetic energy of the molecules in the gas:

$$PV = \tfrac{2}{3}n(\tfrac{1}{2}m\overline{v^2}) = \tfrac{2}{3}E$$

The pressure times the volume of any quantity of gas is equal to two thirds of the total kinetic energy of the gas. This relation, together with its algebraic variants, is called the *ideal-gas law*.

In Chapter 16 we defined a quantity, temperature, in such a manner that the pressure of a gas held at constant volume is proportional to the temperature and the volume of a gas held at constant pressure is proportional to temperature. We can obviously combine these relations to obtain

$$PV = (nk)T \qquad\qquad (17|3)$$

where T is absolute temperature, in degrees Kelvin, and nk is a proportionality constant determined by experiment. This constant will be found to be proportional to the mass of the gas for any particular gas.

A comparison of Eqs. (17|3) and (17|2) shows that

$$nkT = \tfrac{2}{3}E$$
$$\quad\;\; = \tfrac{2}{3}n\overline{E}$$

and so we find that the absolute temperature of a gas is proportional to the total kinetic energy of the molecules of gas; the mean kinetic energy of a molecule, $\overline{E}$, is equal to $\tfrac{3}{2}kT$, where k is a constant of nature called Boltzmann's constant.

We can restate most of the foregoing results in a very simple way. If the temperature of a gas increases by a factor of 4 the average kinetic energy of a molecule must increase by 4 times and therefore the average velocity of the molecules must double. There will be twice as many collisions per second with any section of wall, and the momentum transfer at each collision will double; thus the force on the section, and therefore the pressure on the wall, will increase by a factor of 4. Thus the pressure is proportional to the temperature if the volume is held constant. If the length of the box, dimension a in Fig. 17|1, is reduced by a factor of 2 the volume will be reduced by a factor of 2. Since the molecules will have to travel only half as far in the x-direction there will be twice as many collisions per second with the face bc and the pressure on that face will double. The force on the four sides perpendicular to bc will not be changed, but their area will be reduced by one half; hence the pressure on these sides is also doubled. The pressure is then doubled as the volume is reduced by one half. Or, in general the pressure is inversely proportional to the volume if the temperature is held constant.

Further, the internal energy, U, of an ideal gas depends only upon the temperature of the gas. For the ideal gas we are discussing here, the only internal energy is the kinetic energy of the molecules, which is proportional to the temperature and thus depends only on the temperature.

17|2   *Dalton's laws*

According to the ideal-gas law the relation between the pressure, volume, and temperature of a quantity of gas depends only on the number of molecules of gas and not at all on the mass of the individual molecules. It then follows that equal volumes of different gases held at the same temperature and pressure contain the same number of molecules. The ratio of the masses of the two quantities of gas must be the same as the ratio of the masses of the different molecules. Through extensions of the work of John Dalton, an English chemist of the early nineteenth century, we known that the masses of equivalent volumes of hydrogen (H_2), helium (He), nitrogen (N_2), water vapor (H_2O), and so on are in the ratios of $2:4:14:18$; atomic hydrogen (H), which is unstable, would represent 1 on such a scale. We call these numbers *molecular weights*. Then 1 kg of atomic hydrogen, 2 kg of moleuclar hydrogen, 4 kg of helium, 14 kg of nitrogen, and 18 kg of water all contain the same number of molecules. This quantity of material is given the name *kilogram-mole* (kg-mole) and contains about 6×10^{26} molecules. Inversely, of course, the result that equal volumes of different gases have different masses implies that the individual molecules of these gases have different masses. This important inference of Dalton is a natural consequence of the kinetic theory of gases; the fact that the ratios of the masses of equal volumes of the light gases have the form of simple integral fractions further suggested to Dalton that these molecules are made up as compounds of some fundamental building block and are therefore not fundamental particles themselves. We know now that these fundamental building blocks are the nucleons—the neutrons and protons that make up the atomic nuclei.

It is possible to consider that each gas in a mixture of gases contributes separately to the total pressure according to the number of molecules of that gas that are present. The total pressure is then the sum of the partial pressures. This is Dalton's law of partial pressures.

For example, assume that a container with volume V holds a mixture of three gases at a total pressure of P. There will be n_a molecules of gas a, n_b molecules of gas b, and n_c molecules of gas c, adding up to a total of $n_a + n_b + n_c = n$ molecules of gas. If only gas a were present, the pressure would be

$$P_a = \frac{n_a}{n} P$$

where

$$P = \frac{3}{2} \frac{nkT}{V}$$

For gases b and c, the partial pressures would be

$$P_b = \frac{n_b}{n} P \quad \text{and} \quad P_c = \frac{n_c}{n} P$$

The sum of the partial pressures is obviously equal to the total pressure, P.

Since $n_a + n_b + n_c = n$,

$$P_a + P_b + P_c = P$$

For completeness we add one further notation:

$$R = Nk$$

where $N = 6 \times 10^{26}$, the number of molecules in a kilogram-mole, which is called Avogadro's number (the value is usually listed as 6×10^{23}, the number of molecules in a gram-mole). At normal atmospheric pressure—about 10^5 N/m²—and at 0°C or 273°K, a kilogram-mole of any gas occupies a volume of about 22.4 cubic meters.

Using the relation

$$PV = NkT = RT$$

for 1 kg-mole of gas, and using 22.4 m³ for V, 10^5 N/m² for P, and 273°K for T, we find that

$$R = 8300 \text{ J/°K}$$
$$= 2 \text{ Cal/°K}$$

Then the value of Boltzmann's constant is

$$k = \frac{R}{N} = 3.3 \times 10^{-27} \text{ Cal/°K}$$

$$= 1.38 \times 10^{-23} \text{ J/°K}$$

The total kinetic energy of the molecules in 1 kg-mole of gas is equal to $\frac{3}{2}PV$ or $\frac{3}{2}RT$, which is

$$E = \tfrac{3}{2} \times 8300 \times 273 = 3.35 \times 10^6 \text{ J}$$
$$= 820 \text{ Cal}$$

The gas law for n kg-moles of gas is

$$PV = nRT$$

17 | 3   *Determination of Avogadro's number—the Brownian movement*

Although the product Nm appears in the calculations of the ideal gas law applied to 1 kg-mole of gas, and thus can be measured—Nm is just the total mass of 1 kg-mole of gas—neither the mass m nor the number N enters alone into any of the measurable quantities we have discussed. The value of N is most accurately measured by techniques using measurements of the diffraction of X-rays by crystalline solids. X-rays are essentially light of very short wavelength, and the diffraction of X-rays by crystals is very much like the diffraction of light by a set of slits or bars (see Section 12 | 5) which we call an optical grating; the crystal acts as a three-dimensional diffraction grating where the spacing between the atoms corresponds to the spacing between the slits of an optical grating. Even as the spacing between the atoms in a crystal is very much smaller than the spacing of the slits of a diffraction grating, the wavelength of X-rays is very much smaller than the wavelength of light.

X-rays will be scattered especially strongly at angles such that the amplitudes of the waves scattered from many different atoms will differ in phase by integral numbers of wavelengths and thus interfere constructively. This will be the case when the angle of incidence of the X-rays with a plane of the crystal—a plane that contains many atoms—is equal to the angle of scattering and the relation

$$n\lambda = 2d \sin \theta$$

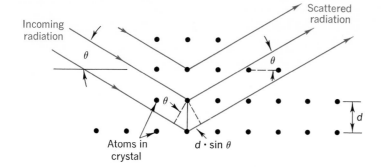

FIG. 17 | 2
*A diagram showing the
geometric relations that
occur in the scattering
of gamma rays from a
crystal.*

holds, where d is the spacing between planes of the crystal, θ is the angle of incidence, and $n\lambda$ is the number of wavelengths of path difference between the amplitudes scattered from adjacent planes. The validity of the relation can be seen by an inspection of the sketch of Fig. 17 | 2. The extra path difference is seen to be equal to twice the value of $d \sin \theta$.

Of course the wavelength of the X-rays must be measured; this can be accomplished by the use of a conventional ruled grating—which is very much like a set of slits—if the X-rays are scattered at very small angles with respect to the grating.

The density of the crystal is measured conventionally. From the density and spacing one can determine the number of atoms per unit mass. We illustrate that procedure using a simple (and artificial) example. Let us assume that an analysis of the X-ray diffraction patterns shows that the atoms are arranged in a cubic lattice—that is, they lie at equally spaced intervals on a rectangular coordinate system as shown in Fig. 17 | 3, where the spacing between atoms is 10^{-10} m. Each atom then occupies a space that is a cube 10^{-10} m on a side, or a volume of 10^{-30} m³. There are then 10^{30} atoms/m³. If the density is 10^4 kg/m³, there will be

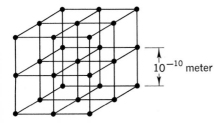

10^{-10} meter

FIG. 17 | 3
*A section of the lattice
of a cubic crystal. The
points represent
individual atoms.*

10^{26} atoms/kg. The value of N, the number of atoms per kilogram-mole, can thus be established from such measurements.

Although this is the most accurate method of determining the number of molecules in a given amount of material, and hence the mass of an individual molecule, it is interesting to note that the value of N can be determined directly by measurements of the Brownian movement, a phenomenon in which one is able to perceive directly the manifestations of discrete molecular collisions.

We can gain some insight into the character of the Brownian movement by considering the behavior of a small cube of light material placed in a box filled with gas at atmospheric pressure. For simplicity let us assume that the cube has dimensions of 1 cm on a side and that the faces of the cube are parallel to the walls of the box. Furthermore, let us assume that we can neglect gravity and that the cube is floating in the box. A cube placed in this way will not move sensibly, even though it is being struck very often by individual molecules. Using the results of our previous calculations, we conclude that $\overline{nv_x}/2$ collisions take place per square meter per second with the faces of the cube that are normal to the x-direction. Here n is the number of molecules per cubic meter. The pressure on the face was shown to be $P = nmv_x$. Knowing n (from the X-ray diffraction results) and m (since nm is just the density of the gas) and P, the pressure, we can calculate the value of $\overline{v_x}$, the average velocity in the x-direction. Then we will find that the number of collisions per second with the face of the cube is about 10^{24} for a typical gas such as air. Now we understand why the cube does not jump around under the bombardment. The force on each face is the result of an extremely large number of collisions with extremely small particles. The number of collisions is so large that the random statistical fluctuations are very small and the average force on each face is very nearly constant and of course cancels out. There is no observable indication of the discrete character of the collisions.

However if the pressure were supplied, not by collisions with 10^{24} molecules/sec, each with a mass of about 10^{-25} k, but by 100 collisions/sec with molecules that weighed 1 gm, we would expect to see the cube buffeted around a great deal, even though the average force would be the same on each side. The discrete character of the interactions, and hence the gas, would be directly observable. One can see qualitatively that the amount of such random motion incited by the irregular buffeting must be related to n, the number of molecules per unit volume, and thus, through the density, ρ, where $\rho = nm$, to the value of the mass m of the individual molecule. The motion of dust particles under the bombardment of individual molecules can be observed under the microscope. The small size of the dust particle means that statistical fluctuations are more important, and their effect on the particle is easily seen. This motion is called the Brownian motion after the English botanist Robert Brown, who noticed the erratic motions of grains of pollen suspended in the atmosphere. This observation, made in 1828, constitutes the first direct evidence of the discreteness of the matter of a gas and thus the existence of molecules.

In 1905 Einstein published calculations that made it possible to understand the Brownian movement quantitatively and determine the value of N (to about 20 percent accuracy). Einstein was unfamiliar with the existence of the effect and deduced that it must exist. He was particularly interested in the problem, since there were many who believed that molecules were unobservable (though the kinetic theory of gases was derived on the assumption that molecules existed), and if they were unobservable the whole concept of molecules was meaningless.

17|4   *Forces between molecules —Van der Waals' equation*

A more sophisticated inquiry into the properties of gases shows that the results concerning the gas law are somewhat modified if we take into account the forces between molecules and hence the collisions between molecules. These collisions establish a distribution of velocities in the gas, but further collisions do not change this distribution. We usually consider a gas only after it has remained in a particular equilibrium condition for a long time. Since collisions are continually occuring, yet the average condition of the gas is certainly constant, we must conclude that the collisions on a whole do not change the distribution of velocities in the gas. Since our previous calculations ignored intermolecular collisions entirely, it seems at first surprising that the existence of such collisions does not affect those results very much. We will not examine this question in detail, but we can gain some insight into the validity of our approximation ignoring collisions by examining the results of a collision. When two molecules collide, the laws of conservation of energy and momentum require that the total energy and total value of the components of momentum in any direction are unchanged. Since these are the quantities that enter into our calculations of the ideal-gas law, it is not surprising that we could neglect the collisions safely.

The existence of collisions does mean that there are forces between the molecules. If there were no forces the molecules would not experience collisions: even if the molecules are assumed to occupy some space, they would pass right through each other unless there are forces between them. We can deduce something of the forces between molecules by noting some of the qualitative properties of matter; for example, water. At high temperatures water is a gas. As the temperature and the average velocity of the molecules become lower, the gas condenses to a liquid. This condensation implies that there exists an attractive force sufficient to bind the molecules together. On the other hand, the liquid water is very nearly incompressible; this implies that there is also a strong repulsive force between molecules that keeps them from getting too close together.

It is convenient to describe the interaction between two mole-

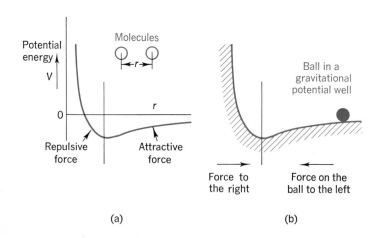

FIG. 17I4
A comparison of (a) the potential energy resulting from the forces between two molecules and (b) the potential energy of a ball on a gravitational surface.

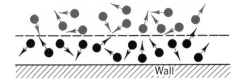

FIG. 17 | 5

The positions and velocities of molecules near a wall. The distance between the dashed line and the wall is much less than the average distance between collisions.

cules by means of a potential-energy diagram such as Fig. 17 | 4a, where the potential energy of the system is the ordinate and the distance between the centers of the two molecules is the abscissa. One can get some feeling for the meaning of such a diagram by considering the parallel between the potential-energy curve of the diagram and the potential energy curve of a surface on the earth where a ball (a molecule) is rolling or sliding on the surface. We see in Fig. 17 | 4b that the ball will be attracted to the left as a result of the slope of the surface, but will be repelled as a result of the steep ascent as it moves far to the left. A rolling ball will enter the trough (potential well), roll up the steep side, reverse direction and roll out as fast as it came in, conserving energy. This is an elastic collision. If it loses energy during the collision, perhaps in collision with another ball, it might be left with too little energy to leave the trough. This is condensation. Note that energy must be taken away (as heat of condensation) in order that the ball be trapped.

The existence of these forces will have some effect on the simple ideal-gas law

$$PV = nRT$$

where n is the number of kilogram-moles of gas. The illustration of Fig. 17 | 5 shows a number of molecules very near the wall of a container. An imaginary line is drawn to separate the molecules farther away. The arrows represent typical velocity vectors. During the instant after the configuration shown by the picture of Fig. 17 | 5, the pressure on the wall will result only from the effects of the molecules that are very near the wall: these molecules are colored black in the diagram. If there is an attractive force between these molecules and those a little farther from the wall, colored red in the diagram, the velocity of the black molecules in the direction of the wall will be reduced; they will not strike the wall quite as hard as otherwise, and the pressure will be reduced. The measured pressure, P, will be smaller than the ideal pressure, P_i, calculated on the basis of the ideal-gas law.

The reduction in pressure will be proportional to the number of collisions per unit time against a unit area that will be affected by the forces. This will be just equal to the number of black molecules in front of the area, or the density of black molecules. The change in pressure will also be proportional to the force holding the black molecules back from the wall, and this is clearly proportional to the density of colored molecules. For 1 kg-mole of gas, this density will be inversely proportional to the volume in which the gas is held, so the reduction in pressure, $P_i - P$, which is proportional to the product of the density of molecules very near the wall and the density of molecules a little further from the wall, will be proportional to $1/V^2$, where V is the volume occupied by the gas; or

$$P_i = P + \frac{a}{V^2}$$

where a is a proportionality constant with a value dependent upon the detailed character of the attractive forces between the molecules.

We repeat the arguments in a manner that may provide some further clarification; if the volume of the gas were doubled, the number of molecules (the black molecules) that were to collide with the wall in the next millionth of a second would be reduced by one half. Since the number of molecules near them, which hold them back by virtue of their attractive forces (the colored molecules), is also reduced by half, the total reduction in the force of the collisions is reduced by a factor of 4. There are only half as many collisions affected, and each of these is affected only half as much when the volume is doubled. The effect is reduced by a factor of 4.

Molecules in the middle of the container are pulled in all ways by the other molecules, so that the total force averages to zero. Near the walls they only pull away from the walls, and their velocity toward the wall is thus reduced and the pressure on the wall is reduced.

There may be, and certainly are, attractive forces between the wall and the molecules that increase the speed of collision

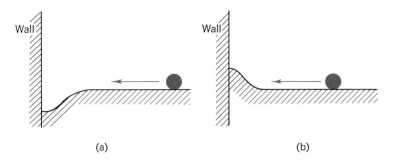

FIG. 17|6
Potential-energy diagrams showing the forces between a wall and a ball: (a) attractive force between wall and ball; (b) repulsive force between wall and ball. Both balls strike the wall and rebound with their energy unchanged.

between the wall and the molecules, even as there are repulsive forces that we consider more directly the cause of the collision. These forces have no effect on the pressure, however. Even as the force the wall exerts on the molecule speeds up the molecule as it nears the wall, from the principle of action and reaction, the gas molecule exerts an attractive force on the wall. The attractive force just compensates for the extra repulsion on the wall due to the extra velocity of the collision. In other words, the total interaction of the molecule with the wall can be considered as of one piece. Only the total change in momentum of the molecule is relevant after the whole collision is considered, including the results of all attractive and repulsive forces.

The two balls in the diagrams of Fig. 17|6 each rebound from the wall with the same final velocity; the ball on the left speeds up as it nears the wall and slows down as it leaves the wall after the collision; the ball on the right slows down as it reaches the wall and speeds up as it leaves. If the collisions are elastic, the balls rebound from the wall and accompanying forces with the same speed with which they approached the wall in each case. In each case the change in velocity in the whole collision is the same, and therefore the momentum transfer to the wall is the same; the forces are irrelevant.

Collisions between the molecules and the wall are not all perfectly elastic. Indeed, it has been shown experimentally that generally the velocity and direction of the individual rebounding molecule has little relation to the original velocity and direction of the molecule. However, if the gas is at equilibrium with the container and with itself, which is to say that the temperature is uniform, the distribution of velocities of the molecules cannot be changed by the collisions. It then follows as a matter of course that the molecules cannot lose any energy to the wall on the average. Although an individual molecule may lose or gain energy upon collision with the wall, the average energy of a large number of molecules will be retained. Thus the average velocity of the molecules will not be changed. Furthermore, if the wall is to be given no torque through the collisions, the average change in the components of the molecular velocity in directions parallel to the wall must be zero. If the total magnitude of the mean velocity is to be unchanged and the parallel components of velocity are to be unchanged, we must conclude that the only mean change of the velocity upon collision will be a change in sign in the component of velocity perpendicular to the wall. The average collision must therefore be exactly the same as an elastic collision with a perfectly smooth plane wall. Our naive approximation is exactly correct.

The short-range repulsive forces between molecules also has an effect as the effective volume available to the molecules is reduced. The actual volume V_i is less than the measured volume of the container V by an amount equal to the volume effectively occupied by the molecules themselves:

$$V_i = V - b$$

where b is the volume taken up by the molecules of the gas (this is actually equal to 4 times the volume of the hard core of the molecules).

The ideal-gas law is now changed by the inclusion of the forces so that

$$P_i V_i = RT$$

goes to

$$\left(P + \frac{a}{V^2}\right)(V - b) = RT \tag{17|4}$$

For n kg-moles of gas,

$$\left(P + \frac{an^2}{V^2}\right)(V - nb) = nRT$$

This equation was first deduced by van der Waals and is called van der Waals' equation. The parameters a and b, which represent the effects of the attractive and repulsive parts of the

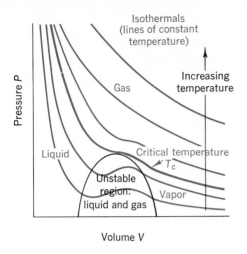

Pressure P

Isothermals
(lines of constant
temperature)

Gas

Increasing
temperature

Liquid

Critical temperature
T_c

Unstable
region:
liquid and gas

Vapor

Volume V

FIG. 17|7
*Isothermal pressure-
versus-volume curves
for a gas that follows
van der Waals' equation.*

molecular forces, are called van der Waals' constants, and of course their values depend upon the particular gas involved.

The behavior of actual gases follow van der Waals' equation very well. Figure 17|7 represents the pressure versus volume curves for a typical gas for different values of temperature, T. At high temperatures, above T_c, the gas can never become liquid, no matter how much it is compressed. At temperatures below T_c, called the critical temperature, the gas will begin to turn to a liquid as the pressure is increased until all of the gas is liquid. Further increases in pressure do not reduce the volume very much: the liquid is not very compressible.

The internal energy of a real gas, where molecular forces are taken into account, differs from the internal energy of an ideal gas inasmuch as the potential energy derived from the molecular forces must be considered as well as the kinetic energy. Since the potential energy, negative for attractive molecular forces and positive for repulsive forces, will depend upon the average distance between molecules and thus the density of the gas, the value of the internal energy, U, will no longer depend only on temperature as it does for an ideal gas. If the density of the gas is low, however, the potential energy will not be large compared to the kinetic energy.

17│5 · *The distribution of molecular energies*

We have stated that the molecules in a gas do not all have the same velocity, because the effects of collisions must result in some distribution of velocities. It is easy to see that the existence of random collisions precludes the possibility of the molecules all having the same velocity even if the collisions are elastic. Figure 17│8 shows a particular possible collision between two molecules having the same velocity: molecule *a* is traveling in the *y*-direction, molecule *b* is traveling in the *x*-direction, each with a velocity *v*. If the molecules are spherical, which is to say that the force between them lies along the line between their centers, the momentum transfer will take place along the line of centers. After the elastic collision, molecule *b* will be stationary and molecule *a* will be traveling in the direction illustrated with a velocity $V = \sqrt{2}v$: after the collision the molecules will have different velocities.

Even as the different molecules of a gas will have different velocities, the molecules will have different kinetic energies. According to our description of gases, the average kinetic energy of the molecules of a gas depends only upon the temperature of the gas and is independent of the characteristics of the molecules, such as their mass or size. If a container holds a mixture of several gases in thermal equilibrium, the average energy of the molecules of one variety will be the same as the average energy of the molecules of another type; there will be an equipartition of energy. This equal division of energy extends to large diversities of size; the mean kinetic energy of a pollen grain sus-

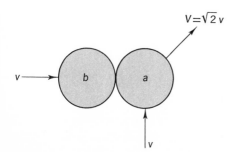

$V = \sqrt{2}\,v$

v

b   *a*

v

FIG. 17│8
A collision between two molecules that have the same magnitude of initial velocity.

pended in air is the same as the mean kinetic energy of an oxygen atom, though the mass of the pollen grain is enormously greater than the mass of the molecule.

A gas molecule that is subject to a conservative force—such as gravity—will have a definite potential energy, and the different molecules can be expected to have a distribution of potential energies even as they have a distribution of kinetic energies. Since there will be a constant exchange between kinetic and potential energy in systems in thermal equilibrium, we can expect that the potential-energy distributions and the kinetic-energy distributions will be closely related. Furthermore, we might expect to find some kind of definite division of the total energy between the kinetic energy of translation and the potential energy: the concept of equipartition of energy might well extended to the various forms of energy storage.

We can determine the distribution of potential energies of the molecules of a gas rather easily for the particular case of a gas in a uniform gravitational field. Each molecule has a potential energy relative to some zero point, such as the ground, such that

$$V = mgh$$

where h is the height of the molecule above the ground, m is the mass of the molecule, and g is the acceleration of gravity. Since the potential energy, V, is proportional to height, h, the distribution of potential energy among the molecules will be proportional to their distribution in height. Even as we know that the pressure—and therefore the number of molecules per cubic meter—decreases with altitude in the atmosphere, we know that the probability of a molecule having a potential energy V decreases as V increases. This qualitative result is correct, interesting, and useful: a quantitative calculation is not difficult.

The diagram of Fig. 17|9a shows a column with constant cross section, which extends upwards indefinitely: the column is filled with a gas at a temperature T. The small layer of gas that is shaded in the diagram must be held up, against the pull of gravity, by the difference in pressure between the top and the bottom of the layer. The force of gravity on the gas will be

$$F = Mg$$

where M is the mass of gas in the layer and g is the acceleration of gravity. If the area of the cross section of the column is A

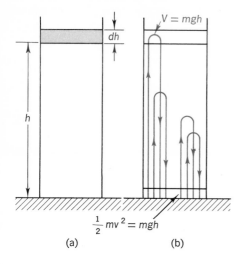

$V = mgh$

dh

h

$$\frac{1}{2}mv^2 = mgh$$

(a)   (b)

FIG. 17·19
*Diagrams showing (a)
the forces on a
cylindrical section of a
gas in a uniform
gravitational field and
(b) idealized trajectories
of single gas molecules
in a gas held at very low
pressure in a
gravitational field.*

and the height of the layer is dh, the volume of the layer will be $A\ dh$. The mass, M, of the gas in this layer will then be equal to the volume of the layer times the number of molecules per cubic meter, n, times the mass, m, of a molecule: or

$$M = nmA\ dh \quad \text{and} \quad F = Mg = nmgA\ dh$$

which must be equal and opposite to the force upward, F', due to the difference in pressure, dP, between the top of the layer and the bottom. Then

$$F' = A\ dP = -F = -nmgA\ dh$$

or

$$dP = -nmg\ dh$$

If n is the number of molecules per unit volume, the ideal-gas law (for the unit volume) takes the form

$$P = nkT$$

Since k and T are constant, a change in P must be reflected in a change in n, and

$$dP = kT\ dn$$

Then we have by equating the two relations for dP, and with a little algebraic manipulation,

$$dn = -\left(\frac{mg}{kT}\right)n\ dh \quad \text{or} \quad \frac{dn}{dh} = -\left(\frac{mg}{kT}\right)n$$

This is just the differential equation DE-EXP, discussed in Section 9|7, and we can use the results of that discussion to write

$$n = n_0 \exp \left(\frac{-mgh}{kT} \right)$$

But mgh is just the potential energy, V, of a molecule, so

$$n = n_0 \exp \left(\frac{-V}{kT} \right) \tag{17|5}$$

where n_0 is the density of molecules at $h = 0$, where $V = 0$.

Equation (17|5) expresses the potential-energy distribution of the molecules in the column of gas. Here n is equal to the number of molecules in a cubic meter of gas at a height such that the potential energy of each molecule is V, and n_0 is equal to the number per cubic meter with zero potential energy.

We can relate this distribution of potential energy with the distribution of kinetic energy among the molecules by a plausible, though not at all rigorous, argument. Since the temperature of the gas is everywhere the same, the average kinetic energy of the molecules is independent of the height: let us further assume that the distribution of kinetic energies among the molecules is also independent of height. Since our calculation of the distribution of potential energies was independent of the pressure of the gas, we might expect that the distribution of kinetic energies among the molecules would be independent of the pressure also. At low pressures molecular collisions could be neglected.

Then the gas molecules will act very much as a set of perfectly elastic bouncing balls constrained to the column. At any instant the number of balls or molecules that reach their peak height, h, and maximum potential energy, V, is proportional to $\exp(-V/kt)$, as suggested by the sketch of Fig. 17|9b. From the law of the conservation of energy, their maximum potential energy, V, must be equal to their kinetic energy, $\frac{1}{2}mv^2$, at the bottom of the column, and we might expect, correctly, that the probability of finding a molecule with a kinetic energy $\frac{1}{2}mv^2$ in an interval near the bottom of the column is proportional to

$$\exp \left(\frac{-\frac{1}{2}mv^2}{kT} \right)$$

Of course, energetic molecules spend less time near the bottom on their "bounce." A molecule A that is traveling with twice the velocity of a molecule B—and has four times the kinetic energy and will reach four times the height—will spend only half as much time as B near the bottom on one bounce. But A's trip up and down takes twice as long, and therefore there must be twice as many molecules in flight at any instant, aside from the exponential factor. The extra number always in flight cancels the smaller time each spends near the bottom, so we are correct in our surmise that the number of molecules per cubic meter near the bottom with a kinetic energy equal to $\frac{1}{2}mv^2$ is

$$n = n_0 \exp \left(\frac{-\frac{1}{2}mv^2}{kT} \right) \tag{17|6}$$

where n_0 is the number with a kinetic energy equal to zero. (More practically, we compare the number in a small energy interval near zero with the number in an equal energy interval near $\frac{1}{2}mv^2$.)

Since our plausible conjecture that the distributions of kinetic energies depend only upon the temperature of the gas and not on the potential or height, the distribution (17|6) holds for any segment of the column.

We have considered here only the potential energy of molecules in a gravitational field and the kinetic energy of molecules moving in one direction. More complex situations, such as the distribution of energies of molecules moving in all directions, require somewhat more complex descriptions. In any case, however, the description of the distribution of energies, E, will be proportional to the Boltzmann factor $\exp(-E/kT)$ even as the distribution will be a special case of a *Boltzmann distribution.*

The character of these results, then, holds quite generally for different phenomena; the distribution of translational kinetic energies, rotational kinetic energies, vibrational kinetic energies, and various potential energies takes much the same form as Eqs. (17|5) and (17|6) for any system in thermal equilibrium. Further, the energy is distributed among the various modes of energy such that each mode (properly defined and properly counted— and that is a subtle process) will have the same average energy and the same distribution of energies: the concept of the equi-partition of energy thus holds generally for all systems in thermal equilibrium.

17|6   *The Boltzmann distribution*
—statistical mechanics

In the last section we deduced the distribution of potential and kinetic energies for molecules in a gas in a gravitational field. As a result of their numerous collisions, both the kinetic and potential energies of individual molecules are continually changing. Indeed, in the course of time each molecule will assume nearly all possible values of potential and kinetic energy. The distribution function then becomes a probability function for any particular molecule, where the value of the function for any parameter, E, is proportional to the probability that the molecule will be found with the value E. For example, we can write the Boltzman distribution of Eq. (17|6) in the form of probability as

$$P(V) = P(0) \ \exp\left(\frac{-V}{kT}\right)$$

which is to say that the probability that a molecule has a potential energy V is equal to the probability that the potential energy is zero multiplied by the factor $\exp(-V/kT)$. (This can be said more precisely; the probability that the molecule has a potential energy with a value between V and $V + dV$, where dV is small, is equal to the probability that the molecule has a potential energy between zero and dV multiplied by the factor $\exp(-V/kT)$.) The curve of Fig. 17|10 shows the character of this variation of probability—or density.

    Since the distribution function can thus be interpreted as a probability function, it then seems that we should be able to determine the character of the function through an appropriate use of the theory of probability and statistics. Since the number of molecules in situations of physical interest is so enormous, analyses in terms of probability—*statistical mechanics*—must replace or complement our understanding of the mechanics of individual interactions. Our use of averages in the consideration of the kinetic theory of the ideal-gas law implied an acceptance of the importance of average behavior. We can demonstrate the use of such ideas in more complex situations, such as the development of energy distributions, in a reasonably simple fashion.

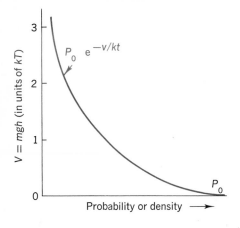

FIG. 17 |10

The density of gas as a function of height in a uniform gravitational field.

It is convenient to consider the probability distribution of the potential energies of molecules occupying a column of gas in a gravitational field, since we have already determined this distribution in another way. It would be necessary for us to develop some special mathematics if we were to deal with the probabilities of very large numbers of molecules occupying a continuous distribution of heights and potential energies, and the mathematics might obscure, rather than illuminate, the essential principles that interest us. Therefore, we will discuss a simplified model in which only four molecules are involved. Let us assume that the average potential energy of the molecules of the gas is is equal to a quantity kT Then the total potential energy of the four molecules is $4kT$. To further simplify the problem, we divide the column of gas into sections such that the potential energy of all molecules in each section can be considered to be the same and equal to some integral value of kT. With this choice of division of the column of gas, all molecular configurations that obey the conservation laws and have a total potential energy of $4kT$ will have equal probability.

There are only a few possible different configurations in this model, and these are shown schematically in the diagrams of Fig. 17|11. The number of different ways of forming each of these configurations is easily determined by simple counting, without the use of any formal mathematics. There are just four different ways of placing three molecules in the section with $V = 0$ and one in the section with $V = 4kT$. If we label the molecules a, b, c and d, we could place either a, or b, or c, or d in the upper section, where the remaining molecules were in the lowest section of the column where $V = 0$. We can list the four possibilities as $(a)_4(bcd)_0$, $(b)_4(acd)_0$, $(c)_4(abd)_0$, and $(d)_4(abc)_0$. There are six ways of placing the molecules such that two have zero potential energy and two each have two units of potential energy, $2kT$. We list the six combinations: $(ab)_2(cd)_0$, $(ac)_2(bd)_0$, $(ad)_2(bc)_0$, $(bc)_2(ad)_0$, $(bd)_2(ac)_0$, and $(cd)_2(ab)_0$. Similarly, there are twelve combinations where two molecules have no potential energy, one has an energy of kT, and one has a potential energy of $3kT$.

All of the configurations are listed in Fig. 17|11. The sum of all of the ways of arranging the molecules is 35; therefore, the probability of each configuration is equal to the number of ways of forming that configuration divided by 35. These probabilities are listed below the particular relevant configurations. The solid points on the graph in the figure represents the probable number of molecules to be found in each section of the column. This is easily calculated for any value of V as the sum of the probabilities of the different configurations multiplied by the number of molecules at that energy. For example, the average number of molecules with zero kinetic energy will be

$$3\left(\frac{4}{35}\right) + 2\left(\frac{6}{35}\right) + 2\left(\frac{12}{35}\right) + 1\left(\frac{12}{35}\right) + 0\left(\frac{1}{35}\right) = \frac{60}{35} = 1\frac{5}{7}$$

The solid line on the graph represents the distribution calculated from expression (17|6). Our result is qualitatively similar, of course. The agreement would have been improved if we had divided our column into more parts. As we approach an infinite

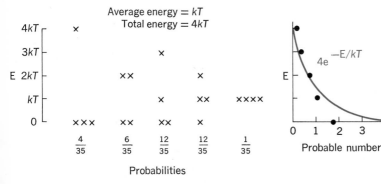

FIG. 17|11
The probable distribution of molecules in a uniform gravitational field.

number of divisions, our results would approach the Boltzmann distribution shown on the graph.

Large classes of problems concern the analyses of macroscopic properties of materials, such as the pressures, temperatures, and densities of gases, which depend upon the statistical or average behaviors of molecular quantities, can be solved using such statistical techniques. The studies of these problems by Maxwell in England, by Boltzmann in Germany, and by Gibbs in the United States, in the last years of the nineteenth century, led to the origin of the area of knowledge we now know as *statistical mechanics*. The simple problem we have examined here is primarily interesting in that as it suggests something of the character of this area of physics.

17|7 *Molecular mean free paths*

The average distance a molecule travels in gas between collisions is called the *mean free path*. For the purpose of discussing the meaning of mean free path it is convenient to consider the molecules as spheres and to neglect the motion of all the molecules except the one whose path is under consideration. Figure 17|12 shows the path of such a molecule. The dashed lines represent the boundaries of a cylindrical region such that any molecule whose center lies within this region will be struck by the moving molecule. Molecule a in Fig. 17|12 will not be struck; molecule b will. If the radius of the molecules is r, the radius of the cylinder of collision will be equal to $2r$ and the cross section for collision, generally written as σ, is

$$\sigma = 4\pi r^2$$

The probability of the moving molecule making a collision in the path length s is equal to the probability of one or more other

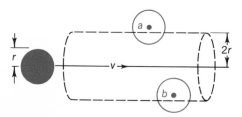

FIG. 17 |12
*A diagram showing the
collision volume of a
moving molecule.*

molecules having their centers in the cylinder of cross section σ and length s. If this probability is sufficiently small that we can neglect the probability of having two molecules in this space compared to the probability of having one, we can approximate the collision probability as just the probability of having one molecule in this volume. This will be equal to N the number of molecules per cubic meter, which is the density of molecules in the gas, times the volume of the cylinder, which is equal to σs. Then

$$P(s) = N\sigma s$$

where $P(s)$ is the probability that the moving molecule will make a collision in the path of length s.

The extension to larger probabilities or larger values of $N\sigma s$ can be understood by considering a special example where the length s is chosen so that the probability of a molecule being within the cylinder that is swept out is 1 percent. The probability that no collision will occur in that path length is then 0.99. The probability of passing a length $2s$ without a collision is then (0.99) (0.99), since, according to the laws of probability, the probability of two independent actions is equal to the product of the probabilities of the two taken independently. The probability of passing through a length $s' = 100s$, such that $N\sigma s = 1$, is then equal to $(0.99)^{100}$, which is about equal to 0.37 and not zero. The exact expression of the probability of *not* making a collision in the length s is

$$P(s)' = 1 - \exp(-N\sigma s)$$

Since the probability that the molecule will make no collisions in the interval s plus the probability that the molecule will make at least one collision must add to 1,

$$P(s)' + P(s) = 1$$

The probability that the molecule will make at least one collision in the distance s is

$$P(s) = \exp(-N\sigma s)$$

It can be shown that the average distance a molecule will travel before colliding, or the *mean free path*, is

$$L = \frac{1}{n\sigma} \tag{17|7}$$

Obviously the mean free path varies directly with the density of a gas, and hence the pressure. A calculation that includes the effect of the velocity of all the molecules shows that the mean free path is less than that noted here by a factor of $\sqrt{\frac{1}{2}}$. This is important only for detailed calculations.

A typical radius for a small molecule, such as a nitrogen molecule, is $r = 2 \times 10^{-10}$ m. We can therefore estimate the collision cross section of a nitrogen molecule in air as

$$\sigma = 4\pi r^2$$

$$= 5 \times 10^{-19} \, m^2$$

We know that at 0°C, and at a pressure of 1 atm, 6×10^{26} molecules occupy 22.4 m³. The number of molecules per cubic meter is thus about $N = 3 \times 10^{25}$, and the value of the mean free path, L, is

$$L = \frac{1}{n\sigma}$$

$$= 6 \times 10^{-8} \, meter$$

At room temperature, 300°C, the velocity of a nitrogen molecule is about 400 m/sec, so the molecule will make about 10^{10} collisions/sec.

17|8 *The conduction of heat by gases*

In Chapter 16 we described the conduction of heat across a uniform section of material by the relation

$$\frac{dQ}{dt} = \frac{KA \, dT}{d} \tag{17|8}$$

where dQ/dt is the heat-transfer rate, usually in Calories per second; A is the cross-sectional area of the section; d is the thickness of the section; and dT is the temperature difference across the section.

For either a gas or a solid we can understand the temperature difference between the two sides of the section in terms of different average kinetic energies of the molecules on the two sides. The average kinetic energy of the molecules on the hotter side of the section is greater than the energy of those on the low temperature side. The excess energy held by the hot side is transferred to the cool side through the interaction of the molecules that make up the material.

In the case of a solid, this transfer might take place through the chain of forces binding molecule to molecule. Thermal conductivity in a gas would be expected to take place as a result of the exchange of molecules, with different average kinetic energies, between the hot and the cool regions.

The conduction of heat through gases can be understood rather well, and quantitatively, in terms of the basic concepts of the kinetic theory. Energy is transferred from hotter surfaces or regions to cooler surfaces or regions by the motion of the molecules. A molecule passing from a hot region to a cooler region passes from a region where the average velocity is large to a region where the average velocity is small; inversely, a particle moving from a cool region to a hot region changes from a slowly moving family of molecules to a set of faster-moving molecules. The fast molecule from the hot region is slowed down by collisions with the slow molecules, though these collisions do slightly increase the average speed of the molecules that collide with the fast molecule. On the other hand, the slow molecule from the cool region is speeded up through the collisions with the fast molecules, but only at the expense of slowing the fast molecules: energy is conserved. In total, the warm region is cooled slightly and the cool region is warmed slightly by the exchange.

We then assume that a molecule that originates in any region carries, on the average, a kinetic energy corresponding to the temperature of that region, and that a molecule that arrives in

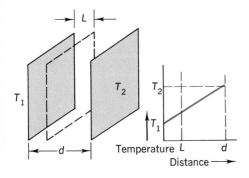

FIG. 17 | 13
A graph showing the variation in temperature of a gas held between two plates at different temperatures.

a region quickly attains a kinetic energy corresponding to the temperature of that region. We can use this hypothesis to make a quantitative calculation of the energy transfered between two faces by a layer of gas, as suggested by the drawing of Fig. 17 | 13. We assume that the two faces are held at temperatures T_2 and T_1, where T_2 is greater than T_1, and that the temperature gradient is constant; that is, the temperature changes linearly with distance from T_2 to T_1. Halfway from surface 1 to surface 2 the temperature is halfway between T_2 and T_1: at a distance L from surface 1 the temperature will be

$$T_L = T_1 + \frac{L}{d}(T_2 - T_1)$$

where d is the distance between the plates.

We have shown that the mean kinetic energy of a molecule is equal to $\frac{3}{2}kT$, where T is the absolute temperature and k is Boltzmann's constant. The average molecule striking surface 1 will have come from a distance L from the wall, where L is approximately equal to the mean free path. The temperature of the gas at position L is thus T_L and the average kinetic energy is therefore $\frac{3}{2}kT_L$. After collision with wall 1, the average temperature will be T_1 and the average energy of the molecules will be $\frac{3}{2}kT_1$. The difference in energy,

$$E_L - E_1 = \frac{3}{2}k(T_L - T_1)$$

$$= \frac{3}{2}k\frac{L}{d}(T_2 - T_1)$$

is the average energy given up to the wall from each collision of a molecule. The number of collisions per unit area per second was shown to be equal to $N\bar{v}$ where N is the number of molecules per unit volume and $\bar{v}$ is the average velocity of the molecule. If the effective area of the wall is A, the number of collisions with the wall in a second will be equal to $N\bar{v}A$ and the energy transfer per second will be equal to the product of the number of collisions per second and the average energy transfer per collision:

$$\frac{dQ}{dt} = Nv A \frac{3}{2}k\frac{L}{d}(T_2 - T_1)$$

In summary, the energy transferred per unit time to a surface is equal to the number of molecules per unit volume, N, times the average velocity of these molecules, $\bar{v}$, times the area of the surface, A, times the average energy carried by a molecule, $\frac{3}{2}kT$, times the temperature gradient, $(T_2 - T_1)/d$. If we compare this result with Eq. (17|8), which defines the thermal conductivity, K, of a material, we find that

$$K = \frac{3}{2}N\bar{v}kL$$

But

$$L = \frac{1}{N\sigma}$$

so

$$K = \frac{3}{2}\frac{k\bar{v}}{\sigma}$$

If we now calculate the value of K in this way for an actual gas, using a reasonable value of σ, we find fairly good agreement with experiment. The agreement for most gases is as good as a factor of 2 even for this very elementary derivation.

Some qualitative aspects of the thermal conductivity in gases are more striking. The conductivity is seen to be independent of N, the number of molecules per unit volume in the gas, and hence independent of pressure. This is intuitively surprising to most of us, but we are now in a position to understand that result on a simple basis. At lower pressure, fewer molecules strike the cold wall, but they come from farther away—from hotter regions— and carry more energy. Also the thermal conductivity varies with $\bar{v}$; as the average velocity is larger, more heat transfers take place. Since $kT = \frac{1}{2}m\bar{v}^2$, $\bar{v}$ is proportional to the square root of the absolute temperature. Therefore, K varies as $\sqrt{T}$, where T is an average temperature of the gas.

At very low pressures—pressures such that the molecule travels, on the average, from wall to wall without a collision—the energy transfer is proportional to the number of collisions with the wall and thus to the number of molecules present: The thermal conductivity is then proportional to the pressure. In such a situation the mean free path, L, is larger than the distance between the walls of the container. For apertures, d, the size of the distance between the walls of a thermos bottle, the pressure must be less than about 10^{-5} atm before the "vacuum" is a good insulator. If the pressure is as high as 10^{-4} atm, the space between walls is hardly a better insulator than if it were filled with air at atmospheric pressure.

17|9   *The specific heats of gases*
—ideal gases

By definition, the specific heat of a substance is the amount of heat, in Calories, required to raise the temperature of 1 kg of the substance 1°C. The properties of gases have been shown to depend in an essential way on the number of molecules per unit volume, and not on the mass of the molecules. We are therefore more likely to obtain general results for gases if we consider, not the usual specific heat, but a molar specific heat defined as the number of Calories required to raise the temperature of 1 kg-mole of gas 1°C (or 1°K).

Since for 1 kg-mole of gas, $PV = RT = \frac{2}{3}E$, the kinetic energy of the molecules of the gas is equal to $\frac{3}{2}RT$. If the temperature of this ideal gas is to increase 1°C, the kinetic energy of the molecules must increase by an amount equal to $\frac{3}{2}R$; since $R = 2$ Cal/°C, the kinetic energy must increase by 3 Cal/°C. Inversely, 3 Cal of heat are necessary to raise the temperature of the gas by 1°C if no energy is lost and no energy is absorbed by the molecules in other ways than increased kinetic energy. For ideal point molecules held in an insulated container this will be the case, and we can conclude that MC_v, the molar specific heat at constant volume of the gas, is 3 Cal/°C. Here M is the molecular weight of the gas molecules and C_v is the specific heat of the gas when the gas is constrained to a constant volume. As the temperature increases, the pressure of the gas on the walls of the container increases; but since the walls do not move the volume is held constant, no work is done by the gas, and no energy is used in doing work. In terms of the first law of thermodynamics,

$$dU = dQ - dW$$

where dQ is the heat introduced into the system and dW is the work done by the system, $dW = 0$, and

$$dU = MC_v \, dT$$

for 1 kg-mole of gas.

Alternatively, we might hold the pressure constant and let the volume increase with temperature. As the temperature changes from T to $T + dT$, the volume will change from V to $V + dV$. The ideal-gas law will hold before and after the temperature change, so

$$PV = RT \quad \text{and} \quad P(V + dV) = R(T + dT)$$

Subtracting the first equality from the second,

$$P\,dV = R\,dT$$

For a change in temperature, dT, of 1°, the pressure times the change in volume, $P\,dV$, is equal to R, which is equal to 2 Cal.

This value of $P\,dV$ represents the work done by the gas in expanding an amount dV against a pressure P. The diagram of Fig. 17|14 illustrates such an expansion where the gas is enclosed in a cylinder constrained by a weightless piston having an area A. As the gas expands, the piston will move upward a distance s such that $As = dV$, the change in volume. The force, F, on the piston will be equal to the pressure on the piston times the area of the piston: $F = PA$. The work, dW, done by the gas in expanding against the pressure will be equal to the force times the distance the piston moves: $dW = Fs$. Altogether,

$$dW = Fs = PAs = P\,dV = R\,dT$$

For a change in temperature, dT, of 1°C, the work done by the gas is $dW = R = 2$ Cal. Using the first law of thermodynamics we

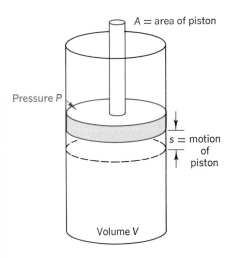

A = area of piston

Pressure P

s = motion of piston

Volume V

FIG. 17|14

Gas enclosed by a cyclinder and constrained by weightless piston.

see that

$$MC_p = dQ = dU + dW = MC_v + dW = MC_v + R$$

again for 1 kg-mole of gas.

The total heat input required to raise the temperature of 1 kg-mole of the gas 1°C as the gas is held at constant pressure will be 5 Cal. The increase in kinetic energy of the gas molecules will require 3 Cal of heat energy, and 2 Cal are required to provide energy for the work done by the gas.

17|10   *The rotation and vibration of molecules*

The molecule of an ideal gas was treated as if it could be described as a point. The position of the molecule at any time was completely described by the values of three spacial coordinates, x, y, and z. The kinetic energy of the molecule, $\frac{1}{2}mv^2$, can be divided into three parts representative of each of the three available directions:

$$\tfrac{1}{2}mv^2 = \tfrac{1}{2}mv_x^2 + \tfrac{1}{2}mv_y^2 + \tfrac{1}{2}mv_z^2$$

as

$$v^2 = v_x^2 + v_y^2 + v_z^2$$

Each of these three parts of the kinetic energy will have the same average value, since there is no preferred direction. This average value will be equal to

$$\tfrac{1}{3}(\tfrac{3}{2}kT) = \tfrac{1}{2}kT$$

where k is Boltzmann's constant. For 1 kg-mole of gas the kinetic energy of motion in each of the three independent directions will be equal to $\frac{1}{2}RT$.

In general, a molecule is a tightly bound complex of many atoms. It is convenient to consider an isolated atom as a particularly simple molecule: then all of our previous arguments also apply to monatomic gases. Since molecules are complexes of atoms, molecules have a considerable structure: they can rotate and vibrate, and the rotational and vibrational modes will represent a storage of energy. We can gain some insight into this by

considering the character of a very simple molecule—the hydrogen molecule—made up of two hydrogen atoms.

Even as the position of one atom of hydrogen at any particular
time is defined by the coordinates x_1, y_1, and z_1, the position of a
second atom of hydrogen is defined by another set of three numbers: x_2, y_2, z_2. The description of two atoms thus requires six
numbers, or six coordinates in six directions. Just as we could
plot the position of atom 1 as a point on a three-dimensional
graph, we could plot the position of the two atoms as one point
on a six-dimensional graph. While the construction of six-
dimensional graphs is rather difficult, six-dimensional mathematics is easily handled. The kinetic energy of the two atoms will
now be

$$E = \tfrac{1}{2}mv_{x1}^2 + \tfrac{1}{2}mv_{y1}^2 + \tfrac{1}{2}mv_{z1}^2 + \tfrac{1}{2}mv_{x2}^2 + \tfrac{1}{2}m_{y2}^2 + \tfrac{1}{2}mv_{z2}^2$$

Each individual term represents part of the total energy of the
two atoms, and each term has an average value of $\tfrac{1}{2}kT$ per molecule or $\tfrac{1}{2}RT$ for 1 kg-mole of this (two-atom) gas (12×10^{26} single
atoms). We call the number of coordinates needed to describe the
system, which is the number of independent directions in which
the system can move, degrees of freedom. One atom has 3 degrees
of freedom, and on the average the atom has an average energy of
$\tfrac{1}{2}kT$ per degree of freedom. Two free atoms have 6 degrees of
freedom, three atoms have 9 degrees of freedom, and so on. On
the average, the energy of the system is equally divided among
the degrees of freedom of the system. This is a most elementary
example of the broad principle of the *equipartition of energy.*

For the preceding example, where the system in question consisted of two free atoms, the result relating the average kinetic
energy to the number of degrees of freedom is trivial and is
meant only to serve as a suggestive illustration. In the case of
ordinary hydrogen gas, the two hydrogen atoms are joined as a
molecule. For our purpose we can consider them rigidly bound at
a small but definite distance from each other. Although we can
still describe the system by means of six numbers, it is clear six
are not needed. If any five numbers are known, for example,
x_1, y_1, z_1, x_2, y_2, it is possible to calculate the sixth, in this case
the value of z_2, if one knows the distance between the two atoms.
There are, then, only five degrees of freedom for the system.
Rather than classify the coordinates of the molecule as we have

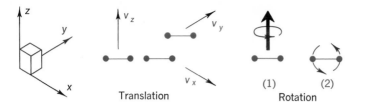

FIG. 17|15
*The independent
translational and
rotational modes of
motion of a diatomic
molecule.*

described, by the position of each atom, it is preferable to define its position by three coordinates representing the position of the center of the molecule and by two angles (resembling latitude and longitude) that describe its angular position. There are thus five degrees of freedom and five kinds of motion. There will be, as usual, three degrees of translation—in the x-, the y- and the z-direction—and two degrees of rotation, about two perpendicular axes, as shown in Fig. 17|15. The third degree of rotation, about the axis between the two atoms, is neglected for the same (not yet explained!) reasons for which we neglected the rotations of individual atoms. Since there are five degrees of freedom, we might expect that the average kinetic energy per molecule is $\frac{5}{2}kT$; the kinetic energy for 1 kg-mole to be $\frac{5}{2}RT$, and the molar specific heat is $MC_v = 5$ Cal/°C.

As noted earlier, the thesis that each degree of freedom should share equally in the kinetic energy is called the equipartition of energy. We have attempted to demonstrate the plausibility of this concept, but our demonstration is by no means a proof. Nevertheless, the idea is valid in classical mechanics. The modifications required by quantum mechanics, which are important and interesting, are taken up later. Although rotational and vibrational energy contribute to the internal energy, U, of a gas of complex molecules, since the energy stored in these modes depends on temperature, it is still true to a good approximation that the internal energy depends only on temperature if the density of the gas is not too high.

At room temperature the simple diatomic molecules H_2, N_2, O_2, CO, and so on all have molar specific heats at constant volume MC_v of 5 Cal/°C, while the monatomic gases helium, neon, argon, and so on have values of MC_v of 3 Cal/°C. Most more complicated molecules, such as CO_2 and H_2O, have a structure in which the atoms are not in a line as they are in H_2, and can spin in three directions. They thus have six degrees of freedom, three translational and three rotational, and we expect that their specific heats will be $MC_v = 6$ Cal/°C. The agreement of the experimental measurements with the simple theoretical description we have constructed is not so good for most of these more complex molecules; the measured specific heats are always somewhat greater than 6 Cal/°C. This deviation from our simple model occurs because the distances between the atoms in the molecule are not exactly fixed; vibration occurs as well as translation and rotation, and energy is stored in the molecule as vibrational energy even as energy is stored in the vibration of a bob suspended from a spring.

Although a vibrational mode accounts for one degree of freedom according to the description we have adopted, this mode takes two shares of energy, one share for the average kinetic energy as usual and one more for the average potential energy— we remember that the average potential energy of a vibrating system is equal to the average kinetic energy. All of the possible modes of motion of a molecule add to $3n$, where n is the number of atoms in the molecule. Of these there will always be three translational modes, at most three rotational modes, and the rest will be vibrational modes. Therefore, the hydrogen molecule, H_2, must have six modes of motion: there will be three translational modes; we have shown that there will be only two rotational modes; therefore there must be one vibrational mode.

Considering that the vibration mode should contain kT of energy and the others each $\frac{1}{2}kT$, the average total energy per molecule should be $\frac{7}{2}kT$, and specific heat should be $Mc_v = 7$ Cal/°C. But experimentally, MC_v is 5 Cal/°C; the vibrational mode does not contribute.

We can understand the sometime failure of vibrational modes to contribute to the specific heat, and the lack of contribution from some rotational modes, such as rotations of single atoms, only from constraints that can be understood through the use of quantum mechanics.

17|11   *Quantum-mechanical constraints*
on specific heats

In the course of the discussion of orbital motion given in Chapter 14, it was shown that the angular momentum of a particle in a circular orbit is quantized; the orbital angular momentum must be equal to $n\hbar$, where n is an integer ($n = 0, 1, 2, \ldots$) and $\hbar$ is a convenient abbreviation for $h/2\pi$. Although only circular orbital motion was discussed in detail, the result is general: any angular momentum is quantized.

The angular momentum of a simple diatomic molecule such as hydrogen, where both atoms have the same mass, is easily computed in terms of the distance between the atoms, a, the mass of the atoms, m, and the angular velocity of rotation, ω. Each atom rotates about the center of gravity of the system with a radius of rotation $a/2$, and the angular momentum of each atom is therefore

$$mv \left(\frac{a}{2}\right) = m\omega \left(\frac{a^2}{4}\right)$$

since

$$v = \omega \left(\frac{a}{2}\right)$$

For the system of two atoms the angular momentum is

$$\frac{m\omega a^2}{2} = n\hbar \qquad n = 0, 1, 2, \ldots \qquad \hbar = \frac{h}{2\pi}$$

The kinetic energy of the two atoms is

$$E = 2(\tfrac{1}{2}mv^2)$$
$$= mv^2$$
$$= m\omega^2 \left(\frac{a^2}{4}\right)$$

and therefore

$$E = \frac{n^2\hbar^2}{ma^2} \qquad n = 0, 1, 2, 3, \ldots$$

There is thus a least energy of rotation corresponding to 1 unit of angular momentum. The value of this least energy for the dumbell-like hydrogen atom, H_2, is very much smaller than kT at room temperature, where T is about equal to $300°K$. Therefore, the hydrogen molecule rotates freely at room temperature, and the energy taken up in this rotation is reflected in the value of the specific heat. The characteristic size of other molecules is as large as or larger than the hydrogen molecule, and the masses are greater, so that all molecules composed of several atoms rotate freely at room temperature.

On the other hand, the effective radius of an atom is much smaller, and the minimum rotation energy of an atom is characteristically of the order of $100kT$ at room temperature; the rotation of an individual atom simply cannot be excited by the comparatively feeble buffetings of the collisions. We can now understand why we can consider individual atoms rather as nonrotational points in our discussions and ignore the fact that they actually have a complex structure of their own. At the temperatures we have considered, thermal energies are very much smaller than the characteristic energies of excitation of these particles; we can consider that the rotational modes—and also the vibrational modes—of the atoms are "frozen" out.

Again from the discussions of Chapter 14 we see that the possible energies of a harmonic oscillator are constrained to the values

$$E = (n + \tfrac{1}{2})\hbar\omega \qquad \omega = \sqrt{\frac{k}{m}} \qquad n = 0, 1, 2, \ldots$$

where k is the spring constant and m is the mass. Although the system will hold a minimum "zero point" energy under any condition, the system can exchange energy freely only if the thermal energy is larger than the energy stored when $n = 1$. When the mass is small and the spring constant is large, this minimum kinetic energy is large—larger than kT at room temperature—and vibration does not occur. This is the case for the hydrogen molecule, H_2, the nitrogen molecule, N_2, the oxygen molecule O_2, and so on. Some molecules having heavier atoms and smaller spring constants do vibrate at room temperature. Their molar specific heats are correspondingly large.

Since the vibrational modes and some rotational modes are "frozen" at room temperatures because the temperature is too low, we might expect the specific heat of hydrogen to increase at high temperatures. Contrariwise, at very low temperatures even the regular rotational modes will be suppressed; only the translational modes will be retained, and the specific heat will be reduced. This behavior is illustrated qualitatively in Fig. 17 | 16.

At low temperatures, well below 100°K, only translation is important. Molecular rotation is frozen out: the smallest kinetic energy is less than kT. The molar specific heat is 3 Cal/°C, characteristic of a point molecule. At higher temperatures, near room temperature, the two rotational modes take part in the

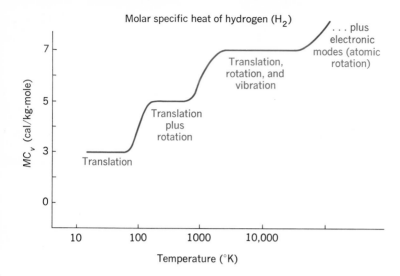

Molar specific heat of hydrogen (H₂)

FIG. 17|16
*The molar specific heat
of hydrogen as a
function of temperature.*

equipartition of energy and the molar specific heat is 5 Cal/°C, that which is characteristic of a diatomic molecule. The vibrational mode is still frozen out; $\hbar\omega$ is larger than kT. However, at much higher temperatures the vibrational mode is again important and MC_v is 7 Cal/°C. At very high temperatures the internal structure of the atom becomes involved. The individual electrons begin to take up energy, corresponding classically to rotation of the individual atoms, and the specific heat continues to increase. At such high temperatures the molecule begins to break up.

17|12   *The specific heat of solids*

The different atoms in solids are fixed, so that translational motion is not allowed. The atoms that make up liquids are also fixed, though not so rigidly. Clearly velocities of the order of hundreds of meters per second, characteristic of the atoms that make up gases, are precluded. These atoms are, however, free to vibrate. Particularly for heavy atoms the binding is not strong, and the spring constants are thus not extremely large. Since the masses, m, are large, the angular frequency, $\omega = \sqrt{k/m}$, is not great, and the least kinetic energy $\hbar\omega$ is not so great. Therefore the vibrational modes share in the kinetic energy. Each atom can vibrate

TABLE 17|1 *Molar specific heats of some elements*

Substance	M	MC_V
Aluminum	27	5.8
Iron	56	6.36
Copper	63	6.01
Sulfur	32	5.68
Carbon (diamond)	12	1.44
Carbon (graphite)	12	1.92
Boron	11	2.6
Silicon	28	4.8

in three independent directions x, y, and z. Since each mode takes up $\frac{1}{2}kT$ for kinetic energy and $\frac{1}{2}kT$ for potential energy, the total energy per atom is $3kT$. For 1 kg-mole of atoms the energy is $3RT$ or 6 Cal. Then the molar specific heat of all such solids should be $MC_V = 6$ Cal/°C. Table 17|1 presents some experimental values.

We note that the heavier atoms follow the rule fairly closely, while the specific heats of the lighter elements fall below the rule. The small masses and large spring constants result in the freezing out of the vibrations. The same element in different crystalline forms may have different spring constants and hence different specific heats, as in the case of graphite and diamond.

PROBLEMS

17|1 A billiard table (no pockets) has dimensions a m by b m. We assume that there is no friction and balls bounce off of the side rails elastically. There are N balls on the table; each has a mass of 100 gm: the total kinetic energy of all the balls is E. Find the average force per unit length on the sides or rails of the table.

17|2 A volume V holds n kilograms of gas of molecular weight G, at a pressure P and a temperature T. Assume that all quantities, P, V, n, G, T, are held constant except those mentioned, and that the gas behaves as an ideal gas.

(*a*) What is the change in T required to double P?

(*b*) What is the change in T required to double V?

(c) What is the change in n required to double V?

(d) What is the change in V required to double P?

(e) What is the change in P required to double V?

(f) What is the change in n required to double T?

17|3   A ball weighing 1 kg bounces around in a box, making perfectly elastic collisions with the walls. The box is a cube 1 m on a side. The velocity of the ball is 100 m/sec. The experiment is conducted in outer space, where gravity is negligible. In each part of the problem assume that all these conditions are held constant, with the exception of the condition named in the question.

How will the average pressure on the walls vary as:

(a) The number of balls is increased to 10?

(b) The velocity of the balls is doubled?

(c) The size of the box is changed so that it is 2 m on a side?

(d) The mass of the ball is doubled?

17|4 $N = 6 \cdot 10^{26}$ molecules/kg-mole. The molecular weight of nitrogen is 28, atmospheric pressure is 10^5 N/m², 1 kg-mole of gas occupies 22.4 m³ at room temperature, 300°K. What is the average speed of a nitrogen molecule?

17|5   Compressing a gas increases its temperature. Explain this qualitatively from the view of kinetic theory; that is, from the effects of collisions on the walls of the container. (The billiard-table analogy of Problem 17|1 may help here.)

17|6   Discuss, qualitatively, the evaporation of water at room temperature from the view of kinetic theory and the potential-well model of the forces between molecules. Why does evaporation cool a liquid?

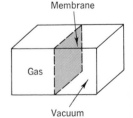

17|7   A gas at temperature T fills the left-hand side of the container shown, which is separated from a vacuum in the right-hand side by a membrane. The membrane breaks. If there are no forces between molecules (an ideal gas) the temperature of the gas, after it expands to fill the whole container remains the same. Why?

17|8   Three molecules have a total potential energy of $3kT$. If the molecules can be considered to occupy only levels where the potential energy is 0, kT, $2kT$, or $3kT$, what is the average number of molecules to be found in each of the four levels?

17|9   Spherical clusters of stars are known that contain thousands of stars. The mutual gravitational attraction of these stars holds such a cluster together. The stars are in motion and can be considered to make collisions with each other (that is, two stars will approach each other so that the gravitational forces between them result in a change in their motion; only very seldom do they collide as two balls might strike each other). Discuss the cluster qualitatively from the view of kinetic theory, where the cluster of stars is considered as a "gas" of stars. In particular: Can one define a pressure and temperature of the gas? How will the average velocity of the stars change if the cluster shrinks or expands? Will stars evaporate (escape) from the cluster? If stars evaporate from the cluster, how will the average velocity of the stars in the cluster be affected? If stars are drawn into the cluster, how will the average velocity of the stars in the cluster be affected? Can a heat of evaporation of the cluster be defined? How will the average velocity of a star in the cluster depend upon the radius of the cluster and the number of stars in the cluster?

17|10   Assume that there are very strong attractive molecular forces between the molecules in the container of Problem 17|7. Will the temperature of the gas change when the membrane breaks? Why?

17|11   The two diagrams show the variation of potential energy, V, with respect to the distance, r, between molecules of two different gases. One of the gases condenses to a liquid at atmospheric pressure at 300°K, the other condenses only at 20°K. Why are they different? Which one condenses at the higher temperature? Why?

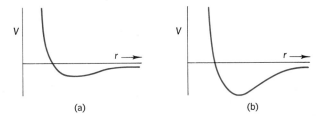

(a)   (b)

17|12   For which of the two gases discussed in Problem 17|11 will the value of van der Waals' constant, a, be larger? For which will b be larger?

17|13   Careful measurements of the specific heat of a diatomic molecule such as hydrogen at low temperatures can be used to determine the distance between the atoms in the molecule. Explain this qualitatively.

17|14 A billiard table 2.0 m long and 1.0 m wide holds 25 balls randomly spaced. A cue ball is stroked from one end of the table toward the other end. The radius of each ball is 2 cm. How far will the cue ball travel, on the average, before colliding with another ball?

17|15 The density of atomic nuclei in interstellar space in the galaxy is about 1 nucleus/m³. The density of nuclei in air, at normal pressure, is 3×10^{25} nuclei/m³. If the mean free path of a cosmic-ray proton in air is about 1000 m, and if cosmic rays travel at the speed of light (3×10^8 m/sec), how long, on the average, will a cosmic ray travel in space between collisions?

17|16 The table lists the molecular weights, temperatures, pressures, and molecular cross sections for four containers holding different gases. Arrange the containers in order of increasing thermal conductivity of the gases they contain.

Container	Gas	M	T ($°K$)	P (atm)	σ ($\times 10^{-20}$ m^2)
(a)	Hydrogen	2	300	1	1
(b)	Oxygen	32	300	1	2
(c)	Helium	4	300	2	2
(d)	Hydrogen	2	600	2	1

17|17 Nitrogen gas has a molar specific heat at constant volume, MC_v, of 5 Cal/°C. The gas is enclosed in a cylinder under a weighted piston such that the pressure is held constant at 3 atm. How much heat must be added to increase the temperature of 1 kg-mole of the gas 10°C?

17|18 At an altitude of about 6 km on earth the density of the atmosphere is about half the density at sea level.

(*a*) On another planet where the atmospheric composition and the temperature is about the same as on earth, the acceleration of gravity at the surface is 5 m/sec². At what height will the density fall to half that at the surface?

(*b*) If the temperature of the earth were twice what it is—that is, about 600°K—at what height would the density fall to half that at the surface?

(*c*) If the air on the earth were replaced by helium, at what height would the density fall to half that at sea level? (Take the molecular weight of helium as 4 and the molecular weight of air as 28.)

17|19 Methane gas, CH_4, consists of one carbon atom and four hydrogen atoms. Draw a graph of MC_v, the molar specific heat at constant volume, from very low temperatures to very high temperatures, showing the changes in specific heat. Label the values of MC_v qualitatively. The temperature scale is to have only qualitative significance.

17|20 Table 17|1 shows that diamond has a lower specific heat at room temperature than graphite. What does this tell you about the character of the forces holding the carbon atoms in place in these different crystals? Is this result in accord with what you know about the physical character of graphite and diamond?

17|21 The deuterium molecule is a diatomic molecule just like the hydrogen molecule, except that the deuterium atom has double the mass of the hydrogen atom. The graph shows schematically the molar specific heat of hydrogen as a function of temperature. Copy this graph and draw a curve showing the specific heat of deuterium also; show the qualitative similarities and differences between deuterium and hydrogen. (Note that the angular momentum of a rotating diatomic molecule is mva, where m is the mass of the atom, v is the velocity of the atom, and a is the distance between the atoms.)

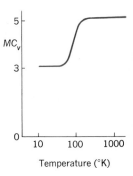

Temperature (°K)

17|22 The properties of a gas under a pressure P are such that the average distance a molecule of the gas travels between collisions is 1 mm. Two parallel plates of area A are immersed in the gas and are 10 cm apart. One plate is at a temperature of 300°K, the other is at 310°K. Under these conditions the heat transfer between the plates is J Cal/sec. What will be the value of the heat transfer if

(*a*) The temperature of the warmer plate is increased 5°K and the temperature of the cooler plate is dropped 5°K?

(*b*) The temperature of the warmer plate is 620°K and the cooler plate is at 600°K?

(*c*) The pressure is reduced to half the original pressure?

(*d*) The Temperature of the plates is held constant but the plates are moved together so that they are 5 cm apart?

(*e*) If the pressure is reduced by a factor of 1000, the thermal transfer is measured as J' Cal/sec. What will the value be if the pressure is reduced further by a factor of 2?

(*f*) The original gas is exchanged with the gas having the same specific heat at the same pressure but such that the molecular weight is four times that of the original gas. What will be the value of the heat transfer?

18 | 1   *Time's arrow—order to disorder*

WE HAVE identified three fundamental conservation laws: the conservation of energy, momentum, and angular momentum. When a ball falls off a picnic table to the surface of the earth, momentum is conserved. In falling, the ball's newly acquired momentum, directed toward the earth's center, is equal to the magnitude and opposite in direction to the earth's acquired momentum directed toward the ball. The total change in momentum throughout the course of the ball's path toward the earth, and during the succession of bounces of diminishing amplitude until the ball finally lies at rest, is zero. Likewise, the total energy is conserved. The potential energy of the ball with respect to the earth is changed to kinetic energy; the kinetic energy of motion of the ball as a whole is changed by a series of inelastic collisions, the bounces, to heat in the ball and the earth, and also the atmosphere, which absorbs small amounts of energy through air resistance. The change in temperature of these materials is the macroscopic measure of microscopic increases in the kinetic and potential energies of a large number (perhaps 10^{24}) of discrete atoms or molecules. But the total energy is unchanged. The total angular momentum of the earth–ball system will also remain unchanged through the history of the ball's fall from the table.

The total momentum is unchanged; the total energy is unchanged; the total angular momentum is unchanged; yet, intuitively, we know that something is changed. What is it that we have somehow lost in our formulation of mechanics that differentiates between the ball on the table and the ball on the ground?

We can sharpen our identification of the intuitive characteristic that differentiates the initial and final position of the ball by considering the character of the event in a motion picture. If the film is run normally through the projector we might observe that the character of the event is in accord with all of the laws of mechanics we have formulated. Further, the action looks normal. If the film is run through the projector backwards, we see the ball resting on the ground begin to move in increasingly large hops until it jumps up onto the table. It is obvious to us that time is going backwards—we cannot believe that the event really happened this way. Yet if we make measurements on the images we will be able to find no evidence of the violation of the laws of mechanics. We *know* that the ball fell off of the table and that it did not jump from the ground to the table. What is it that we have lost, somehow, in our formulation of mechanics that should tell us that the ball will fall to earth and will not rise again? What is it that tells us, intuitively and unerringly, the direction of time; using Sir Arthur Eddington's phrase, what is it that tells us the direction of "time's arrow"?

First, could the ball rise again? What is required in order that the history of the ball's flight be *reversed?* It is clear that all the energy now distributed among the enormous number of molecules and atoms in the earth, the ball, and the atmosphere, would have to be concentrated in such a way as to eject the ball from the ground in increasing jumps until the ball was back on the table. An enormous number of microscopic interactions between molecule and molecule would have to be reversed according to a precise schedule. Is this impossible? Not at all; only improbable. Our measurements on the interactions of individual molecules and atoms show that all of these individual interactions are reversible. But it is most improbable that all of the individual interactions will proceed in such a way as to put the ball back on the table. If all the universe were filled with balls and picnic tables, the probability of such a spontaneous backwards procession of events happening once during the whole age of the universe would still be negligible. This discussion, then, suggests that the direction of "time's arrow" is related to probabilities.

A similar, though simpler, illustration is provided by considering some of the motions of billiard balls on a billiard table.

Now our motion picture shows a set of 15 colored balls arranged in the form of a triangle near one end of the billiard table and a white cue ball moving rapidly toward the stationary triangular set. After the cue ball strikes the other balls, the energy is distributed among them in a generally random or disordered manner. Many balls will be moving around the table, colliding with one another, and roughly sharing the energy. However, if the motion picture shows a randomly moving set of balls that collide with one another in such a way that finally the fifteen colored balls come to rest in a triangle that fits a pool rack and the white ball moves rapidly away with all the kinetic energy, we know something is wrong: we suspect strongly that the film is being run backwards. We are seeing the action with time reversed. If the balls actually took part in such an action, we would consider it most unusual— virtually a miracle. Nevertheless, it is definitely possible—but not very probable: the scattering of the colored balls by the white ball is effectively *irreversible*.

We have intimated that all the individual interactions of elementary molecules and atoms seem to be *reversible*. Certainly the individual collisions of ideal billiard balls are reversible in time if we neglect friction and the small amount of inelasticity involved in the collision of any real balls. Figure 18 | 1a shows, schematically, the collision of two moving billiard balls. The positions of the balls at a specific starting time, t, are shown as a and b, and their velocities are v_a and v_b: the positions at a later time, $t + dt$, after the balls have collided, are shown as a' and b'; the velocities are v_a and v_b. If the situation is reversed in time—if the balls are started at the positions a' and b', as shown in Fig. 18 | 1b, with

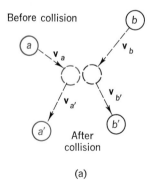

(a)

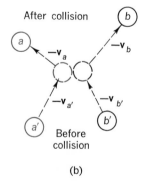

(b)

FIG. 18 |1
(*a*) *A collision of two billiard balls;* (*b*) *the same collision with time reversed.*

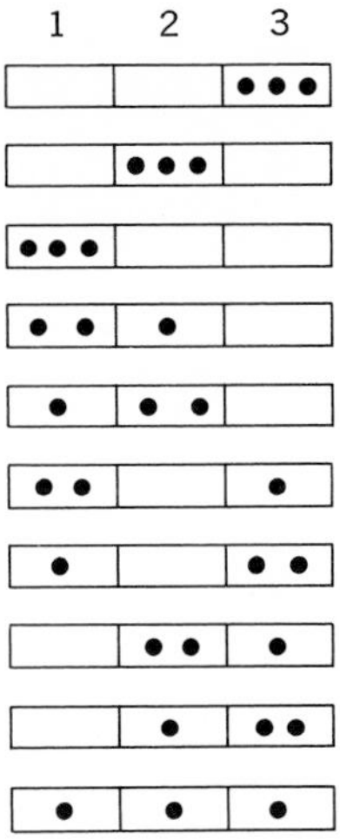

1	2	3		N	P

FIG. 18 |2

Configurations of balls in a box together with the probabilities of the configurations.

velocities that are the reverse of the final velocities of 18 | 1a—the balls will again collide, and after a time dt, the same time that elapsed in the first situation, the balls will be found at the positions a and b with velocities $-v_a$ and $-v_b$. The character of the collisions is independent of the direction of time: we could never tell the direction of the film (or the direction of time) by watching the collision of *one ball with another*.

A third model, much simpler than the others we have discussed, serves to illustrate the subtlety of some of our considerations. Here we consider a box divided by chalk marks into three equal regions. Three balls roll around at random, completely independent of one another, in the box. The numbers beside the box in Fig. 18 | 2 represent various configurations of the balls.

The first represents the configuration where the three balls are all in the third section of the box. There is only one such configuration: labeling the balls a, b, and c, that configuration is ( )( )(abc). The fourth configuration listed in Fig. 18 | 2 has two balls in the first section and one in the second: there are three such configurations—(ab)(c)( ), (ac)(b)( ), and (bc)(a)( ). If the balls are rolling about at random and each ball has an equal probability of being in each of the three parts of the box at any time, the probability of finding the balls in the fourth configuration is three times the probability of finding them in the first configuration where all the balls are in the third

compartment. Since the total number of equally probable configurations is 27, the probability of finding the balls in the
first configuration is $\frac{1}{27}$; the probability of finding the balls in the
third configuration is $\frac{3}{27}$. Each of the six different combinations of
two balls in one region and one ball in a second region has a probability of $\frac{3}{27}$. There are six different ways of putting the three balls
in three different regions—$(a)(b)(c)$, $(a)(c)(b)$, $(b)(c)(a)$, $(b)(a)(c)$,
$(c)(a)(b)$, and $(c)(b)(a)$—so the configuration listed as $(1, 1, 1)$ in
Fig. 18|2 has a probability of $\frac{6}{27}$.

If the balls roll around in the box, continually changing position, all combination will occasionally occur. If we take a picture
of the balls at any time, the probability that the picture of the balls
will show them in the original ordered configuration $(0, 0, 3)$ will
be only $\frac{1}{27}$, while the probability is much larger, equal to $\frac{6}{27}$, that
the balls will be in the disordered configuration $(1, 1, 1)$. If we
use the set of balls and the box as a basis for a gambling game,
we should pay odds of $27:1$ to anyone who bets the balls will be
in the $(0, 0, 3)$ configuration and only $27:6$ or $4\frac{1}{2}:1$ odds for those
who would bet on the $(1, 1, 1)$ configuration.

Now if we begin our game with the balls in the highly ordered
and unusual configuration $(0, 0, 3)$, the system will tend to go
spontaneously to a more disordered configuration such as $(1, 1, 1)$,
while if we start with the disordered configuration $(1, 1, 1)$, there
is a much smaller probability that the system will spontaneously
change to the more ordered configuration $(0, 0, 3)$. The probability of going from order to disorder, from $(0, 0, 3)$ to $(1, 1, 1)$,
is six times as great as the probability of going from disorder to
order, from $(1, 1, 1)$ to $(0, 0, 3)$. The spontaneous reversal of the
order to disorder change is improbable.

It is most important to notice that our construction of the
relative probabilities of the various configurations was essentially
independent of any consideration of the detailed character of the
interactions of the balls with each other or with the walls of the
box. In general, the important statistical conclusions or statistical
laws we will develop are almost independent of the details of
individual interactions. Of course this is why the laws are so
general and so powerful.

When we consider systems that are much more complicated
than the simple system of three balls rolling around in a box
divided into three parts, the improbabilities we found for the
simple systems become impossibilities for analogous actions in

the complex systems. If it is unlikely that the three balls will be
found in one of the three divisions of the box, it is essentially
impossible that the randomly moving balls on the billiard table
will form a triangle of balls that fits a pool rack. The "breaking"
of the pool balls is irreversible. The probability of the ball on the
ground below the picnic table reversing its history and jumping
back up on the table is extremely small—essentially zero. The
action of the ball falling from the table is irreversible. (Of course
we exclude here the interference of outside agencies; pool players
can rack up the balls, a man sitting at a picnic table can pick up
the ball.) These conclusions are almost independent of the detailed character of the interactions of the pool balls on the table,
or of the interactions of the molecules that make up the ball on
the picnic table and the dirt on the ground; again the statistical
results are not sensitive to the character of the detailed interactions.

We emphasize the difference between ordered and disordered
configurations because in many kinds of situations we find that
certain special configurations have important gross features that
are different from those of less special configurations and that
these differences are quite important. Consider a box divided into
two parts; there is an uninteresting configuration where the molecules of air inside the box are evenly divided into the two com-
partments and an interesting configuration where all the air
molecules are on one side and none on the other. Although the
total energy of the two systems will be the same, we can derive
some energy from the second configuration in a simple manner;
we can lead a tube from one side to the other and run a small
turbine or windmill by the impulse of the air passing from the
high-pressure side of the box to the low-pressure side. An experimenter, limited to the box, could extract energy from the unbalanced configuration to run some mechanical device, while he
could not extract energy from the balanced configuration. Energy
would be available from the unbalanced configuration, while no
energy could be extracted from the balanced configuration. We
could have achieved somewhat similar differentiation if we had
put the faster half of the molecules on one side and the slower
half on the other. Again the energy of this configuration would
not be different from the energy when both sides have equal numbers of fast and slow molecules, but it is possible to extract
energy from the nonequilibrium, "interesting" configuration

through a heat engine such as a steam engine. That special configuration again has free energy. The relevance of statistical considerations to the relations between thermal processes and energy —thermodynamics—is clear.

18|2   *The second law of thermodynamics and the concept of entropy*

The distribution of the probabilities of different specific situations or states and the tendency for a physical situation to change always in the direction of situations that encompass higher probabilities leads to definite and important restrictions on real physical processes—restrictions that are not required by the conservation laws and are practically independent of the detailed mechanics of the microscopic world. These restrictions are most important, or at least best defined, in problems of thermodynamics, and the restrictions are codified as the *second law of thermodynamics*. We have discussed the first law, which is, in its essentials, a statement of the law of conservation of energy applied to exchanges of heat energy.

The connection between the behaviors of quantities in the examples of the last section and the restrictions on the character of heat transfer can be illustrated for some simple situations. Consider a room full of gas at room temperature (about 20°C) and atmospheric pressure. If there are no important heat sources or heat sinks (removers of heat), the temperature and pressure in the room will be quite uniform. The microscopic gas molecules will be moving with different velocities in an essentially random fashion. It is definitely possible (though highly improbable) that all the faster molecules might be found at some time on one side of the room and all the slower molecules on the other side. If this were the case the temperatures on the two sides of the room would be very different: the side with the fast molecules would be very hot, and the side with the slow molecules would be very cold. There would not, however, be any violation of the conservation of energy or of the first law of thermodynamics: The total amount of heat in the room would not change. As far as thermal qualities are concerned, the separation of fast and slow molecules would represent a spontaneous or self-acting transfer of heat from one side of the room to the other—after the initial transfer of heat, further transfer would represent *a self-acting transfer of heat from a colder region to a warmer region.*

The final configuration, with all the fast molecules on one side of the room and the slow molecules on the other side, represents an interesting configuration because of the game we play—measuring temperature. Any other equally well defined distribution of hot and cold molecules is equally probable, but most such distributions do not lead to macroscopic differences in temperature and therefore are not interesting. Since there is an enormously larger number of configurations such that the energy or temperature is almost the same on both sides of the room, we can expect to see the temperature the same on both sides almost all the time. If there were only 100 molecules in the average room and the average temperature were 20°C, it would not be unusual to see the temperature equal to 10°C on one side and 30°C on the other; with 10,000 molecules large fluctuations would be quite rare; with 10^{27} molecules so large a fluctuation would be so unlikely as to be miraculous.

Therefore, although it is not strictly impossible for most of the fast molecules to end up on one side of the room and the slow molecules to end up on the other side, the probability is extremely small—so small that we can treat the probability as practically zero. This general conclusion is contained in statements of the second low of thermodynamics.

There are a number of statement of the second law that are equivalent in content, though they sound quite different. A particularly simple and useful statement is due to Rudolf Clausius and dates back to 1850: *Heat cannot flow from lower to higher temperatures in a self-acting way.* For example, no passive (without the introduction of external energy) device can be designed that can extract heat from cold water, making it colder, and use the heat to warm hot water, making it hotter. Such an action is not forbidden by the conservation of energy.

A famous hypothetical design of a mechanism that would segregate heat and cold was presented by the English physicist Maxwell late in the nineteenth century. The device, pictured in Fig. 18|3, consists of a box filled with gas and divided by a partition into two sections. There is a door in the partition guarded by an agile and perceptive demon, Maxwell's demon. This demon is interested in segregating all the hot, fast molecules into the left-hand side of the box and all the cold molecules on the

Hot   Cold

FIG. 18⏐3
*Maxwell's demon
separating fast
molecules from slow
molecules.*

right. To that end, when he sees a slow molecule coming from the
left or a fast molecule from the right he opens the door, letting
it through; otherwise the door is held closed. Soon the left-hand
side of the box will be hot, the right-hand side cold. The total
energy will remain the same, of course; the demon has added no
energy.

If we would invent a self-acting device to do this, even if it
used up some of the heat energy, we would have the next best
thing to a perpetual motion machine. We could bring tap water
into the house at 10°C in winter, separate it into two parts, one
third at 30°C, and two thirds at 0°C, and use the hot portion to
heat the house and the cold portion to run the refrigerator. Of
course our mechanism might not be perfect (the demon might
well need some external energy); we could supply that from our
excess hot water; we could get the hot water at 29° and use the
energy represented in the difference between 30 and 29° to run
the demon. Even if worse came to worst and we needed all the
hot water for operation of the demon, we would still get cheap
refrigeration.

But such a device cannot be built. It violates the statement of
the second law. Such a system, *including the demon,* would constitute a selfacting machine that would segregate heat and cold.
It would transfer energy from a colder to a warmer environment.
If we could analyze the whole system microscopically, we would
find that the system was going, by itself, from a more probable,
disordered situation, to a less probable more ordered situation.

It will not do this for the same reason that a ball will not leap from the ground onto a table.

It is obviously desirable to have some kind of measure of the quantity of disorder of a system in terms of the macroscopic measurements that can be made on the system. Such a measure must be related to the probability of the configuration represented by the system. Let us name this quantity, which we will construct to help describe a statistical property of nature, *entropy:* We will use the symbol S for entropy.

It will be convenient to construct a quantity that will obey the laws of addition as do other physical quantities such as heat or energy. In this case the total entropy of a system must be the sum of the entropies of the parts: if we divide a system with entropy S into two parts, a and b,

$$S = S_a + S_b$$

It can then be seen that entropy cannot simply represent the probability of a system. If we label the probabilities of finding the subsystems a and b in their particular states, w_a and w_b, the probability, W, of finding the whole system as it is, is just the product of the probabilities of the subsystems, even as the probability of two unrelated events is equal to the product of the probabilities of the events taken separately. Then

$$W = w_a w_b$$

Probabilities obey the laws of multiplication. Thus, since we wish to define entropy in a way such that entropy is additive, entropy cannot simply be proportional to probability.

Nevertheless, it is possible to define this additive quantity that we have labeled entropy in a manner such that entropy is related to probability. It is particularly convenient, in this connection, to consider changes in entropy. If the entropies of the parts of the system change, the whole entropy must change: if

$$S = S_a + S_b$$

then

$$S + dS = S_a + dS_a + S_b + dS_b$$

and

$$dS = dS_a + dS_b$$

Such changes, dS, dS_a, and dS_b, should be related to changes in probability of the systems. Let us assume that the probabilities of the two parts of the system, w_a and w_b, both increase slightly as a result of some physical change in the system. Then the total probability, W, will also increase. If w_a increases by an amount dw_a and w_b by an amount dw_b,

$$W + dW = (w_a + dw_a)(w_b + dw_b)$$
$$= w_a w_b + w_a \, dw_b + w_b \, dw_a + dw_a \, dw_b$$

If each of the incremental probabilities dw_a and dw_b is very small, the product $dw_a \, dw_b$ can be neglected. Then subtracting

$$W = w_a w_b,$$

$$dW = w_a \, dw_b + w_b \, dw_a$$

Then dividing by $W = w_a w_b$,

$$\frac{dW}{W} = \frac{dw_a}{w_a} + \frac{dw_b}{w_b}$$

which, of course, is an additive relation: the proportional change in the probability of the whole system is equal to the sum of the proportional changes of the parts. This suggests that we define entropy so that the change in entropy of a system is proportional to the proportional change in the probability of the system:

$$dS = k \frac{dW}{W} \tag{18\,1}$$

where k is a proportionality constant that we will choose to be equal to Boltzmann's constant. It is then obvious that

$$dS = dS_a + dS_b$$

follows from this definition of entropy change.

We will now show that this definition of entropy change can be related to the macroscopic quantities and thus to the results of macroscopic measurements in one special case—which, however, illustrates a completely general result. We will show that

$$dS = \frac{dQ}{T}$$

where dQ is the heat introduced into a system (slowly and reversibly), T is the absolute temperature of the system, and dS is the change in entropy of the system.

For this special case, we will calculate the entropy change involved in a small expansion of the volume holding 1 kg-mole of an ideal gas. We can assume that this volume, V, was extracted from some very large volume, V'. The probability of any one molecule being found in the small volume V is written as $w(1)$ and is obviously proportional to the volume. Therefore,

$$w(1) = aV$$

where a is a proportionality constant. Actually $a = 1/V'$, but this is not important. The probability of finding two molecules in the volume is

$$w(2) = a^2V^2$$

since the probability of two unconnected events is equal to the product of the probabilities of each taken singly. The probability of a coin landing heads is $\frac{1}{2}$, of two coins landing heads is $(\frac{1}{2})^2 = \frac{1}{4}$. Then the probability of finding N molecules in the volume, where N is Avogadro's number, 6×10^{26}, is

$$w(N) = (aV)^N$$

If the volume is larger than a small amount, dV, the probability will differ by a small amount $dw(N)$. Clearly

$$w(N) + dw(N) = a^N(V + dV)^N$$

$$= a^NV^N \left(1 + \frac{dV}{V}\right)^N$$

Using the binominal theorem and noting that $dV/V \ll 1$,

$$\left(1 + \frac{dV}{V}\right)^N = 1 + N\frac{dV}{V}$$

then

$$w(N) + dw(N) = (aV)^N + (aV)^N N\frac{dV}{V}$$

and

$$dw(N) = (aV)^N N\frac{dV}{V}$$

From the relation between entropy difference and probability difference,

$$dS = k\frac{dw}{w}$$

Since $dw/w = N dV/V$, it follows that

$$dS = kN \frac{dV}{V}$$

Or since $Nk = R$, the difference between the entropy value of the mole of the gas held in the volume V and the volume dV is

$$dS = R \frac{dV}{V}$$

Since $PV = RT$ for a mole of gas, $R/V = P/T$ and

$$dS = \frac{P \, dV}{T}$$

This is the difference between the entropy of a mole of gas held in a volume V at a temperature T, and the same gas held in a volume $V + dV$ at the same temperature.

   Entropy, as we have defined it, is a characteristic of a system, just as the temperature or the volume. We can therefore determine the difference between the entropy of a gas contained in a volume V at a temperature T and the entropy of the gas contained in a larger volume $V + dV$ at the same temperature by following the change in entropy as we expand the gas. We choose to expand the gas slowly and reversibly from a volume V to the volume $V + dV$ by letting the gas push against a piston that we slowly withdraw. The gas will do work against the piston equal to $P \, dV$. If the temperature of this perfect gas is to remain constant, the internal energy, U, will be constant and heat must be added to equal the energy expended in work:

$$dQ = P \, dV$$

Then the entropy difference dS between the two states can also be written as

$$dS = \frac{P \, dV}{T}$$

$$= \frac{dQ}{T} \tag{18 | 2}$$

The expression of the entropy change in terms of the reversible heat input is more generally useful than the expression in terms of pressures and volumes.

   Now we see that an increase in the probability of a system

corresponds to an increase in entropy. Even as a system cannot spontaneously change to a state of lower probability (except for very small statistical fluctuations), *the entropy of an isolated system cannot decrease*. This is again a statement of the second law of thermodynamics. We will demonstrate that it is equivalent to the definition of Clausius in terms of heat transfer from cold bodies to hot bodies in the next section.

In the construction of the relation $dS = dQ/T$, we emphasized that the change must be reversible. Even as the piston moved slowly and heat was added to keep the temperature of the gas constant in the example we treated, we could have reversed the piston, slowly compressed the gas, and cooled the gas so as to return to the original condition. If the gas had been contained by a diaphragm such that the gas expanded into a vacuum, increasing the volume from V to $V + dV$, when the diaphragm was broken, the perfect gas would remain at the same temperature even though no heat was introduced: $dQ = 0$. The entropy of the final state of the gas must be the same as if the gas had expanded slowly against the piston, since the final volume and temperature is the same in the two cases. But the explosive expansion is irreversible. For irreversible processes,

$$dS > \frac{dQ}{T}$$

Though we have been concerned with changes in entropy, any system will have a definite total entropy even as it has a definite temperature or mass. The absolute value of the entropy of a system can be established by adding up all the quantities dQ/T required to bring the system, reversibly, from absolute zero to the condition in question. For example, if we are interested in the entropy of a liter of water at a temperature of 300°K, we can find the entropy, in principle, by cooling the water to absolute zero, 0°K, and measuring the temperature of the water as we gradually add heat. We might construct a graph such as suggested in Fig. 18 | 4, where we plot $1/T$ against the heat, Q, that is added. The total entropy will be

$$S = \int_{0°}^{300°} \frac{dQ}{T} \tag{18 | 3}$$

which would be the area under the curve from the origin to the value of Q such that the temperature of the water reached 300°K.

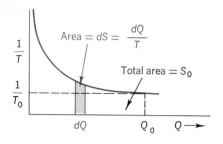

FIG. 18|4
A graph showing the total heat input to a quantity of material plotted as a function of the inverse absolute temperature. The area under the curve is equal to the entropy of the material.

An implicit assumption is made: *The entropy of all systems at a temperature of $0°K$ is zero.* This *third law of thermodynamics* is equivalent to the statement that everything is in perfect order at absolute zero.

18|3   *The Carnot cycle and the thermodynamic scale of temperature*

N. L. Sadi Carnot, an extraordinary French engineer of the early nineteenth century, developed the principle of the second law in his investigations of the efficiencies of the steam engine. He was able to develop important quantitative restrictions on the efficiencies of heat engines and show that these restrictions follow from the second law. It is interesting to analyze the thermodynamic character of an ideal heat engine for a number of reasons: We can observe a direct and practical application of the second law as we show that the heat engines are limited in efficiency by considerations of the second law, which are entirely separate from the laws of mechanics. We can establish a more powerful and general definition of temperature. And we can observe, at least in one case, that the Clausius definition of the second law is equivalent to the statement that the entropy of an isolated system will not decrease spontaneously.

   A heat engine is an engine that changes heat energy into mechanical energy. The steam engine is a characteristic heat engine: the input to the engine is very hot water in the form of steam, and the output is cold water. The heat energy extracted from the water is transformed to mechanical energy by the machine. Less obviously, an internal-combustion engine, such as a gasoline

engine, can also be considered a heat engine. Here the input can
be considered to be the very hot combustion products from the
burning of gasoline in air; the output is the comparatively cold
combustion products as the exhaust. Mechanical energy again
results from the transformation of heat energy. In either the
steam engine or the internal-combustion engine the heat energy
is usually derived from chemical energy produced in the burning
or oxidation of coal or some other fuel, but this is not of interest
to us here; we consider only the heat-to-mechanical-energy part
of the whole cycle.

Schematically all heat engines are rather similar to the ideal
Carnot engine illustrated in Fig. 18|5. Here the engine consists
of a piston acting upon a working substance, which we take to be
an ideal gas in the Carnot cycle; the gas is contained in a cylinder
with conducting walls. There are two large heat reservoirs, a
hot reservoir at a temperature of T_2 and a cooler reservoir at a
temperature of T_1. Presumably the piston is attached to some
mechanism through which mechanical energy can be supplied
and absorbed. The state of the working substance, in this case
the temperature, pressure, and volume of the gas in the cylinder,
is shown on the graph of Fig. 18|5a for different states of the
system as the system proceeds through an engine cycle.

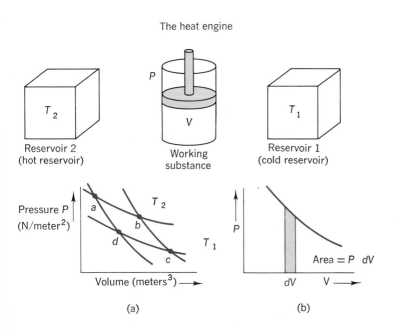

FIG. 18|5
*A schematic version of
the elements of a Carnot
engine, together with P-
versus-V diagrams
illustrating the
thermodynamic
operation of the engine.*

We consider, arbitrarily, that the cycle proceeds by starting at point a on the P versus V diagram. The cylinder is in contact with the hotter reservoir (2) and the temperature of the gas is at T_2. The gas expands, doing work on the piston and the external mechanism attached to the piston. This energy is nominally drawn from the internal energy of the gas, but the energy of the gas is held constant, as the temperature is held constant, by transfer of heat from reservoir 2. For a perfect gas, the internal energy is just the kinetic energy of the molecules, and that kinetic energy depends only upon the temperature. At point b the heat reservoir is removed and the gas expands, doing more work on the piston. This work must represent energy extracted from the internal energy of the gas, so the gas will be cooled during this stage until state c is reached. The temperature of the gas is now infinitesimally larger than T_1. The cylinder is then brought into contact with reservoir 1 at temperature T_1, and heat passes into that reservoir as the gas is compressed (by an external source of energy) to the state d. Since the temperature, and hence internal energy, of the gas is held constant, the work done on the gas during this part of the cycle must be equal to the heat transferred to reservoir 1. Now the reservoir is removed while the outside agency acts on the piston, which continues to compress the gas. This work done on the gas increases its internal energy and therefore its temperature until state a is reached again. This cycle is called a Carnot cycle. In a conventional engine the cycle is repeated as the engine continues to run.

During the cycle the working substance does work on the piston—and thus transfers energy to the external mechanism—during the parts of the cycle shown as a-b and b-c. The external mechanism does work on the piston and thus on the working gas during the parts of the cycle labeled c-d and d-a. Heat is transferred from the hotter reservoir to the gas at temperature T_2 during the part of the cycle a-b, and heat is transferred from the gas to the cooled reservoir at temperature T_1 during the part of the cycle c-d.

Over the whole cycle, the heat engine, consisting of the gas, cylinder, piston, and reservoirs, does a positive amount of work; mechanical energy is transferred to the external mechanism. The work done *by* the heat engine is greater than the work done *on* the heat engine by an amount that is quantitatively equal to the area enclosed by the curve a-b-c-d on the P versus V diagram.

We can understand this conclusion by examining a part of such a cycle as shown in the diagram of Fig. 18│5b. The area enclosed by the narrow rectangle is equal to the height of the rectangle, P, times the width, dV. But $P\, dV$ is equal to dw, an increment of work. The area thus represents the work done by the gas on the piston, or the piston on the gas, depending upon the sign of dV, the change in volume. Then the area under a longer curve is equal to the work done by the system even as the area can be considered to be made up of small rectangles. In this way we see that the work done by the gas in the Carnot cycle of 18│5a is equal to the area under the curve *a-b-c*. The work done on the gas is equal to the area under the curve *c-d-a*. The difference is the work done by the engine through one cycle and is thus the area enclosed by the path *a-b-c-d-a*. This is positive if the path is clockwise, and negative—work done by the outside agency on the heat engine—if the path is counterclockwise.

If we write the heat input to the heat engine from reservoir 2 as dQ_2 and the heat output of the engine, which was deposited in reservoir 1, as dQ_1, the heat used by the machine is equal to $dQ_2 - dQ_1$. From the first law of thermodynamics, which is essentially the law of conservation of energy, this heat used by the machine must be equal to the total work done by the machine. The work output, w, of the machine for one cycle, in joules, is then

$$w = j(dQ_2 - dQ_1)$$

where j is the mechanical equivalent of heat.

The thermodynamic efficiency of the machine, e, is the ratio of the heat that is changed to mechanical energy to the total heat input to the machine. Then

$$e = \frac{dQ_2 - dQ_1}{dQ_2} \tag{18│4}$$

The cycle can also be run backwards: on the *P–V* diagram of Fig. 18│5 we would go from *d* to *c* to *b* to *a*. Instead of expanding the gas in the cylinder and doing work on the outside agency during the parts of the cycle shown as *a-b* and *c-d*, the piston, driven by the outside agency, will compress the gas, and heat will be transferred to reservoir 2. In running the machine in reverse for one cycle, an amount of work w must be provided from an

external source. The heat engine will then extract an amount
of heat equal to dQ_1 from the cooler reservoir and discharge an
amount dQ_2 to the warmer reservoir. Heat will be transferred
from the cooler reservoir (1) to the warmer reservoir (2). The
engine thus acts as a heat pump such as used in a refrigerator.

If we had two reversible heat engines operating over the same
cycle, one of the engines could barely run the other backwards
if the system were absolutely perfect with no friction of any kind.
The work generated by engine number one through the extraction
of dQ_2 Calories of heat from the hotter reservoir (2) could be
used to run the other engine backwards as a heat pump. The first
engine would generate an amount of mechanical energy w that
would just be sufficient to drive the second engine. As the first
engine would extract dQ_2 Calories from the hotter reservoir and
deposit dQ_1 Calories from the cooler reservoir (1), the second
engine would extract dQ_2 Calories from the cooler reservoir and
deposit dQ_1 Calories in the hotter reservoir, restoring the initial
conditions each cycle. Of course all of these could not quite
happen because friction could not be absolutely eliminated.

It is conceivable that the two engines might have different
efficiencies. There might exist an efficient engine, M, that extracts
less heat, dQ_2, from the hotter reservoir than the heat, dQ'_2, extracted by a less efficient machine, M', though they do the same
amount of work, w. Since they both convert the same amount of
heat into work, M must deposit less heat, dQ_1, into reservoir 1
than the heat, dQ', deposited by M'.

$$w = dQ_2 - dQ_1$$
$$= dQ'_2 - dQ'_1$$

If

$$dQ_2 < dQ'_2$$

then

$$dQ_1 < dQ'_1$$

and

$$e = \frac{dQ_2 - dQ_1}{dQ_2} \qquad e' = \frac{dQ' - dQ'}{dQ'} \tag{18|5}$$

and engine M is more efficient than engine M',

$$e > e'$$

Now if the more efficient machine is used to drive the less efficient machine backwards as a heat pump, heat will be transferred by a self-acting machine, or set of machines, from a cooler reservoir to the hotter reservoir. An amount of heat equal to $dQ_1' - dQ_1$ will be extracted from the cooler reservoir each cycle and deposited into the hotter reservoir. But this transfer of heat from a cooler system to a warmer system by a self-acting device violates the Clausius statement of the second law.

We can also consider the change in entropy of the whole system, engines and reservoirs. Rearranging the relation above concerning the heat exchanges in one cycle,

$$dQ_2' - dQ_2 = dQ_1' - dQ_1$$
$$= H$$

where H is positive and represents the total heat transferred to the hotter reservoir from the colder reservoir. The change in entropy of the whole system during the cycle will be

$$dS = dS_2 + dS_1$$
$$= \frac{H}{T_2} - \frac{H}{T_1}$$

where dS_2 is the change in entropy of the hotter reservoir resulting from the heat transferred to that reservoir and dS_1 is the change in entropy of the colder reservoir resulting from the heat transferred from that reservoir. Since $T_1 < T_2$, the change in entropy of this self-acting, isolated, system is negative. But this violates the statement of the second law in terms of the restriction on the change of entropy. Although this is only a special case, the equivalence of the two definitions of the second law is quite general.

The second law—by either definition—will thus be valid only if the heat transferred from one reservoir to the other is zero. Then

$$H = 0 \qquad dQ_1 = dQ_1' \qquad dQ_2 = dQ_2'$$

It then follows that the efficiencies of the machines must be equal

$$e = e'$$

and we have Carnot's theorem: All reversible machines that take in and give out heat at the same temperatures have the same efficiencies. Further, no irreversible machine working between two temperatures can be more efficient than a reversible machine. Indeed, irreversible machines are inevitably less efficient than reversible machines. Real machines are never quite reversible and are never quite as efficient as the ideal Carnot engine.

Now we can use the results on the efficiencies of heat engines to define a temperature scale. If the efficiency of a heat engine depends only on the temperature difference of the input and output, then

$$\frac{dQ_2 - dQ_1}{dQ_2}$$

can depend only on the temperatures T_2 and T_1. Then dividing through by dQ_2,

$$1 - \frac{dQ_1}{dQ_2}$$

must depend only on the temperatures T_1 and T_2 and thus dQ_1/dQ_2 must depend only on T_2 and T_1. Lord Kelvin suggested that the temperature scale be *defined* so that $dQ_1/dQ_2 = T_1/T_2$ This is an absolute scale; it is usually normalized so that the readings are in degrees Kelvin.

With this temperature scale the maximum efficiency of any heat engine can be expressed in terms of the input and exhaust temperatures, T_2 and T_1:

$$e = \frac{dQ_2 - dQ_1}{dQ_2} = 1 - \frac{dQ_1}{dQ_2}$$

$$= 1 - \frac{T_1}{T_2}$$

$$= \frac{T_2 - T_1}{T_2} \tag{18|6}$$

$$\frac{T_1}{T_2} = e - 1$$

One can measure the difference between two temperatures by running a perfect heat engine between the two temperatures and measuring the efficiency. Perfect heat engines are hard to come by, but it can be shown easily, though a bit tediously, that the temperature scale defined by the heat engine is the same as the ideal-gas scale we introduced previously.

18|4   *Some consequences of the second law*

A demonstration of an effect that is immediately perceptible and can be understood simply in terms of entropy is provided by the temperature changes involved in the stretching of a rubber band. When a rubber band is stretched, its temperature increases. When the rubber band contracts, the temperature drops. The lower lip is very sensitive to temperature and the change in temperature is readily detectable if a thick rubber band is held to one's lower lip after various degrees of stretching and release.

Stretching a rubber band results in an alignment or ordering of otherwise unaligned fibers. Since the order is increased, the entropy of the rubber band decreases. If the entropy decreases, from the relation $dS = dQ/T$, where dQ is the heat *input* to the system, heat must be produced by stretching the rubber band. The increased heat then raises the temperature of the band. Inversely, during the contraction, which takes place spontaneously, the entropy increases, and heat is absorbed by the band. This results in a reduction of the temperature of the rubber band, and this cooling is quite noticeable.

The thesis that any isolated system tends, inevitably, to move toward a state of maximum probability or maximum entropy does not mean that subsystems, interacting with other systems of high order or low entropy, do not increase their order or decrease their entropy. A refrigerator cools its contents (and heats the room in which it stands), thus reversing entropy and increasing order, but only at the expense of the increasing entropy of a power source. The entropy of a whole system increases upon any irreversible change and remains the same under any reversible change. According to the second law it will never decrease. The entropy of parts of a system can increase and decrease as a result of their interaction even while the total entropy of the system is unchanged or increasing. For example, in the case of the reversible Carnot cycle, the entropy of the whole system—the cylinder, reservoirs, and some appropriate mechanism to store the mechanical energy without losses—will undergo no entropy change. Individual components of the system will undergo changes in entropy, however. The hotter reservoir will lose heat during the part of the cycle shown as *a-b* on Fig. 18 | 5a. The entropy change of this reservoir will be equal to $-dQ_2/T_2$ during this part of the cycle, and is negative. This does not indicate a breakdown in the second law, since the entropy of the whole system is not decreasing.

Highly ordered crystals grow spontaneously in saturated solutions. There high order and low specific probability or entropy is achieved only at the expense of increased disorder in the surroundings. The total probability of the whole system—crystals, water, air, and so on—increases; the total disorder increases.

Life itself is a most striking example of high organization or low entropy derived from nominally less organized raw materials. It has been suggested that living organisms violate the second law and spontaneously bring order out of chaos. According to this vitalistic hypothesis, this action would differentiate between animate and inanimate things. But there is no evidence for such a violation of the second law, though it is not easy to analyze entropy changes in living processes because they are so complex. Certainly there is no violation of the second law in crystal growth, the inanimate process nearest to life.

We cannot exclude the possibility that there is some fundamental difference between animate and inanimate matter. It is probably safe to say that almost all physicists and the great majority of biologists now believe that no essentially different physical principle is operative in life. However, it seems probable that if some fundamental difference is found it will likely lie in the area of a different statistical law. A few physicists and biologists believe that there is already some suggestion of a breakdown in probability in life processes. It has not been possible to show that life might have first appeared by chance; the best estimates using the theory of probability and the best biological information we have available seem to suggest that the probability of life appearing by accident is very small—essentially zero! However, there are still large uncertainties in such estimates.

The whole universe might possibly have the character of an isolated system. If it can be so considered, we would expect that after a sufficient time the total entropy of the universe would reach a maximum; a condition of maximum probability would ensue. All energy would be evenly dispersed. The temperature would be the same everywhere. No change could occur. The universe would be dead. This eventuality has been called the "heat death of the universe." Actually our knowledge of cosmology and the structure of the universe in space and time is much too incomplete to regard such a hypothesis as more than an amusing fancy.

PROBLEMS

18|1 A box is divided into two parts. When two balls are rolling around at random in the box (which is very much larger than the size of the balls) what is the probability that the balls will be in separate parts of the box? If four balls are rolling around what is the probability that two balls will be in each section of the box? What is the probability that all four balls will be in one section of the box?

18|2 Objects at any temperature radiate and absorb electromagnetic radiation. Although the amount of energy radiated is very much greater for hot bodies, all bodies radiate. An inventor proposes the following device. An enclosure, fitted with walls that are perfect mirrors (we assume that this is possible), contains two objects designed by the inventor. One of the objects, A, emits radiation very strongly but does not absorb radiation; the other body, B, absorbs radiation very well but does not emit radiation very effectively. Energy will therefore be transmitted from A to B. The inventor proposes to pump water through A and B. Cold water will come out of A and hot water will come out of B with no further expenditure of energy.

(*a*) Comment on the validity of the idea behind the design.

(*b*) The second law of thermodynamics leads to a further law: The emissivity and the absorption power of a surface are equal (see Section 16|5). Discuss qualitatively how such a relation might be expected to follow from an examination of the limitations of the experimenter's device.

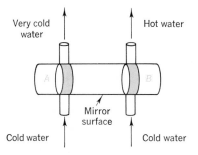

(c) An earthenware jug is heated in a kiln so that it is red hot when it is removed from the kiln. The hole in the mouth of the jug seems to glow the brightest. Why?

18|3 The persistent inventor of Problem 18|2 becomes interested in solar furnaces. A solar furnace is essentially a large lens or mirror designed to focus the sun's rays onto a substance to be heated. Such furnaces are useful and operate up to temperatures or over 2000°C. The inventor proposes to make a very large mirror designed to focus a great deal of energy very sharply to produce temperatures of 100,000°C or even higher.

Comment on this invention; in particular, are there limits to the temperatures that might be reached?

18|4 Each container in the figure is divided into two parts, each holding one liter of water at the designated temperature. Which of these systems has the greatest entropy? How can you show this? (Consider the second law! Detailed calculations are not necessary.)

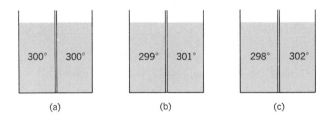

| 300° | 300° | 299° | 301° | 298° | 302° |
| (a) | | (b) | | (c) | |

18|5 Four identical containers are filled with water at various temperatures. Each container is divided into three equal compartments. The water temperatures in the compartments of container a are 20, 10, and 6°C; for container b the temperatures are 12, 12, and 12°C; for container c they are 18, 12, and 6°C; and for d they are 16, 14, and 6°C. List the containers in order of increasing entropy of the water they hold. (Use the second law directly.)

18|6 The heat of fusion of ice is 80 Cal/kg; the heat of vaporization of water is 540 Cal/kg at standard atmospheric pressure. One kilogram of steam at 100°C is used to melt $6\frac{3}{4}$ kg of ice at 0°C. After a certain time all of the ice is melted to water at a temperature of 0°C and all of the steam is condensed to water at a temperature of 100°C. The two quantities of water are not allowed to mix. What is the change in entropy of the system?

18|7 A container having a volume of 2 l. is divided into two equal parts. When one part of the container is filled with nitrogen gas at a temperature of 0°C and a pressure of one atmosphere, the entropy of the gas is S_n. When the gas is allowed to expand to fill the whole container and the temperature is held at 0°C, the entropy is calculated to be equal to $S_n \ln 2$, (where $\ln A$ represents the natural logarithm of A). Under the same conditions of temperature and pressure, the entropy of a liter of oxygen changes from S_0 to $S_0 \ln 2$.

(*a*) What will be the value of the total entropy of the gases when one side of the container is filled with nitrogen at 1 atm pressure, the other side is filled with oxygen at 1 atm pressure, and the temperature is 0°C? What will be the value of the entropy if both sides are filled with nitrogen at 1 atm pressure and 0°C?

(*b*) If the barrier between the two sides is removed when the container is filled with gas in the two ways described in (*a*), how will the entropy change as the gas comes to an equilibrium? What will be the values of the final entropy in the two situations?

18|8 The diagram shows the *P–V* cycle of a certain heat engine. No heat is transferred into or out of the machine during the parts of the cycle labeled *b-c* and *a-d*. The working material is not an ideal gas, though the internal energy of the substance depends only on the temperature.

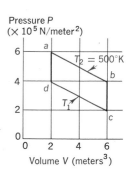

Pressure P
($\times 10^5$ N/meter^2)

(*a*) How much work is done by the machine in one cycle?

(*b*) What is the heat input in one cycle?

(*c*) What is the heat output in one cycle?

(*d*) What is the change in entropy of the working substance in one cycle?

(*e*) What is the change in entropy of the two reservoirs in one cycle?

(*f*) What is the exhaust temperature, T_1?

18|9 One cubic meter of a perfect gas is held at a pressure of two atmospheres (2×10^5 N/m²) and a temperature of 300°K. The gas is allowed to expand slowly against a piston to a volume of 2 m³. Heat is introduced to keep the temperature constant during the expansion. Draw a rough graph of pressure versus volume of the gas, and use this graph to find approximate values of the following:

(*a*) The work done by the gas against the piston.

(*b*) The entropy change of the gas.

Gas at a temperature of 300°K is pumped into one half of a box that has a total volume of 2 m³. The pressure of the gas is 2 atm as before. The second half of the box, separated from the first half by a thin diaphragm, is pumped down to a vacuum. When the diaphragm is broken, the gas fills the whole box to a pressure of 1 atm and the temperature is found to be unchanged at 300°K. No heat was introduced into the gas.

(c) How does the entropy change compare to the change in entropy of the gas expanding against the piston?

18|10   A source of heat generates 100 Cal/sec. The heat is used to heat water from an ambient temperature of 300°K to a higher temperature in order to operate a heat engine, which will then generate mechanical power. In system A the heat is used to heat 2 l./sec to a temperature of 350°K; in system B the heat is used to heat 100 l./sec to a temperature of 301°K. The hot water is then used to drive perfect heat engines that are designed to exhaust the water at a temperature of 300°K. Calculate the useful power generated by the two machines. What are the efficiencies of the two machines?

nineteen   *Electrostatics*

19 | 1   *Coulomb's law*

CONSIDERATION OF THE fundamental forces and the particles that are the sources of these forces lies very near the basis of physics. The electromagnetic forces together with electric charge, the sources of the electromagnetic forces, are now understood better than any other force and perhaps better than anything else in man's experience. Much of this understanding is available to us on an elementary level even as much of our description of the electromagnetic interaction is nearly a hundred years old.

There has existed, at least from the time of the Greeks, a conscious concept of electricity. The word electricity is derived from the Greek word $\eta\lambda\epsilon\kappa\tau\rho\rho\nu$ (electron) meaning "amber." Amber is one of the best insulators or nonconductors of electricity available to a primitive culture. Such an insulator can serve to store electric charge and induce some of the simple, familiar phenomena of electrostatic induction, such as attracting small pieces of dried leaf or other nonconducting debris. It was these properties that brought amber, and thus electricity, to the attention of the Greeks.

Although a considerable amount of information concerning electricity was accumulated up to the beginning of the nineteenth century by very many people, perhaps the most important concepts were developed by that extraordinary man Benjamin Franklin, much of which was published in his book *Experiments*

and Observations on Electricity Made at Philadelphia in America.
In particular, Franklin, perhaps the greatest scientist of his day,
first noted that there are two different kinds of electricity. Our
very terminology—plus and minus, and positive and negative—
stems from Franklin. Although he viewed electricity as a single
fluid, rather than consisting of two separate charges, operationally the single-fluid idea is not so very different from the two-
charge theory and was very useful. Although the development
of Franklin's ideas is intriguing and representative of the best in
scientific thinking, we will concern ourselves with physics rather
than history and commence with some later developments that
summarize an enormous variety of experimental observations.

Our study of electromagnetic phenomena can be considered
as an attempt to construct a description of our observations of
the forces between charged bodies. It is convenient to begin by
considering first the forces between electric charges that are at
rest with respect to each other in an inertial frame of reference.
The area of knowledge concerned with the forces on stationary
charges is called *electrostatics*. The results of the basic observations one can make concerning character of the forces between
stationary charges can be summarized in Coulomb's law and the
principle of superposition, together with the observation that
there are two kinds of charge. Coulomb's law is essentially the
statement that "the force between two charges is proportional
to the product of the strengths of the two charges and is inversely
proportional to the square of the distance between the two
charges." The force has the direction of the line connecting the
two point charges and is repulsive for like charges and attractive
for unlike charges. All the rest of electrostatics can be considered
to consist of amplifications and utilizations of Coulomb's law.

We write this fundamental relation as

$$F = k \frac{q_1 q_2}{r^2} \tag{19|1}$$

where q_1 and q_2 are the values of the charges, r is the distance
between the charges, and k is a proportionality constant. The
equation itself defines charge. The units of charge are largely
arbitrary: in the mks system we define a unit of charge, the coulomb (C), such that k has the value of 9×10^9 N-meter^2/C^2. This
untidy selection of units arises because the coulomb is most
simply defined in terms of practical standardization measure-

ments in terms of the forces between electric currents in a manner such that this number arises naturally. The choice is not intrinsically important, however. It is useful to remember the value 9×10^9 for the duration of the study of electricity.

The coulomb is a very large quantity of static (stationary) electricity. The force between 2 C of charge, 1 meter apart, is 9×10^9 N, equal to the force of 9×10^8 kg weight.

The electrostatic force is similar to the gravitational force in that the magnitude of the force between two charges varies inversely with the square of the distance between the two charges, but differs from gravity in that two different kinds of charge exist, and that repulsive forces as well as attractive forces can result. The direction of the vector force $\mathbf{F}$ in Eq. (19|1) lies along the line between the two charges q_1 and q_2; the force is repulsive if the charges are of the same kind and attractive only if the two charges are of different kind. We give the names *negative* and *positive* to these different kinds of charges. This is to be compared with the source of gravitational force. There is only one kind of mass, and two masses always attract one another.

There is another important difference between electrostatic and gravitational forces on the microscopic level. Electric charge appears to be discrete and to be quantized. No electric charge smaller in magnitude than the charge of an electron has ever been detected, and all charges appear to be integral multiples of this smallest charge. However, there is no evidence that mass, the source of the gravitational force, is quantized. Exceedingly small differences between the masses of different objects have been detected, and though no particle at rest is known to have a smaller mass than the electron, there is no evidence that the mass of the electron is related to any fundamental particularity of gravity.

The similarities between gravity and electricity led Einstein and others to attempt to explain electromagnetic forces in terms of the geometric structure of space in a manner similar to that used to consider gravitation as a distortion of space in the General Theory of Relativity. No equivalence principle is known for electrical forces, however, and these attempts to extend the General Theory of Relativity and construct a Unified Field Theory have achieved no remarkable success.

Although we have not been able to establish a fundamental relation between the electromagnetic forces and gravitational forces, the similar dynamic character of the two forces does

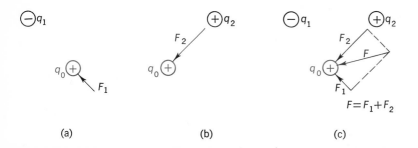

(a)   (b)   (c)

FIG. 19|1

A diagram showing the forces on a test charge that result from the presence of other charges (a) the force on q_0 resulting from the presence of q_1 (b) the force on q_0 resulting from the presence of q_2; (c) the force on q_0 resulting from the presence of q_1 and q_2.

result in some similarities of detailed behavior. In particular, the superposition theorem holds for forces of electrical origin even as it is valid for gravitational forces. The force on a charge q_i is equal to the vector sum of the forces from all other charges, q_1, q_2, q_3, . . . , where the force F_{ij} on q_i resulting from the charge q_i is equal to

$$F_{ij} = k \frac{q_i q_j}{r_{ij}^2} \tag{19|2}$$

where r_{ij} is the distance between the charges, and the direction of the vector force $\mathbf{F}_{ij}$ lies in the direction of the line connecting the charge q_i and the charge q_j. The character of the superposition principle is suggested by the diagrams of Fig. 19|1. As always, the superposition principle holds only if the forces are weak in some sense. This limit, where the superposition principle breaks down, is very large for electromagnetic fields, and a breakdown has been observed directly only through the interaction of electromagnetic waves with the intense electric fields near the surfaces of heavy atomic nuclei.

19|2   *The electric field*

It is convenient to describe the effects of many electric charges on one particular charge, q_j, solely in terms of the magnitude and direction of the total force on q_j. There is a contribution to the total force on q_j from each other discrete charge, q_i, which is described by an expression such as (19|2). We can divide this expression, which is just Coulomb's law, into two parts:

$$F_{ij} = k \frac{q_i q_j}{r_{ij}^2}$$

$$= E_i q_j$$

where

$$E_i = k \frac{q_i}{r_{ij}^2} \tag{19|3}$$

Again the direction of the vectors $\mathbf{F}_{ij}$ and $\mathbf{E}_i$ lie along the line between the two charges. The quantity $\mathbf{E}_i$, defined by the relations (19|3), is the *electric field* at the position of q_j that results from the charge q_i.

The superposition theorem can now be stated in terms of the electric fields. The total electric field at a point is equal to the vector sum of all of the separate fields that result from all separate charges. If the field at a point a that results from the existence of a charge q_i is equal to $\mathbf{E}_i$, the field at a from charges q_1, q_2, q_3, . . . , is just

$$\mathbf{E} = \mathbf{E}_1 + \mathbf{E}_2 + \mathbf{E}_3 + \cdots$$

Since the force on a charge q_j at point a is just

$$\mathbf{F}_j = \mathbf{E}q_j \qquad \text{or} \qquad \mathbf{E} = \frac{\mathbf{F}_j}{q_j}$$

the electric field at point a can be determined by measuring the force on a unit charge at a. We can therefore ignore the origin of the field entirely in our definition of electric field and simply state that the electric field at a point a is equal to the force on a unit positive charge held at the point. The magnitude of the force in newtons is equal to the magnitude of the field in units of newtons per coulomb; the direction of the force is the direction of the field. In practice the introduction of a charge as large as a coulomb will usually upset the distribution of charges that already exists, so we refine our operational definition of electric field and define the field as the force per unit test charge in the limit of very small or vanishing test charge.

The concept of field has been introduced as if it were only a convenience designed to simplify our accounting of nature. This is incorrect only in the implication that any other construct, such as charge, particle, and so on, has any better-founded identity. We will find that the field contains, or holds, energy; a field may carry momentum or contain momentum; and in general it will be necessary to consider the field as having as much reality as any of the other constructs we use. Further, the concept of a field may be as important as any of our other concepts. Even as we are using the concept of a field in order to study the character of electromagnetism, we might consider that one of the intellectually important reasons for studying electromagnetism is that such a study will introduce us to the beginning of an understanding of fields.

19|3 *Lines of force and Gauss' law*

The description of the electric field in terms of *lines of force* is a useful concept introduced by Michael Faraday in about 1840. In this picture or model of the electric field, each charge emits lines of force. The electric field at any point is in the direction of the lines of force through that point, and the magnitude of the field is proportional to the density of lines at that point. This statement can serve as the definition of electric lines of force. With this definition it is easy to calculate the number of lines of force emitted by a charge. Figure 19|2 represents a charge of magnitude q surrounded by a concentric sphere of radius R. From Coulomb's law the electric-field strength at the surface of the

FIG. 19|2

Electric-field lines emitted by a charge at the center of a sphere.

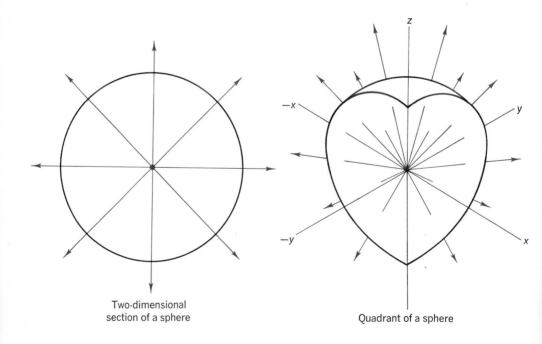

Two-dimensional section of a sphere

Quadrant of a sphere

sphere is equal to $E = kq/R^2$ and the direction of the field is perpendicular to the surface of the sphere: the field is directed outward if the charge q is positive, even as the force on a positive test charge will be directed outward, and the field is directed inward if the central charge is negative. Aside from the sign of the force, positive or negative, the direction, outward or inward, can be considered to result solely from the symmetry of the problem. No other direction can be defined by a point.

From the definition relating field strength to lines of force, the density of the lines of force on the surface of the sphere is equal to the value of E on the surface: The density is thus kq/R^2 lines/m^2, where R is the radius of the sphere. Since the area of the surface of the sphere is $4\pi R^2$, the total number of lines passing through the surface of the sphere is then

$$\text{Number of lines} = (4\pi R^2)\left(k\,\frac{q}{R^2}\right)$$

$$= 4\pi kq \tag{19|4}$$

Obviously this result is independent of the radius of the sphere, R, and most hold generally for any charge, q. In summary: $4\pi kq$ lines of force are emitted by a charge of q. The usefulness of the concept of lines of force largely depends upon this result and therefore upon the long range character of the electrostatic field. If the electrostatic field from a point charge varied with distance in a way different from $1/r^2$, the number of lines through a sphere would depend upon the size of the sphere.

We can extend this result to surfaces more general than a sphere if we consider the relation between the number of lines of force that pass through an area and the normal component of the field with respect to the surface. Let us consider that a uniform electric field is directed upward in Fig. 19|3. An observer carries a meter that measures the component of electric field along the meter, and he is careful to hold the meter perpendicular to the surface on which he is standing. The man standing on the level section measures a value of E_n, the field normal to the surface, equal to E, the total field, while the other man measures a value of $E_n' = E \cos \theta$ where E_n' is the field normal to the surface on which he is standing. That surface is larger, however; dS', the area of the tilted surface, is equal to $dS/\cos \theta$, where dS is the area of the level surface and θ is the angle of tilt of the second surface. Then

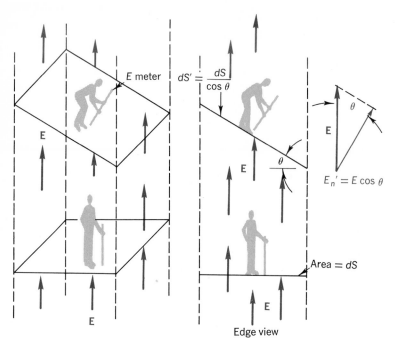

FIG. 19|3
*Electric-field lines
passing through surfaces
that are at different
angles with respect to
the field. The E meter
measures the electric-
field component along
the axis of the meter.*

$$E'_n \, dS' = (E_n \cos \theta) \left(\frac{dS}{\cos \theta} \right) = E_n \, dS$$

But $E_n \, dS$ is just the number of lines of force that pass through the area dS, and it is clear from the left-hand diagram of Fig. 19|3 that the number of lines of force that pass through dS is equal to the number that pass through dS'. Or, in general, the number of lines of force that pass through a small section of surface, dS, is equal to $E_n \, dS$, where E_n is the component of electric field normal to the surface.

It is easy to show that the total number of lines of force that leave any surface is equal to $4\pi kq$, where q is the total charge within the volume enclosed by the surface. Consider at first one charge in a volume enclosed by a surface such as suggested by the drawing of Fig. 19|4a. For simplicity we draw only two-dimensional figures, but the extension of the argument to three dimensions is obvious. Notice that the total number of lines that leave the enclosed region shown in Fig. 19|4a is just equal to the total number of lines emitted by the charge if we count each line once as it leaves the enclosure and subtract one for each line that

enters the volume. The lines that leave the enclosed region between a and b in Fig. 19│4a reenter the region between points
b and c and then leave again between points c and d.

Thus the total number of lines leaving minus the number of
lines entering the region is just equal to the total number of lines
emitted by the charge: this number will be $4\pi kq$, where q is the
total enclosed charge. If the charge is positive, the number of
lines emitted from the enclosure will be positive; if the enclosed
charge is negative, the number of lines will be negative—that is,
the lines of force will enter the region. Of course if there is no
charge in the enclosed region, the total number of lines that will
enter the region will be zero: this does not mean that there will
be no field in the region but, as shown in Fig. 19│4b, that the
number of lines that enter equals the number which leave.

In summary; the number of lines of force that leave the surface of a volume that encloses a charge, q, is equal to $4\pi kq$. Considering the relation between the lines of force leaving a section
of surface, dS, and the electric field normal to the surface, E_n,
we can also state that the sum of all of the quantities $E_n \, dS$, taken
over the whole surface, is equal to $4\pi kq$. In the notation of the
calculus, we indicate the summation over an infinite number of
infinitely small areas, dS, that makes up the whole surface, S, as
an integral:

$$\int_S E_n \, dS = 4\pi kq \tag{19│5}$$

From the principle of superposition it is clear that the charge q in
relation (19│5) represents the sum of all of the charges enclosed

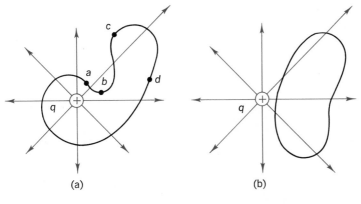

(a) (b)

FIG. 19│4
*A two-dimensional
section showing electric-
field lines passing
through an enclosed
volume.*

by the surface S. This is Gauss' law applied to the electrostatic field. Since $E_n \, dS$ is equal to the number of lines of force that pass through the area dS, Gauss' law can also be expressed as "The total number of lines of force emitted from any closed surface is equal to $4\pi k$ times the sum of the charges held within the surface."

We notice that in the examples we have discussed, lines of force appear only upon emission by a positive charge and disappear only upon absorption by a negative charge. We might generalize this by stating that all lines of force originate upon positive charges and terminate upon negative charges: if the charges are not balanced in a local situation—perhaps there are more positive than negative charges—we can correctly describe the fields that result by assuming that the remainder of the charge that is lacking is to be found on an evenly charged sphere of infinite radius—that is, the excess lines end at infinity. The diagrams of Fig. 19|5 suggest the configuration of lines of force in some particular situations.

What are lines of force? Have they any reality? We should regard the concept of lines of force as a convention, or model, or picture of an electric field and thus as a useful device to establish concepts and to facilitate calculations. Previously forces, such as electric forces, have been related to momentum transfer; in particular, to the transfer of momentum through real moving objects. It is useful to consider lines of force as marking the direction of the momentum carried by such objects. The application of quantum mechanics to fields results in a view of forces transmitted by fields, which, for the case of a single source or

FIG. 19|5

The electric-field near two charges. (Left) the field very near the two charges is like the field near a single charge; the field very far away is also like the field from a single charge. (Right) the field near the charges is like that from a single charge; the field at great distances is very small, like the field from no charge.

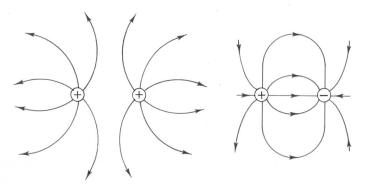

single charge, is quite similar to a picture of lines as trajectories of the particles or photons or quanta that make up the field. At worst, this mechanical picture of the meaning of lines of force is a mnemonic device that helps direct the use of lines of force.

It is important to note that Gauss' law holds only if the strength of the electric field induced by a charge varies inversely as the square of the distance from the charge. If the field decreased with distance faster, as $1/r^3$, for example, fewer lines of force would pass through a large sphere than a small one: lines of force would not begin and end only on charges, but would gradually die away in space as the field dropped off. On the other hand, if the field diminished more slowly, as $1/r$ for example, there would be more lines emitted from the surface of a large sphere than a small sphere about a charge, and the number of lines would have to increase with distance. Inversely, if Gauss' law is valid, then the fields from a point charge *must* fall off with distance as $1/r^2$, where r is the distance from the charge. It is therefore possible, and rather attractive, to consider Gauss' law the fundamental formulation of electrostatics and consider Coulomb's law as a consequence of Gauss' law.

We complete this section by noting that our notation is some-what unorthodox. Usually a parameter $e_0 = 1/4\pi k$ is used. Then Coulomb's law, in this rationalized mks system, has the form

$$E = \frac{q}{4\pi e_0 r^2} \qquad\qquad (19|6)$$

and a charge emits q/e_0 lines of force.

19|4   *Calculations of field strength using Gauss' law*

It is instructive to calculate the electric field produced by certain common charge distributions both for the value of the results and for the purpose of providing further insight into the properties of electric fields and of the concept of lines of force. We first calculate the electric field at a distance R from a uniformly charged sphere of radius r. We take the total charge on the sphere as q. Since the charge is evenly distributed, by reasons of sym-metry, the lines of force are distributed evenly over the sphere and are directed radially as in Fig. 19|6. The total number of

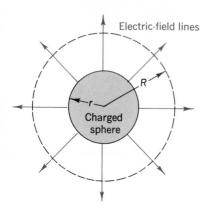

Electric-field lines

FIG. 19 |6
Electric-field lines near an isolated charged sphere.

lines of force is $4\pi kq$, and the lines are evenly distributed over a sphere of radius R with a surface area of $4\pi R^2$. The density of lines, E, is then

$$E = \frac{4\pi kq}{4\pi R^2}$$

$$= k\frac{q}{R^2}$$

the value of the electric field at R. We notice that this is just the same value as for a point charge, q, at the center of the sphere. We deduced the same kind of result upon consideration of gravitational forces. As was the case for gravitational forces resulting from a spherically symmetric body, the electric field from a charged sphere, outside the surface of the sphere, depends only on the distance from the sphere.

FIG. 19 |7
Electric-field lines near a uniformly charged wire.

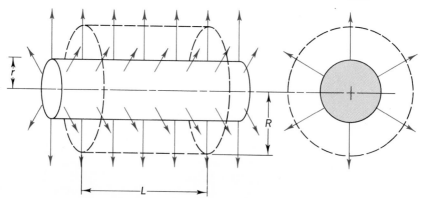

A calculation of the electric field near a long, uniformly charged cylinder is interesting and less trivial. The radius of the cylinder is taken as r; it holds a charge of σ coulombs/meter, the distance of the point of interest from the cylinder is R. Figure 19|7 shows two views of the cylinder, together with the lines of force.

We draw around the cylinder an imaginary cylinder of radius R and L meters long. The lines of force are emitted perpendicular to the axis of the cylinder, again for reasons of symmetry. If the ends of the cylinder are very far away, and we assume that they are, there is no preferred direction. These lines are distributed evenly over the circular area of the cylindrical surface of radius R. The area of the circular part of a section of the cylinder L meters long will be $2\pi RL$ meters^2. The charge held within that cylinder is equal to $L\sigma$ coulombs. The number of lines from this charge is $4\pi kL\sigma$, and the electric field, which is the number of lines per square meter is then

$$E = \frac{4\pi kL\sigma}{2\pi LR} = \frac{2k\sigma}{R} \qquad (19|7)$$

We see that the field outside the cylinder is independent of the radius of the cylinder and depends only upon the distance from the center of the cylinder.

The field near an evenly charged plane surface can be calcu-

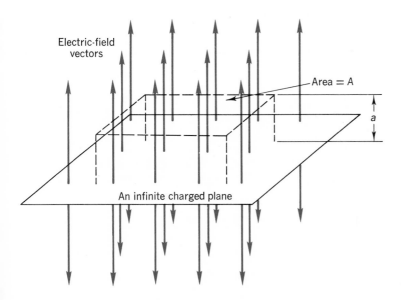

FIG. 19|8
Electric-field lines near a section of an infinitely large, uniformly charged plane.

lated in a similar fashion. We construct an imaginary box about an area, A, as suggested by the diagram of Fig. 19|8. The lines of force are emitted perpendicular to the surface. Again this follows from the symmetry of the situation; if the edges of the plane are very far away, there is no preferred direction other than perpendicular to the plane. If the density of charge is S coulombs/meter^2, there will be $4\pi kS$ lines of force from each square meter —one half up from the surface, one half pointing down. The number through surface A at a distance a from the plane will then be equal to $2\pi kSA$: the number of lines per unit area, which is equal to the electric field, is

$$E = \frac{2\pi kSA}{A} = 2\pi kS \qquad (19|8)$$

It is interesting to notice that the field intensity from the charged sphere, an isotropic distribution in three dimensions, varies as R^{-2}; the field distribution from the charged cylinder, which is isotropic in two dimensions, varies as R^{-1}; while the field from the charged plane, which can change in only one direction, varies as R^0, or is independent of R.

The principal of superposition holds, of course, for the fields from these simple charge distributions even as for individual charges. Thus the fields near two large parallel planes can be represented as in Fig. 19|9. In each case the charge density is S. The plates, charged oppositely in 19|9a, produce twice the field calculated from either plate alone. The fields cancel above and

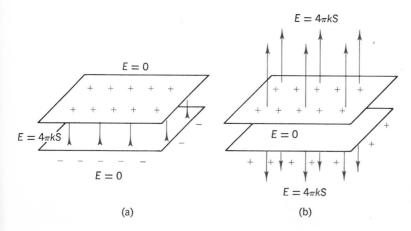

FIG. 19|9
*Electric-field lines near
a pair of uniformly
charged parallel planes.*

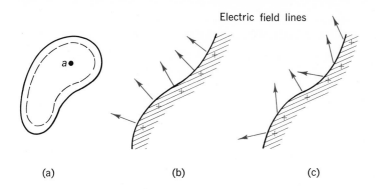

Electric field lines

(a) (b) (c)

FIG. 19|10
*Diagrams illustrating
electric fields (a) inside
conductors and at the
surfaces of (b) charged
conductors and (c)
charged insulators.*

below, resulting in zero field there. The charge distribution of
19|9b results in a cancellation of the field between the plates and
a summation above and below the plates.

Fields near conductors have special characteristics. A conductor is a substance in which a charge is completely free to
move. Further, conductors can be considered to consist of as-
semblies of free charges. Characteristically, metals are conductors, most nonmetals are nonconductors. A neutral conductor
will have equal numbers of positive and negative charges. We
first show that there is no total charge inside a conductor.

Figure 19|10a shows a charged conductor. If a quantity of
charge is placed on a conductor, after a very short time the charge
will be distributed in some fashion and the free charges of the
conductor will no longer be moving—a steady state must be
reached eventually. There will thus be no electric field inside
the conductor at point a. If there were an electric field, the free
charges of the conductor would move, and the conductor would
not be in equilibrium. There can therefore be no net electric
charge within the region bounded by the dotted line, since, by
Gauss' law, if there were a charge q within the region, $4\pi kq$ lines
of force would have to leave that region, and we have just shown
that there are no lines of force in the interior of a conductor.
Therefore, all of the charge must be on the surface of the conductor. If the conductor is hollow, there is no change in these
results: the field is zero inside the conductor.

At the surface of a conductor the lines of force lie perpendicular
to the surface, as shown in Fig. 19|10b. If they did not, as in Fig.
19|10c, there would be a transverse component of force on the
free charges that would move them along the surface. Since we

are discussing steady-state situations after all such motion has ceased, we must conclude that the lines of force at the surface of a conductor will be directed perpendicular to that surface when the charges are at equilibrium. Since all the lines from a charge density of S on the surface extend away from the surface, the field near such a charged surface is equal to

$$E = 4\pi kS \tag{19|9}$$

Even as all these results concerning the distribution of charges on conductors follow from Gauss' law, they also must follow from Coulomb's law. The charge distributions arrange themselves, through the mutual attractions and repulsions described by Coulomb's law, into patterns such that the force at any point on a test charge interior to a conductor is zero, and such that the force on such a test charge near the surface of a conductor is perpendicular to the surface.

19|5   *Electrostatic potential*

The force on a charge, q, in an electric field, E, is

$$\mathbf{F} = \mathbf{E}q$$

If the charge is moved a short distance, $d\mathbf{s}$, the work done on the charge will be

$$dw = (\mathbf{F} \cdot d\mathbf{s}) = q(\mathbf{E} \cdot d\mathbf{s}) = qE\, ds \cos\theta \tag{19|10}$$

where θ is the angle between the direction of motion, $d\mathbf{s}$, and the direction of the field, $\mathbf{E}$. The quantities $(\mathbf{F} \cdot d\mathbf{s})$ and $(\mathbf{E} \cdot d\mathbf{s})$ are the scalar products of the vectors $\mathbf{F}$ and $d\mathbf{s}$ and $\mathbf{E}$ and $d\mathbf{s}$.

The work done per unit charge, dw/q, is a particularly useful quantity, and we give it the name *volt* (V) in the mks system of units. The voltage difference between two points is equal to the work required to take a unit positive charge from one point to the other where the work is measured in joules and the charge in coulombs.

When a charge is moved from a point a to a point b in the presence of an electric field, there will, in general, be a change in energy. The energy change divided by the charge is a characteristic of the field and the points a and b. This difference is called the *potential difference* and is expressed naturally in units of

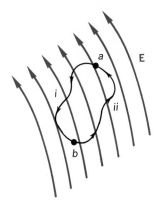

FIG. 19 |11
*Paths in an electric
field.*

joules per coulomb, or volts. Both the meaning and terminology
are nearly identical to those used for gravitational fields.

The work required to take a charge from a to b in a static elec-
tric field is independent of the path. If, in Fig. 19 | 11, less work
is required to take the charge from a to b along path i than along
path ii, one could construct a process that would continually add
energy to the charge without drawing the energy from any known
source. Suppose we take the charge along path i from a to b; we
have to add energy equal to the work done on the charge, W_i.
Then if we return the charge along path ii, work is done on the
charge by the field, equal to W_{ii}. If W_i is less than W_{ii}, the charge
will have received more energy in the circuit than was put into it.
Energy could be extracted every time the charge was sent around
the cycle. If we wish to retain the principle of conservation of
energy, this extra energy must be obtained through some change
in the field or the source of the field. If the sources of the field
are charges that do not move, neither the field nor the sources can
change, and no energy can be transferred to the test charge:
therefore, the total work done on the test charge must be equal
to zero when the test charge returns to its original position. The
electrostatic field, like the gravitational field, is thus a conservative field: the potential difference between two points in the field
depends only upon the position of the points.

The conservative character of the electrostatic field can be
demonstrated explicitly by considering the energy transfer to a
charge in the electric field of another stationary charge. An
arbitrary closed path of a charged particle in the field of a point

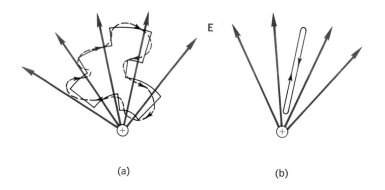

E

(a)   (b)

FIG. 19|12
Equivalent paths in an
electric field. The solid
line in (a) shows one
path; the broken line
shows a nearly
equivalent path. The
radial components of
either path are shown
in (b).

charge is shown in Fig. 19|12a as a dashed line. We can replace this path, in effect, by the nearby path shown as a solid line, where the path is composed of segments that are parallel to the lines of force. No work is done when the particle moves along the segments perpendicular to the lines of force ($dw = qE\ ds\ \cos\theta$, and $\cos\theta = 0$) so we can ignore the perpendicular segments in an analysis of the energy exchange, and the path can be considered as equivalent to a path that moves in and out along a radius vector as suggested by the diagram of Fig. 19|12b. It is obvious that the work done on the test charge as it moves in this path away from the point charge is equal in magnitude and opposite in sign to the work done on the charge as it moves toward the point charge, which is the source of the field. Since any field can be considered as a superposition of fields from single charges, the result is generally valid for all fields.

The potential difference between two points can be calculated in a completely elementary manner only for the special case of a uniform field, such as the electric field very near the surface of a conductor or the electric field between two large plates charged oppositely with equal charge densities, S, as shown in Fig. 19|13. The distance between the plates is d, and we presume that d is small compared to the dimensions of the plates.

The force on a unit positive charge, q, between the plates is directed down, toward the negative plate, and is equal to

$$F = qE$$

$$= q4\pi kS$$

The work done in taking such a charge from the lower to the

upper plate is Fd, the force times the distance. The work, w, is then

$$w = Fd$$
$$= qEd$$
$$= q4\pi kSd$$

This work is independent of the path, of course. The potential difference between the plates is equal to the work done divided by the charge. Then

$$V = Ed$$
$$= 4\pi kSd \qquad\qquad (19|11)$$

where V is the potential difference. The upper plate is considered to be at a higher potential than the lower plate, because work must be done on the standard (+) charge to bring it from the lower to the upper plate. As is the case with gravitational potential, we are always interested in relative potential, and we assign a zero of potential to suit our convenience. Absolute potential probably has no operational meaning. It is generally believed that no experimental result can depend upon the absolute potential even as it appears that no result can depend upon absolute position, absolute time, or absolute velocity.

The potential at a distance from a point charge, or the equivalent, the potential outside a uniformly charged sphere, is identical in form to the relation that describes the gravitational potential outside a spherically symmetric distribution of mass, which was discussed at length in Section 8|3. We will review

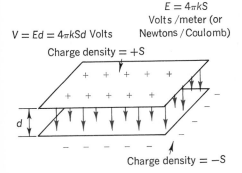

FIG. 19|13
The electric field of a charged parallel-plate capacitor.

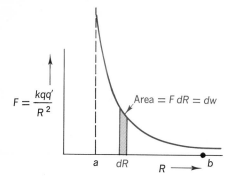

$$F = \frac{kqq'}{R^2}$$

Area $= F\,dR = dw$

$a \quad dR \qquad b$

$R \longrightarrow$

FIG. 19|14

A graph showing the relation between the force on a test charge and the potential energy of the test charge.

those results here in the different notation used for electrostatics. The force on a test charge, q', at a distance R from a charge q or the center of a sphere uniformly charged with a total charge q is equal to

$$F = k\frac{qq'}{R^2}$$

and is plotted as a function of R in Fig. 19|14. The work done in moving a positive charge q' a distance dR toward the charge q is equal to

$$dw = F\,dR$$

where F is the force on the charge. The value of the increment of work dw is just equal to the shaded area under the curve. The total work under the curve between the points a and b will be equal to the work done on the charge in moving the charge from b to a. If we were to measure the area carefully we would find that the work is

$$w = \int_b^a F\,dR = kq'q\left(\frac{1}{a} - \frac{1}{b}\right) \tag{19|12}$$

and the work done per unit charge, or the potential difference, is

$$V = \frac{w}{q'} = kq\left(\frac{1}{a} - \frac{1}{b}\right)$$

which is the potential difference between points b and a. If q is positive, the work done will be positive and point a will be higher in potential than b. A convenient zero of potential in this case is the value of the potential when the test charge is infinitely far away. Then $b = \infty$, $1/b = 0$, and the potential at point a is

$$V(a) = \frac{kq}{a}$$

Since the field distribution from a spherical charge distribution, outside the sphere, is the same as if all the charge were at the center of the sphere, the potential at a point outside the sphere is the same as for a point charge. It then follows that the potential at the surface of a sphere of radius R is $V = kq/R$. Since there is no electric field inside such a sphere, no work will be done in taking a charge from the surface to the inside, and the potential inside of the sphere will be just the same as the potential on the surface.

Even as the potential difference between two points very close together is

$$dV = E \, ds \cos \theta \qquad (19|13)$$

where ds is the distance between the two points, θ is the angle between $\mathbf{E}$ and $d\mathbf{s}$, and E is the electric-field strength in that region, we can write the field strength as

$$\frac{dV}{ds} = E \cos \theta \qquad (19|14)$$

From these relations we can conclude that the potential at every point of a conductor must be the same. Since there is no com-

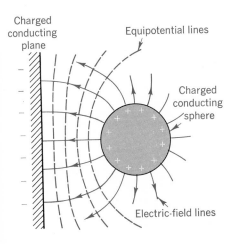

FIG. 19|15

Electric-field lines and equipotential surfaces for a configuration consisting of a charged sphere near a charged conducting plane.

ponent of electric field parallel to the surface of the conductor, for any path along the surface, $dV = 0$. Of course, the field itself is zero below the surface, and the potential will not change along such a path.

Any path designed to cut the lines of force at right angles, such that $\cos \theta$ is zero, will be an *equipotential path*, since the potential will not change along the path. The diagram of Fig. 19|15 shows lines of force (in solid lines) and equipotential surfaces (marked as dashed lines) for a simple charge distribution. The ball is charged positively, the plate negatively, with equal charges. No work would be done in taking a test charge along any equipotential surface even as no work is required to displace an object along a level, frictionless, table—a gravitational equipotential surface.

19|6 *Capacitance and the energy stored in an electrostatic field*

The concept of the *capacitance* of a set of conductors has been found to useful. Capacitance is a property of two conductors and can be defined as the amount of charge that can be held by one of the conductors at unit potential difference between the two conductors. The two conductors are understood to hold equal but opposite charges for the purpose of the definition. A system having a small capacitance can hold only a small amount of charge at a potential difference of 1 V. A system having a large capacitance can hold a larger amount of charge. Such packaged systems are called *capacitors* (in older literature, the word *condenser*, which is inappropriate, is used).

The capacitance of some simple systems can be easily calculated. The calculation of the capacitance of two parallel plates —the parallel-plate capacitor—is simple and interesting. We assume that the plates are of equal area, A, that they each hold Q coulombs of electric charge, and that they are spaced d meters apart. The charge density is then

$$S = \frac{Q}{A}$$

and the electric field is

$$E = 4\pi \frac{kQ}{A}$$

By definition, the capacitance is $C = Q/V$ and

$$C = \frac{A}{4\pi kd} \qquad\qquad (19|15)$$

The unit of capacitance in the mks system is the *farad* (F). The value of the capacitance of a typical parallel-plate capacitor, such that the area of the plates $A = 10^{-2}$ m² and the distance between the plates is $d = 10^{-2}$ m, is about 10^{-11} F. A farad is a very large capacitance, and we ordinarily deal with microfarads (1 μF = 10^{-6} farads) and picofarads (1 pF = 10^{-12} farads). The capacitor discussed above has a capacitance of 88 pF.

The capacitance of a capacitor is invariably increased by the presence of material in the electric field between the conductors. The increase is a result of *polarization* of the material. The positively and negatively charged particles that make up the material may be dislocated by the applied electric field so as to reduce the field and hence the potential difference between the conductors. The diagram of Fig. 19|16 shows the situation schematically for the case of a parallel-plate capacitor. The charge distribution in the material between the plates is distorted in such a way that the material between the plates has an effective layer of charge on its top and bottom surfaces; these charge densities tend to cancel the charge density of the capacitor plates. The effective electric field between the plates is thus reduced, the potential difference is reduced, and the capacitance is increased. If the charge density on the plates is equal to $\sigma = Q/A$, and the induced surface charge is equal to $p\sigma$, where p will be a little less than 1,

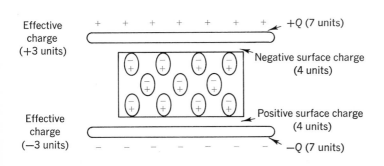

FIG. 19|16

A charged parallel-plate capacitor with a dielectric material between the plates.

the total effective charge density will be

$$\sigma = \frac{Q}{A}(1-p)$$

$$= \frac{Q}{KA}$$

where

$$K = \frac{1}{1-p}$$

The quantity K is called the *dielectric constant,* and the capacitance of a capacitor immersed in substance that has a dielectric constant K is increased by a factor of K.

Since the physical origin of the dielectric effect is the external field induced by the charges on the plates, which results in forces on the electrically charged constituents of the atoms and molecules that tend to separate the charges—either rearrange the charge distributions or align molecules with naturally nonisotropic charge distributions—it is plausible that the dielectric effect should be proportional to the external field for most substances. The value of K is thus approximately independent of the external field. The value of K for water is about 80, for example— a capacitor with water filling the space between its plates will have its capacitance increased by a factor of 80 over its value in vacuum. The dielectric constant of water is unusually high; the dielectric constants of many substances, such as glass, are of the order of 5 to 10; the dielectric constant of gases, such as air, is slightly greater than 1.

Work must be done in taking a small positive charge, dQ, from

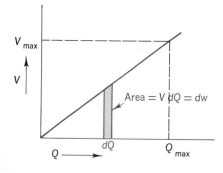

Area $= V \, dQ = dw$

FIG. 19|17
A graph showing the work done in charging a capacitor.

the negative plate to the positive plate of a capacitor. The amount of work is $V\,dQ$, where V is the potential difference between the two plates. Since such an action increases the positive charge by dQ and increases the negative charge by dQ (by taking away positive charge) the capacitor can be charged to any value Q_m in this way.

The total amount of energy required to charge the capacitor to a value of Q_m is easily calculated. Since $V = Q/C$, where C is the capacitance, we can draw a graph of V versus Q as in Fig. 19|17. The increment of work, dw, required to transfer a charge, dQ, from the negative plate to the positive plate of the capacitor is

$$dw = V\,dQ$$

This amount of work is equal to the shaded area in Fig. 19|17. The work done in completely charging the capacitor to a charge of Q is thus the work done in transferring many small charges dQ, and that work would be represented by the total area under the triangle from $Q = 0$ to $Q = Q_m$:

$$w = \int_0^{Q_m} V\,dQ = \tfrac{1}{2}Q_m V_m \qquad\qquad (19|16)$$

Since $C = Q/V$, the total energy stored in the capacitor can also be written as

$$w = \frac{1}{2}\,QV = \frac{1}{2}\frac{Q^2}{C} = \frac{1}{2}\,CV^2$$

where we drop the subscripts and use Q and V to represent the charge of the capacitor and the potential difference between its plates.

Where is this energy stored? The transfer of charge from one plate of a capacitor to the other increases the field between the plates, and it is attractive to consider that the energy is stored in the electric field. In a parallel-plate capacitor we can develop a relation between the energy required to charge the capacitor and the electric field in a particularly simple manner. For such a capacitor,

$$V = Ed$$

and since

$$E = 4\pi\,\frac{kQ}{A}$$

then

$$Q = \frac{EA}{4\pi k}$$

where A is the area of the plates and d is the distance between them; Q is the charge on the capacitor and V is the potential difference between the plates. Then

$$w = \tfrac{1}{2}QV = \frac{E^2 A d}{8\pi k}$$

where w is the energy required to charge the capacitor (and therefore the energy stored in the electric field). The energy stored per unit volume of field is then

$$\frac{w}{Ad} = \frac{E^2}{8\pi k} \quad \text{joules/meter}^3 \tag{19|17}$$

Although this particular calculation pertains to the electric field between the plates of a parallel-plate capacitor, the results are found to hold for any electric field produced by any configuration of charges. The conjecture that energy is stored in the electric field according to the prescription of Eq. (19|17) is thus verified as a description of nature.

Since energy is equivalent to mass through the relation $E = mc^2$, a charged capacitor is heavier than an uncharged capacitor by the mass equivalent of the energy stored in the electric field. This increment of mass, dm, will be

$$dm = \frac{w}{c^2} = \frac{1}{2}\frac{CV^2}{c^2}$$

where c is the velocity of light. This mass is very small compared to the uncharged mass of an ordinary capacitor, but the mass of the electric field is not relatively small for elementary particles and may represent the whole mass of the lightest charged particle, the electron!

PROBLEMS

19 |1   Two very large parallel nonconducting plates are evenly charged positively with a charge density of S coulombs/m². The plates are separated by 1 m. A circular section of one plate having an area of 1 cm² is removed along with the charge on that part of the plate. What is the magnitude and direction of the electric field between the plates? (Use the superposition principle.)

19|2 (*a*) Three equal charges are arranged in an equilateral triangle as shown. Approximately where is the electric field zero? Draw a characteristic set of lines of force.

(*b*) Four equal charges are arranged in a square as shown. Where is the field zero? Draw a set of lines of force.

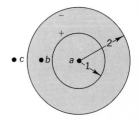

19|3 Draw representative lines of force for each diagram. The diagrams represent the following sequence of events:

(*a*) Two equal opposite charges are placed near each other.

(*b*) A grounded conducting plate is placed between the charges.

(*c*) The negative charge is removed.

(*d*) The ground wire is broken.

(*e*) The positive charge is removed.

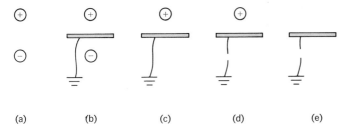

(a)   (b)   (c)   (d)   (e)

19|4 Two concentric conducting spheres 1 m and 2 m in radius are each charged with 1 μC of charge, the inner sphere positively, the outer sphere negatively. What is the value of the electric field at each of the following points?

(*a*) At the center of the spheres.

(*b*) 1.5 m from the center.

(*c*) 2.5 m from the center.

19|5 (*a*) What is the potential (sign and relative magnitude) of the conducting plate relative to the earth in (*b*), (*c*), (*d*), and (*e*) of Problem 19|3?

(*b*) What is the potential difference between the two spheres of Problem 19|2? What is the capacitance of the system?

19|6 Four charges, each of a magnitude q, are placed at the four corners of a tetrahedron 1 m on a side. What is the total potential energy of the system when

(a) All four charges are positive?

(b) Three charges are positive and one is negative?

(c) Two charges are positive and two are negative?

(d) Three charges are negative and one is positive?

(e) All four charges are negative?

19|7 The surface of a sphere of elastic material (such as a soap bubble) is charged evenly with a charge equal to q. An external pressure is applied to the sphere to balance the electrostatic forces so that the total forces on the sphere are equivalent to the force on an uncharged sphere. If the radius of the sphere is r, what will be the value of the applied pressure (force per unit area)?

19|8 A charge of q coulombs is placed 1 cm from the center of a square 2 cm on a side as shown in the drawing. Assume that the square has no electrical properties.

(a) Show that the total electric field passing through the square normal to the area of the square is equal to $\frac{2}{3}\pi kq$. (Use the symmetry of the problem: the square could be a face of an imaginary cube about the charge.)

(b) If the square holds a total charge of q' evenly distributed over a nonconducting surface, what will be the direction and magnitude of the force on the surface?

19|9 Two conducting spheres are connected by a very long, very thin, conducting wire. The spheres are very far from one another and very far from any other charge. The radius of one sphere is 1 m; that of the other is 2 m. If the total charge on the assembly is 1 μC, what is the charge on the 1-m sphere?

19|10 Draw plausible lines of force and equipotential lines for the configurations of charges and grounded conductors shown (the conductors are held at zero potential). Consider that the charges are equal.

19|11 The area of the plates of a parallel-plate capacitor is 1.0 m²; the spacing between the plates is 10 cm. A light pith ball having a mass of 0.1 gm holds a charge of 1 μC. What voltage must be applied to the plates so that the pith ball might be suspended between the plates?

$q\bullet$

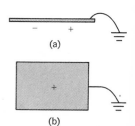

(a)

(b)

19|12 It is probable that the mass of the electron is primarily due to the energy stored in the electric field of the electron.

(a) Estimate the energy in a sphere of radius R about the electron if the field is equal to ke/R^2 throughout the sphere, e being the charge on the electron.

(b) Using Einstein's mass–energy relation $E = mc^2$, find the value of R in terms of e and m, the mass of the electron. (This is, within a small numerical factor, equal to a length called the classical radius of the electron and is about equal to 3×10^{-15} m.)

(c) Using the results of (a) shown that the energy is infinite if the electron is a point.

19|13 The area of the plates of a parallel-plate capacitor is 1.0 m². The spacing between the plates is 10 cm. A slab of copper (which is a conductor, of course) is placed between the two plates of the capacitor. The copper is 8 cm thick and is centered between the capacitor plates so that there is a 1-cm space between the copper and each plate. What is the capacitance between the two plates with the copper in place?

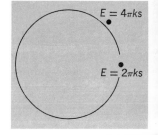

19|14 A sphere made of thin glass, which is a good insulator, is charged evenly with a charge density of $+s$ C/m². A small piece of the sphere, together with the charge, is removed. Show that the electric field on the surface of the sphere is equal to $4\pi ks$, but that it is equal to $2\pi ks$ where the piece is removed. (Remember the superposition principle.)

19|15 A charge of $+Q$ is at a position 0.5 m from a conductor held at zero potential. Consider the distribution of lines of force and equipotential surfaces and show that there will be an attractive force on the charge just as if a charge of $-Q$ were 1.0 m away on the other side of the plane and the plane were removed.

19|16 The area of the plates of a parallel-plate capacitor is 1 m², the spacing between the plates is 10 cm, the potential difference between the plates is 1000 V. The plates are disconnected electrically from the surroundings. The plates are then pulled farther apart so that the new spacing is 11 cm. At this time

(a) What is the potential difference between the plates?

(b) How much work is required to pull the plates apart? (What is the difference in stored energy in the two configurations?)

(c) What is the approximate value of the force between the plates?

19|17   The mass of a parallel-plate capacitor is seen to change from
M to $M + m$ when the capacitor is charged to a value of Q. The area of
each plate is A. For the questions below all quantities remain the same
except the quantity referred to specifically. How will the value of m
vary as

   (a) The charge, Q, is doubled?

   (b) The distance between the plates is doubled?

   (c) The area of the plates, A, is doubled.

20|1 *Ohm's law*

IN GENERAL, if an electrostatic potential difference exists between two points in a medium occupied by any material—liquid, solid, or gas—free electric charges in the material will be induced to move by the action of the electric field. If the potential can be maintained through some agency, the flow of charge will continue: this continuous flow of charge is an electric current. The unit of electric current is a coulomb per second, which is given the particular name of *ampere* (A).

It has been observed experimentally that the current between two such points is proportional to the potential difference between the points for a wide variety of materials and over a wide variety of conditions. This relation is called Ohm's law. Ohm's law belongs in the same category as Hook's law, or the law of friction, which states that the force of friction between two bodies is proportional to the normal force between two bodies. All these laws are approximate rules summarizing observations. The validity of all these laws is limited and the reasons for the ensuing simplicity are rooted in detailed behaviors of complex microscopic phenomena.

The character of the relation between current and potential difference has simple properties that can be illustrated by examining a particularly simple model experiment.

A potential difference of V volts is held across a block of material as shown in Fig. 20|1. It is nearly obvious that the amount of current that will flow will be proportional to the cross sectional area, A; it is plausible (though not at all obvious) that the current that will flow will be proportional to the force on the charges free in the substance. That force will be proportional to the electric field, which is in turn equal to V/L in volts per meter, where V is the potential difference across the block and L is the thickness. Then

$$I = \frac{dQ}{dt}$$

$$= \left(\frac{1}{\rho}\right)\frac{AV}{L}$$

$$= \frac{V}{R}$$

where

$$R = \frac{\rho L}{A}$$

and I is the current in amperes, Q is the charge in coulombs, and $1/\rho$ is the constant of proportionality, written in this fashion for future convenience. Further, we see that I is proportional to V.

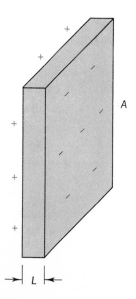

FIG. 20|1
*A diagram used to
show the dependence
of electrical resistance
upon various parameters.
L is thickness, A is area.*

TABLE 20|1   *Specific resistances of some materials*

Substance	ρ (Ω-m)
Copper	1.7×10^{-8}
Iron	1.0×10^{-7}
Carbon (graphite)	8×10^{-6}
Carbon (diamond)	10^5
Quartz (SiO_2)	10^{18}

This proportionality is not limited to the configuration of Fig. 20|1 but holds for the current that flows between two points for any substance and any configuration or shape of the substance. It is then customary to write this general relation as

$$V = IR$$

where R, called the *resistance,* is proportional to ρ and depends upon the configuration and the character of the mediating material. Numerically, ρ, the *specific resistance* of a substance, is equal to the resistance, R, of a cube of material 1 m on a side where the current flows between opposite faces of the cube held at different potentials as suggested by the sketch of Fig. 20|1. The units of resistance are volts per ampere: again a special name is used for this unit called the *ohm.* The symbol for ohm is Ω, omega; the units of ρ are then ohm-meters. Table 20|1 presents some values of ρ for various materials.

20|2   *Conductivity and conductors*

The large differences in the specific conductivities of various materials would seem to indicate the existence of large, easily understood differences in the basic structure of materials. It is probably more nearly correct to consider instead that the basic structure or basic character of different solids is nearly the same for all substances, but that the subtle differences that do exist result in radically different electrical behavior. Although it is not practical for us to consider the structure of solids—solid-state physics—in detail at this time, it is possible to gain some insight into the character of the differences in conductivity of various materials through discussions of simple models of solids that are supposed to represent classical analogues to a reality that can only be described with any kind of precision by the use of quantum mechanics.

Any solid can be considered to consist of a matrix of atoms that are held in position by the forces between atoms. When the forces are such that the atoms are naturally found in very regular patterns, the material has a crystalline structure: most materials have such a regular structure over small regions. Although the exact character of the forces between the atoms that make up a given material depends upon the precise structure of the atoms, for all materials the basic matrix can be considered to be made up from the positive cores or nuclei of the atoms plus the most strongly bound electrons, and for all materials the least tightly bound electrons can be considered free to the extent that they are not held to the position of any single atom. The electrons are negatively charged, and for some materials some of these electrons will move when an electric field is applied to the material; the moving charge constitutes a current in the material: metals conduct electricity in this way. However, no current will flow in certain other materials—the insulators.

According to a characteristic of electrons and some other elementary particles, which is expressed as the *Pauli exclusion principle* (and will be discussed more fully in later chapters), two electrons cannot occupy the same de Broglie standing wave. This can be expressed classically—and we will use a classical model here—by saying that two electrons cannot occupy the same position. Any piece of material can be considered to be like a box where the length and width of the material are the same as the length and width of the box. (We limit ourselves to two dimensions here for convenience.) The electrons that are free in the material are represented as marbles that partially fill the box—marbles also obey an exclusion principle; two marbles cannot occupy the same position. Ordinarily the marbles will form layers in the box. If the number of marbles is just sufficient to form a layer, no marble will easily move. If the box is tilted slightly so that a gravitational force acts on the marbles, tending to push them to one side of the box, they will still not move—no marble current will flow. However, if the number of marbles is such that a full layer is not formed, the marbles constituting the partial layer will roll toward the lower side of the box and a marble current will flow. A third case is interesting also. Let us assume that a disturbance in a system where the top layer is ordinarily full kicks one marble from the complete layer out of that layer to the top of the other marbles. There is now a hole in the layer that was full, and there is one free marble in the otherwise empty next layer. Of course energy had to be added to kick the marble up to a state of higher potential energy, but now the box of marbles is a conductor of marble current. If the box is tilted, the free marble on top will roll down to the lower side of the box and the marbles in the almost filled layer will tend to rearrange themselves so that the hole runs uphill. Such boxes are shown in Fig. 20|2.

Insulators are analogous to the box with complete layers of marbles, while good conductors are similar to the boxes where the top layer is incomplete. The least bound electrons in an insulator completely fill a set of standing waves that have almost the same energy, and no electron can move even if an electric field is present. The electrons in a conductor such as a metal only partially occupy sets of standing waves that have almost the same energy, and these electrons are therefore not so constrained and will move when an electric field is imposed on the material.

Materials such as silicon, germanium, and most forms of carbon are called *semiconductors*. At low temperatures the electrons in a semiconductor essentially fill a set of standing waves that repre-

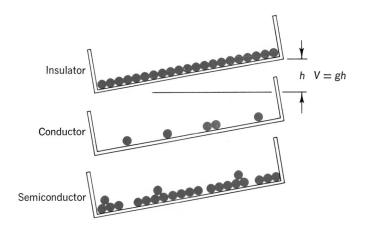

FIG. 20|2
Layers of balls in a box under a gravitational potential difference, used to suggest the character of electrical conductivities in different kinds of material. In the case of the semiconductor, consider that there are filled rows beneath the rows shown and that the box is vibrating with a "thermal" agitation.

sent the same electron energy, even as the marbles in the analogous box might fill a layer where each marble has the same gravitational potential energy. In the case of semiconductors the next
layer, which is ordinarily empty, is very near the filled layer in
energy, and very little energy is required to move an electron
from the filled to the empty level. A parallel might be drawn by
considering that the marbles might be extremely light, so that
very little energy is required to move a marble from the filled
layer to the next layer. In the case of semiconductors this energy
gap between the filled band of energy levels and the conduction
band of energy levels is very small, and the general thermal
agitation is enough to keep some electrons in the conduction
band and some holes in the filled band. The energy gap for insulators is much larger, and such errant electrons are extremely
improbable.

We can consider the difference between insulators and semiconductors in a semiquantitative manner by noting that the energy
of agitation is derived from the thermal energy of the system. The
thermal energy of an electron can be considered to be of the order
of kT, where k is the Boltzmann constant and T is the absolute
temperature. If the energy difference between the energy level
that is filled and the next higher level is not very much larger
than kT, thermal agitation can send electrons into this conduction
band and the substance will be a semiconductor. If the energy
gap is very much larger than kT, the probability of an electron
being ejected by chance into this band will be very small and the
substance will be an insulator.

We thus find that we can usefully divide solid materials into
three classes. Conductors have many electrons in an unfilled
conduction band, and the movement of these electrons under the
influence of an electric field constitutes an electric current. Insulators have essentially no electrons in the conduction band; the
least bound electrons completely fill a set of standing waves in
the material, there is no net movement of electrons when an electric field is applied to the material, and the resistance is very
high. A few electrons from the nominally filled band in semiconductors are thrown up into the conduction band by thermal
agitation, and these electrons, and the holes left in the filled band,
will move under the influence of an electric field, giving rise to
current; the resistance of semiconductors is far lower than that
of insulators, though not so low as for conductors such as metals.

Aside from the limitations of the simple classical discussion of the differences between the conductivities of various materials, we have not discussed the origin of these differences—why do the electrons in a piece of quartz completely fill an energy band, and why do the electrons in a piece of copper only partially fill a band? We can only state here that the origin of these differences is found in an understanding both of the detailed structure of the atoms of the material and in the relations between adjacent atoms. Detailed calculation is required to understand the conductivities of even simple materials, and no complete understanding of all solids has yet been achieved.

We can use a classical modification of the energy-band description of electrical conduction in order to gain some quantitative understanding of the basis for the validity of Ohm's law. We can consider that the electrons in the conduction band are free to move throughout the material in a manner similar to the motion of the particles that make up a classical gas. However, the electrons will undergo collisions with the fixed atoms in the solid and with the boundary of the solid. According to our classical description, the electrons will be in thermal equilibrium with the atoms: the average kinetic energy of the electrons will be the same as the average kinetic energy of the atoms as they vibrate about their equilibrium positions.

This equipartition of energy will always hold if the system is in thermal equilibrium: if the electrons gain energy through some mechanism, they will share this energy with the lattice of atoms in the solid through collisions with these atoms. Indeed, if any electron gains energy, it will lose this extra energy, on the average, during the next collision with the atomic lattice. Then if an electric field, E, is imposed on the solid, the electrons will be accelerated by the force resulting from the field and the velocity will be changed by an amount dv, where

$$dv = a\ dt$$

where

$$a = \frac{Ee}{m}$$

and

$$dt = \frac{L}{v}$$

The acceleration, a, will be equal to the force on the electron, Ee (where e is the charge of the electron), divided by the mass of the electron, m. The relevant time will be the time between collisions, dt, which is equal to the mean distance between collisions with the atomic lattice, L, divided by the mean thermal velocity of the electron, v. We assume, implicitly, that all the extra velocity, and extra energy, is lost in the collision with the lattice.

The change in the average velocity of the electrons that results from the electric field—the drift velocity, u—is equal to the average change in the velocity of an electron that is induced by the field in the time between collisions with the atomic lattice: this is just half the total increment of velocity:

$$u = \frac{1}{2}\,dv = \frac{1}{2}\,a\,dt = \frac{1}{2}\frac{EeL}{mv}$$

and the drift velocity is seen to be proportional to E, the electric field. Since the electric current flowing in a conductor is a measure of that drift and since the electric field in a conductor is proportional to the potential difference imposed across the conductor, this result is equivalent to Ohm's law.

Some of the qualitative aspects of electrical conductivity can be understood to some extent from this simple model. The electrical resistance of metallic conductors, with their partially filled energy bands, increases with temperature. This is due in part to the fact that at high temperatures the thermal velocities of the electrons will be greater, the time between collisions will be shorter, and thus the incremental velocity induced by the electrical field will be smaller. Conversely, the resistance of semiconductors, such as carbon, is found to decrease with temperature because the increase in resistance that follows from the decreased time between collisions of the electrons in the conduction band is more than compensated by the increase in the number of electrons injected into the conduction band by the increased thermal agitation.

We might add here that the differences in heat conduction between good conductors, such as copper, and poor conductors, such as glass, can also be understood qualitatively as a consequence of the difference in electron mobility in such conductors and insulators. Even as the motion of the electrons carries electric current, the electrons also can carry energy and assist in the conduction of heat from one side of a piece of material to the other. The electrons cannot carry any energy in insulators, so the transfer takes place more slowly through the interaction of the atoms that make up the lattice. Typically, then, good electrical conductors, such as the metals, are good thermal conductors, while electrical insulators are poor conductors of heat.

Electric current in liquids and gases takes place through the motion of both positive and negative charges. In water, for example, a small portion of the H_2O water molecules are always dissociated into the charged fragments or ions, H^+ and OH^-, where the superscripts represent the fact that the fragments are charged positively and negatively. Both charges move under the influence of an electric field and contribute to the current.

The number of ions in pure water is small and the conductivity is low—indeed, so low that pure water is a fairly good insulator. Salt, NaCl, is almost completely dissociated into Na^+ and Cl^- ions in a water solution. The conductivity of salt water is correspondingly high.

Gases also conduct electricity slightly under ordinary conditions, primarily as the result of the formation of ions by cosmic rays passing through the gas and by radioactive sources. There is usually a certain proportion of positive and negative ions such as N_2^+ and N_2^- in the atmosphere. The positive nitrogen ion, N_2^+, is an ordinary nitrogen molecule with an electron knocked off; the negative nitrogen ion, N_2^-, is a nitrogen molecule that has captured an extra electron. In general, free electrons are also found in gases, though in air these electrons are quickly captured, usually by the oxygen in the air, occasionally by the nitrogen. All these charged particles move under the influence of an electric field and contribute to the slight conductivity of air.

The atmosphere of the sun is highly ionized because almost all the atoms and molecules have electrons knocked off as a result of the high average energy of the collisions of the particles that make up this extremely hot gas. Correspondingly, the atmosphere contains a very large number of free electrons. Although the gas is electrically neutral over-all, most of the individual free constituents—the molecules, atoms, and free electrons—are electrically charged. Such a gas is called a plasma; since most of the particles are charged, the behavior of plasmas is dominated by the electromagnetic forces between the particles, which have substantial effects at large distances, rather than the short-range forces that account for the collisions between neutral atoms. The behavior that results is so different from the behavior of neutral gases, and of course liquids or solids, that plasmas can be considered a kind of fourth state of matter. Since the material of all stars as well as most of the interstellar gas is ionized and thus forms a plasma, and since this material constitutes more than 90 percent of the material in the universe, the physics of plasmas is of considerable interest. Indeed, we have some hope of using the characteristics of plasmas to create an environment in which we might maintain controlled thermonuclear fusion reactions and thereby produce energy by changing deuterium, a heavy isotope of hydrogen, into helium.

20|3   *Direct-current circuits*

Mechanisms such as batteries, generators, and so on exist that can be employed to sustain a potential difference between points of a conductor in the presence of a flow of current through the conductor. The whole circuit of conductor and the potential-maintaining device constitutes an electric circuit: we now consider the special case where the magnitude of the current does not change with time—the direct-current circuit.

An example of a conventional representation of a simple circuit is shown in Fig. 20|3a. Note the conventions for a battery and for a resistance. A simple line represents a conductor. For the circuits we will study we can assume that the conductors are perfect—their resistance is zero. It is usually convenient to consider one point of a circuit at zero potential. It makes no

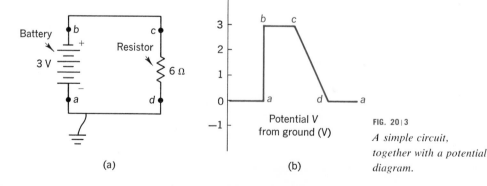

(a)

(b)

FIG. 20|3

A simple circuit, together with a potential diagram.

difference in principle where this point is taken: often there is some point that is actually connected to ground—literally to the earth through water pipes or some other "grounded" conductor. It is particularly convenient to consider this point as the point of zero potential; conversely, any point chosen as a zero potential is usually called the ground, even if not physically connected to the earth.

Figure 20 | 3b shows the potential at various points in the circuit of 20 | 3a relative to ground. It is instructive to follow the current as it travels in a clockwise direction, from plus to minus, in the circuit and consider the effects of the circuit elements on the current. (The electrons actually move in the opposite direction. Our choice of considering a positive current, according to convention, causes no error in practice or in principle.) A charge $+q$, at zero potential at the position of the ground, is lifted through a positive potential V of 3 V by the action of the battery. The battery thus does work on the charge to increase its potential energy by an amount equal to Vq, where V is the "voltage" of the battery. This work is done at the expense of chemical energy of the battery. We will not discuss this rather complex mechanism. Batteries and other sources of energy in a circuit, such as generators, are regarded as sources of electromotive force (emf), which is a name for the increase in potential energy given to a charge passing through the source of emf. Electromotive force is measured in volts. We will use the symbol $\mathscr{E}$ for emf which should not be confused with E, which we will retain as our symbol for electric-field strength.

The charge will move to the resistor at point c without changing its potential, but the potential will drop from c to d as the charge passes through the resistor. The potential at c is 3 V, while at d the potential must be zero since d is connected by a conductor to ground and to point a, which are at zero potential. The change in potential across the resistor must therefore be equal to 3 V, and the charge will have done $3q$ joules of work in passing through the resistor. This work will be evident in the heating of the resistor. From Ohm's law we can relate the voltage drop across the resistor to the current passing through the resistor and the resistance of the resistor; the voltage drop is $V = IR$. Then $I = dq/dt$, the amount of charge passing through the circuit each second, is equal to V/R, where R is the resistance of the resistor. But $V = \mathscr{E}$

and

$$\mathscr{E} = IR$$

The emf, equal to $\mathscr{E}$, is in turn equal to the voltage drop, IR.

This work per unit time done by the battery is

$$\mathscr{E} \frac{dq}{dt} = \mathscr{E}I$$

The work done per unit time by the current on the resistor is

$$V \frac{dq}{dt} = VI$$

$$= I^2R$$

which is equal to the work supplied to the circuit by the source of emf, in this case a battery. Work per unit time is power, so the power supplied to the circuit by the battery is $\mathscr{E}I$, while the power supplied to the resistor by the current passing through it is I^2R.

The work done per unit time by the battery is the power supplied by the battery and is expressed by

$$P_b = \mathscr{E} \frac{dq}{dt} = \mathscr{E}I$$

The work done per unit time by the current on the resistor is

$$P_r = V \frac{dq}{dt} = VI = I^2R = \frac{V^2}{R}$$

There are close similarities between a simple electric circuit and a simple hydraulic circuit. The hydraulic fluid, such as water, corresponds to the electric charge; a pump is analogous to a source of emf; gravitational potential, which is potential energy per unit of mass, is like electric potential, which is potential energy per unit of charge; and the electric current and the fluid current, or water current, are similar. The diagrams of Fig. 20|4 show similar electric and hydraulic circuits. The battery (or other source of emf) can be considered as a device that lifts electric charge up to a potential of 3 V. The ideal battery is limited only in voltage and will lift charge at an infinite rate. The corresponding pump in the hydraulic circuit will lift water to a height of 0.3 m against a gravitational acceleration of 10 m/sec². This ideal pump is limited in the pressure differential it will exert: the pump will

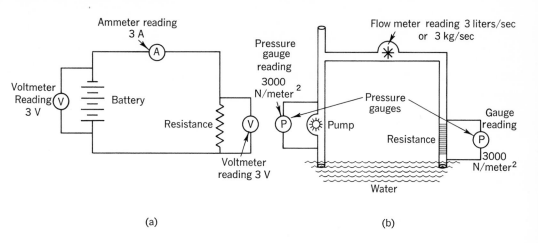

(a)

(b)

FIG. 20|4

(*a*) *A simple electrical circuit; (b) an equivalent hydraulic circuit.*

lift water at an infinite rate, but only to a height of 0.3 m or through the corresponding pressure differential of 3000 N/m².

The battery does 3 J of work as it lifts 1 C of charge 3 V; the pump does 3 J of work as it lifts 1 liter (1 kg) of water 0.3 m. The rate at which the battery pumps the current around is limited by the resistance of the circuit: the current flows through a resistance back to ground, and the voltage drop across a resistance is proportional to the current through the resistance. Since the battery will produce only 3 V of potential difference, the current will flow at a rate such that 3 V potential drop, and no more, occurs across the resistance. The rate at which the pump circulates water through the hydraulic circuit also depends upon the resistance in the circuit. Since the capacity of the pump is infinite, but the pressure difference developed by the pump is limited to 3000 N/m², the pump will pump water at a rate so that the pressure drop across the circuit resistance is just 3000 N/m². Let us assume that in each circuit the resistance is such that a potential drop of 3 units is produced by a current of 1 unit: that is, in the electric circuit the resistance produces a potential drop of 3 V when a current of 1 A is flowing; in the hydraulic circuit the pressure drop across the resistance is 3000 N/m² when one liter/sec is flowing. In that case the battery and the pump are both doing work at a rate of 3 J/sec or 3 W, and in each case the current, electric or hydraulic, is doing work at a rate of 3 W in passing through the resistance. This 3 W will appear as heat in an electrical resistance, heating the resistor. In the hydraulic system the energy will also appear as heat, raising the temperature of the water that passes through and the material in the resistance. Overall, the energy of the battery is transferred to heating the resistor; the energy put into the pump is transferred to heating the water and the hydraulic resistor.

In the diagrams of Fig. 20|4, voltmeters are shown measuring the potential difference across the battery and the resistor, and an ammeter measures the current through the circuit. Pressure gauges measure the pressure drop across the pump and the resistance in the hydraulic system, and a flowmeter measures the current that flows in the system. Voltage thus corresponds roughly to pressure—in this case the correspondence is particularly close if the pressure is measured in units of gh, where g is the acceleration of gravity and h is the head, or height to which the pump will raise the water.

20|4 *Kirchhoff's laws and complex circuits*

The analyses of more complicated circuits can be understood by the use of two single conservation laws relevant to electric circuits. The first is as follows: "The amount of current leaving any point is equal to the amount of current entering the point." If we include all sources and sinks of currents, current is conserved. At any point in a circuit, at any time, the sum of the currents entering a point is equal to zero.

$$I_1 + I_2 + \cdots = 0$$

The second law is very much like a statement of the conservation of energy: "The algebraic sum of all of the sources of emf in any continuous closed path is equal to the sum of all of the potential drops across resistors." This is as much to say that if we take a charge completely around any closed path back to its starting point, the work done on the charge must equal the work done by the charge. No energy is unaccounted for. Around any closed loop in a circuit, at any time, the algebraic sum of all of the sources of emf and the sum of the potential drops across all resistors, (and the sum of the potential differences across other circuit elements such as capacitors) is equal to zero.

$$\mathscr{E}_1 + \mathscr{E}_2 + \cdots + I_1R_1 + I_2R_2 + \cdots$$
$$+ \text{(other potential differences)} = 0$$

Although these rules hold in all circumstances, we will apply them to situations such that the current does not vary with time. We call such currents direct current or dc. We call these two rules Kirchhoff's laws.

Kirchhoff's laws can be used to develop some simple properties concerning the addition of resistors. Figure 2015a shows resistors in series and Fig. 2015b shows resistors in parallel, where series and parallel have the technical meanings illustrated. We are interested in the following problem: What is the effective resistance between a and b? If a and b were connected, in each case, by a single resistance, what value would the resistance have so as to draw the same current as the existing configuration when a voltage $\mathscr{E}$ is applied to their terminals? Using the first of Kirchhoff's laws on the circuit 2013a, we see that the current through the two resistors is the same,

$$I_1 = I_2 = I$$

where I is the current that flows through the whole circuit from a to b. The voltage drop across the resistors is

$$V_1 = IR_1 \quad \text{and} \quad V_2 = IR_2$$

and thus

$$V = V_1 + V_2$$
$$= IR_1 + IR_2$$
$$= IR$$

Therefore

$$R = R_1 + R_2$$

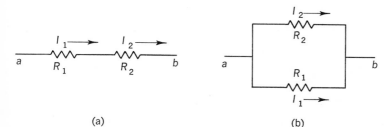

FIG. 2015

Resistances in series (a) and in parallel (b).

where R is the single equivalent resistance. For very many resistors arranged in series,

$$R = R_1 + R_2 + R_3 + \cdots$$

Using the second of Kirchhoff's laws the voltage drop around the loop of Fig. 20|3b must be equal to zero, and

$$I_1 R_1 - I_2 R_2 = 0 \qquad \text{or} \qquad V_1 - V_2 = 0$$

where

$$V_1 = I_1 R_1 \qquad \text{and} \qquad V_2 = I_2 R_2$$

where we choose to take a clockwise path around the loop. Then

$$I_1 R_1 = I_2 R_2 = V_1 = V_2 = V = \mathscr{E} = IR$$

where I is the total current that flows from a to b, and R is the effective resistance. From Kirchhoff's first law,

$$I = I_1 + I_2$$

Therefore,

$$I = \frac{V}{R_1} + \frac{V}{R_2}$$

but $I = V/R$, so

$$\frac{1}{R} = \frac{1}{R_1} + \frac{1}{R_2}$$

which is the rule for the addition of resistances in parallel. For very many resistances in parallel,

$$\frac{1}{R} = \frac{1}{R_1} + \frac{1}{R_2} + \frac{1}{R_3} + \cdots$$

If one notes that $1/R$ is a measure of conducting ability or conductance, the measure of the current conducted through a conductor under a unit potential difference, the addition of inverses is seen to be intuitively plausible.

More complicated problems may be solved using the principles of Kirchhoff's laws. Consider, for example, the circuit of Fig. 20|6. We might ask: What is the current in branch EF and in branch GD? Using the first of Kirchhoff's laws, we see that the current through EF must be equal to the sum of the currents through AE and DE, or 2 A, from E to F. We can now find the current through GD by using the second of Kirchhoff's laws.

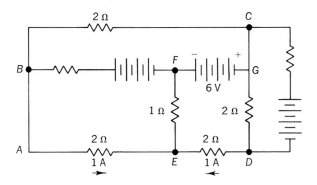

FIG. 20|6

A complex direct-current circuit.

Starting at D and going clockwise around the circuit $DEFG$, we have from D to E, -2 V; from E to F, -2 V; from F to G, $+6$ V. So we must have -2 V from G to D, which would require 1 A from G to D. Using similar arguments one can, step by step, find the current in CB (by finding the voltage around the circuit $AEFGCBA$); finding the current in CD (by using the sum of currents at D); the voltage of the battery in the line CD (by the second law on the loop $DGCD$); the current in CG and FG (by the first law at C and G); the current through FB (the first law at F or B); and the voltage of the battery in FB (using the second law on loops $AEFBA$ or $BFGCB$).

PROBLEMS

Problems 1–5 can be worked by inspection: no scratch paper should be needed. We use the symbol A for ammeter (measuring current) and V for voltmeter (measuring voltage.)

20|1 (*a*) What is the power dissipated in the 3-Ω resistor in the circuit shown?

(*b*) What current does the ammeter read?

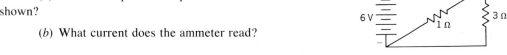

20|2 If the terminals of the 3-V battery in the circuit of problem 20|5 were reversed

(*a*) What would be the reading of V?

(*b*) What would be the reading of V'?

(*c*) What would be the reading of A?

20|3 (*a*) What does the voltmeter read in the circuit shown?

(*b*) What does ammeter *A* read?

(*c*) What does ammeter *A'* read?

(*d*) What is the power supplied by the battery?

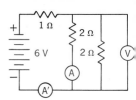

20|4 Calculate all the unknown quantities in the circuit of Fig. 20|6.

20|5 (*a*) What is the reading of *V* in the circuit shown?

(*b*) What is the reading of *V'*?

(*c*) What is the reading of *A*?

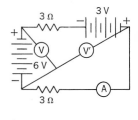

20|6 The cross-sectional area of the left-hand side of the conductor shown is 1.0 cm²; that of the right-hand side is 4.0 cm². Both parts are 1 m long. The whole conductor is made of the same material. When a large current is passed through the conductor, the voltage drop is seen to be 10 V across the whole conductor. What will the voltmeter read?

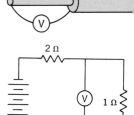

20|7 The voltmeter in the circuit shown reads 10 V.

(*a*) What is the battery voltage?

(*b*) What is the power dissipated in the 2-Ω resistor?

20|8 Each of the 12 wires that make up the cube shown in the diagram has a resistance of 1 Ω. The current that flows from *a* to *b* is 3 A. What is the voltage drop from *a* to *b*? (This can be worked in your head if you use the symmetry of the system. If you don't get the answer in ten minutes, give up. It isn't worth any more effort.)

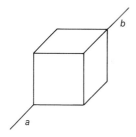

twenty-one

Magnetic fields
and the
electromagnetic field

21 | 1 *The Lorentz transformation of*
the electric field—I

THE FORCE **F** on a *stationary* electric charge q, which results from any assembly of electric charges or currents, is equal to **E**q. This statement is true by definition: it stands as a definition of electric field. If there is no privileged state of motion in the universe, the description of electrical fields in terms of **E** cannot be satisfactory and complete because **E** is defined only with respect to a preferred coordinate system in which the charge is at rest with respect to the observer. A complete description of electrical phenomena must consider the forces on charges that move relative to the observer or, equally, include the measurements made by moving observers. In general, we must construct a description of electrical phenomena that includes the measurements made by different observers in different reference frames, and the description must follow the principle of relativity and not differentiate between inertial reference frames. We must also be able to understand the relations between the electrical measurements made by observers in different frames: we must develop the transformation properties of the electric field with respect to these different inertial reference systems. We must be able to relate the results of the measurements of one man with the measurements of another.

Our definition of the electric field in terms of the force on charges leads to a suggestion of the form of the problem that faces us. Since force has meaning only in its connection with mechanics,

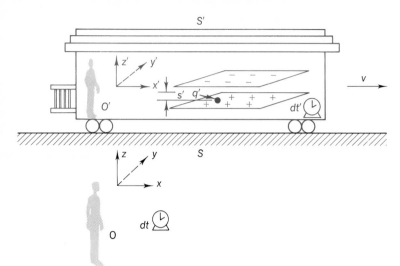

FIG. 21 | 1
Observers in different inertial systems defining the force on a charge.

and since the laws of mechanics can be expressed in covariant forms, forms independent of the state of motion of an observer, only if four-vectors, and their invariants, rather than three-vectors are utilized, we suspect, correctly, that we cannot use the three-vector **E**, alone, to describe forces on moving charges.

The character of the problem we face in constructing a description of electromagnetic phenomena that is valid for all observers in inertial reference frames is illustrated by consideration of the very special set of systems shown in the scene of Fig. 21 | 1. Here an observer, O', on the train, a coordinate system, S', moving with a velocity, v, with respect to an observer, O, on the platform, S, measures the force on a charge, q'. The charge is at rest in the train system, S'. Since all inertial coordinate systems are equivalent according to the principle of relativity, the force, E', on the charge q' measured by O' in the system S' is a measure of the electric field strength on the train at the position of the charge:

$$E' = \frac{F'}{q'}$$

From the view of O, the stationary observer on the platform S, the magnitude of the force on the charge will be different and thus the description of the field must be modified or extended to account for this difference. The electric field, describing the forces between stationary charges, is then a part of the more general *electromagnetic field* which must be defined so as to describe the forces between moving charges as well as stationary charges.

We must then determine the relations that exist between the descriptions of the electromagnetic field in different coordinate systems: we do not understand the electromagnetic field without an understanding of the transformation properties of the field. Since fields are defined operationally in terms of mechanics—the forces on charges—and we understand something of the transformation properties of mechanical quantities, we can derive the transformation relations for fields from a careful analysis of the transformation properties of those mechanical quantities used to describe the fields.

These relations that must exist between the fields in moving and stationary coordinate systems must, then, be determined by considering the results of measurements in those coordinate systems. We proceed by analyzing a particularly simple and well defined situation. The railroad car in Fig. 21|1 carries a large parallel-plate capacitor, which is the origin of an electric field, E'. Observer O' in the train system, S', measures the electric field E' by measuring the force on the charge q'. We may assume that he possesses a clock and a meter stick and that he has made previous measurements and determined the mass of the object holding the charge to be equal to m'. He can then measure the force on the charge by measuring the acceleration of the object caused by the force on the charge. He can determine this acceleration, a', by measuring the distance, s', the charge moves in a short time, t', using his meter stick and clock. Then

$$a' = \frac{2s'}{t'^2}$$

The force on the object must be

$$F' = m'a'$$

and the electric field strength determined by the force on the charge is

$$E' = \frac{F'}{q} = \frac{m'a'}{q}$$

$$= \frac{2m's'}{q't'^2}$$

From our previous results concerning the properties of parallel-plate capacitors we know that the electric field between the plates of the capacitor is equal to

$$E' = 4\pi \frac{kQ'}{A'}$$

where Q' is the charge on the capacitor plates and A' is the area of the plates.

Now we can consider the force on the test charge from the view of the observations of O in the stationary system, S. Some of the quantities measured by O' in the train system, S', will have different values when measured by observer O on the platform. As a result of the relativistic time dilation, the time interval during which the object moves will be measured to be larger by O than by O'; more seconds will elapse according to an observer on the platform than are counted by an observer on the train:

$$t = \frac{t'}{\sqrt{1 - \beta^2}}$$

where

$$\beta = \frac{v}{c}$$

Further, though observer O has measured the mass to be equal to m' kilograms previously when the train was stationary at the platform, he knows that the mass will be measured to be greater by a stationary observer if the mass is in motion and

$$m = \frac{m'}{\sqrt{1 - \beta^2}}$$

The transverse distance the object moves during the acceleration would be measured to be the same by the two observers:

$$s = s'$$

The charges are the same in the two systems:

$$q = q' \quad \text{and} \quad Q = Q'$$

That is to say that we can construct a consistent picture of the interactions of charges by defining charge as a Lorentz invariant.

From the view of O, length in the direction of motion of any object in S' will be contracted, so the length of the capacitor plates will appear to be smaller. The width of the plates or, more precisely, the dimension of the plates transverse to the direction of motion, will be unchanged, so the area of the plates will be reduced in the same proportion as their length.

$$A = A' \sqrt{1 - \beta^2}$$

Correspondingly, the charge density Q/A observed by O on the platform will be larger than the charge density Q'/A' determined by O' on the train, and the electric field measured on the platform, S, by O (perhaps with a test charge) will be greater than the field measured on the train system, S':

$$E = \frac{E'}{\sqrt{1 - \beta^2}} \qquad\qquad (21|1)$$

This relation between the electric fields in the two frames can be verified experimentally by the observers using test charges that are at rest in their reference frames. Their results, which will be in accord with the relation, therefore establish the validity of regarding charge as a Lorentz invariant.

Using the set of relations between the values of the quantities as they are determined in the two reference frames, we can establish relations between the force on the charge as it is deduced from the measurements by the two observers. Noting that $s = s'$,

$$s = \tfrac{1}{2} a t^2 = s' = \tfrac{1}{2} a' t'^2$$

Substituting

$$a = \frac{F}{m} \qquad \text{and} \qquad F' = \frac{F'}{m'} = \frac{E'q}{m'}$$

we have

$$\frac{1}{2} \frac{F}{m} t^2 = \frac{1}{2} \frac{E'q}{m'} t'^2$$

Expressing the primed quantities in terms of the unprimed quantities,

$$\frac{1}{2} \frac{F}{m} t^2 = \frac{1}{2} \frac{qE\sqrt{1-\beta^2}}{m\sqrt{1-\beta^2}} t^2 (1 - \beta^2)$$

If we divide both sides of this relation by $\frac{1}{2}t^2/m$, we have

$$F = Eq(1 - \beta^2)$$

which we can write as

$$F = Eq - \frac{E}{c^2} vqv$$

or   (21|2)

$$F = Eq - Bqv$$

where

$$B = \left(\frac{1}{c^2}\right) Ev$$ (21|3)

and we call B the *magnetic* field. The unit of magnetic field in the mks system of units is the *weber* (Wb) *per square meter* (a bit untidy?): 1 Wb/m^2 is equal to 10,000 gauss (G), where the gauss is the cgs unit of magnetic field.

The situation that was analyzed was chosen for its simplicity and is quite special inasmuch as the field and charge were moving in the same direction with the same velocity. Nevertheless, the results demand an addition to the description we have developed that is valid for stationary charges. In this case we see that if an electric field E' is observed in a system S' moving with respect to a system S with a velocity, v, an electric field E (defined as the force on a stationary unit charge) will be measured in the system S, but the total force on a moving charge will be different from the force on a stationary charge. We describe this difference by defining a new field, the magnetic field B, which induces a force on the charge proportional to the velocity of the charge. The force on the charge will then be

$$F = Eq - Bqv$$

According to this description of the force on electric charges, the force on a charge can be sensibly divided into two parts, one part independent of the velocity of the charge, and one part proportional to the velocity of the charge. *The part that is independent of the velocity defines the electric field at the position of the charge, the part proportional to velocity of the particle defines the magnetic field at the position of the charge.*

In our analysis of the particular system of Fig. 21|1 we found that the measured values of the magnetic field and the electric field in the stationary system, S, were related in a definite way to the measured values of the electric field in the moving system, S'. The magnetic field in that moving system was zero. Since velocity has only a relative meaning, and the two systems are thus essentially symmetric, the form of the relations between the results of the measurements in the two systems must be symmetric. We have deduced that

$$E = \frac{E}{\sqrt{1 - \beta^2}} + a \cdot cB'$$

and

$$cB = \frac{\beta E'}{\sqrt{1 - \beta^2}} + b \cdot cB'$$

where a and b are unknown, since there was no magnetic field, B', on the train system, S'. However, by the symmetry between the two systems we know we can write

$$E' = \frac{E}{\sqrt{1 - \beta^2}} + a' \cdot cB$$

$$cB' = \frac{-\beta E}{\sqrt{1 - \beta^2}} + b' \cdot cB'$$

where a' and a and b' and b differ only in the sign of the relative velocities of the train and platform systems. Even as the train is traveling with a positive velocity with respect to the platform, the platform is traveling with a negative velocity with respect to the train. These four equations are easily solved for the values of a, a', b, and b', and we have

$$E = \frac{E'}{\sqrt{1 - \beta^2}} + \frac{\beta cB'}{\sqrt{1 - \beta^2}}$$

$$cB = \frac{cB'}{\sqrt{1 - \beta^2}} + \frac{\beta E'}{\sqrt{1 - \beta^2}}$$

and (21|4)

$$E' = \frac{E}{\sqrt{1 - \beta^2}} - \frac{\beta cB}{\sqrt{1 - \beta^2}}$$

$$cB' = \frac{cB}{\sqrt{1 - \beta^2}} - \frac{\beta E}{\sqrt{1 - \beta^2}}$$

We used the product cB instead of B to emphasize the relation between these transformation equations and the equations of the Lorentz transformation.

We see now that the electric field, defined in terms of the force on a stationary charge, and the magnetic field, defined in terms of the force on a moving charge, are the two parts of the electromagnetic field. Observers moving with different velocities through the same electromagnetic field will measure different electric fields and different magnetic fields even as they measure different space and time intervals between two events. Their measurements will be related in a definite and well-defined way through transformation relations that are very similar to the relations of the Lorentz transformation.

21|2   *The Lorentz transformation of the electric field—II*

For the examples treated in the last section the velocity of the test charge and the velocity of the electric field were the same. The separation of the term $(v/c)^2$ into two parts, so the magnetic field is proportional to the velocity of the electric field and the force on the charge resulting from the magnetic field is proportional to the velocity of the charge, is artificial inasmuch as we do not know whether this description is valid when the two velocities are different. It is a little more difficult to consider the problem more generally by having the field and the charge moving with different velocities with respect to the stationary observer, O. We outline the procedure and suggest that the reader complete the proof.

In Figure 21|2 we have a capacitor and test charge as in Fig. 21|1, except in this case the capacitor and the accompanying electric field are moving *with respect to the system S'* with a velocity of u. If the field in the system of the moving capacitor is E'', the electric field in the S' system will be equal to

$$E' = \frac{E''}{\sqrt{1 - \beta^2}}$$

where

$$\beta' = \frac{u}{c}$$

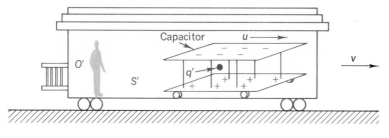

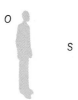

FIG. 21|2
*Observers in different
inertial systems defining
the force on a charge
that results from the
field of a capacitor that
is at rest in a third
inertial system. The
capacitor is moving
with velocity u as
measured by observer
O' on S'.*

The charge q', which is stationary in the system S', will be accelerated in the S' system by the effect of the electric field E'. In a time dt' it will move a distance s' such that

$$s = \frac{1}{2}\frac{E'q}{m'}t'^2$$

Since

$$t = \frac{t'}{\sqrt{1-\beta^2}} \qquad m = \frac{m'}{\sqrt{1-\beta^2}} \qquad \text{and} \qquad s = s'$$

we can write

$$s = s' = \frac{1}{2}\frac{E'q}{m}t^2\sqrt{1-\beta^2}$$

Replacing E' by $E''/\sqrt{1-\beta^2}$,

$$s = \frac{1}{2}\frac{E''q}{m\sqrt{1-\beta^2}}t^2\sqrt{1-\beta^2}$$

But E the electric field measured on the platform, S, will be related to E'', the electric field measured in the system where the capacitor is at rest, according to the relation

$$E = \frac{E''}{\sqrt{1-\beta''^2}}$$

where

$$\beta'' = \frac{w}{c}$$

and w is the velocity of the capacitor with respect to the platform, S. From the relation concerning the addition of velocities,

$$w = \frac{u + v}{1 + (uv/c^2)}$$

It then follows that

$$s = \frac{1}{2} \frac{Eq}{m} t^2 \frac{\sqrt{1 - \beta''^2} \sqrt{1 - \beta^2}}{\sqrt{1 - \beta'^2}}$$

Using the relations

$$s = \frac{1}{2} at^2 \qquad \text{and} \qquad a = \frac{F}{m}$$

together with the addition-of-velocities formula, with a little
elementary but intricate algebra, we have

$$F = Eq(1 - \beta\beta'')$$

$$= Eq - Bqw$$

where

$$B = \left(\frac{1}{c^2}\right) Ev$$

and we have shown that the relations suggest by the results of
the last section are valid, as we surmised, if the velocities of
the field and charge are different.

21|3 *Magnetic fields and electric currents*

From the view of observer O on the platform, S, in Fig. 21|1,
the moving charge held on the capacitor plates represent an
electric current, and therefore the magnetic field he measures
in his frame of reference can be considered to originate from
the current. The relation between magnetic field and current
can be deduced in detail by analyzing the measurements that
might be made in the situation suggested by the sketch of Fig.
21|3. This is similar to the scene shown in Fig. 21|1, except

that the electrical field that acts on the charge q in the train system S' originates from the presence of a long cylinder that carries a charge density of σ' coulombs/meter, as measured by observer O' on the train, instead of the capacitor plates.

On the train system, where both the long charged cylinder and the test charge q are stationary, the electric field at the position of the test charge will be measured to be

$$E' = \frac{2k\sigma'}{r'}$$

where r' is the distance from the charge q' to the axis of the cylinder. This result was obtained in Chapter 19. The electric-field strength at the same point measured by O, the observer on the platform, will be greater:

$$E = \frac{E'}{\sqrt{1 - \beta^2}} = \frac{2k\sigma'}{r' \sqrt{1 - \beta^2}}$$

which follows from the results of Section 21|1 as expressed by the transformation equations (21|4).

We can also understand this increase in the electric field more directly by noting that observer O on the platform will measure the length of any specific segment of the cylinder to be shorter than the measurements of O'. This is the usual Lorentz contraction. A length of the cylinder that is measured to be 1 m

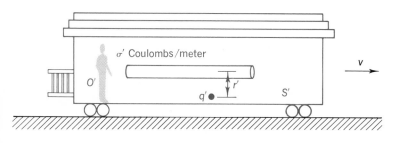

FIG. 21|3

Observers in different inertial systems observing the force on a test charge resulting from a long charged cylinder. The charge density on the rod is σ' coulombs/meter.

long by O' and that holds σ' coulombs of electric charge, will be measured to be only $\sqrt{1 - \beta^2}$ meters long by O on the platform. But O will also measure the charge held by that segment as σ' coulombs. Of course, then, O on the platform will observe a greater charge density than O' on the moving train, and the electric-field strength observed by O will be greater than the field observed by O' by a factor of $1/\sqrt{1 - \beta^2}$. We might consider that the lines of electric field are denser as seen from the platform because of the Lorentz contraction: this is suggested in the drawing of Fig. 21|4.

The analysis now follows that of Section 21|1 and we need not follow it in detail. The force on the charge q will be equal to

$$F = Eq(1 - \beta^2)$$

or

$$F = Eq - Bqv$$

where

$$B = \left(\frac{1}{c^2}\right) Ev$$

We have shown that

$$E = \frac{E'}{\sqrt{1 - \beta^2}}$$

$$= \frac{2k\sigma'}{r'\sqrt{1 - \beta^2}}$$

$$= \frac{2k\sigma}{r}$$

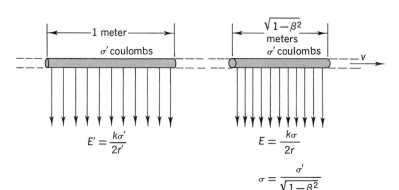

$E' = \frac{k\sigma'}{2r'}$

$E = \frac{k\sigma}{2r}$

$\sigma = \frac{\sigma'}{\sqrt{1-\beta^2}}$

FIG. 21|4
A charged cylinder as observed in two different inertial systems.

where $r = r'$ and $\sigma = \sigma'/\sqrt{1 - \beta^2}$ is the charge density in the platform system, S. Then

$$B = \left(\frac{k}{c^2}\right)\frac{2\sigma v}{r}$$

But σv (coulombs per meter times meters per second) is just the number of coulombs per second that will pass a point on the platform system S and is therefore equal to the electric current as measured in S. Then

$$B = \left(\frac{k}{c^2}\right)\frac{2I}{r} \tag{21|5}$$

where I is the current, is the expression for the magnetic field at a distance r from an electric current of I amperes moving along a long line.

We are also interested in the force exerted on a current in a magnetic field where the direction of the current is the same as the direction of motion of the charge in Fig. 21|1 or 21|3. Since the force on each portion of charge that makes up the current is

$$F = Bqv$$

the force on a length of 1 m of a cylinder carrying a charge density σ, as measured in the platform system, S, will be

$$F = B\sigma v$$

but again $\sigma v = I$ and the force on 1 m will be

$$F = BI$$

and

$$F = BIL$$

on a current I traveling a length of L meters such as a current-carrying wire L meters long.

21|4   *Conventions concerning the direction of the magnetic field*

For the situation pictured in Fig. 21|1 the electric field is directed upward in the z-direction and the velocity is in the x-direction. In order to describe the phenomena we observe, we have invented, or *defined*, a quantity we call a magnetic field, and the effect of this magnetic field on the moving charge is such as to exert a force downward, in the −z-direction. The force on the charge is a vector; the velocity is a vector; in order to construct a complete description of all phenomena concerning moving charges, we find it convenient to further define the magnetic field as a vector field: **B** will be a vector. We *choose* to adopt a description of the electromagnetic field such that the moving electric field induces a magnetic field that is at right angles both to the direction of motion of the field and to the direction of the moving field itself. We choose a sign convention such that the field is in the −y-direction, or out of the paper, in Fig. 21|1. The force on the test charge is then perpendicular both to the magnetic field and to the direction of motion of the test charge.

We are now prepared to analyze a situation such that the direction of the electric field in a moving frame of reference, *S'*, the direction of motion of the moving system (the train system), and the direction of motion of the test charge are all different. We could do this using the same kind of procedures as we used in the analyses of Sections 21|1 and 21|2. Such calculations would be tedious, though simple enough in principle, and we will just write down the results. We would find that we can obtain a complete description of the general results if we consider that the magnetic field, **B**, at a particular point in space is given by

$$\mathbf{B} = \left(\frac{1}{c^2}\right)(\mathbf{v} \times \mathbf{E}) \qquad \text{or} \qquad B = \left(\frac{1}{c^2}\right) vE \sin \theta \qquad (21|6)$$

Where θ is the angle between **v**, the velocity of the charges that are the source of the electric field, **E**, at that point, and the direction of **E**, the field produced by those charges. The direction of the vector field **B** is perpendicular to the directions of **v** and **E** according to the convention shown in Fig. 21|5a.

Then the relation between the direction of the magnetic field, **B**, the direction of motion of the charge, **v**, and the force on this charge is

$$\mathbf{F} = (\mathbf{v} \times \mathbf{B})q \qquad \text{or} \qquad F = vBq \sin \theta' \qquad (21|7)$$

where θ' is the angle between **v** and **B**, and the direction of **F** is

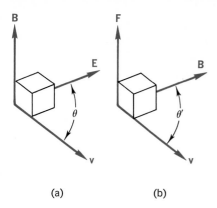

FIG. 21|5
*The vector relations
between* **B, E, v,** *and* **F.**

(a)   (b)

perpendicular to the plane defined by the directions of **v** and **B** according to the convention shown in Fig. 21|5b.

It is useful to consider magnetic-field lines in much the same manner, and for much the same reasons, as we consider electric lines of force. Then a magnetic field of 1 unit—1 Wb/m²—is represented by a density of lines of magnetic flux of 1 line/m² and the direction of the line is in the direction of the field. One line corresponds to 1 Wb of flux.

Since the direction of a line of magnetic flux at a point is always perpendicular to the line from the current to that point, the lines do not diverge from, or connect with, the current. Though the current is the physical source of the magnetic field and thus the physical source of the magnetic lines of flux, the current is not the geometric source in the same sense as a charge is the geometric source of electric lines of force. The diagram of Fig. 21|6 shows the pattern of lines of force about a current that is directed out of the paper. One sees that the lines of force form continuous circles: there is no geometric source or geometric sink; the lines are continuous loops. For more complex patterns of currents the configurations of the lines of force are more complicated, but the lines always form closed paths. Therefore, since there is no geometric source of lines, it is clear that the number of lines that enter any volume is equal to the number that leave the volume. Gauss' law applied to magnetic fields tells us that the total number of lines that leave any volume in space is zero.

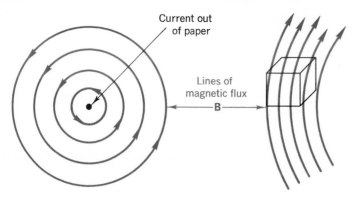

FIG. 21|6
Lines of magnetic flux.

Since the magnetic field was introduced to express or describe the effects of moving charges, and moving charges constitute currents, it is attractive to relate the magnetic field at a point to the position and direction of those currents. It is most convenient to consider the artificial question of the magnetic field from a very short current element; the problem is artificial, since in any real apparatus the current must reach the element through leads connected to the element and leave the element through other leads, and the magnetic fields induced by the currents passing through those leads will be dominant. Nevertheless, such a formulation is very useful because the magnetic field at any arbitrary point produced by an arbitrary configuration of currents can then be deduced by dividing the current configuration into very many short segments, calculating the magnetic field from each segment, and then adding all the field elements vectorially to find the resultant field from the whole configuration.

The expression for the increment of magnetic field $d\mathbf{B}$ produced by a current I passing through a short distance $d\mathbf{L}$ is then

$$d\mathbf{B} = \left(\frac{k}{c^2}\right)\left(\frac{I}{r^3}\right)(d\mathbf{L}\times\mathbf{r}) \qquad (21|8)$$

or

$$dB = \left(\frac{k}{c^2}\right)\left(\frac{I\,dL}{r^2}\right)\sin\theta$$

the Biot-Savart law, where $\mathbf{r}$ is the vector distance from the current element to the point where the field is to be determined and θ is the angle between $d\mathbf{L}$ and $\mathbf{r}$. The direction of the field $d\mathbf{B}$ is perpendicular to both $d\mathbf{L}$ and $\mathbf{r}$ according to the convention shown in Fig. 21|7.

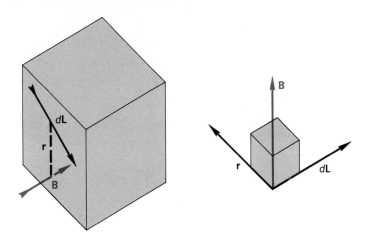

FIG. 21|7
Diagrams showing the vector relations between **r**, *d***L**, *and* **B**.

Similarly, it is necessary to obtain an expression for the force on an element of current in a magnetic field. A current of *I* amperes (coulombs/second) passing through a conductor *dL* meters long is equivalent to the passage of a charge *q*, equal to *I* coulombs, passing through the conductor in 1 sec; that is, at a velocity *v* equal to *dL* meters/second. We can rewrite expression (21|8) to express the force on a current element by replacing *qv* by *I dL*:

$$d\mathbf{F} = I(d\mathbf{L} \times \mathbf{B}) \qquad \text{or} \qquad dF = BI\,dL\,\sin\theta$$

where θ is the angle between *d***L** and **B**. The convention concerning the direction of the field with respect to the direction of the current is the same as for Eq. (21|7), of course, however the relations can be shown usefully in a somewhat different manner as in the diagrams of Fig. 21|8.

As a mnemonic device it is useful to use a "right-hand rule." If the thumb of the right hand is directed in the line of the current,

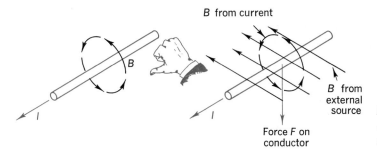

B from current

B from external source

Force *F* on conductor

FIG. 21|8
Magnetic-flux lines near a conductor in a magnetic field.

the fingers will curl in the direction of the magnetic field produced by the current. Again as a mnemonic device, it is useful to consider that lines of magnetic field that travel in the same direction tend to repel each other, while lines of field that are oppositely directed tend to attract each other. If one considers the lines connected mechanically to the source, the direction of the resultant forces between currents and fields—and currents and currents—is easily deduced.

There are a host of such mnemonic devices, and their use is a matter of personal preference.

Using these conventions concerning the directions of the magnetic field and the complete calculations concerning the relations between the values of the quantities measured in the system S', moving with a velocity v in the x-direction with respect to the stationary system S, which we have mentioned (but not completed ourselves), we can write the relations between the electric-field components measured in the moving frame and the electric and magnetic fields in the rest frame as

$$E_x = E'_x \qquad\qquad cB_x = cB'_x$$

$$E_y = \frac{E'_y - \beta c B'_z}{\sqrt{1 - \beta^2}} \qquad cB_y = \frac{cB'_y + \beta E'_z}{\sqrt{1 - \beta^2}} \qquad\qquad (21\,|\,9)$$

$$E_z = \frac{E'_z + \beta c B'_y}{\sqrt{1 - \beta^2}} \qquad cB_z = \frac{cB'_z - \beta E'_y}{\sqrt{1 - \beta^2}}$$

The equations that express directly the values of the quantities measured in the moving system, B' and E', with the values of E and B, the quantities measure in the stationary system, are the same except that the sign of v (and hence β) is reversed: that is, the platform, S, is moving in the $-x$-direction according to observer O' in the train system, S'. Notice the similarity of these equations to the equations of the Lorentz transformation applicable to relativistic four-vectors.

We must keep in mind that this whole apparatus, consisting of two three-dimensional vectors **B** and **E** together with the relations between them, was constructed in order to *describe* the forces between charges. Inasmuch as the description is complete, not redundant, and correct, no other description can be fundamentally different, but descriptions that have quite different forms are certainly possible. The value of this particular description lies in the close relation between the base quantities, the components of **E** and **B**, and the measurable forces on charges in a coordinate system where the measuring apparatus is at rest.

As a pedagogic point: it is important to understand the character and the origin of the relations developed in this section; it is not important to memorize relations such as Eqs. (21|9).

21|5   *Ampere's law*

If a line *a-b* is constructed in the *y*-direction in the diagram of Fig. 21|1 or Fig. 21|9 and the line is at rest in the platform system, lines of electric field will cross the line *a-b* as the capacitor moves by. If the length of the line in the field is L and the velocity of the capacitor is v, all the electric field lines in an area equal to Lv, as measured in the platform system, will be cut by the line in the *y*-direction in 1 sec. If the field strength is E, as measured in the rest system, the density of electric field lines will be equal to E lines/m², and the number of lines crossing the constructed line *a-b* in 1 sec will be equal to EvL. We recall that the magnetic field strength in the *y*-direction was equal to $(1/c^2)Ev$. Therefore, in this particular case,

FIG. 21|9
An observer and a moving electric field.

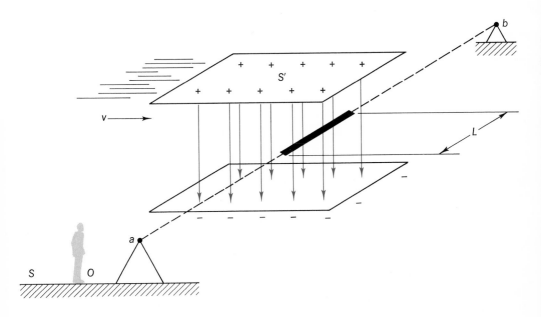

$$(\mathbf{B} \cdot \mathbf{L}) = \left(\frac{1}{c^2}\right) \text{ (number of electric-field lines}$$

$$\text{cut by } L \text{ in 1 sec)} \qquad (21\,|\,10)$$

where, as usual, $(\mathbf{B} \cdot \mathbf{L}) = BL \cos \theta$ is the product of the component of magnetic field in the direction of L times the length L. This relation is not restricted to the particular case we examined but is completely general and thus equivalent to the expressions of $(21\,|\,9)$.

This expression of the relation between the magnetic field and a moving electric field can be used to calculate the magnetic field near a long current-carrying wire. If the magnitude of the current carried by the conductor of Fig. $21\,|\,10$ is I, the magnitude of the charge carried past point a is I coulombs per second. From each charge of magnitude I there issues $4\pi kI$ lines of force. All of these lines of force eventually cut the dashed circle, which is drawn in a plane normal to the conductor with its center at a and radius r. For the case of a steady current, $4\pi kI$ lines of force must cut the circle every second. Using Eq. $(21\,|\,10)$, we then have

$$BL = B2\pi r$$

$$= \left(\frac{1}{c^2}\right) 4\pi kI$$

where the length of the wire cutting the electric lines of force is $2\pi r$. Then our result is the same as derived previously from fundamental considerations in Section $21\,|\,3$,

$$B = \left(\frac{k}{c^2}\right) \frac{2I}{r} \qquad (21\,|\,11)$$

for the magnetic field near a long current carrying wire.

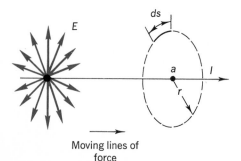

Moving lines of force

FIG. 21 |10
Electric-field lines moving past a closed path.

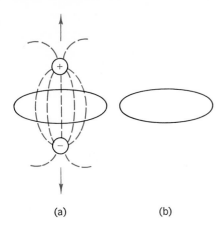

(a) (b)

FIG. 21|11
*Electric charges near a
closed path.*

The electric lines of force that cut a path need not emanate from a current passing through the closed path. Figure 21|11 illustrates a situation where the motion of charges that do not pass through a loop results in lines of electric field cutting the loop and therefore, by our rules, generating a magnetic field. Positive and negative charges near the loop are moved very far away in the direction shown by the arrows. The electric field lines that pass through the loop in Fig. 21|11a leave by passing through the loop as the two charges draw farther apart. Since the field component B along the direction of a segment of the loop, ds, at the position of ds, is equal to $(1/c^2)$ times the number of lines that cut ds per second, the sum of the components B along all the elements ds that make up the whole loop will be equal to $(1/c^2)$ times the number of lines that cut the whole loop per second. Of course this is just the number of lines that leave the loop in a second. We summarize this in the relation

$$\oint (\mathbf{B} \cdot d\mathbf{s}) = \left(\frac{1}{c^2}\right) \text{(number of lines of } E \text{ that leave the region}$$

enclosed by the loop per second)

Here the symbol $\oint$ is borrowed from the notation of the calculus and means the sum or integral of all the contributions around a path.

If a current passes through the loop, there will also be a contribution to the magnetic field at the position of the loop from the moving electric fields carried by the moving charges that make up the current. If we should travel in a circle about a current-carrying wire and measure the components of magnetic field along the circle, we would find that the sum of all the products $(\mathbf{B} \cdot d\mathbf{r})$ that we would measure as we traveled around the whole circle would be equal to $2\pi r B$. At each interval of circumference, dr, the magnetic field along the direction of the circumference would be equal to $(k/c^2)\, 2I/r$ [from Eq. (21 | 11)]. Since the distance around is equal to $2\pi r$, the product will be

$$\oint (\mathbf{B} \cdot d\mathbf{r}) = \left(\frac{k}{c^2}\right) \frac{2I}{r}\, 2\pi r$$

$$= \left(\frac{k}{c^2}\right) 4\pi I \qquad\qquad (21 | 12)$$

The result (21 | 12), calculated for a circular path of radius r is obviously independent of the value of r and thus holds for any circle centered at the wire. It is not difficult to demonstrate the the result holds for any path about the current, since any path can be approximated closely be segments that follow the circumferences of circles and segments that follow the radii of circles. Since the magnetic-field direction is always perpendicular to a radius vector, only the circular parts contribute to the total field along the path. The path shown in Fig. 21 | 12c is presented as an example of an irregular path that can be closely approximated by a path made up of radial and azimuthal segments. The total contribution from the radial segments to the sum of magnetic field components along the path is zero, while the contribution of the circular parts, and thus the whole contribution, is expressed by the relation of (21 | 12).

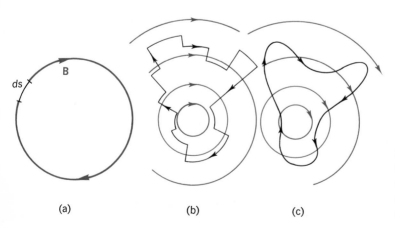

(a)   (b)   (c)

FIG. 21 | 12
Closed paths in the magnetic field about a wire carrying a current.

The most general expression for the summation (or integral) of the components of magnetic field times path distance around a closed loop must thus include the contributions from currents that pass through the loop as well as any change in the number of lines of electric flux that link the loop. This can be expressed

$$\oint (\mathbf{B} \cdot d\mathbf{s}) = \oint B \, ds \cos \theta$$

$$= \left(\frac{k}{c^2}\right) 4\pi I + \left(\frac{1}{c^2}\right) \text{(rate of change in the number of}$$

$$\text{lines of electric flux through the loop)} \qquad \textbf{(21|13)}$$

Here $\cos \theta$ is the angle between the direction of the path and the direction of the field $\mathbf{B}$, and I is the sum of the currents that flow through the loop defined by the path. This relation between magnetic fields and changing electric fields is *Ampere's law*.

It is important to recognize that, in general, magnetic fields will be found anywhere in space near a current or moving charge, and Ampere's law can be considered as an expression that allows the calculation of the field anywhere. The paths of summation or integration need not be, and generally are not, marked by anything physical. The results hold for all paths and thus for all space.

21 | 6   *Faraday's law*

By definition the part of the force on a moving charge that is proportional to the velocity of the charge is induced by a magnetic field. The magnitude and direction of the field are defined in such a way that the force on the charge, q, is expressed as $\mathbf{F} = q(\mathbf{v} \times \mathbf{B})$. From the view of an observer, O', who moves along with the charge in a "train" system, S', in which the charge is stationary, the force on the charge, $\mathbf{F}' = \mathbf{E}'q$, is a measure of the electric field, $\mathbf{E}'$, at the position of the charge. The magnetic field moving past O' on the train is equivalent to, or produces, an electric field in the S' system.

A particular example that serves to illustrate these relations is shown in Fig. 21 | 13. A train traveling in the negative x-direction with velocity v carries an electric charge, q, that is stationary in the train system, S'. The train and charge pass through the jaws of a large electromagnet mounted on the platform. From the

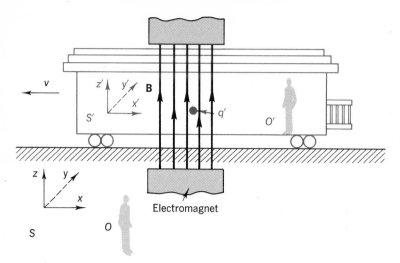

FIG. 21|13

*An observer in a moving system considering the force on a charge that results from a stationary magnetic field. A large electromagnet attached to the platform produces a magnetic field **B**. The charge q' is stationary in the train system.*

view (or according to the measurements) of observer O on the platform, there is a force on the charge directed in the y-direction (into the paper) that is equal to

$$F = qBv$$

where F is the value of the force and B the value of the magnetic field strength determined by O. The observer on the train also observes a force on the positive test charge, which is directed in the $-y$-direction and indicates to him the presence of an electric field such that

$$F' = qE'$$

If he carries on further measurements, he will also determine the existence of a magnetic field, B'.

It would not be difficult to conduct an analysis of the relations between such measurements in the two systems in the same spirit, and using the same techniques, as in Sections 21|1 and 21|2. If we should do this, we would find that

$$E' = B'v \qquad\qquad (21|14)$$

Indeed, our results of Section 21|1, as expressed in the Eqs. (21|4), give us just the relation (21|14) with a little algebraic manipulation.

It is interesting to express the particular relation between the electric field observed in a system and the value of the magnetic field moving through the system in a manner that allows further generalization of the kind expressed by Ampere's law. Now we consider ourselves on the train system, S', and examine the magnetic field that appears to be moving by us with velocity v, as suggested by the diagram of Fig. 21 | 13.

If a line a-b is constructed in the y-direction in the diagram of Fig. 21 | 14 and the line is at rest in our train system, S', lines of magnetic flux will cross the line a-b as the magnet sitting on the platform moves by us with velocity v. If the length of the line in the field is L and the velocity of the magnet is v, all the lines of magnetic flux in an area equal to Lv, as measured in our train system, will be cut by the segment L in 1 sec. If the field strength is B', as measured in the train system, the density of magnetic flux lines will be equal to B' lines per square meter and the number of lines crossing the constructed line a-b in 1 sec will be equal to $B'vL$. Since the electric field strength in the y-direction was $E' = B'v$, therefore in this particular case

$$(\mathbf{E'} \cdot \mathbf{L}) = (\text{number of magnetic field lines cut by } L \text{ in 1 sec})$$

where $(\mathbf{E'} \cdot \mathbf{L}) = E'L \cos \theta$ is the product of the component of magnetic field in the direction of L times the length L. The change in flux through a closed loop, s, can be related to the components of field along the increments of path ds as

FIG. 21 | 14
An observer in a stationary system considering the effects of a moving magnetic field.

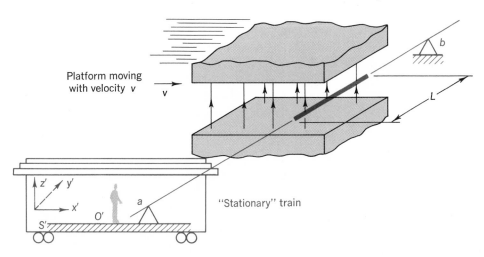

Platform moving
with velocity v

v

L

z' y'

x'

O'

a

"Stationary" train

S'

b

$$\oint (\mathbf{E} \cdot \mathbf{ds}) = \oint E \, ds \cos \theta$$

$$= \text{(rate of change in the number of}$$
$$\text{magnetic field lines through } s) \qquad (21\,|\,15)$$

This relation is called Faraday's law, and like Ampere's law, which it resembles closely, is completely general.

Therefore, even as changing electric fields are equivalent to, or generate, magnetic fields, changing magnetic fields generate electric fields.

The electric fields set up by changing magnetic fields can induce currents in conductors. Consider a straight segment of a conductor length L meters that is stationary in some reference frame. If this conductor is cut by ϕ lines of magnetic flux per second, an electric field is induced along the conductor such that $EL = \phi$, and there will be a force, F, on any free charge, q, in the conductor such that $F = Eq$, where the direction of the force is along the conductor. The potential difference between the two ends of the conductor is then equal to $V = EL$ volts. If the conductor is part of a circuit, the free charge in the conductor will be forced into motion by the field, E, and a current will flow. The potential difference across the segment of conductor will constitute an emf equal in magnitude to ϕ, the number of lines of flux that cut the conductor per second.

If the magnetic field is stationary and the conductor is moving, there will be a force on any charge held in the conductor even as that charge is moving in a magnetic field. For simplicity we

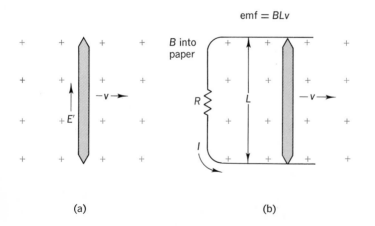

(a)

(b)

FIG. 21|15
Forces and current induced by a conductor moving in a magnetic field. In (a) the conductor moves through the field, incuding an emf per meter of E'. In (b) the ends of the moving conductor contact an external circuit so that a current I flows through the circuit.

examine the specific case where the direction of the magnetic field, **B**, is perpendicular to the direction of motion of the rod, **v**, and the length of the rod, L, is perpendicular to both **v** and **B**, as suggested by the drawing of Fig. 21|15. The force on each free charge, q, in the rod will then be equal to

$$F = Bvq$$

Since B is the number of lines of flux per square meter and the moving conductor will sweep out vL square meters per second, ϕ, the number of lines of flux cut per second by the conductor, will be $\phi = BLv$. The force on the charge in the conductor will then be such that $F = (\phi/L)q$, which is just the same force as if the magnetic field had been replaced by an electric field, E', where $E' = \phi/L$. The emf developed along the length of the conductor will be just the same as if an electric field, E' were induced by the change in flux, or emf $= E'L = (\phi/L)L = \phi$.

Although the result was developed for this special case for simplicity, the conclusions are quite general; the emf developed across a length of conductor is equal to the number of lines of flux the conductor cuts per second, whether the conductor moves or the field moves.

21|7   *Maxwell's equations and the symmetry between E and B*

The essential results of the study of the electromagnetic field can now be summarized.

1. *Gauss' law applied to the electric field:*

(net number of electric lines of force leaving a volume) $= 4\pi kQ$

(21|16)

where Q is the total charge within the volume.

2. *Gauss' law applied to the magnetic field:*

(net number of magnetic lines of force leaving a volume) $= 0$

3. *Ampere's law:*

$$\oint (\mathbf{B} \cdot d\mathbf{s}) = \left(\frac{k}{c^2}\right) 4\pi kI + \left(\frac{1}{c^2}\right) \text{(rate of change in the number of}$$

electric lines of force that link the loop)

4. *Faraday's law:*

$$\oint (\mathbf{E} \cdot d\mathbf{s}) = \text{(rate of change in the number of magnetic lines of force that link the loop)}$$

The four laws are called, collectively, *Maxwell's equations.* Usually they are written in the more elegant and abstract (and precise) notation of the vector calculus. Together with the pondermotive equation, which relates the fields to the forces on charges, Maxwell's equations summarize the classical properties of the electromagnetic field. The pondermotive equation is

$$\mathbf{F} = \mathbf{E}q + q(\mathbf{v} \times \mathbf{B}) \tag{21|17}$$

The four Maxwell's equations are valid in any inertial reference system. We did not follow history in our development of these relations through the use of the principles of relativity and equations of the Lorentz transformation. Originally Maxwell's equations were developed as a summary and description of experimental observations on the forces between charges. Then Lorentz used these equations to develop the transformation equations that bear his name. Even as we used the Lorentz transformation equations to develop the whole of Maxwell's equations starting from electrostatics alone, Lorentz used the experimentally based Maxwell's equations to develop the transformation equations. In this way the study of electromagnetism led to the theory of relativity.

In the domain of the very small, such that units of the dimension of energy times times that are of the order that Planck's constant, h, most be considered, there are some modifications to descriptions of phenomena based solely on Maxwell's equations.

The symmetry between $\mathbf{E}$ and $\mathbf{B}$ exhibited in Maxwell's equations, which was also evident in the transformation equations (21|9), is striking. Indeed, if we consider $\mathbf{E}$ and $c\mathbf{B}$ as the fundamental field quantities, the equations are completely symmetric with the exception that electric charges and currents have been observed but not magnetic charges (or poles, as they are usually named) or, of course, magnetic-pole currents.

Magnetic poles would have properties analogous to those of electric charges. Each pole would emit $4\pi kg$ lines of magnetic field, Bc, where g is the strength of the pole measured in coulombs. The force between two poles would be

$$\mathbf{F} = \mathbf{B}cg + g(\mathbf{v} \times \mathbf{E}) \tag{21 | 18}$$

The force on a stationary magnetic pole would be a measure of the magnetic field, $\mathbf{B}$, and the force on a moving pole would be proportional to the velocity of the pole and the magnitude of the electric field, $\mathbf{E}$.

Although electric charges are familiar to us, magnetic poles are not. Not only does electric charge exist, but it appears that charge is quantized. All quantities of electric charge represent integral multiples of a quantity e, equal to 1.6×10^{-19} C. Most elementary particles carry either 0, 1, or -1, units of such charge.

From the general symmetry of the fields we might expect to find magnetic poles as well as charges. Indeed, Dirac has shown that the interaction between particles holding an electric charge and particles holding a magnetic pole is consistent with the de Broglie wave character of particles that has been generally observed only if the value of the magnetic pole, g, is such that $keg/c = \frac{1}{2}n\hbar$, where e is the value of the electric charge, n is some integer, $n = 1, 2, 3, \ldots$, and $\hbar$ is Planck's constant divided by 2π. Of course, if for any possible values of e and g the product is finite, as implied by Dirac's relation, and if a finite least value of g exists, some smallest value of e must exist and all other values of e must be integral multiples of this value. Therefore, if magnetic poles exist we can connect the observed quantization of charge, which otherwise is not understood at all, to the Dirac condition and the existence of magnetic poles. However, though their particular properties suggest that they should be easily detected, we have found no evidence for such magnetic poles. Magnetic poles probably do not exist.

Why, then, do we have electric charges and not magnetic poles? It is interesting to break this question down into two parts. Why is there an asymmetry: we have electric and not magnetic charges? And why do we have only one of the two possibilities?

Our answer to the first part is that as far as we know, there is no asymmetry. If this universe, or some other one, were so constituted that there was no electric charge and that elementary particles held 1 unit, 1.6×10^{-19} C, of magnetic charge, that universe would be indistinguishable from ours. If we could communicate with the inhabitants of that universe, we could not determine whether they lived in an electric or a magnetic universe by any description they could give us of any possible phenomena. Do we, then, live in an electric or magnetic universe? The question is meaningless. We have *named* our charge electric charge.

As to the second part of the question, as of now we have no answer. Indeed, the possibility that poles exist has not been excluded.

21 | 8   *Electromagnetic waves*

Changing charge and current distributions generate changing electromagnetic fields. If the charge on a capacitor is reversed, the electric field near the edge of the capacitor will also change, as suggested by the sketch of Fig. 21 | 16a. If the charge of the capacitor is reversed regularly, many times a second, the field will also change with that frequency. We can also consider the magnetic field generated by a current loop as suggested in Fig. 21 | 16b. If the direction of the current is alternated regularly, the direction of the magnetic field will also change with the frequency of alternation. The electric field from the charged capacitor, as well as the magnetic field from current loop, extends out very far—essentially to infinity. As the direction of the current

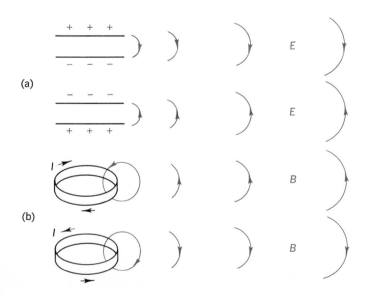

FIG. 21 | 16
The electric field far from a charged capacitor and the magnetic field far from a current loop.

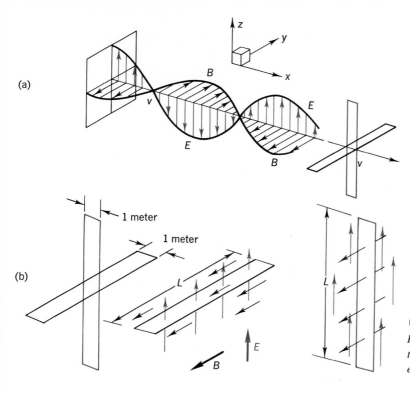

(a)

(b)

FIG. 21|17

Diagrams used to deduce the velocity of electromagnetic waves.

in the current loop changes or as the sign of the charge on the capacitor changes, the direction of the field must change. We might now ask ourselves, "does the change in direction of the field, far from the capacitor or inductor, change instantly as the fields in the capacitor or inductor change sign, or is there a time lag for propagation of the signal?"

To answer this we first ask the question, "How does a wave or other electromagnetic disturbance propagate itself?" We remember that a changing electric field produces a magnetic field according to simple rules; likewise, a changing magnetic field induces an electric field. If we were to be complete, Fig. 21|16 might also have shown magnetic fields and electric fields, respectively, induced by the changing electric and magnetic fields. Thus an oscillating electric field generates an oscillating electric field, and so on, and we have waves. We use these ideas quantitatively to determine the velocity of an electromagnetic wave.

It is convenient to determine the velocity of a particular wave that might lend itself to an especially simple treatment. The diagram of Fig. 21|17a shows schematically the electromagnetic-

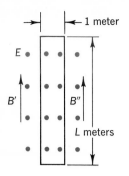

FIG. 21|18
*A diagram showing the
relation between a
changing electric field
and a magnetic field.
From Ampere's law, if
E increases from
E to E + DE in one
second, the flux through
the rectangle increases
by L DE, and B″L −
B″L = (1/c²)L DE.*

field configuration of a wave traveling in the *x*-direction; the wave is polarized so that the electric field vectors lie in the *x*-*z* plane and the magnetic field vectors lie in the *x*-*y* plane. We further assume, for numerical convenience only, that the frequency of the wave is very low; less than a cycle every few seconds.

In the path of the wave we construct two rectangles: one in the *x*-*y* plane normal to the electric field and one in the *x*-*z* plane normal to the magnetic flux. For the sake of definiteness, and to keep our considerations numerical rather than abstract, let us assume that each of these rectangles is 1 m wide and a much larger distance, *L* m, in length. Now we consider the relations between the electric and magnetic fields at some particular time. Of course the fields will vary both in space and in time at this particular space and at this particular time.

The argument may be followed most easily with the aid of the diagrams of Fig. 21|18. The value of the electric field can be taken as *E* and thus there will be *EL* lines of flux through the rectangle. If the field changes by an amount *DE* during 1 sec, the number of lines of flux through the rectangle will change by an amount equal to *L DE*. By the Ampere's law this means that the sum of the quantities *BL* taken around the rectangle must be equal to $(1/c^2)L\ DE$. If *B* did not change with distance over the 1-m distance between the lines marking the rectangle, the sum would be zero. Therefore the value of *B* must vary over that interval such that the change in *B* in 1 m, *dB*, is

$$dB\ L = \left(\frac{1}{c^2}\right) L\ DE$$

or

$$dB = \left(\frac{1}{c^2}\right) DE \qquad\qquad (21|19)$$

Using the same kind of argument and Faraday's law, we can relate the change in the magnetic field in 1 sec, DB, with the difference in the electric field over 1 m, dE:

$$L\ dE = L\ DB$$

or

$$dE = DB \qquad\qquad (21|20)$$

Now we must relate DB to dB and DE to dE. During 1 sec, the position of the wave moves a distance equal to v m where the velocity of the wave is v m/sec. If the amplitude of the wave varies by an amount dE in 1 m, the amplitude will vary by an amount equal to $v\ dE$ over a distance of v m. Since the change in the amplitude in 1 sec, DE, is the same as the change in the amplitude in v m,

$$DE = v\ dE$$

and, similarly,

$$DB = v\ dB$$

Using these relations and the results of Eqs. (21|19) and (21|20),

$$dB = \left(\frac{1}{c^2}\right) DE$$

$$= \left(\frac{1}{c^2}\right) v\ dE$$

$$= \left(\frac{1}{c^2}\right) v\ DB$$

$$= \left(\frac{1}{c^2}\right) v^2\ dB$$

which can hold only if the velocity of the wave, v, is equal to c, the velocity of light.

With the numbers we used in order to gain some physical feeling for the origin of the relation between Maxwell's equations and the requirement that electromagnetic waves travel with the speed of light, we were restricted to very low frequencies and very long wavelengths. Obviously this is not really relevant, as we could have chosen extremely small time intervals and extremely small widths of the rectangle.

It is interesting to note that the results follow from relations between electric and magnetic fields that are valid for any coordinate system, and therefore the velocity of electromagnetic waves is the same for any coordinate system, and this follows from Maxwell's equations. Though we started from the Theory of Relativity in discussing the relations we eventually classified as Maxwell's equations, these equations summarized experimental observations that were made long before the Theory of Relativity was formulated. The nonclassical concept that the velocity of light would be the same for any observer, moving with any velocity, is thus implicitly part of the work of Maxwell. The contradictions between electromagnetic theory and the classical view of space and time was known by such men as Lorentz and Einstein and led rather directly to Einstein's work on relativity.

21 |9   *Electromagnetic radiation*

The time lags that must necessarily occur in the propagation of any change or disturbance lead to the concept of radiated energy. We are not prepared to consider this quantitatively, but we can gain some qualitative insights from simple consideration. We have emphasized that lines of force do not just abruptly vanish when currents or charge distributions are neutralized, but they retain continuity and shrink away. For the sake of definiteness

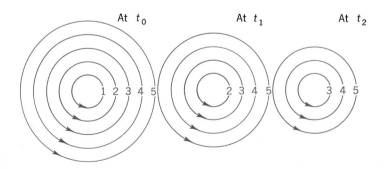

FIG. 21 |19

Magnetic-field lines induced by a current that is alternating direction every second.

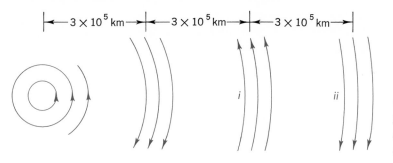

FIG. 21 | 20
*Electric field lines from
a charge that is changing
sign every second.*

we consider the magnetic lines of force about a current-carrying
wire where the current is traveling in a direction such as to come
out of the paper. Figure 21 | 19 shows the lines of force as a func-
tion of time as the current is decreased. The individual circles
can be considered to contract into the wire. (This is a bit fanciful
inasmuch as it gives individual lines of force too much reality—
they are of course, a symbol.) Now we consider that the current
is reversed, and reversed in 1 sec. The lines of force farther away
then 300,000 km, where the velocity of light is 300,000 km/sec,
would not have time to shrink back into the wire and disappear.
If the current oscillates, we will have at some instant a situation
very like Fig. 21 | 20, where the field portions denoted as *i* and
ii are lost to the wire. That field can never get back. It is a radiated
field, and the energy it contains will continue on, outward, at the
speed of light, and will be lost to the oscillating circuit. The effect
on the circuit of this loss of energy is very much as if a resistor,
dissipating energy, had been placed in the circuit.

   Although an exact calculation of the energy lost by radiation
is somewhat complicated, we can use dimensional analysis together with some physical insight to examine the energy radiated
per second by a charge, q. The result cannot depend upon the
velocity of the charge because a system moving with constant
velocity is equivalent to a system at rest, and certainly a charge
at rest does not radiate energy. It is plausible that energy loss
is related to the acceleration of the charge, a. Certainly the energy
radiated will depend upon the magnitude of the charge. It seems
very likely that the radiated energy will vary with the square of
the charge as the energy stored in the field depends upon the
square of the field strength, which in turn is proportional to the
square of the charge, and it is this energy that is radiated. Another natural parameter is c, the velocity of propagation of the

field. If the velocity were infinite, the field could get back to the wire in Fig. 21|20 and there would be no radiation. We can expect that the power that is radiated must be inversely proportional to some power of the speed of light.

From these parameters we wish to construct a quantity that has the dimensions of power, or energy divided by time, to represent the rate of radiation of energy by the charge. Recalling that kq^2/R has the dimensions of energy (this is the potential energy of two charges separated by a distance R) and noting that a^2/c^3 has the dimensions of $(1/LT)$, we can construct the quantity

$$\frac{kq^2a^2}{c^3}$$

which has the dimensions of power, or energy divided by time. This tells us that the power radiated by a charge varies as the square of the charge and as the square of the acceleration of the charge. An exact calculation shows that

$$P = \frac{2}{3}\frac{kq^2a^2}{c^3} \tag{21|21}$$

The dimensional calculation was almost quantitatively correct. Since the acceleration of a charge in an oscillating circuit is proportional to the square of the frequency, the energy radiated by a circuit is proportional to the fourth power of the frequency.

PROBLEMS

21|1 From an analysis of the physical sources of an electric field and the sources of a magnetic field show that the electric field, **E**, is a vector and the magnetic field, **B**, is an axial vector: that is, show that **E** behaves like a displacement upon reflection in a mirror, while **B** behaves like angular momentum upon reflection.

21|2 A magnetic field of 1 Wb/m² (typical of values produced by an electromagnet) is directed into the paper.

(a) What are the direction and magnitude of the force on a wire in the plane of the paper carrying a current of 100 A toward the top of the paper? Toward the left-hand side of the paper?

(b) Discuss the forces on a circular loop of wire in the plane of the paper such that the current is clockwise. Counterclockwise.

21|3 A metal plate 10 m square holds an electric charge Q coulombs. At time $t = a$, an observer measures the electric field 1 m below the center of the plate and finds an electric field, E_a, equal to 100 V/m; the magnetic field, B_a, is measured to be zero. Later, at a time $t = b$, another plate moving by with a velocity $v = \sqrt{\frac{3}{4}}c$ passes just over the first plate. At that instant the observer on the ground notes that the two plates have the same length and width. The electric field, E_b, measured at this time is found to be zero. An observer riding on the moving plate also measures the electric and magnetic fields 1 m above the center of that plate, finding the values of E_b' and B_b'. Before the moving plate came near the stationary plate, he had also measured the electric and magnetic fields and found values of E_a' and B_a'.

(a) What is the value of B_b?

(b) What are the values of E_a, E_b', B_a', and B_b'?

(c) What is the value of the charge on the moving plate?

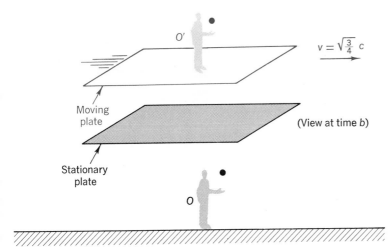

O'

$v = \sqrt{\frac{3}{4}}\ c$

Moving plate

(View at time b)

Stationary plate

O

21|4 Find the magnitude and direction of the magnetic field at the center of a circular loop of wire 1 m in radius in which a current of 100 A is moving in a clockwise direction.

21|5 A parallel-plate capacitor has round plates 1 m in radius, separated by 1 cm. The capacitor is charged to a potential of 10,000 V and then discharge in 10^{-6} sec. Assuming that the capacitor discharges in such a way that the voltage changes linearly with time, what will be the (approximate) value of the magnetic field at the edge of the capacitor during the discharge?

21|6   Two long parallel wires are separated by 0.1 m; each carries a current of 10 A in the same direction.

(*a*) What is the magnitude and direction of the force per meter between the wires?

(*b*) How will the force change if the distance between the wires is doubled? If the currents are both reversed? If one current is reversed? If both currents are doubled?

21|7   A proton (mass equal to 1.6×10^{-27} kg) is seen to travel in a circle 0.1 m in radius in a magnetic field of 1.0 Wb/m².

(*a*) What is the velocity of the proton?

(*b*) What is the frequency of revolution of the proton about the circle?

(*c*) Show that the frequency of revolution is independent of the velocity of the proton (this is the cyclotron condition).

21|8   Starting from the Eq. (21|4), show that $E' = B'v$ [Eq. (21|14)]. Note that $E = 0$.

21|9   A magnetic field of $B = 2$ Wb/m² passes normally through a square loop of 2 turns of wire with a resistance of 0.1 Ω. The loop has dimensions 0.5 m by 0.5 m. The field value drops linearly to zero in 0.5 sec. What is the energy dissipated in the resistance of the wire?

21|10   An electron is moving in a circular orbit in a magnetic field as shown in the diagram. The electron is moving with a velocity very near the velocity of light; the radius of the orbit is 0.5 m. The magnetic field is increased by an amount equal to 1.0 Wb/m in a time of $\frac{1}{100}$ sec. Assume that the electron remains in orbit.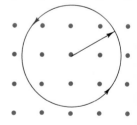

(*a*) What is the value of the electric field at the position of the orbit?

(*b*) If the charge of the electron is -1.6×10^{-19} C, how much does the energy of the electron increase during the increase in magnetic field?

(*c*) What is the potential difference in volts through which the electron would have to pass to gain the same energy?

21|11   An electron having a charge e and a mass m moves clockwise in an orbit of radius r with a velocity v.

(*a*) If the force on the electron is generated by the electric field of a charge, Q, at the center of its orbit, what is the value of the charge?

(b) What is the value of the magnetic field in the center of the orbit generated by the electron? (Note: the moving electron constitutes a current).

21|12 The moving conducting rod shown in the diagram is in electrical contact with a stationary conductor, all in a magnetic field. A force is exerted on the rod so as to move it to the right with a velocity of 1 m/sec.

(a) What is the force on a charge, q, in the conductor?

(b) What is the value of electric field that would be required to give the same force on the charge in the absence of a magnetic field?

(c) What is the value of the current flowing through the circuit?

(d) What is the power dissipated in the resistor?

(e) What is the value of the force on the rod that results from the interaction of the magnetic field with the current in the rod?

(f) What is the mechanical power required to effect the movement of the rod? (Disregard friction.)

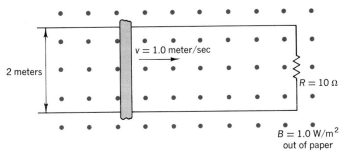

21|13 A current of I amperes flows counterclockwise in a conductor that forms a circle 1 m in radius in the plane of the paper. The magnetic field at the center of the circle is 1 Wb/m² out of the paper. A current I', is then introduced into a conductor in the form of a circle 10 cm in radius that is concentric with the larger circle such that the field goes to zero in the center.

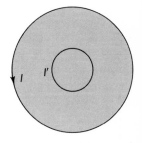

(a) What is the value of the ratio of I'/I, and what is the direction of the current I'?

(b) If the current in the outer loop is increased at the rate of I A/sec what is the value and direction of the emf induced in the inner loop? (An accuracy of about 20 percent is sufficient.)

21|14 Use equations 21|9 to show that $(E \cdot E) - c^2(B \cdot B)$ is a Lorentz invariant.

21|15   A guillotine blade 1 m wide with a mass of 1.0 kg falls toward a victim from a considerable height. A large magnetic field of 1.0 Wb/m² is directed out of the paper in the region of the guillotine. The blade plus the rest of the system forms a closed electric circuit as shown in the drawing, with a resistance of 10^{-2} Ω. Although the blade fell very quickly when there was no magnetic field, now it seems to slide down so slowly that the victim will not be harmed. Why does it fall slowly? What is the maximum velocity it will reach after it falls for a while?

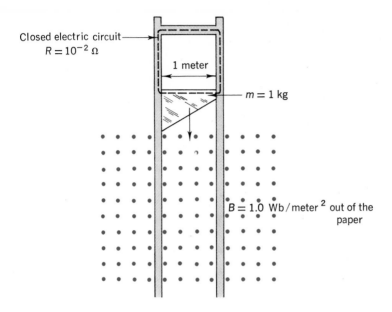

21|16   A magnetic field *B* of 1 Wb/m² is in a direction out of paper. A conducting rod making contact with a conducting ring 1 m in radius makes 1 revolution/sec. The end of the rod is connected to the ring through a 1-Ω resistance. What is the power dissipated in the resistance?

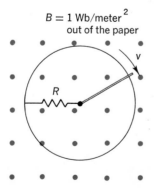

21|17 The moving conducting rod shown in the diagram is in electrical contact with a stationary conductor, all in a magnetic field. A force is exerted on the rod that is sufficient to move it to the right with a velocity of 1 m/sec.

(*a*) What is the current in the circuit?

(*b*) What is the power dissipated in the resistor?

(*c*) What is the mechanical power required to effect the movement? (Neglect friction.)

(*d*) What is the force on the rod?

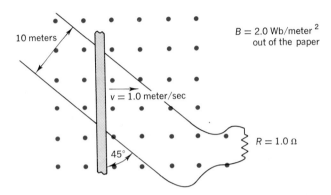

21|18 Two parallel capacitor plates, separated by 0.01 m, are connected by a conducting wire. When the plates are moving with a velocity of 10 m/sec through a magnetic field of 2 Wb/m², as shown in the diagram, the wire is broken. When the plates are examined afterward, they are found to be charged.

(*a*) Where did the charges on the plate originate?

(*b*) What was the potential difference between the plates when they were examined afterward?

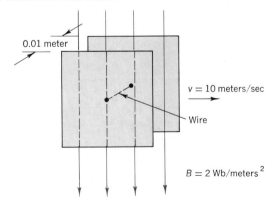

21| 19 (*a*) A charge moves in a circle of radius *r* with a velocity *v*. What is the frequency of radiation?

(*b*) The velocity of the charge is doubled. Will the charge radiate more energy, less, or the same amount? Why?

21| 20 A charged particle is traveling from left to right in an electric field, **E**, which is directed toward the bottom of the paper and a magnetic field, **B**, directed into the paper: $E = 1000$ V/m; $B = 0.5$ Wb/m². The particle travels *in a straight line*. What conclusions can you draw concerning the velocity of the particle?

twenty-two *Alternating-current circuits*

22 | 1 *The magnetic field of a solenoid*

THE COMPLEXITIES OF THE interactions between moving charges, expressed as the interactions between electric fields, magnetic fields, and currents, results in a complex and useful technology concerned with the transfer of energy and information. The storage of energy in the form of electric and magnetic fields is particularly important. We have considered some of the properties of stored electric fields in our analysis of capacitance and capacitors; we can consider some of the properties of magnetic fields in an analysis of *inductance* and inductors. Even as we studied the parallel-plate capacitor in detail because of its simplicity, we shall study the solenoid in detail as an example of the simplest of *inductors*.

We have shown that the sum of the components of magnetic field along a path around a current is independent of the path and

$$\oint (\mathbf{B} \cdot d\mathbf{s}) = \oint B \, ds \cos \theta$$

$$= \left(\frac{k}{c^2}\right) 4\pi I$$

where I is the current and θ is the angle between the increment of path, $d\mathbf{s}$, and the magnetic field, $\mathbf{B}$. The symbol $\oint$ again means

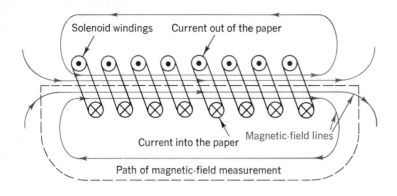

the integral, or sum, of the quantities taken around the whole path. We will use this result to calculate the magnetic field inside a long solenoid. This will be useful inasmuch as it allows us to introduce the concept of inductance in a quantitative manner and, eventually, to compute the energy stored in the magnetic field.

A solenoid is a cylinder wound as a helix with turns of wire. We consider a solenoid D meters long wound with N turns of wire per meter through which passes a current I. The diameter of the solenoid is irrelevant as long as it is small compared to the length. In such a solenoid the magnetic-field distribution will be similar to that suggested in the diagram of Fig. 22|1. Notice that the magnetic-field strength is very much greater inside the solenoid than outside. We choose to consider the field around a path, such as the path represented by the dashed line in the diagram, that passes around all of the wires of the solenoid. The total magnetic field along this path times the path length will then be expressed as

$$\oint B \, ds \cos \theta = \left(\frac{k}{c^2}\right) ND4\pi I$$

where ND is the total number of turns making up the solenoid. Since the field is very small outside the solenoid, only the path inside the solenoid contributes substantially to the path integral: then

$$\oint B \, ds \cos \theta \approx BD$$

and

$$B = \left(\frac{k}{c^2}\right) 4\pi NI \tag{22|1}$$

Since the position of the path inside the solenoid is irrelevant for the purpose of this argument, the magnetic field is the same at any point inside the solenoid. Since B is equal to the density of lines of magnetic flux, BA is equal to ϕ, the total number of lines of magnetic flux that pass through the solenoid, where A is the cross-sectional area of the solenoid.

22|2   *Inductance*

Since the flux density, B, inside the solenoid is expressed by the relation (22|1), and the cross-sectional area is A, the total flux is

$$\phi = BA$$

$$= 4\pi \left(\frac{k}{c^2}\right) NIA \qquad (22|2)$$

where ϕ, the total flux, is measured in webers.

For a circuit configuration that consists of two concentrically wound solenoids, as shown in Fig. 22|2, all the lines of flux that link the inside solenoid, a, also link the outer solenoid, b, and the flux through the two solenoids is the same:

$$\phi_a = \phi_b$$

Therefore a change in the flux through solenoid a will also represent a change in the flux through b. This change in flux will produce an induced emf in each turn of solenoid b. Since ϕ_a, the flux through solenoid a, is proportional to the current in a, I_a, the flux through b will also change as the current I_a changes. The voltage induced in b will be

$$\mathcal{E}_b = N_b D_b \frac{d\phi_b}{dt}$$

where N_b is the number of turns per meter of b, D_b is the length

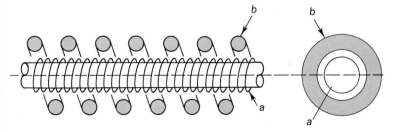

FIG. 22|2

Two concentric solenoids.

of solenoid b, and $d\phi_b/dt$ is the rate of change of the flux through b. The total emf induced in b is equal to the emf induced per turn, times the total number of turns, $N_b D_b$.

Since

$$\phi_a = 4\pi \left(\frac{k}{c^2}\right) N_a I_a A_a = \phi_b$$

then

$$\frac{d\phi_b}{dt} = \frac{d\phi_a}{dt} = 4\pi \left(\frac{k}{c^2}\right) N_a A_a \frac{dI_a}{dt}$$

where dI_a/dt is the rate of change of the current in a with time. The emf induced in solenoid b will be

$$\mathcal{E} = N_b D_b \frac{d\phi_b}{dt}$$

$$= N_b D_b 4\pi \left(\frac{k}{c^2}\right) N_a A_a \frac{dI_a}{dt}$$

or

$$\mathcal{E}_b = M_{ba} \frac{dI_a}{dt}$$

where

$$M_{ba} = 4\pi \left(\frac{k}{c^2}\right) N_b D_b N_a A_a \tag{22|3}$$

where we call M_{ba} the *mutual inductance* between circuits a and b.

If an emf of 1 V is induced in circuit b when the current in a is changing at the rate of 1 A/sec, the value of the mutual inductance, M_{ba}, is 1 *henry:* the unit of mutual inductance is named the henry (H).

In general, any two circuits will interact. The specific case of two concentric solenoids was chosen here because the mutual inductance is easily calculated. It can be shown—though not here—that

$$M_{ba} = M_{ab}$$

for any two circuits. If

$$\mathcal{E}_b = M_{ba} \frac{dI_a}{dt} \quad \text{and} \quad \mathcal{E}_a = M_{ba} \frac{dI_b}{dt}$$

then

$$M_{ba} = M_{ab}$$

It is therefore convenient to use the symbol M for the mutual inductance between two circuits and to drop the subscripts.

It is important to note that the mutual inductance between two circuits is completely defined by the geometry of the circuits and is independent of any electrical properties of the circuits.

Even as the change in flux in solenoid b, which results from the change in current in a in Fig. 22|2, produces an emf in b, the change in flux is solenoid a will induce an emf in solenoid a itself. The calculation of the magnitude of the emf induced in a follows the same steps as the calculation of $\mathscr{E}_b$ even as the basic mechanisms are equivalent. The results of Eq. (22|3) are immediately applicable with every subscript b replaced by a. Then

$$\mathscr{E}_a = L \frac{dI_a}{dt}$$

where   (22 |4)

$$L = 4\pi \left(\frac{k}{c^2}\right) N_a^2 D_a A_a$$

where L is the *self-inductance* of the single solenoid a.

In any circuit

$$E = L \frac{dI}{dt}$$

where $\mathscr{E}$ is the emf induced in the circuit by the change in current, I, and L is the self-inductance of the circuit. The unit of self-inductance is also the henry.

The direction of the emf must be such as to oppose the change in current that induces the emf. For example, a current that is increasing and positive, according to some convention, will induce an emf that is in a direction to produce a negative current. This rule is Lenz's law.

22 |3   *The energy stored in a magnetic field*

The calculation of the self-inductance of a long solenoid is particularly useful because that result can be used to compute the energy stored in a magnetic field. Since the emf induced by a

changing current is opposed to the change, power must be supplied to a solenoid if the current is increasing according to the
relation

$$P = \mathscr{E}I$$

$$= LI\frac{dI}{dt}$$

where P is the power, $\mathscr{E}$ the emf, and I the current, all measured
at the same time. The energy, dw, transferred to the solenoid in
a brief time interval, dt, by the external agency supplying the
solenoid with the increasing current will then be

$$dw = P\, dt$$

$$= \mathscr{E}I\, dt$$

$$= LI\left(\frac{dI}{dt}\right)dt$$

Cancelling the factors dt in the numerator and denominator,

$$dw = LI\, dI$$

The diagram of Fig. 22|3 shows a graph where LI is plotted
against the current I. The shaded area then represents the quantity $dw = LI\, dI$. The total energy required to raise the current
from zero to some value, I_m, is thus the sum of the many increments dw and is equal to the area under the curve from zero to
I_m. This energy is

$$w = \tfrac{1}{2}LI^2 \qquad\qquad\qquad (22|5)$$

Since no mechanical parameter has changed (and the extra kinetic
energy of the electrons carrying the current is negligible), this
must be the energy stored in the magnetic field.

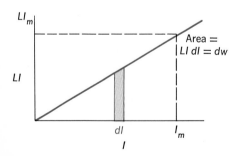

FIG. 22|3
*The current I through
an inductance of
magnitude L plotted
against LI.*

Expressing L in terms of the parameters of the solenoids,

$$w = \frac{1}{2} \, 4\pi \left(\frac{k}{c^2}\right) N^2 A D I_m^2$$

With some algebraic manipulation,

$$w = \left(\frac{1}{8\pi}\right) \left[4\pi \left(\frac{k}{c^2}\right) NI\right]^2 AD \left(\frac{k}{c^2}\right)^{-1}$$

Since

$$B = 4\pi \left(\frac{k}{c^2}\right) NI$$

we can write

$$w = \frac{B^2 AD}{8\pi \left(\frac{k}{c^2}\right)}$$

Since DA is the volume, V, occupied by the magnetic field in the solenoid,

$$\frac{w}{V} = \frac{B^2}{8\pi \left(\frac{k}{c^2}\right)} \quad \text{joules/meter}^3$$

Although the calculation was made for a field produced in a very special manner, the result holds generally for all magnetic fields.

In Chapter 19 we showed that

$$\frac{w}{V} = \frac{E^2}{8\pi k}$$

Again we see that E and Bc play symmetric roles in the description of the electromagnetic field.

22|4   *Transient currents in circuits containing inductance and capacitance*

In order to understand the electrical characteristics of any circuit such that the current is changing, it is necessary to consider the inductance and capacitance of the circuit.

We first analyze the flow of current in a simple circuit where a capacitor discharges through a resistor. An appropriate circuit is shown in Fig. 22|4. The switch is thrown first to the left and

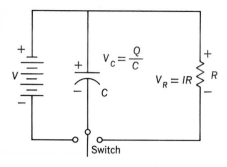

FIG. 22|4

A circuit containing a capacitor and a resistor.

the battery charges the capacitor to a voltage V, generating an electric field between the plates of the capacitor. We will not concern ourselves with the details of the current flow during this operation, which merely establishes the initial conditions for the discharge of the capacitor. Then the switch is thrown to the right, the battery is disconnected from the circuit, and the capacitor is discharged through the resistor.

We can now consider how the current through the resistor, the voltages across the capacitor and resistor, and the charge held by the capacitor vary with time. At the instant the switch is thrown to the right, the voltage across the capacitor, V_C, is equal to V, the battery voltage. If we consider the clockwise direction around the circuit as positive for definiteness, the voltage across the resistor, V_R, must be equal in magnitude but opposed in direction to the voltage difference across the capacitor. Around the whole circuit,

$$V_C + V_R = 0$$

Since $V_C = Q/C$, where Q is the charge held by the capacitor and C is the capacitance, and $V_R = IR$, where I is the current flowing through the resistor and R is the resistance, we have

$$\frac{Q}{C} = -IR$$

The current through the resistor comes from the charge leaking off the capacitor, so $I = dQ/dt$, the rate of change of the charge on the capacitor. Then

$$\frac{Q}{C} = -\frac{1}{R}\frac{dQ}{dt}$$

or, with a little algebraic manipulation,

(a) $\dfrac{dQ}{dt} = -\left(\dfrac{1}{RC}\right)Q$ or   (b) $\dfrac{dQ}{Q} = -\left(\dfrac{1}{RC}\right)dt$

The form (a) is familiar as the "compound interest" differential equation, DE-EXP, solved in Chapter 9. We can take the solution from that result:

$$Q = Q_0 \exp\left(-\dfrac{t}{RC}\right)$$

where Q_0 is the charge on the capacitor at the time $t = 0$, when the switch was thrown. Since $V_C = Q/C$, and $I = V/R$, we have

$$V_C = V_0 \exp\left(-\dfrac{t}{RC}\right) \quad\text{and}\quad I = I_0 \exp\left(-\dfrac{t}{RC}\right) \qquad (22\,|\,6)$$

where V_0 and I_0 are the initial voltages and currents: $V_0 = V$, and $I_0 = V/R$, where V is the battery voltage, which is the initial voltage on the capacitor. The graphs of Fig. 22|5 show the variation of voltage and current with time.

In some respects the character of the decay of the charge (and also the decay of the current and voltage) is more nearly evident from the relation (b). The ratio dQ/Q is the proportional change in the charge Q. The equation, in this form, states that the proportional change in Q (or in V_C or I) is the same for any equal time interval, dt, and is inversely proportional to the product RC.

We might consider a particular example as an illustration. Let $C = 10^{-6}$ F, and $R = 10^7\ \Omega$; RC, the *time constant* is then 10 sec (RC has the dimensions of time). Then in one second the charge on the capacitor will decrease about 10 percent, the voltage on the capacitor will decrease about 10 percent and the current through the resistor will decrease 10 percent.

We can consider another simple circuit containing an induc-

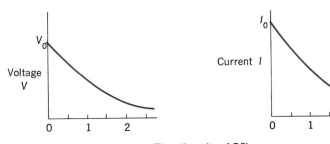

Voltage V

Current I

Time (in units of RC)

FIG. 22|5

The voltage across the capacitor and the current through the resistor plotted as a function of time as the capacitor discharges.

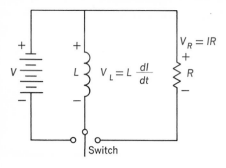

FIG. 22|6

*A circuit containing
an inductor and a
resistor.*

tance, L, and a resistor, R, in a similar fashion. When the switch
is thrown to the left in the circuit of Fig. 22|6, a current, I_0,
flows through the inductance, producing a magnetic field about
the coils. Then the switch is thrown (instantaneously) to the right.
There is now no source of emf, and we expect the current to stop.
But if the current stops, the magnetic field must cease to exist,
and for the magnetic field to cease it must change. A changing
magnetic field induces an emf across the inductor, which will
serve to produce a current through the resistor. In particular,

$$V_L + V_R = 0$$

where V_L is the voltage (or the emf) induced across the inductor
and V_R is the voltage across the resistance. Since $V_L = L\ dI/dt$
and $V_R = IR$, we have

$$L\frac{dI}{dt} = -IR$$

and then we can write

(a) $\dfrac{dI}{dt} = -\left(\dfrac{R}{L}\right)I$ (b) $\dfrac{dI}{I} = -\left(\dfrac{R}{L}\right)dt$

—the same type of equation, DE-EXP, that described the discharge of the capacitor through the resistor. The proportional
change in I is the same for any equal interval, dt, and is inversely
proportional to the time constant of the circuit, L/R, which,
again, has the dimensions of time. The solution of the equation
has the form

$$I = I_0 \exp\left(-\frac{R}{L}t\right) \quad \text{or} \quad V = V_0 \exp\left(-\frac{R}{L}t\right) \tag{22|7}$$

where $V_0 = I_0 R$ is the voltage across the resistance at time $t = 0$

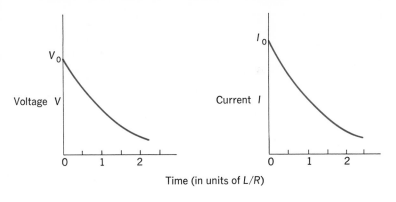

FIG. 22|7
The voltage across the inductor and the current through the resistor plotted against time.

when the switch was thrown. The curves of Fig. 22|7 show the variation of current and voltage with time; the graphs are similar to those of Fig. 22|5 even as the equations 22|6 and 22|7 are similar.

An especially interesting and important phenomenon occurs in circuits that contain inductance and capacitance. We consider an analysis of the currents and voltages in the circuit of Fig. 22|8, where the capacitor, C, is charged to the battery voltage, V, and then discharged through the inductance, L, as the switch is thrown to the right.

Again the sum of the voltages around the circuit must be zero, and

$$V_C + V_L = 0$$

where $VC = Q/C$ and $V_L = L \, dI/dt$; therefore,

$$\frac{Q}{C} + L\frac{dI}{dt} = 0$$

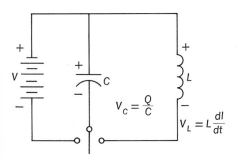

FIG. 22|8
A circuit containing an inductor and a capacitor.

Since

$$I = \frac{dQ}{dt}$$

then

$$\frac{dI}{dt} = \frac{d^2Q}{dt^2}$$

Therefore,

$$\frac{Q}{C} + L\frac{d^2Q}{dt^2} = 0$$

or

$$\frac{d^2Q}{dt^2} = -\left(\frac{1}{LC}\right)Q$$

This is the equation, DE-SHM, that also describes simple harmonic motion where $(1/LC)$ corresponds to ω^2, the square of the angular frequency. The results or solutions of the equation must therefore have the same form as the solutions of the equation for simple harmonic motion:

$$\frac{d^2x}{dt^2} = -\omega^2 x$$

where $\omega = 2\pi f$ and f is the frequency. We thus know immediately that the circuit of Fig. 22|8 will oscillate with a frequency

$$f = \frac{\omega}{2\pi} = \frac{1}{2\pi}\sqrt{\frac{1}{LC}}$$

We write down the solutions of the two equations side by side to emphasize the similarity of the results.

Oscillating LC circuit	*Simple harmonic motion*
$Q = Q_0 \cos \omega t$	$x = x_0 \cos \omega t$
$\dfrac{dQ}{dt} = I = -Q_0\omega \sin \omega t$	$\dfrac{dx}{dt} = v = -x_0\omega \sin \omega t$
$\dfrac{d^2Q}{dt^2} = \dfrac{dI}{dt} = -Q_0\omega^2 \cos t$	$\dfrac{d^2x}{dt^2} = a = -x_0\omega^2 \cos \omega t$
Where Q_0 is the initial charge on the capacitor and I_0 is zero.	Where x_0 is the initial position of the system and v_0 is zero.

In each case the subscript 0 indicates the initial value at the time $t = 0$.

In summary, the charge on the capacitor of the circuit of Fig. 22 | 8, the current through the inductor, and the rate of change of the current through the circuit all vary with time in a manner similar to the variation of the kinematic quantities of a mechanical system moving with simple harmonic motion. If we compare the electric circuit to the mechanical system of a bob oscillating at the end of a spring, we find that the capacitor in the circuit corresponds to the spring in the mechanical system; the inductance in the circuit plays much the same role as the mass of the bob in the mechanical system; and the position of the bob corresponds to the charge on the capacitor, while the velocity of the bob corresponds to the current through the inductance. Although the mass of the bob corresponds to the value of the inductance in the circuit, the spring constant corresponds to the inverse of the value of the capacitance: a small capacitance corresponds to a stiff spring, a large capacitance is similar to a weak spring.

It is amusing, and perhaps instructive, to describe a hydraulic system that is a very close parallel to an electric circuit such as we are considering. The diagrams of Fig. 22 | 9 show such similar circuits. The electrical capacitor is equivalent to an elastic rubber diaphragm placed in the hydraulic circuit, and the electrical inductor is equivalent to the coil of tubing, which holds a very large mass of water. The electrical resistor is equivalent to a physical resistance in the hydraulic circuit designed so that the current that flows through it is proportional to the pressure difference across it.

The current flowing in the hydraulic system is equivalent to the electric current; the volume of water displaced past the equilibrium position of the diaphragm corresponds to the electric

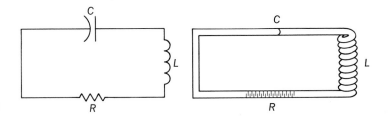

FIG. 22 | 9

An electric circuit containing inductance, resistance, and capacitance, together with an analogous hydraulic circuit.

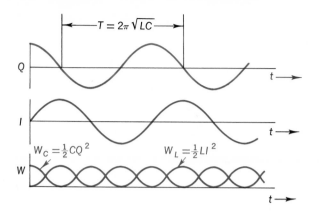

FIG. 22|10

The charge on the capacitor, the current through the inductor, and the energy stored by the inductor and by the capacitor, plotted as a function of time for an oscillating LC circuit.

charge on the capacitor. The mechanical potential energy of the stretched rubber diaphragm is similar to the electric potential energy of the charged capacitor, while the kinetic energy of the moving mass of water in the coil of tubing corresponds to the energy in the magnetic field of the electrical inductance.

The graphs of Fig. 22|10 illustrate the variation of the charge on the capacitor and the current through the inductor as a function of time for a circuit such as that shown in Fig. 22|8. The values of the energy stored in the electric and magnetic fields are also shown as they vary with time. The energy stored in the circuit alternates between storage in the electric field of the capacitor and the magnetic field of the inductance very much as the energy stored in an oscillating mechanical system alternates between kinetic energy and potential energy. In both cases, of course, the total energy stored in the system is constant. At any instant when the charge on the capacitor is Q and the current through the inductance is I,

$$w_{\text{tot}} = w_L + w_C$$

$$= \tfrac{1}{2}CQ^2 + \tfrac{1}{2}LI^2 \tag{22|8}$$

22|5   *Alternating-current circuits and resonance*

Alternating currents—currents that vary with time sinusoidally—are sufficiently important that it is worthwhile considering the character of alternating-current (ac) circuits specifically. Fig.

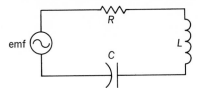

22|11 shows a simple ac circuit where a resistor, a capacitor, and an inductor are connected in series with a source of alternating emf.

Let us assume that a current flows through the circuit as a result of the emf. The current will vary with time according to a relation

$$I = I_m \sin \omega t$$

where, $\omega = 2\pi f$, f is the frequency, and I_m the maximum current. From our previous results concerning the equations of simple harmonic motion applied to the LC circuit of the last section,

$$Q = -\frac{I_m}{\omega} \cos \omega t \quad \text{and} \quad \frac{dI}{dt} = I_m \omega \cos \omega t$$

The voltage across the capacitance is equal to Q/C, and the voltage across the inductance is equal to $L\, dI/dt$; therefore,

$$V_C = -I_m \left(\frac{1}{\omega C}\right) \cos \omega t \quad \text{and} \quad V_L = I_m(\omega L) \cos \omega t$$

while the voltage across the resistor is simply

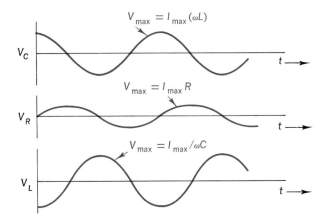

FIG. 22|12

The voltage across the various circuit elements as a function of time for an oscillating RCL circuit.

$$V_R = IR$$

$$= I_m R \sin \omega t$$

The graphs of Fig. 22|12 show the instantaneous voltages across the various circuit elements as a function of time. According to Kirchhoff's laws, the total voltage across all of the circuit elements must be equal to the emf at any time. If the current varies according to the relation

$$I = I_m \sin \omega t$$

the sum of the voltages across the resistance, the capacitance, and the inductance will be

$$E = V_R + V_C + V_L$$

$$= I_m R \sin \omega t - I_m \left(\frac{1}{\omega C}\right) \cos \omega + I_m(\omega L) \cos \omega t$$

Using the relations

$$\cos \omega t = \sin(\omega t + 90°) \qquad \text{and} \qquad -\cos \omega t = \sin(\omega t - 90°)$$

we can write

$$E = I_m R \sin \omega t + I_m \left(\frac{1}{\omega C}\right) \sin(\omega t - 90°)$$

$$+ I_m(\omega L) \sin(\omega t + 90°) \qquad \qquad \textbf{(22|9)}$$

We have shown that the amplitudes of waves of the same frequency that differ in phase can be added very much as vectors, where the amplitude of the wave corresponds to the length of the vector and the phase angle corresponds to the angle the vector makes with some arbitrary coordinate. Figure 22|13 represents the voltages across the various circuit elements in a circuit such as that shown in Fig. 22|11 as vectors and shows also the vector sum of these voltages, which must be equal to the emf vector.

With a little trigonometry we can write down the magnitude of the emf in terms of the voltages across the separate elements, and the phase of the emf with respect to the phase of the current. Expressing the emf $\mathscr{E}$ as

$$\mathscr{E} = V_m \sin(\omega t + \phi) \qquad \qquad \textbf{(22|10)}$$

where

$$V_m = \sqrt{(V_L - V_C)^2 + V_R^2}$$

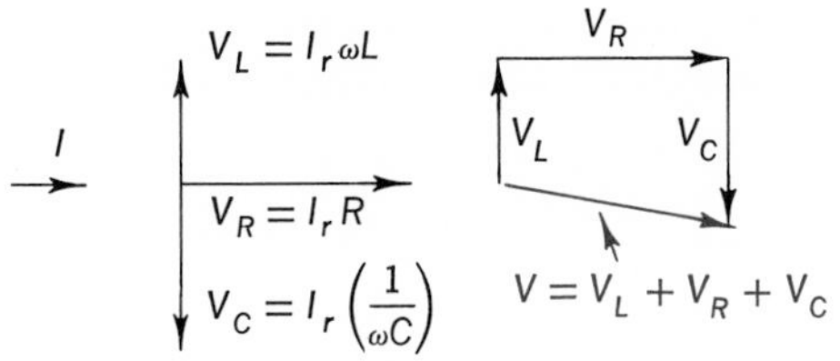

FIG. 22 | 13

A vector construction showing the relations between the voltages across the various circuit elements when a current I passes through a capacitor, a resistor, and an inductor, all in series.

and

$$\tan \phi = \frac{V_L - V_C}{V_R}$$

It is obvious upon inspection of Eq. (22 | 9) that the quantities ωL and $1/\omega C$ have much the same kind of meaning and the same dimensions as resistance: ωL is the *inductive reactance* and $1/\omega C$ is the *capacitive reactance* of the circuit, both measured in ohms. Collectively we call these quantities, together with R, the re-sistance, the *impedance* of the circuit.

For circuits that contain only resistance, only inductance, or only capacitance, the relations between the maximum voltage and the maximum current take the form

$$V_m = I_m R \qquad V_m = I_m(\omega L) \qquad V_m = I_m \left(\frac{1}{\omega C}\right)$$

a result that follows directly from Eq. (22 | 9).

If we divide the vector voltages shown in Fig. 22 | 13 by I_m, we obtain vectors with the same relative magnitudes and the same directions that have the dimensions of impedance. These vectors are proportional to the quantities R, ωL, and $1/\omega C$ and the vector sum is the total impedance of the circuit, Z. From Eq. (22 | 10) we can establish the magnitude of the impedance as

$$Z = \sqrt{(X_L - X_C)^2 + R^2}$$

where

$$X_C = \frac{1}{\omega C} \qquad \text{and} \qquad X_L = \omega L$$

The vector relations, shown in Fig. 22 | 14, are clearly similar to the relations shown in Fig. 22 | 13.

The impedance of the inductance and the capacitance of the

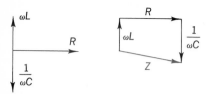

FIG. 22|14

*A vector diagram
showing the relations
between the impedances
of a resistor, a capacitor,
and an inductor in a
series circuit.*

circuit of Fig. 22|11 will vary with the frequency of the source of
the emf. At high frequencies the reactance of the inductance will
become large, while the capacitive reactance will become small.
At low frequencies the reverse will occur: the reactance of the
capacitor will be large, and that of the inductance will be small.
At a frequency such that

$$\omega L = \frac{1}{\omega C} \quad \text{or} \quad \omega^2 = \frac{1}{LC} \quad \text{or} \quad \omega = \sqrt{\frac{1}{LC}}$$

the reactances of the two elements will be equal, the reactance of
the capacitor will cancel the reactance of the inductance, and the
total impedance of the circuit will be equal to the resistance of
the circuit,

$$Z = R$$

This is the lowest impedance the circuit can present for a given
magnitude of emf, and the current will therefore be a maximum
at this frequency, which is called the *resonant* frequency.

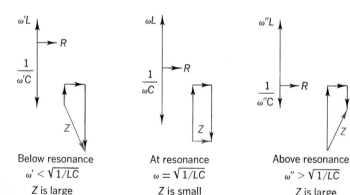

Below resonance	At resonance	Above resonance
$\omega' < \sqrt{1/LC}$	$\omega = \sqrt{1/LC}$	$\omega'' > \sqrt{1/LC}$
Z is large	Z is small	Z is large

FIG. 22|15

*Vector diagrams showing
the voltages across
the various circuit
elements of a series
circuit for frequencies
below resonance, at
resonance, and above
resonance.*

The diagrams of Fig. 22|15 show schematically the vector diagram of typical impedance relations at frequencies below resonance, above resonance, and at resonance.

Voltage amplification can be produced by a resonant circuit. Let us assume that the reactance of the capacitor and of the inductance is X ohms at resonance, while the resistance is R ohms. At resonance the impedance of the circuit, Z, will be equal to the resistance, R. If the maximum emf is V volts, the maximum value of the current that will flow in the circuit will be $I = V/R$ amperes. But the maximum voltage across either the inductance or the capacitor will be equal to

$$V_L = V_C = IX \quad \text{volts}$$

$$= V\left(\frac{X}{R}\right)$$

If X is very much larger than R, the voltage across the inductance or the capacitance will be much larger than the input voltage.

We are not often as interested in the maximum currents or maximum voltages when we discuss alternating currents as we are in average current. The instantaneous power absorbed by a resistance is

$$P = I^2 R$$

For a current that varies sinusoidally, the power absorbed at any time, t, is

$$P = (I_m \sin \omega t)^2 R$$

$$= I_m^2 R \sin^2 \omega t$$

Since

$$\sin^2 \omega t + \cos^2 \omega t = 1$$

and over a long period of time the average value of $\sin^2 \omega t$ must be the same as the average value of $\cos^2 \omega t$, and since certainly the average value of 1 is 1, the average value of $\sin^2 \omega t$ must be equal to $\frac{1}{2}$. Then

$$P = \tfrac{1}{2} I_m^2 R$$

where P is the average power. The square root of the average squared current, $\frac{1}{2} I_m^2$, which we will write simply as $\bar{I}$, is thus a useful average. It has the same properties concerning resistance loss and power as direct current.

$$\bar{I} = \sqrt{\tfrac{1}{2}I_m^2}$$

$$= 0.707 I_m$$

The average power loss in a resistance is therefore

$$\bar{P} = \bar{I}^2 R$$

which is the same form as for dc power losses. The same means (averages) can be used to define a "root-mean-square" (rms) voltage,

$$\bar{V} = \sqrt{\tfrac{1}{2}V_m^2}$$

$$= 0.707 V_m$$

The standard relations that were defined for dc circuits involving only resistance holds now for alternating current circuits also if the rms currents and voltages are used consistently. These are the voltages and currents read on standard ac ammeters and voltmeters. Then

$$\bar{P} = \bar{V}\bar{I} \qquad \bar{P} = \bar{I}^2 R \qquad \bar{P} = \frac{\bar{V}^2}{R}$$

and

$$\bar{V} = \bar{I}(\omega L) \qquad \bar{V} = \bar{I}\left(\frac{1}{\omega C}\right)$$

PROBLEMS

22|1   (*a*) A square loop of wire having a resistance of 0.001 Ω is placed 1 m from a very long straight wire carrying a current of 100 A: this current drops to zero in 0.1 sec. What is the maximum current in the loop? (It is convenient to estimate that the field everywhere in the loop is the same as at the center.)

   (*b*) The current in the loop is changed from 0 to 100 A in 1 sec. What emf is induced in the long wire?

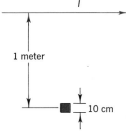

22|2   A solenoid has a measured inductance of 1.0 H. A current of 10 A flows through the solenoid.

   (*a*) What is the value of the energy stored in the magnetic field of the solenoid?

   (*b*) The solenoid (a coil of wire) is stretched to double its length without changing its cross-sectional area. How is the energy storage changed?

(*c*) How much will the energy storage change if the cross-sectional area of the solenoid is doubled? If the number of turns is doubled?

22| 3 The current described by the graph flows in the circuit shown. Draw three graphs showing the voltage across the resistance, across the inductance, and across the capacitance as a function of time.

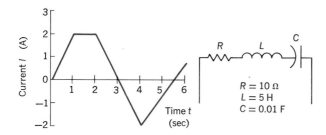

$R = 10 \, \Omega$
$L = 5 \, H$
$C = 0.01 \, F$

22| 4 If the inductance in Fig. 22 | 6 is 1.0 H, the resistance is 0.01 Ω, and the voltage V_L is 100 V at time $t = 0$, what will the current be at this time? After a very long time, how much energy will have been dissipated in the resistor?

22| 5 (*a*) A switch is thrown in a circuit like that shown in Fig. 22 | 4, where $V = 10$ V. At the end of 1 sec the voltage across the capacitor is 5 V. What will the voltage be after 2 sec? After 4 sec?

(*b*) If V in Fig. 22 | 4 is 100 V, C is 10^{-6} F, and the R is 1 Ω, how much energy will be dissipated in the resistor when the switch is thrown to the right? If the resistance is 100 Ω, how much energy will be dissipated in the resistor?

22| 6 A solenoid wound as a torus (shaped like a doughnut) is 1 m in diameter with a cross-sectional area of 0.01 m². The magnetic field generated by a current of 10 A is found to be equal to 0.01 Wb/m².

(*a*) What is the inductance of the solenoid?

(*b*) What is the total number of turns of wire used to wind the solenoid?

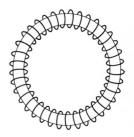

22| 7 The maximum measured voltage across the capacitor, C, is an oscillating LC circuit, such as that shown in Fig. 22 | 8, is 1 V. If the value of the inductance, L, is 10^{-3} H, (*a*) What is the maximum rate of change of the current in the circuit (in amperes per second)?

(*b*) If the value of the capacitance is 10^{-6} F (1 μF) what is the maximum value of the current flowing in the circuit?

(*c*) What is the value of f, the frequency of oscillation?

(*d*) How should the capacitance be changed so the frequency is doubled?

22|8 The value of the resistance in a circuit configuration like that of Fig. 22|11 is 1 Ω, the inductance is 1 H, and the capacitance is 10^{-4} F. The emf varies sinusoidally with a maximum value of 1 V.

(*a*) What is the resonant frequency?

(*b*) What is the maximum value of the current at resonance?

(*c*) What is the voltage across L at resonance?

(*d*) What is the voltage across C at resonance?

(*e*) What is the voltage across R at resonance?

(*f*) What is the value of the maximum energy stored in the electric field of the capacitor at resonance? In the magnetic field of the inductor?

(*g*) What is the current in the circuit (to a few percent) when the frequency is twice the resonant frequency?

(*h*) What are the voltages across C, L, and R, when the frequency is twice the resonant frequency?

(*i*) If, under some circumstances, the maximum voltage across R is 1 V, and the maximum voltage across L is 1 V, what will be the value of the maximum voltage across R and L combined (that is, the reading of an appropriate voltmeter connected across both R and L)?

twenty-three The atom—I
The structure of the
hydrogen atom

23|1 *The nuclear atom*

THROUGH THE first years of the twentieth century the atom was considered to be an indivisible fundamental particle. Through analysis of the spectra of light emitted by atoms in magnetic fields, it was known that the atom held electric charges that had properties similar to those of free electrons in some ways. The whole atom was electrically neutral. Although the distribution of positive and negative electricity in the atom was unknown, it was a popular conjecture that the negative electrons were spread through some positive matrix, rather as raisins in a pudding. All such ideas were swept away by the experiments of a remarkable New Zealand-born Englishman, Ernest Rutherford, which showed that most of the mass of the atom is contained in a small, positively charged nucleus and that the electrons therefore form some kind of light outer material.

Rutherford and his collaborators bombarded thin gold foils with alpha particles from naturally radioactive sources. For the purpose of this discussion the alpha particles, which are the nuclei of helium atoms, can be considered simply as rather heavy, positively charged particles that are traveling at a considerable velocity—about 3 percent of the speed of light. Rutherford believed that only electrical forces would act on the alpha particle as it shot through the atoms in the foil, and in this he was correct because the nuclear forces play no important role. If

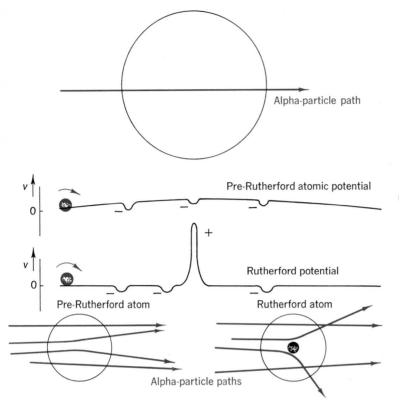

Alpha-particle path

Pre-Rutherford atomic potential

Rutherford potential

Pre-Rutherford atom

Rutherford atom

Alpha-particle paths

FIG. 23 I1
Diagrams illustrating the distribution of potential for a pre-Rutherford model of the atom and for the nuclear atom introduced by Rutherford. Characteristic alpha-particle trajectories suggested by the two models are also shown.

the charges were spread out over the whole atom, even if the charge were found in small discrete pieces, he expected that the alpha particles would never be strongly deflected by the atom—the atom would be "soft" and semitransparent. But if the mass and charge were concentrated somewhere in the atom in a "hard" core, the alpha particles would sometimes be scattered at large angles.

The diagrams of Fig. 23 I1 suggest something of the character of the interaction to be expected between the positively charged alpha particle and the different models of the atom. The upper diagram is supposed to represent a possible path of an alpha particle through the atom where the path passes very close to the center of the atom. The other two curves represent schematically the potential energy of the system as the alpha particle passes along the path. If the positive and negative charges are spread through the atom, there will be small forces of varying sign on the alpha particle; but since the energy of the alpha particle is quite large, the forces will not deflect the particle very much. This is the pre-Rutherford model of the atom. However, if all the positive charge is collected in one place, at the nucleus of the atom, the forces will be quite large if the alpha particle passes close to the nucleus. If this happens, the alpha particle will be sharply scattered.

It is useful to consider the two-dimensional analogy where the alpha particle is represented by a ball rolling across a surface and the forces on the alpha particle correspond to dips and hills in the surface. The pre-Rutherford atom would be very much like a slightly raised surface, corresponding to a positively charged matrix of matter about the size of the atom, with many small dips that correspond to the effects of the negatively charged electrons that were known to exist in the atom. The alpha particle—or ball—moving with high energy and considerable

FIG. 23|2

A diagram suggesting the potential near the nucleus of the nuclear atom and the trajectory of an alpha particle scattered by the nucleus.

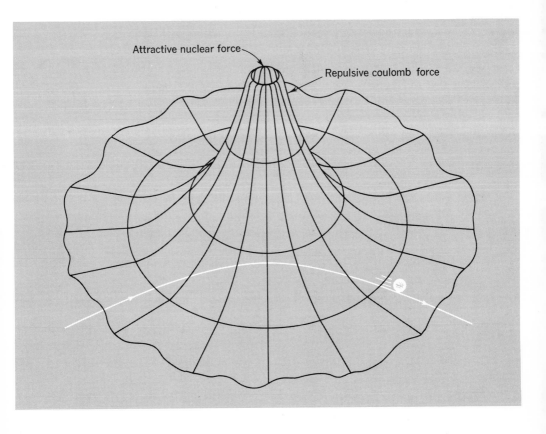

Attractive nuclear force

Repulsive coulomb force

momentum, would never be deflected much as it passed through the atom—or passed over the surface. However, if all the positive charge was concentrated together with most of the mass of the atom in a nucleus at the center of the atom, the forces on any alpha particle that passed very close to that nucleus would be quite large, and the alpha particle would be strongly deflected.

The diagram of Fig. 23|2 shows an expanded view of the potential surface very near such a nucleus and the path of an alpha particle scattered as a result of the strong repulsive electro-static forces. The alpha particle is scattered by the heavy, posi-tively charged nucleus very much as a rolling ball might be de-flected by the potential hill, which simulates the repulsion of the nucleus on the alpha particle.

Figure 23|3 shows, schematically, the experimental design used by Rutherford to investigate the structure of the atom. Alpha particles from a radioactive source were used to bombard a thin gold foil: gold was used because the total positive charge of a gold atom was known to be large and it is easy to produce very thin gold foils. The scattered alpha particles struck screens coated with a zinc sulfide compound. Single alpha particles create enough light upon striking such zinc sulfide screens so that they can be seen by men who are properly dark adapted. (If you look at the dial of your luminous wrist watch at night, after you have been in the dark for half an hour, you can see the individual flashes easily—hold the watch right up to your eye.) The large-angle deflections of individual alpha particles by the nuclei in the gold foil could thus be observed directly by ob-servers using low-power microscopes that directed the light into the eye efficiently. Detailed angular distributions were observed that were in accord with distributions calculated on the basis that the scattering occurred as a result of the Coulomb repulsion from a very small core that carried all of the positive charge of the atom and much of the mass. If the mass of this nucleus was

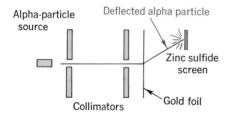

FIG. 23|3

A schematic diagram showing the character of the Rutherford scattering experiment.

not large, the alpha particle would brush the nucleus away and the angular distribution of the scattered alpha particles would be different. We now know that the nuclear mass represents almost all of the mass of the atom: the outer cloud of electrons accounts for less than 0.05 percent of the total atomic mass.

It was thus Rutherford's work that showed us that the atom is made up of a very small but massive positive core, surrounded by a much larger, but tenuous, negative cloud.

23|2 *The classical mechanics of the hydrogen atom*

The nucleus of the hydrogen atom, the lightest and therefore presumably the simplest of the atoms, is a single proton: a single electron comprises the outer region. The hydrogen atom is thus a compound of an electron and proton held together by electrostatic forces. The proton is much heavier than the electron, having a mass about 1835 times that of the electron. According to our conventions, the proton carries a positive unit electric charge, and the electron a negative unit charge, of 1.6×10^{-19} C.

We have shown that we must describe a particle in a box in terms of standing waves, where the waves are the de Broglie waves of the particle, if the momentum of the particle times the length of the box is of the order of h, Planck's constant of action. The walls of the box constrain the position of the particle by exerting a force on the particle. The electrostatic force between the proton and the electron may hold the electron in a small region about the proton very much as the walls of a box. Since the characteristic momentum times the size of the "box" or atom will be found to be small and of the order of h, it is clear that we must finally understand the structure of the hydrogen atom in terms of standing waves of the electron inside the region allowed by the forces on the electron. Since an electron may be attracted to a proton even at very large distances such that the classical concepts must be a good approximation, we can analyze the classical behavior of an electron and a proton to gain some insight into the more abstract problem of constructing a description of the atom in terms of standing waves.

We therefore analyze the structure of the atom by considering the electron and proton as particles in the primitive sense and investigate the dynamic character of their interaction. From the application of Coulomb's law, the force between the two particles, F, will be attractive:

$$F = \frac{ke^2}{a^2}$$

where e is the magnitude of the unit charge and a is the distance between the electron and proton. Still considering the electron and proton as discrete particles, we equate the force between them with the centripetal force required to keep the electron in an orbit about the proton. Though elliptical orbits are possible when the force between the particles varies as the inverse square of the distance between the particles, even as the orbits of planets about the sun are ellipses, we will make the restrictive simplifying assumption that we need consider only the simplest of ellipses—a circle—at this time. Since the proton is very much heavier than the electron, we use the further simplification that the center of the electron's orbit is at the position of the proton (rather than a position $\frac{1}{1835}$ parts closer to the electron). The centripetal force must then be

$$F = \frac{mv^2}{a}$$

where m is the mass of the electron. Equating this to the electrostatic force,

$$\frac{ke^2}{a^2} = \frac{mv^2}{a}$$

Multiplying both sides of this equation by $a/2$,

$$\frac{1}{2}\frac{ke^2}{a} = \frac{1}{2}mv^2$$

The left-hand side of the equation is one-half of the negative potential energy, V, the right-hand side is just the kinetic energy of the electron, T. Thus we have

$$\frac{1}{2}\frac{ke^2}{a} = -\frac{1}{2}V$$

$$= \frac{1}{2}mv^2$$

$$= T$$

It is most convenient to use as a zero of potential energy the potential energy of the two particles when they are very (in-finitely) far from one another. Since the force between the electron and the proton is attractive, energy must be added to the system in order to pull the electron and proton apart; the potential energy of the system must be negative.

The total energy of the system, E, is the sum of the two partial energies:

$$E = V + T$$

$$= -\frac{ke^2}{a} + \frac{1}{2}mv^2$$

Using the results from the previous relations,

$$E = -\frac{1}{2}mv^2$$

$$= -\frac{1}{2}\frac{ke^2}{a} \qquad\qquad (23|1)$$

where again the negative sign means that work must be done on the system of the electron in orbit about the proton to take the electron to a position at rest very far from the proton. We give the name *binding energy* to this required energy.

All the above considerations are identical to those used to describe bodies in orbit in a gravitational field. The only sub-stitution that is necessary is the replacement of $Gm'm/a^2$, where G is the gravitational constant and m and m' are the masses of the particles, with $ke'e$, where k is the electrostatic constant and e and e' are the electric charges of the two bodies.

23|3 The Bohr model of the hydrogen atom

The preceding classical description of the orbits of an electron in the electrostatic field of the proton must be valid under con-ditions such that quantum effects are not important. We know that classical mechanics works very well for large momenta. Then the classical description should be adequate if the de Broglie wavelength of the electron, $\lambda = h/p$ where p is the momentum, is small compared to the radius of the orbit, a, the only other linear dimension. We can then use the classical trajectory of the electron in an orbit as a good approximation for large orbits, to which we can further apply the constraints required by the concept of the wave character of the electron. If the orbit is to be well defined, and if the character of the orbit is to be constant in time, there must be an integral number of de Broglie waves about the circumference of the orbit—a concept that was discussed in detail in Chapter 14. It then follows that

$$n\lambda = 2\pi a$$

since

$$\lambda = \frac{h}{mv} \frac{nh}{mv}$$

$$= 2\pi a$$

Since mva is the angular momentum of the electron moving about the orbit, we have, again, the quantization of angular momentum:

$$mva = n\hbar \tag{23|2}$$

where $\hbar$ (phonetically, "aitch bar") is the symbol for $h/2\pi$.

From the two relations (23|2), which defines the quantization of angular momentum, and (23|1), which relates the binding energy to the potential energy and the kinetic energy of the electron in its orbit, one can develop the relations of the *Bohr model* of the hydrogen atom. With a little algebraic manipulation,

$$m^2v^2a^2 = n^2\hbar^2$$

$$= 2ma^2 \left(\frac{1}{2} mv^2 \right)$$

$$= 2ma^2 \left(\frac{1}{2} \frac{ke^2}{a} \right)$$

$$= ke^2 ma$$

Dividing the first and last member of the chain of equalities by m^2v^2a, we determine the radius of the orbit:

$$a = \frac{n^2\hbar^2}{mke^2} \tag{23|3}$$

Using this relation for a, the total energy is

$$E = -\frac{1}{2}\frac{ke^2}{a}$$

$$= -\frac{1}{2}\frac{k^2e^4m}{n^2\hbar^2} \tag{23|4}$$

The characteristic radii and characteristic energies are small: for $n = 1$, the smallest orbit, the radius a is equal to 0.53×10^{-10} m, and the total energy is about -2.1×10^{-18} J; the minus sign indicates that energy must be added to the system to take the electron out of orbit and out of the sensible attraction of the proton. That energy therefore represents a *binding energy* of the atom in that state.

Niels Bohr, then a young Danish physicist working in Rutherford's laboratory, reached these results concerning the structure of the atom in about the same way as outlined here in about 1913, except that the quantization of the angular momentum was introduced on a more nearly ad hoc basis. De Broglie's insights into the wave character of matter came much later, in about 1925.

23|4   *The correspondence principle— corrections to the Bohr model*

Now we will examine in retrospect the degree of validity of the ideas we have used: in particular, can we justify this mixture of particle and wave arguments? The particle arguments concerning orbits are certainly almost exactly valid for large orbits and large objects. We have ample experience concerning such objects. We also have a considerable and reliable body of data that strongly suggests that electrons act as waves. These two considerations show that our equations are valid for large values of the quantum number, n. This *correspondence principle* derives from the necessity of wave mechanics giving the same answers as ordinary classical mechanics in the macroscopic regions. The *correspondence principle* is a statement that in the limit of large quantum numbers, n, or small wavelengths, λ, any correct equations of quantum mechanics must be the same as those of classical mechanics.

Although the validity of Eqs. (23|3) and (23|4) is essentially established for large values of n from our knowledge of classical mechanics and our knowledge of the wave character of electrons, we have not determined whether these equations describe nature adequately for small values of n. We might gain some insight into the defects of the semiclassical quantum-mechanical treatment of (23|3) and (23|4) by considering the character of the orbit that corresponds to the $n = 0$ state with angular momentum zero. The total energy of the state will be infinite if Eq. (23|4) holds and the radius of the orbit is zero: the electron and proton will occupy the same point of space. Even if we believe that the electron will be excluded from the exact position of the proton and will merely be very close to the proton, perhaps touching it in some sense, the binding energy would be extremely large. Such a result is not in accord with the general principles of quantum mechanics. Though the (negative) potential energy will become very large when the electron is very near the proton, the wavelength of the electron must be very small if it is to be so sharply localized. A small wavelength corresponds to a high momentum and thus a large (positive) kinetic energy.

We can consider the size of the region occupied by the electron as well as the total energy of the electron—the sum of the potential energy and the kinetic energy—in a semiquantitative way by estimating the potential and kinetic energies of an electron for standing waves that represent different degrees of localization of the electron. The diagrams of Fig. 23|4 represent a set of such waves where the de Broglie amplitude of the electron is plotted as a function of x, the distance between the electron and proton in the x-direction. For this state the variation of the amplitude in the y-direction and z-direction will be the same. The square of the amplitude, u, at any point, x', is proportional to the probability that the electron is at a distance x' from the proton. There will therefore exist some average value of the distance, a_0, and some average value of the potential energy,

$$V = -\frac{ke^2}{a_0}$$

The electron standing waves shown in Fig. 23|4 have effective wavelengths, λ, that are very nearly equal to $\lambda = 2\pi a$. Clearly the standing wave of Fig. 23|4a represents a longer wave than 23|4b. Since the wavelength $\lambda = h/p$, where p is the momentum

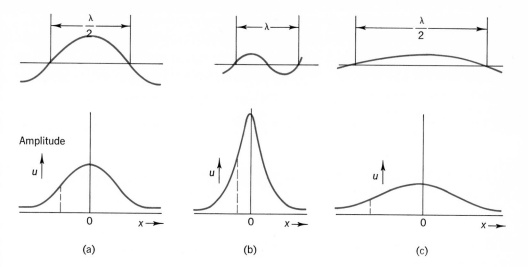

(a)   (b)   (c)

FIG. 23 |4
Diagrams showing
possible de Broglie
wave amplitudes of an
electron very near a
proton.

of the electron, the kinetic energy, equal to $p^2/2m$, is about

$$T = \frac{h^2}{2m\lambda^2}$$

since

$$\lambda = 2\pi a_0$$

$$T = \frac{\hbar^2}{2ma_0^2}$$

and the total energy, the sum of the potential energy and the kinetic energy of the electron, is expressed approximately as

$$E = V + T$$

$$= -\frac{ke^2}{a_0} + \frac{\hbar^2}{2ma_0^2}$$

If the electron is very close to the proton on the average, as in Fig. 23 |4b, the value of a_0 will be small and the magnitude of both the potential energy and the kinetic energy will be large. If the value of a_0 is reduced by a factor of 2, the (negative) potential energy will increase by a factor of 2 but the (positive) kinetic energy will increase by a factor of 4. For small values of a_0 the total energy will increase as a_0 becomes small, since the positive kinetic energy will increase faster than the negative potential energy; and therefore an electron localized to a point—

or a very small region—cannot be bound by a potential that varies as $1/a$: our semiclassical model of the hydrogen atom breaks down at $n = 0$.

If the electron is very far from the proton, as suggested by Fig. 23|4a, both the kinetic energy and the potential energy will be very small and thus the total energy will be small and the electron will not be strongly bound by the proton. The graph of Fig. 23|5 suggests the way the potential energy, the kinetic energy, and the total energy will vary with the value of a. From a classical viewpoint we would expect the state to occur such that the negative total energy (the binding energy) will be at a maximum. This condition will obtain, just as in the classical orbit calculations, when

$$T = -\frac{1}{2}V \quad \text{and} \quad E = V + T = -\frac{1}{2}\frac{ke^2}{a_0}$$

or

$$E = -\frac{1}{2}\frac{k^2e^4m}{\hbar^2} \quad \text{and} \quad a_0 = \frac{\hbar^2}{mke^2} \tag{23|5}$$

You can prove this easily if you have a little calculus.

The results expressed in Eq. (23|5) agree with observations made of hydrogen atoms and thus also are in agreement with the results of detailed calculations using a complete quantum-mechanical analysis. Further, these relations are just the same as the relations of Eqs. (23|3) and (23|4) for a value $n = 1$. This suggests to us that the Eqs. (23|4) and (23|3), established with the use of the correspondence principle, are correct with one revision: the angular momentum for circular orbits is not equal

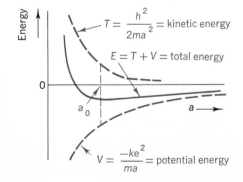

FIG. 23|5

The potential energy, kinetic energy, and total energy of an electron near a proton, plotted as a function of the mean distance between the electron and proton.

to $n\hbar$ but instead is $(n-1)\hbar$, and the state with angular momentum zero, where the electron is closest to the proton, does not have infinite binding energy. This change does not violate the correspondence principle, since, for macroscopic observations on large orbits, n is an enormously large number and the difference between n and $n-1$ is not detectable.

23|5   *The hydrogen atom according to wave mechanics*

The previous discussion of the atom concerned a semiclassical model, the Bohr model, in which the classical equations of motion of the electron in the electric field of a proton were slightly modified by noting that the angular momentum should be quantized; that is,

mva = nħ

All of these conclusions, only suggested and made plausible by this discussion, are precisely reached by solving well-defined three dimensional wave equations of a character determined according to prescriptions that are very much as implied by our qualitative considerations. Although the procedures required to obtain the exact results require more mathematical apparatus than we are prepared to use, we can usefully consider qualitatively some properties of the solutions—the properties of the standing waves that describe the electron bound to the proton. We will be particularly interested in the relations between the standing waves and the semiclassical orbits of the Bohr model.

It is difficult to describe a three-dimensional standing wave, since four dimensions are actually required for the representation—three spacial dimensions plus one dimension to represent the amplitude. However, we can describe the wave by discussing the variation of the amplitude in various directions, since for rather subtle reasons, which arise from the symmetry of the atom, it is possible to consider the variation of the amplitude of the wave in certain different directions separately.

To introduce the particular methods we choose to describe the wave, we first look at one- and two-dimensional standing waves in a classical medium. Figure 23|6 shows the displacement of a string at a particular instant where the string is oscillating with a definite frequency in a standing-wave mode. The observer

Observer measuring
amplitude of wave

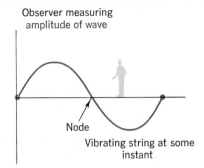

Node

Vibrating string at some
instant

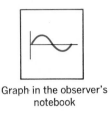

Graph in the observer's
notebook

FIG. 23|6

A standing wave and
the description of the
wave.

can walk along the string, frozen in time, measure the displacement, and then construct a plot of displacement versus distance
along the string. This graph (which will look very much like the
position of the string) will be an adequate representation of the
configuration of the string in that standing wave. Notice that
aside from the boundaries, there is one node for this particular
configuration, which is marked in the diagram. For a higher
overtone, which would vibrate with a greater frequency, there
will be more nodes. Obviously the wavelength is shorter if there
are more nodes and the frequency is therefore higher.

One can construct a similar description of a two-dimensional
wave: for example, an observer could measure the displacement
of a circular drumhead at some particular time, where the drumhead is vibrating with some definite frequency, and make a clay
model of the drumhead that would certainly reflect the pertinent
characteristics of the standing-wave mode of the drumhead.
However, the observer could also measure the amplitude as he
moved from the center of the drumhead to the outer edge and
construct a graph of the displacement as suggested by the sketch
of Fig. 23|7b. He could also walk around in a circle, concentric
with the edge of the drum, record the amplitude and plot a graph.
The two graphs will contain all the information that might be
found on the clay model. We can represent the amplitude over
the two-dimensional face of the drum in two separate one-dimensional plots, plots of the variation of amplitude with radius and
the variation of amplitude with azimuthal angle about the drumhead, only because of the symmetry of the drum: the drum is
round. But we often deal with symmetric situations: atoms have
a spherical symmetry, and the electrostatic force between the
electron and the proton depends only upon the distance between
them; the force is spherically symmetric.

For a two-dimensional standing wave the nodes consist of lines. Dashed lines are used to mark the nodal lines on the surface of the drum shown in Fig. 23|7; the boundary can be considered to form another nodal line, making four nodal lines altogether. The concept of wavelength is somewhat obscure on such a surface, but it is qualitatively clear that the mean wavelength along the surface of the drum will be smaller if there are many nodal lines. Even as the frequency of a vibrating string is then greater if there are many nodal points, the frequency of a vibrating drumhead, vibrating in one frequency, will be greater if there are more nodal lines.

The boundary condition on the string, which constrains the possible set of standing waves, is the condition that both ends are tied down and the amplitude of the standing wave must be zero at each end. A similar boundary condition holds for the drumhead. The drumhead is constructed such that the edge of the surface is held down, and the standing wave on the drumhead must have an amplitude that is zero at the edge of the drum. The boundary condition constraining the standing waves of an electron bound to a proton in a state of negative energy—that is, energy must be provided to tear the electron completely away from the proton—is similar: the probability of the electron being very far from the proton is zero and thus the de Broglie amplitude of the wave must go to zero for large distances from the proton.

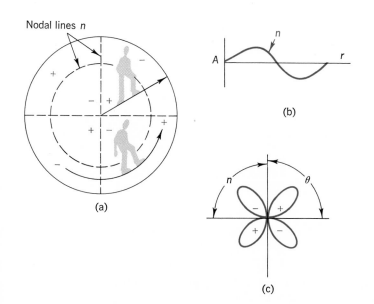

FIG. 23 |7
A two-dimensional standing wave. (a) A vibrating drumhead at a particular instant "+" means deflection upward, "—" means downward. Two observers are shown measuring the amplitude, one along a radial path, the other along an azimuthal path. (b) Graph of amplitude versus radius constructed by the first observer. (c) Polar graph of amplitude versus angle constructed by the second observer.

Before attempting to discuss in detail the particular standing waves that are to represent the states of the hydrogen atom, we may find it useful to review briefly the character of the de Broglie standing waves discussed in Chapter 14. The total energy, E, of a state is constant (and negative if the electron is bound to the proton), though both the kinetic and the potential energy will vary with the distance, r, between the electron and proton. In general,

$$E = T + V$$

or

$$T = \frac{p^2}{2m}$$

$$= \frac{ke^2}{r} - |E| \tag{23|6}$$

where p is the electron momentum and $|E|$ represents the absolute value of the total energy, or $|E|$ is the binding energy of the electron–proton system. The de Broglie wavelength of the electron is $\lambda = h/p$, and the standing wave at any point, taken in a particular direction, will have a shape very much the same as a sine wave of wavelength $\lambda = h/p$, where p corresponds to the component of momentum of the electron in that direction. In classical physics the value of the kinetic energy can never be negative; the particle will simply never be found at any place where the total energy will be less than the potential energy and the kinetic energy must be negative. Of course this is not the case over the very small distances of atomic physics, and negative kinetic energy, and thus (mathematically) imaginary momenta, are important. At any point where the momentum in some direction must be imaginary, the standing wave in that direction will have the shape of the function $\exp(-|p|r/\hbar)$, where $|p|$ is the absolute value of the momentum.

It is hardly necessary to add that the foregoing remarks are not intended to provide any precise formula for the construction of the standing waves, but they may be useful in providing a qualitative background for the discussion of the waveforms as derived exactly using mathematical techniques that are beyond our present interest.

A typical set of maps for the amplitudes of a particular standing wave, or state, or orbit, of the hydrogen atom is shown in Fig. 23|8. Here the observer makes three maps, which describe the amplitude of the de Broglie wave for the three-dimensional

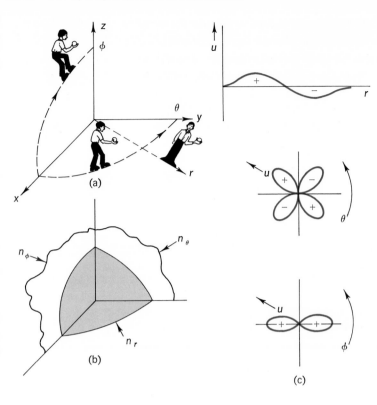

(a)

(b)

(c)

FIG. 23 |8

Description of a three-dimensional standing wave. (a) Observers with amplitude meters measuring amplitude with respect to radius r, θ, and ϕ. (b) An octant showing nodal surfaces. (c) Observers' maps of the variation of amplitude with radius, θ, and ϕ.

standing wave. We might assume that the observer is armed with a meter that measures the de Broglie wave amplitude and constructs the map from the reading of the meter. This is, of course, an imaginary procedure on two counts: aside from the difficulty of recruiting observers who are sufficiently small, we believe that the amplitude of a de Broglie wave is not directly observable or measurable. We only actually see or observe intensities, which are the squares of the amplitudes we construct to provide a description of the phenomena of mechanics. The observable quantity is thus the square of the amplitude, u^2, where the value of $u^2\, dV$ at any point is equal to the probability of finding the electron in a small volume, dV, about that point.

Even as the waves on a one-dimensional string could be classified in terms of the number of nodal points on the line of the string, and the waves on the two-dimensional drumhead showed nodal lines on the plane of the drumhead, the three-dimensional de Broglie waves, which represent the probability distribution for the electron of the hydrogen atom, have nodal surfaces. There are four nodal surfaces for the wave shown in the diagrams of Fig. 23|8: two of the surfaces are planes intersecting the x-y plane at a definite values of θ, and the other nodal surfaces are spherical surfaces with definite radii, r. It is a convention to consider the surface at infinity as a nodal surface, since the wave must vanish at infinity. Just as the states of a vibrating string or vibrating drumhead can be classified in terms of the number of nodal points or nodal lines, the states of the hydrogen atom can be classified usefully in terms of the number of nodal surfaces of the standing wave.

23|6   *Standing waves and orbits*

Even as the elementary Bohr model of the atom, where the electron is pictured as moving in a classical orbit about the proton, correctly describes many aspects of the observations or the results of experiments conducted on the hydrogen atom, there must be a close relation between the semiclassical orbit representation of the atom and the wave-mechanical description. The diagrams of Fig. 23|9 show a set of standing-wave patterns together with the classical orbits that correspond to these states in the Bohr model. The state at the left can be recognized as a state such that the angular momentum of the electron about the proton has a value of $2\hbar$ or $L = 2$, and the direction of the angular momentum is perpendicular to the paper, corresponding, then, to an orbit in the plane of the paper. We can deduce all of this from an inspection of the "maps" of the wave amplitude u, as u varies with angle. As one procedes in a full circle about the path in the θ-direction, taken here as in the plane of the paper, the sign of u changes four times: we have passed through two full waves. If the radius of our path about the proton is r, the circumference is equal to two wavelengths: $2\pi r = 2\lambda$. Then, since

$\lambda = h/p$,

$$2\pi r = \frac{2h}{p}$$

and

$$pr = 2\left(\frac{h}{2\pi}\right)$$
$$= 2\hbar$$

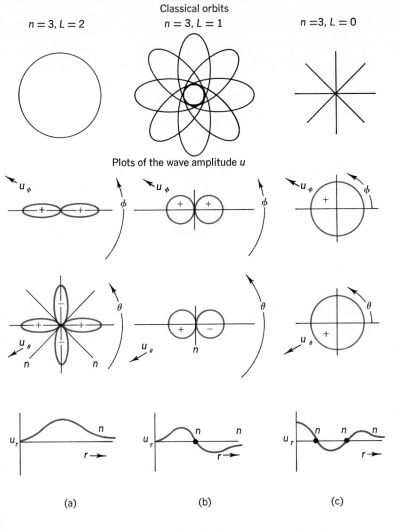

FIG. 23 19

Descriptions of the states of the hydrogen atom having a principle quantum number n = 3. The classical orbits are shown, together with the graphs that define the character of the de Broglie wave descriptions.

where $pr = mvr$ is the angular momentum of the electron about the proton. The diagram or map showing the value of the amplitude u as a function of ϕ shows no change in the sign of u, so the component of angular momentum perpendicular to a plane perpendicular to the paper is zero. The total angular momentum of the state is thus 2 units and the direction of the angular momentum is perpendicular to the paper.

The diagram of the value of u as a function of r again shows no change in the sign of u, thus no wavelengths in the r-direction, and thus no flow of momentum in the r-direction toward and away from the proton. An electron in a classical orbit that is a circle will have no component of motion toward or away from the proton, which suggests that this state corresponds to a classically circular orbit in the plane of the paper where the electron moves with 2 units of angular momentum; the angular momentum is equal to $2\hbar$; the *angular momentum quantum number L* equals 2.

The second state, shown in Fig. 23|9, can be analyzed similarly. There is only one wavelength in the traverse about the θ-direction, and none in the ϕ-direction, signifying that the state has a total angular momentum of 1 unit directed out of the plane of the paper: $L = 1$. There are now two nodes in the radial wave, suggesting some motion in the radial direction. A particle with energy E moving in a classical elliptical orbit will have less angular momentum than a particle with the same energy moving in a circular orbit, but the elliptical orbit represents a certain amount of motion toward and away from the focus which is the proton in this case. This standing wave, thus corresponds to a classical orbit that is an ellipse.

The de Broglie amplitude representing this state goes to zero at the origin of the coordinate system, which is the center of the classical orbit. This results from the centrifugal force associated with the presence of angular momentum. We can consider the centrifugal force very much as a normal repulsive force—which is infinitely strong at the origin—and the effect of this force is to reduce the probability of finding an electron near the origin. This zero in amplitude does not represent a nodal surface, and we do not count this in our accounting of the nodes of the standing waves.

The third state, Fig. 23|9c, shows a standing wave such that there are no wavelengths about either the θ-path or the ϕ-path, but there are three nodes in the radial wave. There is then no angular momentum at all, only motion of the electron back and forth toward the proton. This state then corresponds to the set of classical orbits such that the electron moves back and forth through the proton in a straight line like the bob on a pendulum.

Upon inspection of the diagrams or maps showing the wave function, u, for the three states of Fig. 23|9, it is clear that there are three nodal surfaces for each of these waves. From the results of an exact calculation of the wave equation (which we have not carried out, of course) we know that the total energy, E, is the same for each of these states and corresponds to the energy calculated from the Bohr formula of Eq. (23 | 5) if the quantum number, n, is taken as 3. This is just the number of nodal surfaces in the standing wave—a result that holds generally: for all standing waves of the hydrogen atom the *principle quantum number, n,* is equal to the number of nodal surfaces of the standing wave; the larger the number of nodal surfaces the larger the total energy and the smaller the binding energy.

We might add that the average distance between the proton and the electron for any given state is almost the same for the semiclassical Bohr model and for the wave-mechanical description of the state.

In the course of the discussion centered about the states of Fig. 23 | 9, only standing waves were considered, and only states such that the angular momentum was directed perpendicular to the paper. Of course, a standing wave is a superposition of running waves in opposite directions, so these states can be considered combinations of two states such that the angular momentum in a z-direction is equal to $+L\hbar$ and $-L\hbar$. Even as we use the symbol L for the magnitude of the total angular momentum in units of $\hbar$, we use the symbol m for the value of the component of angular momentum in a particular direction of "quantization," in this case the z-direction. For any state there must be an integral number of wavelengths about the circle in the x-y plane of the paper, or in the θ-direction of Fig. 23 | 9. If the total angular momentum is L there may be L waves, or $L-1$ waves, or $L-2$ waves, down to zero waves, corresponding to a component of angular momentum in the z-direction equal to $L\hbar$, $(L-1)\hbar$, . . . , $-(L-1)\hbar$, $-L\hbar$, and thus values of the quantum number m equal L, $L-1$, . . . , $-(L-1)$, $-L$. There will be $2L+1$ values of m, ranging from L to $-L$.

It is desirable to comment on the character of these descriptions of the hydrogen atom. When we say that a state can have only a specific integral value for the component of angular momentum in some arbitrary direction, what do we mean? Certainly we might choose some slightly different direction: how would the results differ then?

We choose to comment on these rather difficult and subtle questions (rather than attempt to answer the questions categorically) by examining a set of familiar observations that can be understood classically as well as quantum mechanically. Let us consider the polarization of a beam of light by a dichroic material such a piece of Polaroid. If the beam of light comes out of the paper in a z-direction, we can place the Polaroid so that only the half of the light that is polarized in an x-direction (which we might take as toward the top of the page for definiteness) will be transmitted and the half that is polarized in the y-direction will be absorbed. Physically the Polaroid acts so as to absorb completely any component of the electric field in the y-direction and to transmit the component in the x-direction. We might consider that we have determined by our observations that the beam of light consisted originally of a part polarized in the x-direction and a part polarized in the y-direction. But we could have set the Polaroid at a different angle and divided the beam of light into two parts in another way! Obviously there is an infinite number of ways to align a coordinate system. But the light can be divided into only two parts even as the electric field transverse to the direction of propagation of the light can be separated into only two independent components.

An atom, with a total angular momentum of $L\hbar$, may be more complicated than the beam of light, inasmuch as the atom will have $2L + 1$ different states rather than the two states of a light beam, but the general character of the description is otherwise the same. We can divide the states of an atom into $2L + 1$ separate states in an infinite number of ways even as there is an infinite number of ways to align a coordinate system, but once we have decided on a coordinate system, the atomic states can only divided into $2L + 1$ sensibly different parts.

PROBLEMS

23| 1　The binding energy of the lowest state of the hydrogen atom is 13.6 electron volts (eV), where $1 \text{ eV} = 1.6 \times 10^{-19}$ J. The radius of the orbit in the semiclassical Bohr model is 0.53×10^{-10} m.

(*a*) What is the binding energy of the state with the quantum number, n, equal to 2? Equal to 4? Equal to 70?

(*b*) What is the radius of the Bohr orbit for the state with $n = 2$? $n = 4$? $n = 70$?

(*c*) What is the binding energy of one electron to a helium nucleus, which has twice the charge of a proton?

(*d*) What is the radius of the Bohr orbit of the lowest state of one electron bound to a helium nucleus?

23|2 Using the semiclassical Bohr model,

(a) What is the value of v/c, where v is the velocity of the electron, in the first Bohr orbit of a hydrogen atom?

(b) What is the value of v/c for a electron in the third Bohr orbit?

(c) What is the current in amperes in the classical model for the electron in the first Bohr orbit? In the third Bohr orbit?

(d) What is the magnetic field at the position of the proton when the electron is in the $n = 3$, $L = 2$ Bohr orbit? (Use the semiclassical Bohr model, of course.)

23|3 A large sample of atoms each with a total angular momentum of $L = 1$ are in a container (these could be nitrogen atoms for example). We make the statement that $\frac{1}{3}$ of the atoms are oriented such that their angular momentum vectors are pointing up; also $\frac{1}{3}$ are pointing down; $\frac{1}{3}$ are pointing east; $\frac{1}{3}$ west; $\frac{1}{3}$ north; $\frac{1}{3}$ south. All of these statements can be considered correct. How can this be?

23|4 List all different states of the hydrogen atom with $n = 4$ by their different quantum numbers L, and m; there are 16 different states.

23|5 Draw graphs showing the variation of the wave function, u, for the electron in a state of the hydrogen atom such that $n = 2$, $L = 1$, and $m = 1$. Show the amplitude as it depends on r, θ, and ϕ.

23|6 In what way do the de Broglie wave functions of the hydrogen atom differ for states with angular momentum $L = 0$, and the principle quantum number, n, equal to 1, 2, 3, and 6?

23|7 What are the values of the quantum numbers n and L for the hydrogen-atom state described by the graphs of the de Broglie amplitude shown here?

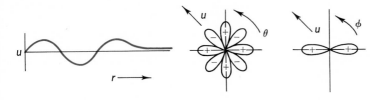

23|8 Noting that the binding energy of an electron–proton system in the ground state (the state with the largest binding energy) is 2.1×10^{-18} J (or 13.6 eV) and the radius of the Bohr orbit is 0.51×10^{-10} m,

(a) What will be the binding energy and orbit size of a muon–proton system in the ground state? (The muon is an elementary particle which appears to be exactly like an electron except that the muon mass is 207 times as great as the electron mass.)

(*b*) An antiproton can be considered at this time to be exactly like a proton except that all electrical charges are reversed in sign. The antiproton is thus negative, whereas the proton carries a positive charge. The antielectron is called the positron and can be considered to be exactly like the electron except that the positron carries a positive unit charge instead of a negative charge. How will the energy levels and standing-wave states of an antihydrogen atom (made up of an antiproton and a positron) differ from the energy levels and states of the hydrogen atom?

twenty-four   The atom—II
Radiation and the
exclusion principle

24|1   *Electromagnetic radiation from the atom*

ACCORDING TO THE Bohr model of the hydrogen atom, the electron moves about the proton in an orbit that has the form of an ellipse or circle. From the correspondence principle we know that this model must be very mearly valid if the principle quantum number, n, is large. An electron in such an orbit continually undergoes an acceleration toward the center of the orbit. According to our classical calculations concerning radiation, an accelerating charge will radiate energy in the form of electromagnetic waves. We must therefore expect that an atom will radiate electromagnetic energy in general.

The character of the electric field that results from the combination of a positive charge and a negative charge is suggested by the drawing of Fig. 24|1a. If the negative charge rotates about the positive charge, the field at a particular point will change with time. The changing field that will result from the movement of the negative charge (the electron) about the positive charge (the proton) will be very nearly that described by rotating Fig. 24|1a about the positive charge as suggested by the sketch of Fig. 24|1b.

The electric-field vector, at a point in the plane of the orbit far from the system, will lie in the plane of the orbit and will

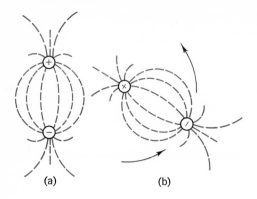

(a)   (b)

FIG. 24│1

The electric-field lines connecting a positive charge and an equal negative charge: the negative charge is rotating about the positive charge.

vary in intensity sinusoidally in time as suggested by the graph of Fig. 24│2a. The electric field at a point far from the orbit, in a direction perpendicular to the orbit, will vary with time approximately as shown in Fig. 24│2b. The electric vector will lie in a plane approximately normal to the vector from the orbit to the point under observation. Notice that in this case the magnitude of the field does not vary, only the direction. In each case the time scale on the diagrams extends to one full revolution of the charge in orbit. The field variations for the points in the plane of the orbit are the same as one would expect from a charge oscillating with simple harmonic motion with the same frequency as the frequency of revolution. Indeed, from an edge-on view, a particle moving in an orbit will appear to move in a manner that is identical to a particle oscillating with simple harmonic motion.

The electric field at points far from the rotating system that lie

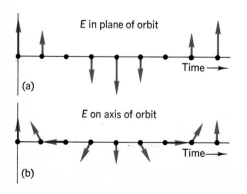

E in plane of orbit

Time →

(a)

E on axis of orbit

Time →

(b)

FIG. 24│2

The electric-field vector as a function of time (a) at a position in the plane of the orbit, far from the orbit, and (b) at a position on the axis of the orbit, again far from the orbit.

in the plane of the orbit will be *linearly polarized:* the magnitude of the field will vary with time, but the field vector will always lie along the same line. The field at points far from the system in a direction perpendicular to the plane of the orbit will be *circularly polarized:* the magnitude of the field will be constant, but the direction of the field vector will rotate at the same frequency as the frequency of rotation of the electron about the proton. Energy will be radiated by the rotating (and therefore accelerating) charge in the form of electromagnetic waves, even as any change in an electric field results in some radiated energy. At optical frequencies the electromagnetic radiation is light: the atom emits linearly and circularly polarized light.

These are classical concepts. Since quantum mechanics must give the same answers as classical mechanics when the quantum numbers are large (the correspondence principle), electrons in large Bohr orbits must radiate energy even as they induce changing electric fields. Furthermore, they must emit polarized radiation according to the classical prescriptions.

According to the classical description of the hydrogen atom, which must be nearly valid for very large orbits, the electrons must spiral in toward the proton as they lose energy through radiation. The smaller orbits correspond to states of less energy (or greater negative energy) than the larger orbits. This classical description of radiative energy loss must be modified by quantum-mechanical considerations that tell us that the electrons can have only discrete energies: the electrons must therefore lose energy in discrete amounts. The smallest energy change will correspond to the energy lost in changing from a large orbit, corresponding to a large quantum number, n, to the next-lower-energy orbit, corresponding to a smaller quantum number $n - 1$. The energy difference is

$$dE = E_n - E_{n-1}$$

where

$$E_n = -\frac{1}{2}\frac{k^2 e^4 m}{n^2 \hbar^2} \quad \text{and} \quad E_{n-1} = -\frac{1}{2}\frac{k^2 e^4 m}{(n-1)^2 \hbar^2}$$

Then

$$dE = \frac{1}{2}\frac{k^2 e^4 m}{\hbar^2}\left[\frac{1}{(n-1)^2} - \frac{1}{n^2}\right]$$

We rewrite the quantity in the brackets as

$$\frac{1}{(n-1)^2} - \frac{1}{n^2} = \frac{n^2 - (n-1)^2}{n^2(n-1)^2} = \frac{2n-1}{n^4 - 2n^3 + n^2}$$

which, for very large values of n—in the limit of the correspondence principle—is almost exactly equal to

$$\frac{2n}{n^4} = \frac{2}{n^3}$$

Using this approximation, which is valid in the classical limit when n is very large, we have for the energy difference

$$dE = \frac{k^2 e^4 m}{n^3 \hbar^2} \tag{24 | 1}$$

We can also calculate the frequency of revolution of the electron in such an orbit. From our previous results concerning the Bohr model the radius a_n of a circular orbit associated with the principle quantum number n is

$$a_n = \frac{n\hbar}{ke^2 m}$$

and

$$mva_n = n\hbar$$

or

$$v = \frac{n\hbar}{ma_n}$$

The frequency of revolution is equal to the velocity of the electron divided by the distance traveled in one revolution, which is the circumference of the orbit:

$$f = \frac{v}{2\pi a_n}$$

$$= \frac{n\hbar}{2\pi m a_n^2}$$

Substituting for a_n,

$$f = \frac{k^2 e^4 m}{2\pi n^3 \hbar^3}$$

Comparing this result with the previous expression (24 | 1) for *dE*, we have

$$dE = 2\pi\hbar f \quad \text{or} \quad dE = hf$$

The energy of the atom is lost in discrete amounts or *quanta* equal to *hf*, where *f* is the frequency of revolution of the electron and therefore the frequency of oscillation of the electromagnetic field.

Our discussion has been limited to the analysis of radiation by electrons moving in perfectly circular orbits in the classical limit of the correspondence principle. Even for classical orbits some radiation will be emitted at higher frequencies, harmonics of the fundamental, if the orbits are elliptical. This radiation would correspond to changes of several units of the principle quantum number, *n*, in the Bohr model even as the frequency would be several times the frequency of the fundamental transition where *n* changes by 1. The relation

$$dE = hf \tag{24|2}$$

will still hold, though the change in energy now represents the energy difference between orbits or states that have values of *n* that differ by more than 1 unit.

Indeed, relation (24|2) is completely general and holds for all states of atoms, molecules, nuclei, and elementary particles— indeed, for all systems of electric charges and currents. Then with complete generality,

$$dE = E_i - E_j = hf \tag{24|3}$$

where E_i and E_j are the energies of different stationary states of the electrical systems—or different orbits of the hydrogen atom. Inversely, all of these systems, and specifically the proton– electron system that we call the hydrogen atom, can only absorb electromagnetic energy in such a way that the system changes states or changes orbits. Since the orbits correspond to specific energies, only specific energies can be absorbed. Relation (24|3) thus holds for absorption as well as emission.

The change of orbits in the classical model of circular orbits demands not only a change of energy but also a change of 1 unit, $\hbar$, of angular momentum. If we are to retain the laws of conservation of energy and conservation of angular momentum, we must assume that the radiation carries off that amount of energy and angular momentum. The absorption of radiation by the atom is thus associated with the absorption of a specific quantity of energy and a specific quantity of angular momentum even as the radiation by the atom occurs in discrete quanta of energy and angular momentum.

The circularly polarized light emitted normal to the plane of the orbit thus carries off one unit of angular momentum—an intuitively plausible result. The direction of the angular-momentum vector is in the direction of propagation of the light for light coming out of the paper from an electron rotating as in Fig. 24 | 1b. The linearly polarized light emitted in the plane of the orbit can be considered as a superposition of two circularly polarized quanta—one left-circularly polarized and the other right-circularly polarized. Only one unit of angular momentum is carried away: the probability is $\frac{1}{2}$ that it is right circularly polarized.

Unpolarized light emitted from an ordinary source, such as the sun or a tungsten filament, can be considered to consist of a very large number of incoherent photons, half left-circularly polarized and half right-circularly polarized.

24 | 2   *Energy levels and spectra*

Using the relation $dE = hf$ and the expression (23 | 4) for the energies of the various states of the hydrogen atom, we can express the whole set of possible energy differences between states of the atom, and thus the whole set of possible frequencies of electromagnetic radiation emitted by hydrogen atoms, as

$$dE_{ij} = \frac{1}{2} \frac{k^2 e^4 m}{\hbar^2} \left(\frac{1}{n_i^2} - \frac{1}{n_j^2} \right)$$

$$= hf_{ij} \qquad\qquad (24 | 4)$$

where n_i is the principle quantum number for the final state and n_j is the principle quantum number of the initial state of the atom. Even as the atom only exists in specific orbits or states associated with specific total energies, the atom can emit radiation only at discrete frequencies. The set of frequencies comprises the *spectrum* of the hydrogen atom. A large set of atoms highly excited to states with large values of n, perhaps by sparks or electric arcs in hydrogen gas, will radiate as the electrons jump to lower-energy orbits or states with smaller values of n. Under such circumstances a very large number of different frequencies of emitted radiation will be observed.

The particular set of frequencies expressed by Eq. (24|4), with $n_i = 2$, was known in the nineteenth century. Johann Balmer, a sixty-year-old Swiss high school teacher, working during his summer vacation, first expressed these frequencies as a rational numerical series rather like Eq. (24|4). Balmer's analysis of the numerical relations between the frequencies that correspond to the first four terms of the series, where $n_i = 2$, and $n_j = 3, 4, 5$, and 6, which he published in 1885, was a fundamental step in the development of the Bohr model of the hydrogen atom and thus of quantum mechanics. These four terms of the *Balmer series* represent frequencies that are in the visible region of the spectrum: the first term of the Lyman series, where $n_i = 1$, is in the ultraviolet, and the terms of the other series are in the infrared.

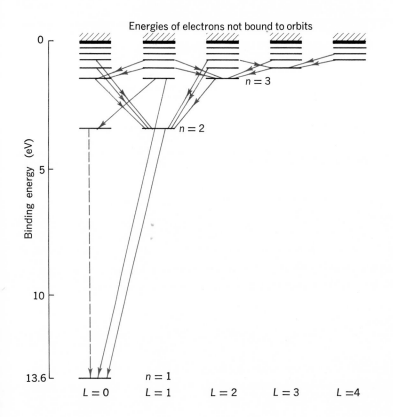

FIG. 24|3
The lower energy levels of the hydrogen atom, together with the transitions between the levels. The solid lines represent the allowed transitions where the angular momentum of the atom can change by one unit. The dashed line shows a forbidden transition, which can, however, occur with reduced probability.

Since the frequencies of emitted light are proportional to the energy released when an electron "jumps" from one orbit to another, it is convenient to construct an *energy level diagram* that gives the energies of the various states and thus the energies of the transitions. Such a schematic presentation of possible emission frequencies is shown in Fig. 24|3.

The states (or orbits) are shown by straight lines and labeled by the principle quantum number, n, and the angular-momentum quantum number, L. Each such state is shown as $2L + 1$ lines representing, schematically, the number of separate orientations of the orbit (or directions of the angular momentum). The energy scale is not in joules but in the measure we call *electron volts*. Even as. a joule is the amount of energy required to transfer a coulomb of charge through a potential difference of 1 V and is therefore a "coulomb volt." An "electron volt" is the energy required to transfer the electron charge through a potential difference of 1 V. One electron volt is equal to 1.6×10^{-19} J, as one electronic charge is equal to 1.6×10^{-19} C.

Since the photon carries off 1 unit of angular momentum, only transitions that change the angular momentum by 1 unit are "allowed." For these allowed transitions, $DL = \pm 1$, where DL is the change in L. (For reasons we will not discuss here, some of the forbidden transitions, such that the angular momentum does not change by just 1 unit, do occur, but the probability of such transitions is usually low.)

24 |3   *Photons—the Compton effect and the photoelectric effect*

We have discussed, in detail, only one very particular source of radiation, or sink of radiation, and found that such radiation carries energy in discrete quanta of size $E = hf$ and that each quantum carries an angular momentum equal to $\hbar$. Further, absorption is also restricted to such units. These results, derived from the behavior of the hydrogen atom, actually hold for all electrical systems and hold for all absorption and emission of electromagnetic radiation. No observation of electromagnetic radiation of any kind has ever resulted in the detection of a quantity of radiation that differs from the quanta so defined. It is then sensible, and in accord with our observational attitude towards physics, to condense this information about electromagnetic phenomena in the statement that electromagnetic radiation travels in quanta, which we call *photons*. Each photon carries an energy E equal to hf, where f is the frequency of the radiation, and an angular momentum equal to $\hbar$. From classical analyses of electromagnetic waves, we know that the photon must travel with the speed of light, c, and that the photon must carry an amont of momentum $p = E/c = hf/c$. All these characteristics are just those of a particle with an instrinsic angular momentum or spin of $\hbar$. The de Broglie wavelength of the particle is

$$\lambda = \frac{h}{p}$$

$$= \frac{h}{(E/c)}$$

Since

$$E = hf$$

then

$$\lambda = \frac{h}{(hf/c)}$$

$$= \frac{c}{f}$$

which is just the relation between frequency, wavelength, and velocity for any wave and, in particular, for electromagnetic waves. The electromagnetic wave is thus a de Broglie wave for the photon. The probability of finding a photon in a volume dV is proportional to the energy stored in that volume, which in turn is proportional to the square of the amplitude of the wave—that is, the square of the electric-field strength or the magnetic-field strength.

We can use the Special Theory of Relativity to express the mass of the photon in terms of the energy and the momentum of the photon:

$$m_0 = \frac{1}{c}\left[\left(\frac{E}{c}\right)^2 - p^2\right]$$

But $p = E/c$; therefore, the rest mass of the photon, m_0, is equal to zero! The photon is a particle with a spin of $\hbar$ and a rest mass

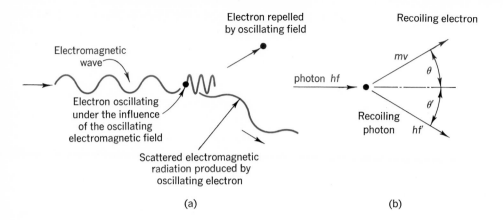

Electron repelled
by oscillating field

Recoiling electron

Electromagnetic
wave

photon *hf*

Electron oscillating
under the influence
of the oscillating
electromagnetic field

Recoiling
photon   *hf'*

Scattered electromagnetic
radiation produced by
oscillating electron

(a)

(b)

FIG. 24 I4

*A classical picture (a)
and the quantum-
mechanical picture (b)
of the scattering of
radiation by an electron.*

equal to zero; but this does not preclude its carrying energy and momentum.

The particle aspect of these packets of electromagnetic energy or photons is particularly evident when collision-type processes between radiation and free electric charges, such as electrons, are considered. Figure 24 I 4a is meant to illustrate some aspects of the scattering of an electromagnetic wave by a free electron. Classically we consider such a process as follows: The oscillating electric field, E, produces an oscillating force on the electron, which causes the electron to move in simple harmonic motion where the energy of the electron is supplied by that field. The oscillating electron sets up an oscillating electric field, E', and radiates energy. The electron is therefore gradually pushed away by forces associated with this exchange of radiation.

According to the (correct) quantum-mechanical description of the process, the absorption of energy by the electron does not take place gradually and continuously; the electron absorbs energy and momentum in impulses just as if photons collided elastically with the electrons. When the frequency of the electromagnetic radiation is very large, and the energy held by a photon is large, single collisions are often observed. The constraints of conservation of momentum and conservation of energy then result in definite relations between the momenta and energy of the scattered particles. The collision is shown schematically in Fig. 24 I 4b.

From the conservation of energy,

$$hf = hf' + \tfrac{1}{2}mv^2 \qquad\qquad (24\ I\ 5)$$

From the conservation of the transverse component of momentum,

$$mv \sin \theta = \frac{hf'}{c} \sin \theta' \tag{24|6}$$

From the conservation of the longitudinal component of momentum,

$$\frac{hf}{c} = \frac{hf'}{c} \cos \theta' + mv \cos \theta \tag{24|7}$$

Where m is the electron mass and v is the electron velocity.

We see that the photon scatters, losing energy. The energy loss manifests itself in the reduced frequency of the scattered photon. These discrete collisions of photons with electrons were first observed by Compton, and this particle-like scattering of the photon by an electron is called the *Compton effect*.

When low-frequency electromagnetic radiation, such as radio waves, is incident on an electron, we find that the subsequent motion of the electron is very much the same as we might expect from classical considerations. If the frequency of radiation is low, the energy carried by a single photon will be extremely small. The energy taken up by the electron must therefore be transferred by the collisions of very many photons, and these photons will act together so that the results of the many collisions follow the classical prescriptions. Of course, this is an example of the applicability of the correspondence principle.

The inverse of the Compton effect, the scattering of photons by charged particles, also occurs in nature. High-energy photons (X rays) are found as a part of the cosmic radiation that fills the interstellar regions of the galaxy, and some part of the high-frequency electromagnetic radiation appears to be derived from the collisions of the very-high-energy charged particles in cosmic rays with the low-frequency, low-energy, photons of the starlight.

When electromagnetic waves of sufficiently high frequency are incident upon metal, electrons are immediately ejected from the metal. The maximum kinetic energy of the electrons is observed to be

$$E_m = \tfrac{1}{2}mv^2$$

$$= hf - \phi \tag{24|8}$$

Where f is the frequency of the radiation and ϕ is a characteristic of the metal called the *work function* and is a measure of the energy required to extract an electron from the metal. This result is completely independent of the intensity of the radiation and depends only on the frequency. No matter how intense the radiation, no electron will be ejected if $hf < \phi$. On the other hand, even if the intensity of the radiation is very small, if $hf > \phi$, electrons will be ejected as soon as the radiation strikes metal: the emission of electrons begins instantaneously after the radiation begins.

According to a classical explanation, we would expect the electrons to gradually absorb energy from the field until they had enough energy to escape. This would be at the time the metal became extremely hot—indeed, heating does occur, but only after a long time. This effect is independent of frequency and depends only on the energy supplied to the metal. The immediate emission of electrons, with their energy related to frequency, can be understood only if discrete packets or quanta of energy are delivered to individual electrons. This *photoelectric effect* is thus, again, a quantum-mechanical effect—not explicable in classical terms. Einstein received the Nobel prize for his explanation, in 1905, of the photoelectric effect.

Again, the inverse also occurs. High-energy electrons striking metal, or any other material, generate high-energy photons, which are called X-rays. Classically we can understand the generation of electromagnetic radiation, since the electrons undergo an acceleration—or deceleration—as they stop. The maximum frequency of the radiation is not derivable classically, however: but from the particle or photon description of electromagnetic radiation required for consistency with the quantum mechanics of particles, the maximum frequency is obtained from a variation of Eq. (24 | 8),

$$hf = \tfrac{1}{2}mv^2 + \phi \qquad\qquad (24\,|\,9)$$

where f is the maximum frequency of the photons produced by electrons of mass m and velocity v. The maximum energy of the photon is thus just equal to the total energy of the electron plus the small additional energy of absorption of the electron described by the work function, ϕ.

24|4 *Identical particles and the exclusion principle*

The intensity of a standing de Broglie wave at any point is proportional to the probability of a particle being in a small volume
about that point. The sum or integral of the intensities of the wave
over all small volumes will be equal to the total number of particles represented by the standing wave. We might consider a
specific standing wave or state such that the total intensity over
the whole volume occupied by the wave corresponds to one
particle in the state: this might be the state of a particle in a box,
for example. Then if the amplitude of the standing wave is increased by a factor of $\sqrt{3}$, the intensity, which is proportional
to the square of the amplitude, will be increased by a factor of 3:
there will be three particles in the box, all in the same state. Assume the box with mirror walls contains an electromagnetic standing wave in a mode such that the frequency of the wave is f, and
the energy stored in the box is $3hf$; that is, three photons are stored
in the box. The energy may have been introduced into the box
through three discrete operations; the box may have been opened
to starlight to trap an amount of radiation to raise the energy from
zero to hf; then the box may have been opened to sunlight to
trap the second photon, and to the light of a candle to catch the
third photon and raise the stored energy to $3hf$. (In all of this we
speak with considerable poetic license; the experimental procedures described here are hardly practical.) Now the box holds
an electromagnetic standing wave of a frequency f and energy
equal to $3hf$. Further, the wave is completely described in terms
of the amplitude of the wave, which represents a state of three
photons. It now makes no sense to number the three photons—
all photons are identical—and by stating that there are three
photons in the box we are merely assigning a magnitude to the
amplitude of the wave. The acceptance of the absolute equivalence of the three photons is equivalent to assigning an identity
to the three photons and then stating that any ordering of the
three cannot make any observable difference. We might number
the photon from the starlight as 1, the photon from the sun as 2,
and the photon from the candle as 3, and write the amplitude of
the wave as $A(1, 2, 3)$ where 1, 2, 3 represents some order, per-

haps the order of reception of the photons: but since the 3 photons are indistinguishable, $A(1, 2, 3) = A(1, 3, 2) = A(2, 3, 1)$, and so on. The final result is independent of the order in which the state was filled, since the photons are identical. *If we exchange any two photons, the amplitude remains the same.* This rule holds not only for photons but for every set of identical particles that have integral values of their intrinsic angular momentum or spin —$0\hbar$, $1\hbar$, $2\hbar$, and so on (we recall that the photon has a spin of $1\hbar$). We call these particles *bosons* after the Indian physicist (and botanist) J. C. Bose.

We can gain some understanding of the observable consequences of this absolute identity of particles by considering certain characteristics of simple systems. Let us assume that we have a large set of systems such that each system has two states —such as two standing waves of a particle in a box or two Bohr orbits of a hydrogen atom—and these systems hold two particles distributed randomly among the states. In general, some of the systems will have two particles in one state and none in the other, while some systems will have each state occupied by one particle. If the particles are not identical, what is the probability that each state is occupied by one particle? What proportion of the systems have one particle in each state? The diagrams of Fig. 24|5a show the various equivalent possibilities: it is clear that half of the systems will have a particle in each of the two states.

If the particles are identical bosons, the two configurations with one particle in each state will not be distinguishable and will represent but one possibility instead of two. The probability of two states being occupied will then be $\frac{1}{3}$ instead of $\frac{1}{2}$. The numbers or labels attached to the particles are now irrelevant.

Although the statistics of the nonidentical particles is similar to what we might expect classically, the statistics of the identical particles has no clear classical counterpart. If we throw two balls, colored red and green, into a box divided into two equal parts by a partition, the probability of finding the two balls in different parts of the box will be $\frac{1}{2}$ if the throws are made randomly. As we make the balls more nearly identical by painting both red, the probability will not change. Even if the balls were so nearly alike that we could not differentiate between them by any measurement that we can make in practice, the probability of finding the two balls in different parts of the box would still remain at the value of $\frac{1}{2}$.

The balls are not really identical: if we made more subtle tests we would surely find some difference. And the two sides of the box represent, not two different states, but two different sets of states where each set represents an extremely large number of differentiable states: there are very many ways in which one ball can rest in one side of the box. When we talk about states in the microscopic realm where we must use quantum mechanics, we mean but one unique standing wave or orbit, and when we say that the particles are identical, we use the term *identical* in an absolute manner that has, effectively, no classical counterpart. The *Bose statistics* of the two elementary particles in the two states of Fig. 24|5b, is a quantum-mechanical concept.

Some particles are observed to have half-integral values of $\hbar$ as their intrinsic angular momentum; $\frac{1}{2}\hbar$, $\frac{3}{2}\hbar$, $\frac{5}{2}\hbar$, and so on. Of course, this does not fit into our simple standing-wave picture of angular momentum: how can one have one-half standing wave around a circle? If $s\hbar$ is the value of the angular momentum, there are $2s + 1$ different orientations, just as was the case for particles with integral angular momentum. These particles are called *fermions*, after Enrico Fermi. The electron and the proton both have a spin of $\frac{1}{2}$ and are thus fermions.

Aside from their half-integral spin, fermions have another unusual property: two identical fermions are never observed in the same state. If we perform the model experiment exhibited

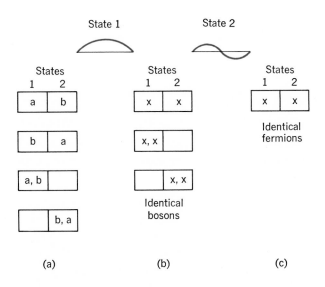

FIG. 24|5

The different possible distributions of two particles among two different states or standing waves. Particles that are not identical are labeled a and b.

in Fig. 24|5 with fermions, we will find that all of the systems have the two particles in different states. We are able to include this property of fermions in the description of nature we call quantum mechanics by postulating that the amplitude of a state of two (or more) identical fermions changes sign upon the interchange of the two (any two) fermions. If two fermions occupy the same state, interchanging the two particles cannot change anything; but the amplitude of the wave must change sign: the paradox is removed only if two identical fermions cannot occupy the same state. The probability of the two identical fermions occupying the two different states of Fig. 24|5c is therefore 1 rather than $\frac{1}{2}$ for the different particles and $\frac{1}{3}$ for the identical bosons: the statistical probabilities are different. We say that fermions obey *Fermi–Dirac statistics*.

The nearest classical equivalent to an occupation of the same state by two particles is the occupation of the same point in space by two particles. If two electrons occupy the same point, an exchange of the two particles cannot result in any change; but according to the exclusion principle such an exchange must change the sign of the de Broglie wave that describes the state of the two particles. Therefore two electrons cannot occupy the same point in space.

This "exclusive" property of fermions is known as the *Pauli exclusion principle*, after W. Pauli who first clearly expressed this formulation of the character of nature. We cannot expect to relate these properties of fermions, the exclusion principle, and the half-integral spin to classical models and our macroscopic experience. Pauli has shown that the two properties are related to each other and to the requirement that no signals travel faster than light even in the microscopic world of quantum mechanics. We admit these ideas as experimental facts or as constructs that directly account for experimental observations.

24 |5   *The periodic table of the elements*

We can now understand much of the bases of Mendeleev's Periodic Table of the Elements from the character of the electronic structure of the atoms determined by the exclusion principle. The energy levels or orbits of the heavier atoms, where the nucleus has a larger charge than the charge of the proton, are much the same as the Bohr orbits of the hydrogen atom, except that the energies are greater and the radii smaller. Since the charge of the nucleus is greater than 1, the nucleus can hold more than one electron before the atom is neutral—of course, a neutral atom will not attract another electron strongly.

The proton or hydrogen nucleus has an electric charge of one unit and will thus hold one electron. If the atom is not excited, the electron will be found in the least energetic state that is available, which is the $n = 1$ state: the only spacial state, or orbit, with $n = 1$ has zero angular momentum. The helium nucleus has a charge of 2 and will therefore hold two electrons which, again, will normally occupy the least energetic states that are available. Both of the electrons will go into the $n = 1$ space state or orbit, though the electron is a fermion. Since the electron has a spin of $s\hbar = \frac{1}{2}\hbar$ and since there are $2s + 1$ sensibly different orientations of a state with spin of $s\hbar$, there are $2(\frac{1}{2}) + 1 = 2$ different orientations or spin states of the electron. Since one electron in an orbit can point "up" and the other can point "down," they can be differentiated and are not identical: the exclusion principle does not operate, and the two electrons can occupy one orbit or space state. When two electrons occupy the $n = 1$ *shell*, the shell is filled; the exclusion principle forbids the occupation of that state by any more electrons.

The lithium nucleus has a charge of 3 and will therefore hold three electrons. Two of the electrons will fill the $n = 1$ shell, and the third will go into the lowest energy state that is left. This will be a state of the $n = 2$ shell; there are four spacial states for electrons comprising the $n = 2$ shell, one $L = 0$ state and three $L = 1$ states; each of these can be occupied by two electrons with their spins in opposite directions. The elliptical $L = 0$ state will have a little lower energy than the circular $L = 1$, state as the elliptical orbit will penetrate inside the positions of the inner electrons and thus the electron in that orbit will be attracted by a larger average charge than the electron in the circular orbit. Therefore, the third electron of the lithium atom will occupy the $n = 2$, $L = 0$ orbit.

The state or orbit with $n = 2$ and $L = 0$ will be filled in the beryllium atom, which holds four electrons. Starting with boron, with a charge of 5, the $n = 2$, $L = 1$ state will begin to fill: carbon, with a charge of 6 will have two electrons in that state, ni-

TABLE 24 | 1 *Electronic shell structure of the lighter elements*

n	L	Number of states $2(2L+1)$	Element	Number of electrons	
1	0	2	H	1	2 states in
			He	2	$n=1$ shell
2	0	2	Li	3	
			Be	4	
2	1	6	B	5	
			C	6	8 states in
			N	7	$n=2$ shell
			O	8	
			F	9	
			Ne	10	
3	0	2	Na	11	
			Mg	12	
3	1	6	Al	13	
			Si	14	
			P	15	
			S	16	18 states in
			Cl	17	$n=3$ shell
			Ar	18	
3	2	10	K	19	
			Ca	20	
			.	.	
			.	.	

trogen will have three, oxygen with a charge of 8 will have four electrons, flourine will have five, and the shell will be filled with six electrons in the case of neon, which has a nuclear charge of 10 and will hold ten electrons.

Electrons are added to other nuclei in the same way filling up the Bohr states in order of their decreasing binding energy. Table 24 | 1 lists the electronic configurations of the lighter nuclei.

The chemical properties of an atom are determined largely by the character of the outermost, least strongly bound electrons. As a result, the elements with corresponding outer-electron configurations, as the various electron orbits are filled, will have similar chemical properties. The chemically similar inert gases, helium, neon, and argon, have electronic configurations that represent closed shells or completed orbits: the $n = 1$ shell is closed with helium; the $n = 2$ shell is closed with neon; and the $n = 2$, $L = 1$ shell or orbit is closed or filled at argon. The chemically similar alkali metals, lithium, sodium, and potassium, each have one electron outside of a closed shell.

The electronic structure of the heavier elements is more complicated; the effective charge acting on electrons in highly elliptical orbits, which get very close to the nucleus, is greater than the charge acting on electrons in nearly equivalent circular orbits, which are screened from the nucleus by the electrons in the more tightly bound shells. As a result of this, the lowest energy, most strongly bound states with $n = 4$, which have highly elliptical orbits such that $L = 0$, are more strongly bound than the most circular orbits with $N = 3$. Although the level structure is thus more complicated than that suggested by our simple picture, it is defined by the same general concepts. The Periodic Table of Mendeleev is therefore understood in terms of the electronic structure of the atom, which in turn is determined by the constraints of the quantum conditions and the exclusion principle.

PROBLEMS

$h = 6.6 \times 10^{-34}$ J-sec; $e = 1.6 \times 10^{-19}$ C; $c = 3 \times 10^8$ m/sec; $ke^2/\hbar c = 1/137$; $a_0 = 0.5 \times 10^{-10}$ m; 1 eV $= 1.6 \times 10^{-19}$ J; if $hf = 1.0$ eV, $\lambda = 1.23 \times 10^{-6}$ m.

24|1 The power radiated by a moving charge was expressed as $P = dE/dt = \frac{2}{3}ke^2a^2/c^3$, where a is the acceleration of the charge and e is the charge. Using this expression, the Bohr model, and the correspondence principle,

(a) Estimate the time it takes for a transition to take place from the second Bohr orbit to the first.

(b) If the charge of the nucleus were 2 (that is, one electron about a helium nucleus), would the transition be faster or slower than for the hydrogen atom?

24|2 When radiation (light) containing all wavelengths passes through cold hydrogen gas, absorption lines are found (in the ultraviolet) that correspond to emission lines of the same wavelengths as are observed when electronic transitions take place to the $n = 1$ state of the atom. No other absorption lines are noted. When light from the sun is analyzed, absorption lines are found that correspond to emission lines that represent transitions to the $n = 2$ state of the atom as well as the $n = 1$ state. Explain the origin of the difference between the two observations. (This answer is not to be found directly in the text.)

24|3   If the eye can see electromagnetic radiation such that the wavelength is greater than 0.4×10^{-6} m (violet) and less than 0.7×10^{-6} m (red), what lines of the hydrogen spectrum lie in the visible region?

24|4   Although most of the light from the sun originates in transitions of the hydrogen atom, all frequencies are radiated, not just the frequencies calculated from the Bohr model and observed in the spectra from low-pressure gas-discharge tubes in the laboratory. Why the difference? (Again the answer is not to be found specifically in the text.)

24|5   Light having a wavelength of 0.4×10^{-6} m (violet light) interacts with a stationary free electron, which then recoils with a kinetic energy of 1.0 eV. What is the wavelength of the scattered radiation?

24|6   Light from a hydrogen-discharge tube is incident upon a substance, b, having a work function, ϕ, equal to 1 V. What minimum voltage, V, must be applied to plate a so that no electron from b will reach a?

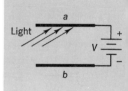

24|7   Electrons fall through a potential difference, V, into a region containing hydrogen gas at a very low pressure. A spectroscopist measuring the light emitted from the gas upon the electron bombardment notes the presence of transitions from the $n = 2$ state to the $n = 1$ state, but no others. What is the value of the voltage V?

24|8   Three particles fall randomly into three states of a system. If the particles have spins, assume that they are all pointing in the same direction. What is the probability of there being one particle in each of the three states

(*a*) If the particles are not identical?

(*b*) If the particles are identical bosons?

(*c*) If the particles are identical fermions?

24|9   (*a*) What is the radius of the classical $n = 2$ orbit, and what is the binding energy in that orbit for a lithium nucleus that has a charge of 3 units and is doubly ionized (that is, it is holding only one electron)?

(b) What is the radius of the $n = 2$ orbit, and what is the binding energy when the lithium nucleus is holding three electrons and the $n = 1$ shell is filled?

24|10 Write the electron configuration of boron (charge 5)

(a) For electrons as they are.

(b) For electrons if their spin were $\frac{3}{2}\hbar$.

(c) For electrons if their spin were zero and they were bosons.

24|11 In a universe such that the spin of the electron is $\frac{3}{2}\hbar$, what is the nuclear charge of the two lightest inert gases?

24|12 Prove that a free-moving electron cannot emit or absorb 1 photon. (Show that energy and momentum cannot both be conserved in such actions.)

24|13 The frequency of photons emitted by a certain atomic transition is measured to be f by an observer O near the excited atoms. An observer O', d m below O, measures the frequency as $f' = f(1 + gd/c^2)$, where g is the acceleration of gravity. Show that this result follows from the relations $E = mc^2$ and $E = hf$ (see Eq. 24|7).

25 | 1   *The short-range nuclear force*

THE NUCLEUS of the hydrogen atom is a proton. The nuclei of heavier atoms are made up of many neutrons and protons, which are closely related fermions with a spin of $\frac{1}{2}\hbar$. The neutron and proton masses are nearly equal and about equal to 1835 times the mass of the electron, the neutron being slightly the heavier. The proton is positively charged with a unit (electronic) charge; the neutron is neutral. We call them, together, *nucleons*.

Heavy nuclei are built up from large numbers of neutrons and protons: the bismuth nucleus, for example, consists of 83 protons and 126 neutrons. Nuclei are small on the atomic scale: the radius of the bismuth nucleus is about 6×10^{-15} m, or about 10^{-4} times as large as the hydrogen atom—or the bismuth atom. With 83 protons packed into a very small region, the electrostatic repulsion of the protons is very large. The only other force observable on the macroscopic scale is gravity, and the gravitational forces that hold the protons together in the nucleus are very much smaller than the electrostatic forces that push them apart—the ratio of the strength of the forces is about 10^{38}! We must therefore postulate some other force, which we call the *nuclear force,* not discernible macroscopically, that serves to hold the nucleus together.

We can draw some important conclusions concerning nuclear forces by considering some qualitative properties of nuclei. The

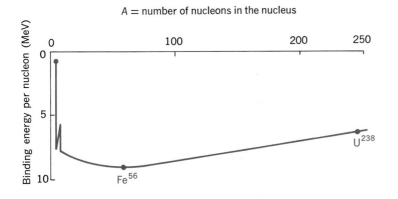

FIG. 25 | 1

The binding energy per nucleon, plotted against the number of nucleons in the nucleus.

graph of Fig. 25 | 1 shows the binding energy of nuclei per nucleon in millions of electron volts, or MeV, plotted against the total number of nucleons. This is just the total binding energy divided by the total number of nucleons: that is, the total energy required to seperate the nucleus into individual neutrons and protons widely separated from each other, all divided by the total number of nucleons. The curve is smoothed; it does not reflect the fluctuations of 1 MeV or so from nucleus to nucleus.

Except for the very lightest nuclei, the binding energy per nucleon is about constant at 8 MeV per nucleon. We note also that this value is much larger than typical atomic binding energies even as the nucleus is much smaller than the atom.

The constancy of the binding energy per nucleon tells us that the energy required to extract 1 nucleon from a nucleus is independent of the size of the nucleus. This differs from what we would expect if the nuclear force were a long-range force like gravitation or electrostatic forces. The energy required to remove 1 kg of matter from Jupiter is much greater than the energy required to remove 1 kg from the moon—all against gravitational forces. On the other hand, the energy required to remove 1 kg of water and disperse it into individual molecules as steam is the same—the heat of vaporization of water—whether the water is evaporated from a small saucepan, a pond, or the Atlantic Ocean. Here the forces holding the water molecules together are the short-range, van der Waals forces. The kilogram of matter on Jupiter was attracted sensibly, by every other kilogram of matter of Jupiter. Each water molecule is sensibly attracted only by its near neighbors. The analogy of nuclear binding to liquid condensation is thus obvious and suggests to us that nuclear forces, though they are very strong, have a very short range. This, of course, also explains the result that they do not manifest themselves particularly in macroscopic situations. The nuclear force between two pebbles, 1 cm apart, is immeasurably small.

25|2   *The Yukawa theory of the nuclear force and the pi meson*

The characteristics of the short-range nuclear forces were first expressed, semiquantitatively, by the Japanese physicist Yukawa in 1935. The electromagnetic force can be considered to take place through the agency of the electromagnetic field. The quanta of this field—the particles associated with this field—are photons, and photons have no rest mass; only the mass associated with the energy of motion of the electric field. Yukawa suggested that the nuclear force is transmitted also by a field. The nuclear charge must be much larger in magnitude than the electric charge, since nuclear forces are stronger than electrostatic forces, but the quanta of the nuclear field must have a finite mass, whereas the mass of the photon, which carries the electromagnetic force, is zero. Yukawa was able to show that a short-range force must result if the mediating particle has a finite rest mass. We can examine this very important idea using a combination of results from the special theory of relativity and from quantum mechanics.

First we discuss qualitatively the characteristics of a force between two stationary nucleons that arises from the exchange of a massive particle between them. We assume that the basic mechanism can be described in terms of the emission of the particle, which we call a meson, by one of the nucleons and the absorption of the particle by the other. If we write the nucleon mass as M, the total energy of the system before the exchange and after the exchange is equal to $2Mc^2$; but during the exchange the total energy must be greater at least by the rest-mass energy of the meson. If the meson mass is m, the total energy will therefore be equal to $(2M + m)c^2$, and it would appear that energy is not conserved in the process. But from the uncertainty principle the energy cannot be determined or defined to an accuracy greater than dE, where

$$dE \; dt \approx \hbar$$

where dt is the time of observation. Taking $dE = mc^2$ as the amount of excess energy, we see that there is no violation of the conservation of energy if the whole exchange is over in a time $dt \approx \hbar/mc^2$. In that time the meson cannot travel farther than a distance, a, equal to $c\, dt$; that is, the meson cannot travel faster than light. This distance, which is then the range of the force, will be about equal to

$$a = c\, dt$$

$$= c\, \frac{\hbar}{dE}$$

$$= c\, \frac{\hbar}{mc^2}$$

$$= \frac{\hbar}{mc}$$

where m is the meson mass: if the meson mass is large, the force will have a short range.

It is possible to derive much more detailed conclusions concerning the character of the nuclear force within the bounds of elementary procedures. The meaning of these procedures is particularly clear when they are also applied to the electrostatic force, which is familar to us.

The electrostatic force between two protons can be considered to result from the exchange of photons between the two protons. If the protons do not move appreciably, no energy is exchanged and the energy, E, of the photon must be zero. From the relation between energy, E, momentum, p, and rest mass, m, derived from the special theory of relativity,

$$m^2 = \left(\frac{E}{c^2}\right)^2 = \left(\frac{p}{c}\right)^2 \tag{25|1}$$

Since the photon has zero rest mass, the momentum, p, of the photon that is exchanged between the two protons is also zero. The de Broglie wave amplitude for a photon emitted from a source at the origin takes the form

$$A = A_0 \left(\frac{1}{r}\right) \cos\left(\frac{pr}{\hbar}\right)$$

which is the form for a wave moving outward from a source in a three-dimensional space. This form would be valid for any wave, such as a sound wave, for example, if the wavelength were equal to p/h and the amplitude at a distance r_0, very near the origin, where equal to r_0A_0. For a value of momentum equal to zero, $p = 0$, $\cos(0) = 1$, and the amplitude of the wave, A, varies with distance from the origin as $1/r$. The intensity is therefore proportional to $1/r^2$. If we consider that the momentum transferred between the two charges will be proportional to the number of photons absorbed by the charge, which will be proportional to the intensity of photons at the position of the charge, the momentum transfer per second, which is the force, will be proportional to $1/r^2$. Of course, this is just the relation familiar to us from Coulomb's law.

Following Yukawa, we can now use the same kind of reasoning to examine in more detail the character of the force between two nucleons when the force results from the momentum transferred between the nucleons by the exchange of a massive meson.

Again, if the nucleons are stationary, no energy will be exchanged and the energy of the mesons will be equal to zero. Then from Eq. (25 | 1),

$$p^2 = -m^2c^2$$

where m is the rest mass or invariant mass of the dominant meson, the pi meson, or the pion. The momentum is then imaginary:

$$p = imc$$

where

$$i = \sqrt{-1}$$

and

$$\frac{pr}{\hbar} = \frac{imcr}{\hbar}$$

The de Broglie wave then has the form

$$A = A_0 \left(\frac{1}{r}\right) \exp\left(-\frac{mcr}{\hbar}\right) \quad \text{or} \quad A = A_0 \left(\frac{1}{r}\right) \exp\left(-\frac{r}{a}\right)$$

where $a = \hbar/mc$ has the dimensions of length and is called the *Compton wavelength* of the pion. The close relation between the functions "exp" and "cos" was noted in Chapter 9. In the limit of zero mass for the pion, the amplitude varies with distance as $1/r$ (as $\exp(0) = 1$) and the intensity varies at $1/r^2$, again as the Coulomb force.

The force between the two nucleons separated by a distance r, which is mediated by the exchange of pions, is proportional to the momentum exchanged per second and thus to the number of mesons exchanged per second. This is in turn proportional to the density of mesons at a distance r and therefore to the intensity of the de Broglie wave at r. Thus

$$F \propto A_0^2 \left(\frac{1}{r^2}\right) \left[\exp\left(-\frac{r}{a}\right)\right]^2$$

We can carry the parallel between the electromagnetic force and the nuclear force further. Even as we write

$$F = \frac{ke^2}{r^2}$$

for the electrostatic force between two protons, where e is the electric charge of the proton, we can write

$$F = \frac{kg^2}{r^2} \left[\exp\left(-\frac{r}{a}\right)\right]^2 \tag{25|2}$$

for the nuclear force between two protons, where g is the mesonic charge, or strong-interaction charge, of the proton: g is measured in coulombs.

Nuclear forces can be either attractive or repulsive, depending upon the detailed interaction of the nucleon with the pions. The force between two nucleons separated by distances of the order of a is known to be attractive.

At close range the nuclear forces are much stronger than the

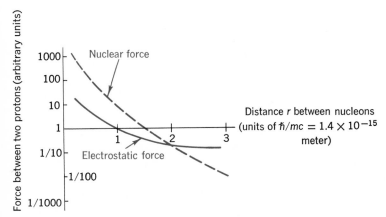

FIG. 25|2
The magnitude of the nuclear force and the magnitude of the electrostatic force between two protons plotted as a function of the distance between the two protons.

electrostatic forces between two protons. Since the nuclear forces are about 100 times as strong as the electrostatic forces, the nuclear charge, g, is about 10 times as large as the electrical charge, e. At large distances the factor $[\exp(-r/a)]^2$ becomes extremely small and the nuclear force becomes correspondingly small—very much smaller than the electrostatic force. When the distance, r, between the two nucleons is equal to a, the force is reduced by about a factor of 10 as a result of the exponential factor arising from the finite mass of the meson. The relative strength of the nuclear force and the electrostatic force between two protons, as a function of the distance between the two protons, is suggested by the graph of Fig. 25|2. At small distances the nuclear force is very much larger than the electrostatic force; at large distances the nuclear force becomes very much smaller than the electrostatic force.

The length $a = \hbar/mc$, the *Compton wavelength of the meson*, is therefore called, conveniently, the range of nuclear forces: the detailed result is then the same as the result of the elementary estimate using the uncertainty principle. Note that according to this convention for the range of forces, the range of the electrostatic force, with the mass of the photon equal to zero, is infinite.

The similarity of the electromagnetic field and the meson field associated with the nuclear force is shown further when radiation is considered. When an electric charge is accelerated, the electromagnetic field is changed and parts of the field are torn off; photons are emitted. When a nucleon, which is a source of the meson field, is accelerated sufficiently, parts of the meson field are torn off and mesons are emitted. In order to conserve energy, the energy lost by the accelerating charged particle must be equal to the energy of the photons; $E = hf$. Since photons can have very low frequencies, f, and thus very low energies, photons may be emitted for any change in the motion of a charge. Since mesons have a rest mass, at least as much energy must be given to the nucleon as the rest mass of the meson, mc^2, in order for mesons to be radiated. Therefore, only very violent accelerations of nucleons, generally from the result of collisions of very energetic particles, result in the emission of mesons. Mesons are observed to be produced in the course of these collisions, and the mass of the lightest of these mesons, the pi meson or pion, has been measured to be about 270 times the electron masses or about $\frac{1}{7}$ the nucleon mass. It is from these measurements of the pion mass that we get the value of $a = \hbar/m_\pi c = 1.4 \times 10^{-15}$ m for the range of the nuclear force.

Although the general character of the description of nuclear forces that has been presented here is essentially correct, the actual interaction between two nucleons is rather more complex. There are other mesons besides the pion or pi meson that contribute to the nuclear force; forces that result from the exchange of two or more mesons must be considered; and the various meson fields have different transformation properties than the electromagnetic field. The complications that arise from these factors have not been completely resolved, and we do not yet have as complete a description of nuclear forces as of electromagnetic forces.

25 |3 *Nuclear systematics and nuclear structure*

Nuclei behave very much like liquid drops in some respects—a consequence of the importance of short-range forces between the nucleons that make up the nucleus. Inside a nucleus, a nucleon will not feel a strong force, since the sum of the forces from the nucleons that uniformly surround the interior nucleon will necessarily add up to zero; the interior nucleon will be pulled almost equally in all directions, and the total force will therefore be nearly zero as shown in Fig. 25|3. A nucleon at the surface of the nucleus will be pulled toward the center by the interior nucleons, and there will be no compensating pull away from the center. There will thus be a certain total force on the nucleon holding it in the nucleus. The force on a water

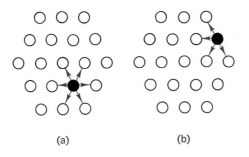

(a) (b)

FIG. 25|3
A schematic version of nucleons in a section of a nucleus, which suggests the character of the total force on interior nucleons and nucleons at the surface of the nucleus: (a) no total force on an interior nucleon; (b) a nucleon at the surface is attracted toward the center.

molecule on the surface of a water droplet is similar in character and is responsible for the surface tension of water. Even as the surface tension of water tends to force a small amount of water into a spherical shape, or drop, if no other forces are important, the surface tension of nuclear matter acts in such a way as to tend to force small amounts of nuclear matter—such as nuclei— into shapes that are nearly spherical.

A nucleon in a nucleus is thus very much like a nucleon in a spherical box: in the center of the nucleus or box there is no force on the nucleon; at the ends of the nuclear box there is a force that holds the nucleon inside the surface. We might therefore suspect that we can describe the state of a nucleon in the nucleus by a de Broglie standing wave very much like a standing wave in a box or the standing wave that describes the state of an electron in an atom. From this view the nucleus is very much like an atom: the neutrons and protons occupy particular standing waves or orbits in the nucleus even as electrons occupy specific orbits in atoms. At first thought this is surprising, since the density of nuclear matter is so great and the interactions between nucleons are so strong that one would expect the nucleon in the orbit to undergo a collision before the orbit was completed— indeed, before it were hardly started. That such collisions do not occur is a consequence of the exclusion principle; almost all of the states or orbits to which the nucleon could be scattered are occupied by other nucleons, and the struck nucleon, therefore cannot easily change orbits. Therefore, collisions cannot often take place.

Some of the nucleon orbits are very much like circles; some are very much like ellipses with large eccentricities. The nucleons in the largest orbits tend to pull the rest of the nuclear matter— that is, the other nucleons—along with them as a result of the strong attractive forces between the nucleons. The shape of the nucleus may thus be distorted, and many nuclei have shapes that deviate from a sphere. Nuclei exist that resemble oblate or prolate spheroids, such as suggested by the sketches of Fig. 25|4, as well as nearly perfect spheres.

We recall that a particular orbit or standing wave can be occupied by two electrons in an atom where the two electrons have their spins in opposite directions. A particular orbit or standing wave can be occupied by four nucleons in a nucleus even as there are four distinguishable nucleons; two neutrons

FIG. 25|4

Characteristic dominant orbits of outer nucleons of a nucleus, together with resulting nuclear shapes. (a) A circular orbit and a section of the oblate spheriod shaped nucleus that may result. (b) An elliptical orbit and a section of the prolate spheroid shaped nucleus that may result.

with spins in opposite directions and two protons with spins in opposite directions. Shell structures then exist in nuclei very much as shells exist in atoms. The simplest closed shell in atomic structure is represented by the helium atom with the first orbit filled with two electrons. The simplest closed nuclear shell is the helium nucleus, which consists of two neutrons and two protons in the same state or orbit. The fact that ordinary helium is a closed-shell atom and also a closed-shell nucleus is an accident. Since the character of the forces (or boxes) is different for atoms and nuclei, the shell structure is quite different.

Even as atoms with a given number of electrons are ordinarily found in the state of lowest energy—or lowest mass—since all other states will eventually decay to the lowest state by radiating energy, nuclei with a given number of nucleons will ordinarily be found in one of a few states that have the lowest energy or smallest mass. All other states will eventually decay into one of the lightest or least energetic states. Since some kinds of nuclear decay (beta decay, to be discussed later) operate in such a way as to change neutrons to protons or protons to neutrons, the lightest states will have a ratio of neutrons to protons that represents the tightest possible binding of all of the nucleons. The study of the constitution of nuclei can therefore be informative as to the dependence of the nuclear force upon the identity of the nucleons involved. In particular, we might determine the relative strength of the force between two neutrons, or two protons, or a neutron and proton.

The solid line in the diagram of Fig. 25|5a shows the locus of the stable nuclei on a plot of the number of neutrons versus the number of protons in the nucleus. The curve is schematic and designed to show the general character of nuclei; not all nuclei are listed. In particular, stable nuclei exist with the same

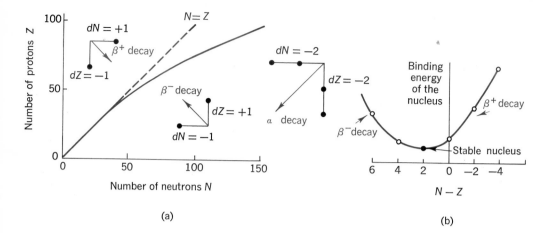

FIG. 25 I5

number of protons but different numbers of neutrons: these sets are called *isotopes* and have the same chemical properties. Conversely, nuclei with the same number of neutrons but with different numbers of protons are called *isobars*.

Plots showing (a) the loci of stable nuclei on a plot of neutron number N versus proton number Z, and (b) the binding energy for a typical nucleus with A nucleons as a function of the number N − Z, the excess of neutrons over protons. The stable nucleus is shown as a solid circle; the other nuclei are unstable with respect to beta decay.

Nuclei that lie off the stability curve of Fig. 25 I5a are unstable toward the change of a neutron to a proton or vice versa; that is, their binding energy would be increased or their mass decreased if a nucleon were transmuted. Since this can occur through beta decay, which we will discuss at more length later, these nuclei are unstable. The graph of Fig. 25 I5b shows a plot of binding energy or mass as a function of the difference between the number of neutrons and protons for nuclei with a given number of nucleons. The bottom of the curve, marked by the solid point, represents the locus of the stability curve of Fig. 25 I5a.

As we anticipated, the schematics of nuclei, as represented in the diagrams of Fig. 25 I5, does lead to qualitative conclusions concerning the character of nuclear forces. If the forces between two neutrons were attractive and very much larger than the forces between two protons, we would expect that it would require much more energy to separate a nucleus consisting of 12 neutrons into separate nucleons that it would to separate a nucleus consisting of 12 protons into separate protons; that is, we would expect that the binding energy of the neutron system to be much greater than the binding energy of the proton system and therefore that the neutron system would be lighter than the proton system. In fact, the lightest system of 12 nucleons is the system we know as the nucleus of carbon, which consists of 6 protons and 6 neutrons. This general result, shown clearly in Fig. 25|5a, that the stable light nuclei have equal numbers of neutrons and protons, suggests strongly that neutron–neutron forces and proton–proton forces are nearly equal. The electrostatic repulsion that results from the Coulomb forces of the very many protons in heavy nuclei is such that the effective attractive forces on the protons in the nucleus tend to be less than the forces on an equivalent neutron, so the heavy nuclei have more neutrons than protons.

A careful examination of specific nuclei is even more informative. The nuclei C^{14}, N^{14}, and O^{14} each consist of 14 nucleons. Their structure is such that each can be considered to be made up of a core of 6 protons and 6 neutrons, such as the C^{12} nucleus, plus 2 nucleons. Thus C^{14}, an isotope of carbon, is C^{12} plus 2 extra neutrons; N^{14}, normal nitrogen, is C^{12} plus an extra neutron and an extra proton; and O^{14}, an isotope of oxygen, is C^{12} plus 2 extra protons. The added nucleons go into the same orbit, state, or standing wave, and the 2 neutrons and 2 protons must have their spins in opposite directions, since they are fermions and the exclusion principle does not allow two identical fermions to occupy the same state. The diagrams of Fig. 25|6 represent the configurations symbolically in order to facilitate the counting of the various bonds of force.

From an inspection of the diagram it is clear that each of the outer nucleons makes 6 neutron–proton bonds with the core and 6 bonds that are either neutron–neutron bonds or proton–proton bonds. Since the equivalence of neutron–neutron forces and proton–proton forces was established, each of the outer nucleons will be bound to the core with the same energy if we can neglect electromagnetic forces. Since the charge of O^{14} is 8 (unit charges of 1.6×10^{-19} C), the charge of N^{14} is 7, and the

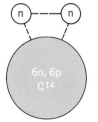  

FIG. 25|6

A schematic diagram of the triplet set O^{14}, N^{14}, and C^{14}, designed to show the different force bonds that contribute to the binding energy.

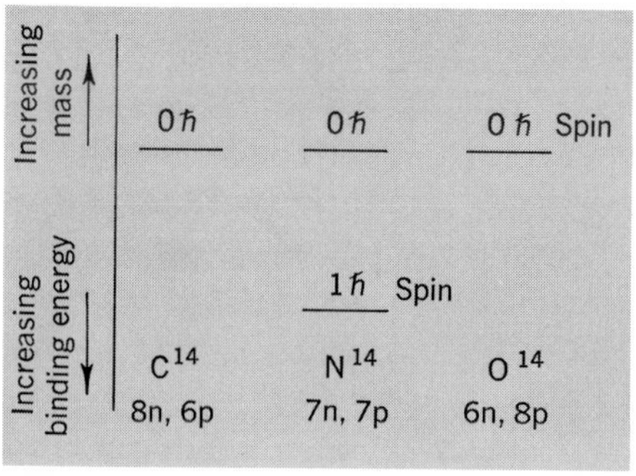

FIG. 25|7

The masses, or binding energies, of the lowest states of O^{14}, C^{14}, and N^{14}.

charge of C^{14} is 6, the energy stored in the electrostatic field of O^{14} is greater than the electrostatic energy of N^{14}, which is greater than the electrostatic energy of C^{14}. When this difference is taken into account, the corrected masses of the three spin-zero states are almost identical, as shown in Fig. 25|7.

If the masses of the three nuclei are equivalent, then the binding energies of the three nuclei must be equal. The binding energies can be equal only if the forces between the two outer nuclei are equal; the force between a neutron and proton must be the same as the forces between two protons or the forces between two neutrons. If the neutron–proton force were greater than the proton–proton force or the neutron–neutron force, it would take more energy to break up N^{14} than either C^{14} or O^{14}. Then N^{14}, with the greater binding energy, would have the smaller mass. The equivalence of the mass (corrected for electromagnetic forces) thus establishes the equivalence of neutron–proton force and the neutron–neutron and proton–proton forces.

In summary, the nuclear force between two nucleons is independent of the labels neutron and proton, and thus independent of the charge of the nucleon. As far as nuclear forces are concerned, the forces are *charge independent*; we can consider that there is only one *nucleon*—with two different charge states even as there are two different spin directions.

There is a considerable body of evidence concerning the charge independence of nuclear forces. We have presented only one small, but convincing part of the evidence.

For completeness, we mention that the forces between two nucleons can depend upon their relative spin orientation. The spin $1\hbar$ state of N^{14} shown in the diagram of Fig. 25|7 is a state very much like the spin $0\hbar$ state, except that the two "outer" nucleons have their spins in the same direction, whereas the spins are antiparallel for the spin $0\hbar$ states. Since the spin angular momentum is a vector, and the spin of the nucleons is $\frac{1}{2}\hbar$, the total spin will be equal to $1\hbar$ when the spins are parallel and $0\hbar$ when the spins are antiparallel. We observe the forces are different—the force between the nucleons with their spins parallel is greater. Equivalent spin $1\hbar$ states of O^{14} and C^{14} do not exist, since the two nucleons are in the same orbit and the exclusion principle forbids having two neutrons or two protons with their spin directions the same in the same orbit.

25|4   *Nuclear transitions—gamma decay and beta decay*

Electromagnetic transitions involving the emission of photons occur in nuclei even as such transitions occur in atoms. In atomic processes the radiation can be considered to result from the acceleration of electrons; in nuclear processes the radiation results from the acceleration of protons, or occasionally from changes in the direction of the intrinsic electric currents of either protons or neutrons. Since the different states of nuclei may have energies that differ by the order of a million electron volts rather than the typical energy differences of atoms of about a volt, nuclear photons have energies very much larger than the energies of atomic photons. These very-high-energy photons were not originally recognized as electromagnetic phenomena and were called gamma rays. They are identical in character to X rays.

Some nuclei are not appropriately balanced in their neutron–proton ratio. The solid circles on the diagram of Fig. 25|5b represent such nuclei. A more tightly bound nucleus would result if protons would change to neutrons or neutrons to protons.

Such nuclei may undergo β decay through the mechanism of a fourth force, which we call the *weak-interaction*. (The other three forces are gravity, the electromagnetic force, and the strong nuclear force.) This weak nuclear force or weak-interaction allows a neutron to decay into a proton by emitting an electron and an antineutrino, or a proton may decay into a neutron by emitting a positron and a neutrino even as the existence of electromagnetic forces allow an orbit of a hydrogen atom with a large quantum number to decay to an orbit with a smaller quantum number and smaller energy or mass by emitting a photon. Sometimes a nucleus can become lighter if a proton decays to a neutron (since there may be more binding energy). The proton then emits a positive electron or positron and a neutrino. These basic reactions are

$$n \rightarrow p + e^- + \nu^- \quad \text{and} \quad p \rightarrow n + e^+ + \nu$$

The electron, e^-, and the positron, e^+, are related as antiparticles, as are the neutrino, ν, and the antineutrino, ν^-. We will discuss the relation between particles and antiparticles, as well as the properties of neutrinos, later.

The transitions that result in the emission of electrons are called β-ray transitions for historical reasons again; the original investigators did not immediately relate the radiation they observed with electrons and gave the name β rays to the radiation.

The rate at which the orbit of a hydrogen atom changes by radiation is proportional to the square of the electric charge of the electron. The effective weak-interaction charge is very small—about 10^{-5} times the electric charge—and so β-decay processes typically go slowly. The average time for a neutron to change to a proton is about 10 min.

Electron β decay thus indicates an increase in the number of protons in the nucleus by 1 and a corresponding decrease in the number of neutrons; positron β decay represents a change of a proton to a neutron. These changes are shown schematically in the diagram of Fig. 25 | 5a.

25 | 5   *The neutrino*

It was noticed very early in the study of radioactivity that the energy of the electron emitted in the β decay of a particular nuclear species was not the same for every decay. Further, the energy of the electron was always less than the energy associated with the mass difference between the original nucleus and the final nucleus.

$$E_e < (M_i c^2 - M_f c^2)$$

where E_e is the total energy of the electron emitted in course of the β decay, and M_i and M_f are the masses of the initial and final nuclei. Later it was seen that the process as observed did not conserve either linear momentum or angular momentum: the momentum and angular momentum of the final nucleus plus the electron was not the same as the momentum and angular momentum of the initial nucleus. It is not at all inconceivable, only unattractive, to conclude that energy and momentum are not conserved on the microscopic scale of the nucleus. However, there are definite correlations between the values of the missing quantities that allow further insights into the character of the β-decay process.

The magnitude of the missing angular momentum is always $\frac{1}{2}\hbar$, and the missing energy, E, and the missing momentum, p, are related as

$$p = \frac{E}{c} \qquad \text{or} \qquad \frac{E^2}{c^4} - \frac{p^2}{c^2} = 0$$

These are just the relations that would obtain if the energy, momentum, and angular momentum were carried away by a particle with an invariant mass equal to zero and an intrinsic angular momentum or spin of $\frac{1}{2}\hbar$.

Any entity to which we give a name, be it an electron or a cow, represents a construct that is a more or less concise summary of a number of observations. A large object that is observed to give milk, has soft brown eyes, and moos, is, by definition, a cow to a small child. The results of a few more observations are required by a more critical audience of farmers or biologists: nevertheless, the word or construct *cow* represents the sum of a set of observations. Likewise the concept *electron* signifies and summarizes a large number of observations or experiments.

In the same spirit we can give the name *neutrino* to the set of missing dynamic quantities in β decay. Of course, we are very much interested in correlating the properties of this neutrino with the properties of other concepts we have constructed in the course of classifying the occurrences of nature. In particular, if this neutrino has further particular characteristics, it is possible to deduce the distribution of neutrino energies and hence the distribution of electron energies that will occur in the decay of a particular nuclear species. The first such calculation was made by Enrico Fermi, and the results of the calculation were eventually found to be in essentially perfect agreement with observation. The concept of the neutrino was therefore very nearly the same as the concept of a particle with no rest mass, like the photon, which was given off in β decay.

If this concept were really identical to the particle concept, the free neutrino should have some interaction with matter. If a particle interacts with other matter with sufficient strength to be created, the particle must interact with matter after it is created in a detectable manner. Since the strength of the weak interaction is very small, neutrinos are produced only very feebly. They might therefore be expected to interact very feebly, and it must be difficult to detect their interaction. Typically, a neutrino can be expected to travel through a heavy material such as lead an average distance about equal to the distance from the sun to the farthest planet, Pluto, before experiencing a collision. Since the interaction is so weak, observation of the interaction is quite difficult, and such interactions, which establish definitely that the neutrino shares the essential character of other particles, were first observed only comparatively recently, in 1956 by Cowan and Reines.

25|6   *Nuclear transitions—alpha-particle decay of nuclei*

Nuclei, particularly heavy nuclei, also decay through the emission of particles with two units of positive electric charge and a mass about 4 times that of the nucleon. Historically these particles were called alpha particles; we know now that they are identical to the nuclei of helium atoms. An examination of the systematics of the binding energy of nuclei, such as the diagram of Fig. 25|1, shows that the total binding energy will be increased if a heavy nucleus breaks up into two fragments: the mass of the two fragments will be less than the mass of the original nucleus. This excess mass will be observed in the form of the kinetic energy of the resultant fragments. Nuclei split in two specific ways: a heavy nucleus may decay into a slightly lighter nucleus and an alpha particle or helium nucleus; or, more rarely, the nucleus may undergo *fission* and split into two medium-weight nuclei.

We will first discuss alpha decay and consider a reaction

$$X_Z^A \rightarrow X_{Z-2}^{A-4} + \alpha_2^4 + Q$$

where the X represents a nucleus; the superscript is the number of nucleons in the nucleus and the subscript is the charge or number of protons in the nucleus. The symbol Q represents the energy released in the decay; the sum of the kinetic energies of the residual nucleus and the alpha particles will be equal to Q. The curve of Fig. 25 | 1 is not sufficiently well defined to allow the determination of sufficiently accurate binding energies so that the mass differences between elements can be accurately determined, but the general decrease in binding energies from a value near 8.7 MeV per nucleon for $A = 100$, to values of about 7.7 MeV for $A = 200$ is exhibited clearly. From this, with a little tricky arithmetic and the value of 7 MeV for the binding energy per nucleon of the alpha particle, it can be shown that the average value of Q for the alpha decays of heavy nuclei will be near 5 MeV.

What will be the magnitude of the mean decay time of a typical nucleus that decays through alpha-particle emission? The strength of the strong nuclear forces responsible for the decay is very large, so that we might expect that the change would occur very quickly, perhaps as quickly as the time it would take an alpha particle to move a distance equal to the radius of the nucleus. Knowing the size of the nucleus and the velocity of a typical alpha particle, we find that that time is about 10^{-22} sec. Instead, the lifetime for decay is very long: the mean life of the most abundant isotope of uranium, U^{238}, is more than 6×10^9 yr—about the same as the age of the solar system.

These long lifetimes can be understood in detail through analyses that consider the wave nature of the particle, which were first presented by G. Gamow and by F. U. Condon. It is illuminating to consider the forces on an alpha particle near a nucleus. Far from the nucleus the alpha particle is strongly repelled by the electrostatic field of the nucleus, since both the alpha particle and the nucleus are positively charged. Only when the alpha particle is very close to the nucleus, literally touching its surface, do the attractive, short-range nuclear forces manifest themselves. These strong forces act to attract the alpha particle. The whole pattern of attractive and repulsive forces can be expressed by the diagram of Fig. 25 | 8 showing the potential energy of the alpha particle and nucleus system as a function of the distance between the center of the nucleus and the center of the alpha particle.

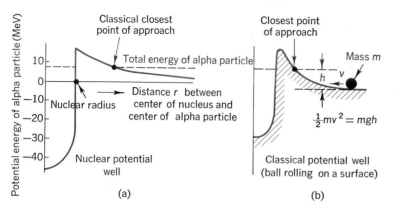

FIG. 25 18

(a) *The potential energy of an alpha particle in the field of a nucleus;* (b) *the analogous potential energy of a ball near a hole banked with earth.*

We now consider, classically, the motion of an alpha particle headed toward the nucleus with a velocity such that its kinetic energy, far from the nucleus, has a value represented by the height of the dashed line in the diagram. The alpha particle will be slowed by the electrostatic repulsion and will stop at the point designated by the arrow, where all its kinetic energy will be turned to potential energy. It will then rebound back to where it started. This is almost exactly like a classical system where the potential-energy curve of Fig. 25|8 represents a profile of a surface in a gravitational field, such as a macroscopic surface on the earth, and the particle is a ball rolling or sliding toward the hole. Even though the hole is deep, and the total energy of the ball would be at a minimum if the ball fell into the hole, it will never get there unless it has enough energy to get over the hill or *potential barrier.*

Similarly, if the ball is in the hole, though it is bouncing around with a kinetic energy corresponding to the value marked by the dashed line on the diagram of Fig. 25|8, which is much more than sufficient to allow it to escape if there were no barrier, it cannot get out unless some extra energy is supplied to lift it over the potential barrier.

The nucleons inside the nucleus occupy various states or orbits. Since they are fermions, the exclusion principle keeps them from all occupying the orbit with least energy. Some sets of four nucleons, corresponding to the alpha particle, must occupy states or orbits that are such that these nucleons have rather high energies, corresponding to the dashed line of Fig. 25|8. Like the ball, in a classical picture, the alpha particle could not escape the nucleus and alpha decay could not occur. However, the result is different if we consider the system, correctly, from the view of the quantum mechanics.

We must therefore describe the system of the nucleus and the alpha particle as a de Broglie wave. We might expect the amplitude of the wave to have a form such as

$$A = A_0 \left(\frac{1}{r}\right) \cos \left(\frac{pr}{\hbar}\right)$$

where A is the amplitude of the system when the alpha particle is separated from the nucleus by a distance r, A_0 is a constant, and p is the momentum of the alpha particle,

$$p = \sqrt{2MT}$$

Here T is the kinetic energy of the alpha particle and M is the mass of the alpha particle. We assume, implicitly, that the alpha particle is much less massive than the nucleus. The kinetic energy of the alpha particle is equal to the total energy minus the potential energy

$$T = E + V$$

If the total energy of the alpha particle is designated by the dashed line in Fig. 25|8, the kinetic energy will be negative between the point of closest approach in the classical sense, which is designated by the arrow, and the edge of the nucleus. In this region the potential energy is greater than the total energy. The momentum of the alpha particle, $p = \sqrt{2MT}$, will thus be imaginary in the mathematical sense. We have noted that the wave therefore varies as the "exp" function rather than a trigonometric function:

$$A = A_0 \left(\frac{1}{r}\right) \exp \left(-\frac{pr}{\hbar}\right)$$

where $p = |\sqrt{2MT}|$. Since the value of T varies over the non-physical region, the exact behavior of the de Broglie amplitude is complicated, but the general character of the variation is suggested by the diagram of Fig. 25|9.

The amplitude of the wave is seen to be very much smaller outside the nucleus than inside, but there is some amplitude outside! Some of the wave has leaked out: the alpha particle will escape from the potential well, unlike the classical results.

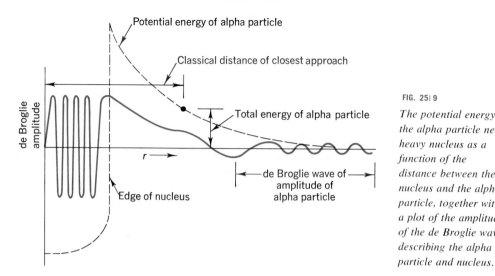

FIG. 25|9

The potential energy of the alpha particle near a heavy nucleus as a function of the distance between the nucleus and the alpha particle, together with a plot of the amplitude of the de Broglie wave describing the alpha particle and nucleus.

For alpha particles in heavy nuclei, the amplitude of the wave outside the nucleus is very small, and thus the probability of finding the alpha particle outside the nucleus is very small and the mean lifetime is therefore large.

25|7 *Nuclear transitions—half-lives*

The intensity of de Broglie waves at a point is proportional to the probability that a particle is near that point. This interpretation of the de Broglie intensity in terms of probability leads immediately to a statistical character of the decays of unstable states. It is illuminating to consider the special case of the alpha-particle decay of a heavy nucleus such as uranium: in particular, we will use the description of the state introduced in Section 25|6 to introduce the subject of alpha decay.

The uranium nucleus was described, implicitly, as a thorium nucleus plus an alpha particle. The de Broglie wave amplitude was very large when the alpha particle was inside the nucleus and very small when the alpha particle was far from the nucleus. Outside the nucleus the alpha particle has a certain energy (near 6 MeV) and thus a certain velocity directed away from the residual thorium nucleus. If we were to find the system in a state such that the alpha particle was inside the thorium nucleus, we would describe our observation by stating that the uranium nucleus had not decayed. If we were to find the alpha particle at a distance L away from the thorium nucleus, we would conclude that the nucleus had decayed and that the decay had occurred at a time equal to L/v before the time of observation, where v was the velocity of the alpha particle.

If the probability of finding an alpha particle outside the nucleus, but inside the sphere that has a radius equal to the distance the particle could travel in 1 sec, is 1 percent of the probability of the alpha particle being found inside the nucleus, the decay rate is 1 percent/sec. If a large set of such nuclei exist at a certain time, t_0, 1 percent will decay during the next second; of the 99 percent left, 1 percent of those will decay in the next second. After 69 sec only 50 percent will be left; after 138 sec only 25 percent of the nuclei will remain. We call the time in which half of the particles decay—or the probability of decay is $\frac{1}{2}$—the *half-life:* the half-life of the hypothetical nucleus discussed here will be 69 sec. The average lifetime is the mean life. The mean life is a little longer than the half life: the half-life is 0.693 times the mean life: the mean life of the nuclei considered here would be about 100 sec.

We note that any previous history is irrelevant! This is a characteristic, indeed a definition, of random events. If you flip a coin and it comes up heads 5 times in a row, the probability of its coming up heads on the next throw is still $\frac{1}{2}$. All quantum phenomena are determined by the laws of probability, and all decay processes—the alpha decay of nuclei, the beta decay of nuclei, and the electromagnetic decay of an excited state in a hydrogen atom—follow the same statistical laws of behavior. Of course, the decay rates, and therefore the half-lives, of the different species can differ enormously. A U^{238} nucleus has a half-life of nearly 5×10^9 yr, while the N^*, an elementary-particle state, has a half-life of less than 10^{-23} sec. But the statistical character of their decays is essentially the same. The decay rate, or half-life, is a characteristic of a state, just as its mass or angular momentum.

According to our discussion, the probability of a nucleus (or any other state) decaying in a time dt is determined by the character of the nucleus and is independent of any past history of the nucleus. The probability can be expressed as

$$P = \left(\frac{1}{\tau}\right) dt$$

where $1/\tau$ is a proportionality constant. If there are a very large number of such nuclei, N, in the sample the number, dN, that will decay in a time dt is equal to the number of nuclei present, N, times the probability, P, of a nucleus decaying in that time. Then

$$dN = -NP \quad \text{or} \quad dN = -N\left(\frac{1}{\tau}\right) dt \qquad (25\,|\,3)$$

where the minus sign signifies that the number of nuclei will decrease in the time dt. This is a differential equation of the type DE-EXP discussed in Chapter 9, and the solution is

$$N = N_0 \exp\left(-\frac{t}{\tau}\right) \qquad (25\,|\,4)$$

where N is the number of states at a time t, N_0 is the number of states at time $t = 0$, and τ is the *mean life* of the state. From the second equation of (25 | 3) we see that the number of states that decay per unit time is inversely proportional to the mean life. If the mean life is 100 sec 1 percent will decay per second.

Since, from Eq. (25 | 3), the number of states decaying per second is proportional to the number of states that have not yet decayed, the counting rate of an instrument measuring the decays will vary with time just as the population varies with time.

25 | 8   *Nuclear reactions*

In Chapter 24 we observed that the electromagnetic radiation of an excited atom is reversible: even as an atom will emit a photon when an electron moves from a highly excited state to a lower state, as the atom absorbs a photon the electron moves from a low state to a state of higher energy. Even as the atom will emit only certain discrete frequencies of electromagnetic frequencies, the atom will absorb only those discrete frequencies that correspond to the energy differences between the states, or electron orbits, of the atom. If the energy of the photon is very large, an electron may be completely ejected by the atom as the photon is absorbed. These represent examples of atomic reactions with photons.

Nuclei interact with electromagnetic radiation in much the same way. Even as an excited nucleus can decay to a state of lower energy by emitting a gamma ray (which is a high-energy photon), the nucleus will absorb photons or gamma rays and change from a low-energy state—usually the lowest possible energy state, or ground state—to an excited state, or higher energy state. These states are discrete, just as the states of the hydrogen atom are discrete, and only gamma rays of specific frequencies and specific energies, which correspond to the energy differences between the ground state of the nucleus and the excited states, will be absorbed. The different states of the hydrogen atom can be described accurately in terms of different orbits of the electron. The nucleus is more complicated, but some of the excited states of the nucleus can be described in terms of different orbits of a nucleon. For transitions to these states, we can consider that the interaction of the gamma ray causes a change in the orbit of the nucleon, just as the interaction of a lower-energy photon can cause an electron to change orbits in the hydrogen atom. Just as very-high-energy photons incident on atoms can eject an electron from an atom—ionizing the atom—very-high-energy gamma rays can eject neutrons or protons from a nucleus.

An atom that has its full complement of electrons is electrically neutral; the negative charges of the electrons cancel the positive charge of the nucleus, and the atom will not strongly attract further electrons. There is no such cancellation of the nuclear forces; a stable nucleus will still attract another nucleon near the surface of the nucleus even as a drop of water exerts an attractive force on a molecule of water near its surface. Although a positively charged proton will be repelled by the positively charged nucleus and a slow proton will not ordinarily reach the nuclear surface and be affected by the short-range nuclear forces, a slow neutron, electrically neutral, may drift close to the nuclear surface and then be strongly attracted to the nucleus and absorbed. Even as the absorption of a water molecule by a drop of water heats up the water through the heat of condensation, the absorption of the neutron by the nucleus heats the nucleus by the addition of the binding energy of the neutron; the binding energy of the neutron corresponds to the heat of condensation of the water molecule. The "hot," or excited, nucleus formed by the absorption of the neutron will typically "cool" to the ground state by emitting electromagnetic energy in the form of gamma rays.

Even as a photon is absorbed by an atom only if the energy of the photon is such that the final energy of the atom fits some energy level, the neutron will be absorbed only if the final energy of the new nucleus fits some energy level. Neutrons will then be captured only at certain *resonance* energies. We use the term *resonance* because both the mathematical description, and indeed the physical reality, resemble the resonances we observe in mechanical and electrical systems. In this case, the resonance is a resonance of the neutron de Broglie wave in the complex system of the nucleus. Sometimes the extra energy the nucleus obtains by the condensation of the neutron will be again concentrated in one neutron near the surface of the nucleus, and that neutron will break free or evaporate with the same kinetic energy as the original incident neutron. Although the energy of the incident and emitted neutron will be the same, the original direction of the incident neutron will be lost, and we can consider that the nucleus scattered the neutron. Since the energy that had been dispersed among the various nucleons will be concentrated on one neutron "accidentally" only after a long time on the average, the energy can be known very precisely and the energy spread or the width of the energy level is very small.

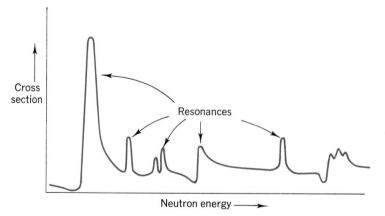

Cross section

Resonances

Neutron energy ⟶

FIG. 25|10

A graph showing the cross section of the sulfur nucleus for neutrons as a function of the energy of the neutrons.

This is a reflection of the uncertainty principle,

$$dE \, dt = \hbar$$

where dE is the width of the resonance and dt is the lifetime. We might consider that the excited nucleus decays by the emission of the neutron after a time dt. Figure 25 | 10 shows a typical curve of the variation of neutron scattering with energy where the effects of energy levels are important. The scattering probability is very large where the energy of the neutron matches the energy of a state of the new *compound nucleus* (the target nucleus plus the incident neutron), and the probability is comparitively small where no such match takes place. The scattering probability is measured in terms of the effective area of scattering. The cross section for neutron scattering at the position of an energy level may be near λ^2, the square of the de Broglie wave length of the neutron, while the background scattering cross section will be of the order of the nuclear size. The narrow resonances correspond to very long-lived states—where the energy of the state is therefore well defined—while the broader resonances correspond to short-lived states where, according to the uncertainty principle, the energy cannot be so well defined.

Protons and alpha particles also interact with nuclei in a similar manner. The coulomb repulsion reduces the probability that the proton or alpha particle will reach the nuclear surface and thus reduces the probability of nuclear scattering. Of course, electrostatic scattering, such as the scattering observed by Rutherford will still take place. The proton and alpha-particle resonances tend to be narrower than the neutron resonances because the charged protons and alpha particles must tunnel through the potential barrier as discussed in Section 25 | 6: The lifetimes of these states are therefore long: the energy spreads or widths are small.

Resonance effects are important when the de Broglie wavelength of the incident particles is not small compared to the nuclear size and thus the energy of the incident particles is not extremely large. At very high energies, when the de Broglie wavelength of the incident particles is very small, the collisions are more nearly classical. The incident neutrons or alpha particles or protons simply knock pieces off the nucleus. The pieces of nuclear matter knocked off are, of course, neutrons and protons themselves.

As shown on the binding-energy diagram of Fig. 25 | 1, the binding energy per nucleon is greater for nuclei of moderate mass than for the heaviest nuclei. Energy will therefore be released if a heavy nucleus splits into two lighter nuclei, even as the mass of the heavy nucleus is greater than the mass of the two pieces. The probability of this happening spontaneously is small for reasons that are similar to those that reduce the probability of alpha decay: there is a potential barrier. If enough energy is added to a heavy nucleus, it will split quickly into two parts—a process called *fission*. A great deal of energy, perhaps 30 MeV, must be added to a nucleus such as lead or bismuth before fission will occur. Heavier nuclei, such as uranium, will fission quickly if 6 or 7 MeV are added. For very heavy nuclei, much heavier than uranium, fission will occur spontaneously, which is why such elements do not occur in nature. Nuclei become increasingly unstable with size, since the electrostatic repulsion increases with size and the number of protons, while the nuclear part of the binding energy for each nucleon remains the same because the nuclear forces are short range and the exclusion principle keeps the nucleons from crowding too close together.

In certain very heavy elements, such as the uranium isotope U^{235}, or plutonium, fission can be induced by the absorption of a slow neutron by the nucleus. Almost all nuclei absorb slow neutrons. This process is analogous to the absorption of water-vapor molecules by a water droplet: even as the condensation of water vapor heats up the droplet through the heat of condensation of the water (540 Cal/kg), the absorption of neutrons heats up a nucleus by an amount equal to the heat of condensation of the neutron. This nuclear heat of condensation is just the binding energy per nucleon and is thus about 8 MeV per nucleon. Therefore the absorption of a neutron by U^{235} produces a "hot" nucleus, U^{236}, which splits into two parts.

Since the binding energy per nucleon is larger for the smaller pieces of matter that result from the fission, each piece has considerable extra energy—each piece is very "hot." These hot fragments cool down to stable nuclei in various ways, but an important part of the cooling takes place through the evaporation of neutrons. The hot droplets of nuclear matter cool off through the boiling off of neutrons, even as hot water droplets cool off through the evaporation of molecules of water. Typically, about 3 neutrons are emitted per fission.

If each of the 3 neutrons is absorbed by U^{235}, the 3 fission reactions that would occur would release 9 neutrons; if each of these were absorbed and produced fission, 27 neutrons would be produced in the third generation of the chain. Eventually—and quickly—the reaction would run away in an explosive fashion that would be unsuitable for the controlled production of power. A nuclear power reactor is therefore designed with a control system that absorbs some of the neutrons so the multiplication number is 1 instead of 3. Explosive devices differ from reactors, then, in that they are designed such that the chain reaction proceeds very quickly with a large multiplication factor.

A uranium nucleus or a plutonium nucleus has a binding energy equal to about 7.7 MeV per nucleon; the mass of the nucleus is about 0.8 percent less than the mass of the individual nucleons. These nuclei undergo fission to form medium-weight nuclei that have a binding energy of about 8.7 MeV per nucleon and a mass equal to about 0.9 percent less than the mass of the constituent nucleons. Upon fission, then, a mass equal to about 0.1 percent of the original heavy-nucleus mass is transformed specifically into energy. This energy is extracted from power reactors as heat and used to drive generators and other mechanisms in conventional ways. It is important to emphasize that the change of mass to energy is not specific to nuclear reactions such as fission, but is a part of any energy production. Gasoline, plus the oxygen used in the combustion of the gasoline, has a greater mass than the water and carbon dioxide that comprise the production products in just the same manner as uranium has more mass than the medium-weight nuclei that are the ashes of the fission process. Of course there is a considerable quantitative difference in the proportion of mass changed to energy: the proportion is near 0.2 percent for the fission process, while the change in chemical processes is seldom as large as 1 part in 10^9.

Until the advent of the extraction of power from nuclear fuels, almost all of man's sources of power could be traced to the energy the earth has received from the sun. Wind and water power depend on recent energy transfer, while the combustion of coal and oil releases solar energy stored by plant life in the past. The energy in the nuclear fuels does not originate in our sun, however; it now seems probable that these heavy elements were created in the explosion of a supernova long before the creation of the solar system. The burning of nuclear fuel therefore must represent a last extraction of energy from the explosion of a star.

25|10 *Fusion*

Since the masses of the heavy nuclei are less than the free masses of the nucleons that make up the nuclei, any process that results in the fusion of free nucleons, such as the proton, into heavier nuclei must involve the release of large amounts of energy. The fusion of a free electron and a free proton into a hydrogen atom results in the release of 13.6 eV of energy, the binding energy of the hydrogen atom. In the same sense the binding of 4 nucleons into a helium atom will result in the release of about 30 MeV, the binding energy of the helium nucleus. The binding energy of the hydrogen atom is equal to about 1 part in 10^8 of the atomic mass, while the binding energy of the helium nucleus is nearly as large as 1 percent of the nuclear mass; therefore, the energy release per unit mass in the fusion of nuclei is very large compared to the energies of similar atomic processes. Also, since the universe appears to be made up largely of free nucleons, the total energy available for fusion is immense.

Such fusion reactions provide the source of energy for almost all stars (very young stars draw upon their gravitational potential energy as they condense from gas). For most stars the important fusion reactions are those that result in the production of helium from hydrogen, or helium nuclei from protons, which are the nuclei of the hydrogen atom. Two sets of nuclear reactions are involved in this change. Since both are rather complicated, we will not discuss them in detail here, but it is interesting to note that the specific energy production in stars, in terms of energy produced per second per kilogram of stellar matter, is very small. Since most stars, like our sun, can be considered to be at equilibrium, the total energy produced by the whole sun must be equal to the total energy radiated by the sun. A typical star, such as our sun, radiates energy from its surface at a rate that is near 10 kW/cm²: this is about a factor of 10 greater than a hot tungsten filament. But this energy must be equal to the energy produced in a cone that has a base area equal to 1 cm² and a length equal to the radius of the star: in the case of the sun this radius is about 7.5×10^{10} cm and the cone contains about 3×10^7 kg of material. The power produced per kilogram is small—about 10^{-4} W/kg, which is about ten thousand times less than the metabolic energy production of a human being. The production of energy per kilogram in the sun is less than the energy production of a hibernating mud turtle! But the sun is very big.

The reactions that proceed in the sun are not, then, likely to be useful for power production on the earth. However, there are other fusion reactions that proceed with much more speed and generate much more power per unit mass, which are likely sources of power for human consumption. The most important reactions are

$$\text{d} + \text{d} \rightarrow \text{H}^3 + \text{p} + Q \qquad \text{and} \qquad \text{d} + \text{d} \rightarrow \text{He}^3 + \text{n} + Q' \quad \textbf{(25 |5)}$$

where d is a symbol for the deuteron or the nucleus of deuterium (heavy hydrogen), an isotope of hydrogen. The deuteron is a loosely bound system of 1 proton and 1 neutron; H^3 is the nucleus of tritium, another isotope of hydrogen with one proton and two neutrons; He^3 is an isotope of helium having two protons and a neutron; p and n are the proton and neutron; and Q and Q' are energies produced in the reactions, which will appear as the kinetic energies of the reaction products. The value of both Q and Q' is near 2.5 MeV: the reactions thus produce that much energy. The tritium nucleus, H^3, eventually changes to the helium isotope He^3 through a beta-decay transition, so we might say that the heavy-hydrogen nucleus, the deuteron, is changed or fused into an isotope of helium.

Since the deuteron has a positive electric charge, two deuterons repel each other and will not ordinarily ever get close enough together so that the reactions of (25|5) will ever take place. However, if the deuterons are moving very fast, the impact of the collision between two deuterons can be sufficiently great that the repulsion is overcome; they interact with each other, and the reactions will occur. In order to create a large number of deuterons moving with such great energies, deuterium gas must be heated up to temperatures that are extremely high according to usual standards: sufficient collisions to produce measurable power will occur only if the temperature is near a million degrees! Of course, nothing material can withstand such temperatures, but it seems that it may be possible to create magnetic fields with sufficient strengths and of appropriate shapes to contain the fast-moving charged deuterons. There is hope that such a "magnetic bottle" may be designed that can contain the deuterons at a high enough temperature so that fusion takes place and useful power is generated.

The reactions of (25|5) are also the reactions that provide most of the energy in an explosion of a hydrogen bomb. The necessary high temperatures are produced briefly by the explosion of a fission bomb of uranium or plutonium, together with an intermediate set of reactions involving the neutrons from the fission bomb and an isotope of lithium.

PROBLEMS

$e = 1.6 \times 10^{-19}$ C; 1.0 MeV $= 1.6 \times 10^{-13}$ J; 4180 J $= 1$ Cal; $c = 3 \times 10^8$ m/sec; $\hbar/m_\pi c = 1.4 \times 10^{-15}$ m.

25|1   One kilogram of nucleons contains about 6×10^{26} nucleons.

(*a*) What is the mass of a nucleon in MeV/c^2?

(*b*) If a pion has a mass $\frac{1}{7}$ that of a nucleon, how much energy (in MeV) must be supplied to make a pion?

25|2   If the meson charge of a proton is equal to 10 times the electric charge, what is the approximate ratio of the nuclear and electric forces between two protons separated by a distance of 10^{-16} m?

25|3   The K meson has a mass about 3.5 times greater than that of the pion. If the nucleon has a K meson charge equal to the pion charge, will K mesons contribute to the nuclear force between nucleons as much as pions? Why or why not?

25|4   How would you expect the curve of Fig. 25|5a to look if the proton–proton attractive force were stronger than the neutron–neutron force?

25|5   A particular nuclear species decays radioactivity in a manner such that it emits alpha particles, beta particles, and gamma rays. These emissions are recorded by separate specially designed counters. During a 10-min run the alpha counter records 1000 counts, the beta counter records 10,000 counts, and the gamma counter records 5000 counts.

During the next 10 min the alpha counter records 200 counts, while the records of the gamma counter and beta counter are lost. What is the probable number of counts recorded by the gamma counter in the third run of 10 min (during the time from 20 to 30 min after the counting started)?

25|6 (*a*) Which of the masses of O^{14}, N^{14}, and C^{14}, shown to be equal in Fig. 25|7, would be greater if the attractive neutron–proton force were greater than the proton–proton force or the neutron–neutron force?

    (*b*) Which state will have the greatest mass when the correction for electromagnetic effects is not made? Which will have the smallest mass?

25|7 The products of the alpha-particle decay of heavy nuclei are often radioactive, emitting negative beta rays (electrons), but never emitting positive beta rays (positrons). Why is this the case?

25|8 The counting rate of a counter surveying an unknown sample is 1000/sec at 9:00 a.m., 200/sec at 10:00 a.m. and 100/sec at 11:00 a.m. What can you conclude concerning the composition of sample?

25|9 Using the binding-energy chart of Fig. 25|1, which gives the binding energy of helium (2 neutrons plus two protons) as 8 MeV per nucleon,

    (*a*) What is the energy released in changing 4 protons into helium (in MeV)?

    (*b*) If 1 kg of hydrogen (protons) is changed to helium, what is the mass equivalent of the energy released?

    (*c*) How much water can be turned to steam by the energy released in changing 1 kg of hydrogen to helium? (The heat of vaporization of water is 540 Cal/kg).

25|10 Estimating binding energies from the graph of Fig. 25|1,

    (*a*) How much energy (in MeV) is released when a uranium nucleus splits into two approximately equal parts?

    (*b*) What portion of the mass of the uranium nucleus is changed to energy?

25|11 Free neutrons are produced high in the atmosphere when atmospheric nuclei are broken up by very-high-energy cosmic rays. These neutrons are absorbed by the nuclei of the nitrogen atoms in the air to form the radioactive isotope of carbon C^{14} by the reaction

$$N^{14} + n \rightarrow C^{14} + p$$

The C^{14} nucleus is unstable and decays back to N^{14} by the process

$$C^{14} \rightarrow N^{14} + e^- + \nu^-$$

where the half life of the C^{14} nucleus is 5700 yr. Living plants and animals exchange carbon dioxide with the atmosphere so that metabolic carbon contains the same proportion of C^{14} as the carbon in the atmosphere. There is usually no further exchange after the organism is dead.

The radioactivity of carbon from trees felled by the Wisconsin glaciation is about 25 percent as intense as the activity from trees cut down now. When did this last ice age take place? What assumptions must you make in coming to this conclusion?

twenty-six **Fundamental particles and forces**

26 | 1 *The fundamental forces and the elementary particles*

OUR STUDY OF THE electromagnetic field has given us some insights into the deep and fundamental relationships between forces and particles. In particular, it appears that the mass of particles is partially or wholly derived from the energies of the fields for which the particle serves as a source. We believe, then, that the mass of the electron is thus largely the mass corresponding to the energy of the electromagnetic field the electron generates as a result of its charge. From this view a particle can be considered to be essentially a source of force, or a source or singular point in a field; implicitly, the field is the important concept. Conversely, we know that we can consider the field of force as consisting of particles, even as the electromagnetic field can be described as a spectrum of photons: thus the concept of the field might be considered as merely a convenient description of the behavior of a set of particles. Further, it is evident that no operational meaning can be given to a particle except through its interaction with other particles and thus through the forces that act on the particle.

If a particle were acted upon by no force whatsoever, the particle would be undetectable in principle and could not have any physical meaning. On the other hand, a force or field that acted on no particle would be equally meaningless. Clearly, then, inquires into the nature of particles and the nature of the forces that act on the particles, or the fields that act as a description of these forces, are joined. We cannot consider particles and fields, or forces, separately in any meaningful way.

We now know of four separate forces, or at least classes of forces. If two protons are very close together, the total force between them can be divided into four parts, each quite different from the others, and in the limit of our present understanding, each is independent of the others. The major part of the force between the two protons results from the *strong-interaction*. We can characterize the strength of that interaction by the quantity

$$\frac{kg^2}{\hbar c} \approx 1$$

Here g is a strong-interaction charge of the proton, measured in the same units as electric charge. The particular mode of expression, where the square of the charge is divided by the product of the fundamental constants $\hbar$ and c, is chosen because the resulting combination is dimensionless—a pure number—and because the force will be proportional to the charge on each nucleon: hence the square of the charge. The strong-interaction is the force responsible for the binding of nuclei—hence the nuclear force. The electromagnetic force between the two protons is weaker than the strong interaction, since

$$\frac{ke^2}{\hbar c} = \frac{1}{137}$$

where e is the electric charge of the proton, the electromagnetic force is only about 1 percent of the nuclear force. A third part of the total force between the nucleons arises from the *weak interaction*, which is responsible for beta decay in nuclei. We may consider that the weak interaction is about 10^{-6} as strong as the strong interaction, and the measure of this strength is contained in a factor

$$\frac{kf^2}{\hbar c} \approx 10^{-6}$$

where f is the weak-interaction charge of the proton. In many, or most, circumstances, the effective weak-interaction strength is about $(10^{-6})^2 = 10^{-12}$ as strong as the strong-interaction. We interpret this result, in a manner we will discuss in more detail later, by considering that most weak-interactions, like the beta decay of nuclei, take place in two steps, each of which has a probability or strength of 10^{-6}, and that the effective strength is therefore the product of the two effects and equal to $(10^{-6})(10^{-6}) = 10^{-12}$.

The fourth and by far the weakest force is the gravitational force. We write this in the conventional form and also in a somewhat unusual form to emphasize the parallels between the various forces:

$$\frac{G m_\mathrm{p}^{2}}{\hbar c} = \frac{k m^{2}}{\hbar c} \approx 10^{-38}$$

where m_p is the mass of the proton in kilograms and G is the gravitational constant; m is the mass of the proton in the same units as the coulomb—m is thus a kind of charge. The gravitational force is about 10^{-38} times as great as the strong interaction and about 10^{-36} times the strength of the electromagnetic forces. The gravitational "charge" of the proton is about 10^{-18} as large as the electric charge of the proton.

These four forces differ from one another in many ways other than magnitude. The character of the charge or source of the field, the character of the quanta that carry the field, and the way the fields appear to observers moving with different velocities are all different for the different forces.

We will therefore discuss the particles that are so closely related to these forces in their role as the sources of the fields or the repository of the charges that are the sources of the fields, and as the quanta of these fields. This is in analogy to our description of the electromagnetic interaction, where the source of the field is the charge on a particle and the quantum of the field is the photon. It is possible that the particles we will discuss are completely described, and thus completely defined, by the charges they carry and by their intrinsic angular momentum or spin.

Further, we shall limit our discussion to the consideration of particles that cannot simply be described as a composite of two other particles. We will not, then, concern ourselves with the hydrogen atom, which can be treated quite accurately as a composite system of a proton and electron, or the deuteron, which we can consider as a composite state of a neutron and proton bound together by the nuclear force. The remaining particles are called *elementary particles*, where the term elementary has not, at this time, any particularly precise definition nor profound meaning.

26 | 2   *The electromagnetic field*

We name the source of the electromagnetic field "electric charge," and this electric charge is quantized. A smallest electric charge seems to exist that is equal to 1.6×10^{-19} C, and no smaller charge is known: further, all larger charges seem to be multiples of this smallest, fundamental, electric charge. We know of no compelling reason why electric charge is quantized. We have mentioned a point raised by Dirac, which we will restate in a different manner: If electric charge were not quantized, and if magnetic charges existed, it would be possible to make measurements more accurate than allowed by the uncertainty principle. Since magnetic charges are not known to exist, this interesting point is, as yet, empty.

We know even less of the origin of the magnitude of the charge —the origin of the number $\frac{1}{137}$. Sir Arthur Eddington, a brilliant British astronomer and physicist, published, just before his death in 1944, a very difficult paper purporting to provide an explanation of the value of this number. It appears that no one but God and Eddington, and perhaps not Eddington, ever understood the paper. Certainly the consideration of the origin of all pure numbers that occur naturally in the universe constitutes a question of consequence: we may be very far from being able to provide any kind of answer to this question, however.

There are two kinds of fundamental electric charge, which add to zero; we call these, conventionally, positive and negative charges. For each kind of particle having a positive charge, there also exists a particle of the same mass having the opposite electric charge: these two particles are considered to be antiparticles. Electric charge is conserved: as far as we know, the total charge in any closed system is constant, though pairs of equal positive and negative charges—such as particle anti-particle pairs—can be created or annihilated, the total charge will be conserved, where the total charge is defined as the amount of positive charge minus the amount of negative charge.

On the other hand, the photon, which is the field quantum of the electromagnetic field, is not conserved. Photons are created and annihilated by charge; indeed, the magnitude of a charge is essentially a measure of the probability of the charge creating or absorbing a photon. We will explore this type of description of the relation between fields and their sources in more detail later.

The photon appears to have a rest mass of zero. From the arguments we used in discussing the range of the nuclear force, we know that the electrostatic field from a point charge should vary with distance, r, as

$$E = \frac{ke}{r^2} \left[\exp \left(-\frac{r}{r_0} \right) \right]^2$$

where r_0, the range of the force, is equal to $\hbar/mc$, where m is the mass of the field quantum, in this case the photon. If m were very large, the range of the electrostatic force would be small, even as the range of the nuclear force is small as a result of the large mass of the mesons that are the photons or quanta of the nuclear-interaction field. Since we know from simple experiments in the laboratory that the electrostatic field is not much weakened over a span of meters, the mass of the photon is immediately shown to be very small, less than 10^{-20} times the mass of an electron. Of course if m is zero, then r_0 is infinite, and the field takes the familiar form of Coulomb's law:

$$E = \frac{ke}{r^2}$$

A more direct, though less sensitive, determination of the mass of photon can be established from measurements of the velocity of light for light of different frequencies. If the photon has a finite rest mass, high-energy photons would travel faster than low-energy photons: violet light would travel faster than red light. This can be seen by an examination of the relativistic relations between energy, rest mass, and velocity:

$$E = \frac{m_0}{\sqrt{1 - \beta^2}}$$

so that

$$\beta = \frac{v}{c}$$

$$= \sqrt{1 - \left(\frac{m_0}{E} \right)^2}$$

where E and m_0 are the energy and rest mass of the photon. Then v, the velocity of the photon, depends upon the ratio of the energy of the photon to the rest mass of the photon. The photon velocity is equal to c and independent of the photon energy only if the mass of the photon is zero. Since there is no evidence for any dispersion of photon velocities—all photons appear to travel with the same velocity in free space—it appears that the mass of the photon is zero.

26|3   *The gravitational field*

The gravitational interaction is similar to the electromagnetic interaction in that it is a long-range interaction; the gravitational force between two bodies varies as $1/r^2$, where r is the distance between the bodies. Therefore, if the gravitational field is to be described in the same manner as the electrostatic field, we must conclude that the rest mass of the quantum of the gravitational field, called the graviton, must also be zero. There are striking differences between the two interactions, however: there are positive and negative electric charges and attractive and repulsive electromagnetic forces, but there is only one kind of gravitational charge or mass, and gravitational forces are always attractive. The electromagnetic mass is quantized and all charges are integral units of the quantity $e = 1.6 \times 10^{-19}$ C, but gravitational charge (mass or energy) is not quantized as far as we know. Extremely small mass differences and energies are known to exist. Although quantum effects have never been observed in gravity, and it is hardly obvious that any operational meaning can be applied to the graviton, the quantum of the gravitation field, it is almost certain, curiously, that if the graviton exists at all its spin must be $2\hbar$.

The very weakness of the gravitational field, combined with the lack of quantization of mass, has made it difficult to construct a quantum theory of gravitation. The radius of the gravitational Bohr orbit, the smallest orbit of the hydrogen atom if the proton and electron had no charge but were held together only by their gravitational attraction, would be

$$a_{\mathrm{g}} = \frac{\hbar^2}{m_{\mathrm{e}} G m_{\mathrm{e}} m_{\mathrm{p}}}$$

where m_e and m_p are the masses of the electron and proton and G is the gravitational constant. This is just the electromagnetic Bohr radius with Gm_em_p substituted for ke^2, but it is about 10^{40} times larger, even as the force is smaller, and is about equal to the radius of the universe! Using the same kind of analogy we can consider the rate of emission of gravitons from an excited (ordinary) hydrogen atom. The rate of emission of photons is proportional to ke^2, and about 1 photon is emitted per 10^{-8} sec; the rate of graviton emission might therefore be expected to be similar except that the charge is smaller; instead of ke^2 the effective charge factor would be Gm_em_p and the rate of emission of gravitons would be about 1 graviton in 10^{32} sec, which is a time greater than the age of the universe! It is thus difficult to attach an operational meaning to the quantization of the gravitational field; the extreme weakness of the gravitational field compared to other forces is more than a quantitative difference, it is a qualitative difference.

The gravitational force, perhaps as a result of its weakness, is unique at present, in that we have been able to construct a view of the universe in which gravity does not exist as a force but only as a geometric consequence. The General Theory of Relativity has the result of reducing the problem of the description of the motion of several bodies from dynamics to kinematics, where dynamics is the study of the effects of forces on bodies, and kinematics is the study of the motion of bodies without reference to forces. If we consider only gravitational effects, all bodies always travel in straight lines. These are straight lines in a curved space, however.

The unacceptable idea of action at a distance is thus supplanted by *two* different hypothesis. Electromagnetism (and the strong and weak interactions) act through the exchange of particles, while gravity is the result of a distortion of space—a change in geometry. This is rather an embarrassment of success; two entirely different hypotheses to explain two quite similar characteristics of nature. Most physicists believe that these two ideas represent different faces of some more generally valid description. There has been considerable effort devoted to including electromagnetism in the geometry of space–time and to quantizing the gravitational field (hence gravitons). But no remarkable success has been achieved in either endeavor.

26 | 4   *The strong-interactions*
—baryons and mesons

The sources of the strong-interactions are particles that are called, collectively, *baryons*. The neutron and proton are the lightest of the many baryons. We can consider that the baryons carry a strong-interaction charge analogous to electric charge, though much larger. Indeed this is essentially the definition of a baryon— a particle with a strong-interaction charge. Since the meson charge is much larger than the electric charge, the energy stored in the accompanying meson field is much larger than the energy stored in the electric field of an electron, and the masses of baryons are very large compared to the mass of the electron—thus the origin of the name baryon from a Greek word meaning heavy.

Even as electric charge is conserved, baryons appear to be conserved. Even as the total positive charge minus the total negative charge will remain the same in a closed system, the number of baryons minus the number of antibaryons will remain the same. Even as pairs of positive and negative charges can be created or annihilated, pairs of baryons and antibaryons can be created and annihilated. We find it convenient to invent a concept of baryon number to describe this kind of result. We then can consider that baryon number is conserved like electric charge. According to this description, baryons, such as the neutron and proton, have a baryon number of $+1$, while antibaryons, such as the antiproton or antineutron, have a baryon number of -1. Since a pair consisting of a baryon and an antibaryon have a total baryon number of 0, the conservation of baryon number does not preclude the annihilation or creation of the baryon–antibaryon pair.

There are a large number of different baryons, which appear to be related in a way we will discuss later when we consider the symmetry properties of the elementary forces. All baryons are fermions having half-integral values of spin, $\frac{1}{2}, \frac{3}{2}, \ldots$, units of $\hbar$, and they have various values of electric charge and various values of a quantity we call hypercharge. It is appropriate to define and discuss hypercharge when we concern ourselves with the symmetries of nature. For each such baryon there exists an antibaryon with the opposite charge and electrical properties as well as the opposite hypercharge and baryon number. This is part of a general characteristic of nature that for any particle there is an antiparticle, where the sums of all conserved discrete properties, such as charge and baryon number, are equal to zero.

Another set of particles, the mesons, comprise the quanta of the strong-interactions. The mesons have zero baryon charge; they are bosons, with integral values of spin, 0, 1, 2, . . . , units of $\hbar$; and like protons they are not conserved. Mesons are created and absorbed by baryons just as photons are created and absorbed by electric charge. The different varieties of mesons have different values of electric charge and hypercharge and various values of mass. The lightest mesons are the pi mesons or pions, with a mass about 270 times the electron mass. As we noted in Chapter 25, the pions are primarily responsible for the nuclear force. There are three charge states of the pion, π^+, π^0, and π^-, where the superscript represents the charge in units of the electron charge.

It is sometimes especially convenient to discuss the interactions of elementary particles with the aid of schematic diagrams that represent typical behaviors of particles as a function of time. These *world diagrams* represent the configurations of the particles as a function of time. For example, the diagram of Fig. 26|1a shows a proton that emits a positive pion, meanwhile becoming a neutron, and then reabsorbs the pion. The dashed line does not represent any kind of trajectory of the pion, only that both the pion and the neutron existed over this period of time. Notice that both electric charge and baryon number are conserved at the two vertices of the diagram. Each vertex represents a boson emitted or absorbed by a fermion: we are proceeding on the assumption—which is not yet firmly established—that all fundamental processes can be described in terms of diagrams with such vertices; that is, that the most basic transition is al-

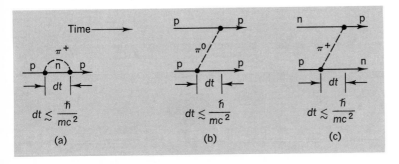

FIG. 26 |1
Diagrams showing interactions that contribute to nuclear forces.

ways the emission or absorption of a field quantum by a source particle.

Energy is not obviously conserved according to the procession of events suggested by the diagram. During the time in which the proton was changed to a neutron and pion, it would seem that energy was not conserved. A free neutron and pion have much more mass, and more energy, than an isolated proton. However, if this situation persists for only a very short time, dt, the uncertainty principle expressed as

$$dE \, dt = \hbar$$

where E is the total energy of the state and dt is the time of observation, suggests that we cannot know the mass of the system to an accuracy better than

$$d(mc^2) = dE$$
$$= \frac{\hbar}{dt}$$

where m is the total mass of the system. Then if

$$dt \lesssim \frac{\hbar}{dm \, c^2}$$

where dm is the extra mass of the system or the mass of the pion, there is no measurable violation of the conservation of energy. Since we can discuss only measurable things in a well defined sensible way, there is no violation of the law of conservation of energy at all. Of course, the final results, observable over a long period of time, must conserve energy. The particle that takes part in the interaction during the time energy is not counted is called a *virtual* particle.

As a useful example, we can represent the meson transfers that account for the major part of the nuclear force in terms of these world diagrams. The diagram of Fig. 26|1b shows the exchange of a neutral meson between two protons, an exchange that represents a basic contribution to the force between the two nucleons, Note that the pion can only be "free" for a time of the order of $\hbar/m_\pi c^2$. Thus if it were to travel at the speed of light it could only travel a distance of $\hbar/m_\pi c$, which is the range of the nuclear force as we found in Chapter 25. The transition shown in Fig. 26|1c shows a meson exchange that contributes to the force between a neutron and a proton. Notice that although the neutron and proton change identities, there is 1 neutron and 1 proton after the exchange as there is 1 neutron and 1 proton before the exchange: since elementary particles of a species are identical, this exchange cannot be identified operationally, and the meson transfer is therefore part of the description of a force between a neutron and proton.

As a practical matter, nearly independent of our degree of sophistication, it is almost necessary to find schematic descriptions of the microscopic phenomena dealt with by the apparatus of the quantum-mechanical description of fields. These diagrams, together with some conventions concerning the interpretation of the diagrams, can be considered as such a description. Although such descriptions are useful to the point of necessity as guides to reason, all firm conclusions and detailed extensions of the concepts presented by the diagrams must rely on meticulously prepared logical foundations and hence upon precise mathematical descriptions. Our comments, which are guided qualitatively by the diagrams, are thus largely verified by detailed calculations that we will not discuss.

Even as the gravitational interaction differs from other interactions qualitatively because of its extreme weakness, the strong-interactions show some important qualitative differences from the other interactions as a result of their great strength. We have emphasized that the magnitude of the charge of a particle is a measure of the intensity, and thus the probability, of the emission of a field quantum. The charge is equally a measure of the probability of absorption of a field quantum. It is a useful approximation to consider that the square of the charge, expressed in the dimensionless units we have adopted, is about equal to the probability of the field containing a quantum. Since $ke^2/\hbar c$ is equal to $\frac{1}{137}$, we can consider that a particle having a charge of e will be emitting and absorbing photons such that the probability of a photon being in the field at any instant is about $\frac{1}{137}$: if we should suddenly remove the particle at the speed of light, the probability is about $\frac{1}{137}$ that a photon will be left behind—or emitted. Since the strong-interaction charge, $kg^2/\hbar c$, is about equal to 1, the probability of a meson being in the field of a baryon is about 1, and the probability of a meson being left behind if a baryon is suddenly removed is about equal to 1.

Less obviously, the same probability holds if the transition takes place in different ways with respect to time. The diagrams

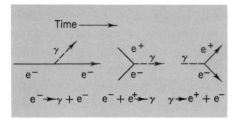

FIG. 26|2
Diagrams showing closely related transitions.

of Fig. 26|2 show transitions that are equivalent in this sense. An electron emitting a photon and remaining an electron has the same probability as the annihilation of an electron and a positron to form a photon, which again has the same intrinsic probability of a photon producing a positron–electron pair. Notice that in the sense of this description, a particle traveling toward the inter-action in time is equal to an antiparticle traveling away from the interaction in time. The electron and positron are antiparticles; the photon and antiphoton are the same.

As a result of the great strength of the strong-interaction, the structure of a baryon and the accompanying field is very complex —much more complex than the structure of a particle such as the electron and the electromagnetic field. The diagrams of Fig. 26|3 suggests the origin of this considerable difference. An electron is usually just a bare electron, as shown at time t_a in

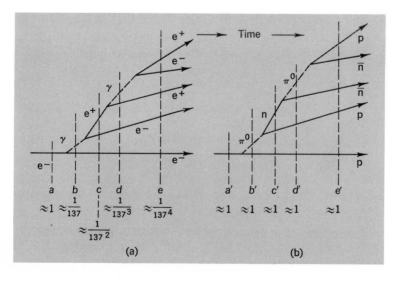

FIG. 26|3
Diagrams showing the complex structure of an electron and a proton.

Fig. 26|2a; rarely, with a probability of $\frac{1}{137}$, it is an electron plus a photon such as shown at time t_b; very rarely, with a probability of $(\frac{1}{137})^2$ the photon produces an electron–positron pair, and the configuration is similar to that at t_c; the field will consist of a photon and a pair even less frequently, as at t_d, and two pair, such as shown as t_e, less often yet. Each extra transition is less probable by a factor of about $\frac{1}{137}$, and the field is usually very simple.

Qualitatively, the possible fields about a proton can be considered in a similar fashion. Sometimes the proton is just a bare proton, as shown in Fig. 26|3b at time $t_{a'}$. Sometimes it will be a proton plus a meson, such as shown at $t_{b'}$. And sometimes there will be the original proton plus a proton–antiproton pair as at $t_{c'}$, and so on. But since each of these fundamental emissions and absorptions represented by the vertices has a probability of the order of 1, in some crude approximation, all of these configurations are about equally probable and the baryon field is never simple.

The simplicity of the electromagnetic interaction allows us to perform extraordinarily precise calculations that are in accord with the extraordinarily precise observations of electromagnetic phenomena that have been made. As a result of the complexity of the strong-interaction, progress has been much slower, and our ability to calculate strong-interaction processes—and hence our understanding of those processes—is quite incomplete.

26|5   *The weak-interactions*

All fermions are sources of the weak-interaction. Our understanding of the weak-interaction is seriously incomplete, but we believe that a photon of the weak-interaction field probably exists. We call this as yet unverified particle the W particle. There are presumably positive and negative W particles; if a neutral W particle exists, it does not seem to play much of a part in the weak-interactions. In order to account for what we do know about the weak-interactions, the W must be a boson with a spin of $1\hbar$ like the photon. If the mass of the W were as small as two proton masses, direct evidence for the existence of the W would now exist: the absence of such evidence established the W mass as greater than the mass of two nucleons—if the W exists at all!

It appears that there are three separate conservation laws for

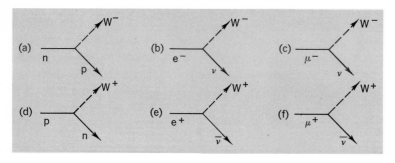

FIG. 26|4
Diagrams showing transitions that are fundamental to the weak interactions.

the fermions that are the sources of the weak-interaction. We mentioned the conservation of baryons in the last section. The fermions that do not hold a strong-interaction charge and emit and absorb mesons are called *leptons*. And we now know that there are two kinds of leptons: (1) the electron and the electron–neutrino together with their antiparticles, the positron and the antielectron–neutrino; and (2) the negative muon and the muon–neutrino with their antiparticles, the positive muon and the anti-muon–neutrino. Both the electron leptons and the muon leptons can be considered to have separate lepton numbers, where the particles have the number $+1$ and the antiparticles have the number -1. Again, in any closed system the number of electron leptons minus the number of antielectron leptons will be conserved, and the number of muon leptons minus the number of antimuon leptons will be conserved. Particle–antiparticle pairs of either the electron leptons or the muon leptons can be created or destroyed.

The muon is much heavier than the electron: the muon mass is equal to 207 times the electron mass. All neutrinos seem to have a rest mass of zero. Aside from the difference in mass, no difference between the electron and the muon has ever been detected.

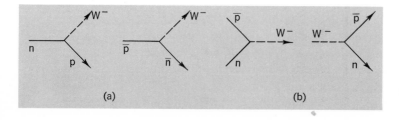

FIG. 26|5
Equivalent transitions.

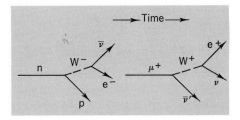

FIG. 26|6

Diagrams exhibiting the beta decay of a neutron and of a positive muon.

This strange situation—two sets of particles exist that are different, yet almost exactly alike in so many ways—is one of the important problems of physics.

The weak-interaction charge of all fermions appears to be the same, and thus the probability of the emission of a W by a baryon and by either of two kinds of leptons is the same. The various fundamental weak-interactions are suggested by the diagrams of Fig. 26|4. The reactions are

(a) $n \rightarrow p + W^-$

(b) $e^- \rightarrow \nu + W^-$ (ν is the electron neutrino)

(c) $\mu^- \rightarrow \nu' + W^-$ (μ is the muon, and ν' is the muon neutrino)

(d) $p \rightarrow n + W^+$

(e) $e^+ \rightarrow \bar{\nu} + W^+$ (ν is the electron antineutrino)

(f) $\mu^+ \rightarrow \bar{\nu}' + W^+$ ($\bar{\nu}'$ is the muon antineutrino)

Note that charge, and baryon number, and both kinds of lepton number are conserved in the emission of W particles. Here e^-, μ^-, ν, and ν', are considered as leptons and e^+, μ^+, $\bar{\nu}'$, and $\bar{\nu}'$ are antileptons. All these transitions can be reversed in time according to the prescription introduced previously; a particle traveling away from the interaction in time is equal to an antiparticle moving toward the interaction. The W^+ and W^- are related to each other as particle and antiparticle. Thus the transition of 26.4a can also take the forms of Fig. 26|5, for example.

Since the W (if it exists) must be very heavy, none of the transitions shown in the diagrams of Fig. 26|4 can occur and conserve energy; therefore, they can occur only as virtual transitions, and the actual decay of particles through the weak-interactions must take place through two-step processes that conserve energy. The diagrams of Fig. 26|6 show the decay of the neutron to a proton and an electron and an anti-neutrino, and the decay of a positive muon to an electron and two neutrinos. Note that charge, baryon number, and the two kinds of lepton numbers are conserved at each vertex. Since the W is very massive, energy is not conserved during the time the W is in existence, but the time is so short that the uncertainty principle precludes any operational violation of that conservation law. Since the masses of the proton, electron, and neutrino are smaller than the neutron mass, energy can be conserved over-all, which is required by the conservation law. Likewise, the masses of the electron and the two neutrinos are less than the mass of the muon, so the reaction can proceed and conserve energy.

The transition takes place in two steps; since the weak-interaction charge $kf^2/\hbar c$ is about 10^{-6}, the effective transition strength is about 10^{-12}. A weak-interaction transition thus takes about 10^{12} times as long as a similar strong-interaction transition and about 10^{10} times as long as an equivalent electromagnetic transition. Lifetimes for particles that can decay only through the weak-interactions are thus rather long on the scale of time of fundamental processes. The lifetime of the neutron is about 100 sec and the mean life of the muon is about 2×10^{-6} sec.

26|6   *Summary*

We have described all of the fundamental interactions in much the same way: a force between two source particles results from the exchange of a field quantum and the other source particle absorbs the quantum. The differences between the forces arise,

TABLE 26|1   *Properties of the fundamental interactions*

Interaction	Source	Strength $kq^2/\hbar c$	Field quanta	Spin of quanta
Strong	Baryons	1	Mesons	$0, 1\hbar, 2\hbar, \ldots$
Electro-magnetic	Charges	$\frac{1}{137}$	Photons	$1\hbar$
Weak	Fermions (baryons and leptons)	10^{-6}	W	$1\hbar$
Gravity	Mass	10^{-40}	Gravitons	$2\hbar$

then, largely from the different strengths of the charges, where the charge is a measure of the probability of emission and absorption of the quantum, and also from different conservation laws regarding the sources, and different properties of the field quanta. This description is aesthetically attractive, and is certainly nearly correct as a description of electromagnetic forces and the strong-interactions, but may not be completely adequate for gravity or the weak-interactions.

Table 26|1 summarizes some of the important information available concerning the various known interactions.

PROBLEMS

26|1 How would you expect nuclear forces to be affected if the interaction strength, $kg^2/\hbar c$, were doubled?

26|2 How would you expect nuclear forces to be affected if the mass of the pion were doubled?

26|3 In the collision of very-high-energy protons with other protons, both pions and photons are produced directly in the collision. Estimate the ratio of the number of pions and photons produced in a large number of such collisions.

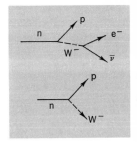

26|4 Why does a neutron decay into a proton in the two-step process $n \rightarrow p + W^-$, $W^- \rightarrow e^- + \bar{\nu}$ instead of the one-step process $n \rightarrow p + W^-$?

26|5 Consider these diagrams to represent reactions between two protons at very high energies. Order the diagrams as to your estimate of their relative probability. Make numerical estimates of the ratio of the probabilities if you can.

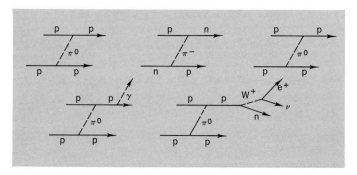

26 |6 The mean life of the neutron is about 1000 sec. If the strength of the weak-interaction, $kf^2/\hbar c$, were increased by a factor of 2, what would be the value of the lifetime? Why?

26 |7 The reactions represented by these diagrams are all impossible. Show why for each diagram.

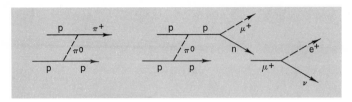

26 |8 Upon hitting solid material, such as lead, a very-high-energy proton will be stopped in a meter or less, a very-high-energy muon will travel through very many meters of lead, while a high-energy neutrino will usually pass through the whole earth before even making a collision. Explain this result qualitatively.

26 |9 (*a*) What physical processes are represented by these two diagrams?

(*b*) Estimate the relative probability of the two processes.

(*c*) The importance of process (a) suggests that the superposition principle does not hold very well for the strong-interactions. What does this mean? Why is it likely to be true?

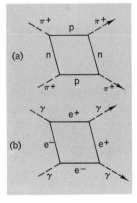

twenty-seven Symmetries and conservation laws

27|1 *Space–time symmetries and the classical conservation laws*

MOST, IF NOT ALL, conservation laws are related to the existence of symmetries or invariances in nature. Before we explore the consequences of such symmetries or invariances and their explicit relations to conservation laws, it is useful to analyze the meaning of these concepts by considering the nature of some very elementary symmetries.

The diagram of Fig. 27|1a shows a circle with an observer standing at the center. Let us assume that half the circle is painted green and half red. If the observer is color blind, the enclosure is *invariant* with respect to rotation of the observer: the observer will see or otherwise perceive the enclosure in just the same way, no matter how he is oriented. Of course the symmetry is broken if he can detect the color in some way. For some purposes the circle is symmetric: for some purposes it is not. The character of the symmetry depends upon the tool used to measure or determine the orientation of the observer.

An observer will see the circle in the same way for an infinite number of orientations: further, the invariance is continuous: the view is the same as he slowly turns around. The observer in the center of the triangle of Fig. 27|1b sees a threefold, discontinuous symmetry. If he whirls around with his eyes closed and then stops and opens his eyes and looks around, he will not know

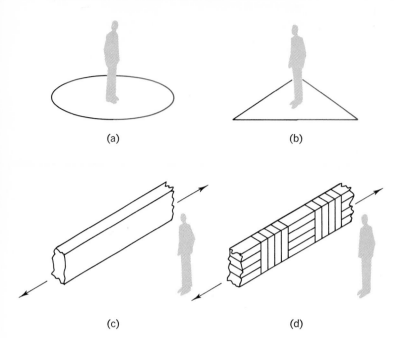

(a)   (b)

(c)   (d)

FIG. 27|1
Various symmetries with respect to rotation and translation of the observer or the environment.

what direction he is facing up to a threefold uncertainty. The view is invariant with respect to a rotation of 120° by the observer (or the triangle). Again the triangle would exhibit a symmetry to anyone concerned only with form, but might not be symmetric to anyone who could observe that the sides were painted different colors.

The symmetry group need not be closed. Fig. 27|1c shows a man in front of a wall that extends forever without change in size, shape, or color. Of course he cannot, then, tell where he is by inspection of the wall. There is a complete and continuous invariance with respect to position along the wall. The observer is hardly better off as far as geographic clues are considered when he is standing in front of the wall of Fig. 27|1d. Here the wall is figured with a recurring pattern: he can tell where he is with respect to the pattern, but there is an infinite number of repeated patterns. There is an invariance with respect to discrete intervals along the wall.

It seems possible to understand many of the conservation laws developed in our description of nature in terms of such symmetries or invariances of nature. The classical conservation laws, the conservation of energy, momentum, and angular momentum, appear to be related to invariances in the space–time description of nature. In particular, it has been possible to understand the law of conservation of energy as a consequence of the invariance of nature with time. If the results of any experiment are to be independent of the time when the experiment is performed, energy must be conserved. If time is relative, if no experimental measurement can detect absolute time, if all of the universal constants—the velocity of light, Planck's constant, the charge of the electron, and so on—are to be independent of time, conservation of energy will follow as a consequence.

In a similar fashion, conservation of momentum follows naturally from the invariance of nature with respect to place. If position is wholly relative, if no conceivable experiment can give results that depend upon the position of the laboratory, if the constants of nature do not vary with position, conservation of momentum follows as a consequence.

The conservation of angular momentum is a consequence of the rotational symmetry of the universe. Nature appears to be invariant with respect to angle. There seems to be no absolute zero of angle, no intrinsically preferred plane or direction. The velocity of light is the same in all directions. The gravitational force from a sphere or the electrostatic field from a charged sphere is the same in all directions.

All of these statements can be relevant only in closed systems or isolated laboratories. The momentum of a ball thrown upward from the earth's surface is not itself conserved: the ball comes to a stop, reverses its motion, and falls to the ground. It is the total momentum of earth and ball that we believe is conserved. Our laboratory must either include the earth or be closed to the earth, excluding the earth and effects of the earth.

The reasoning behind these statements is not easily available to us; however, we can construct some examples of asymmetric "universes" in which angular momentum, linear momentum, and energy are not conserved, which may serve as useful illustrations of the concepts involved. These universes will consist of rooms or laboratories holding an observer and some suitable apparatus, as suggested by the drawings of Fig. 27 | 2. Except for the influences that are manifestly introduced in the drawings and in the discussion, we assume that nothing external to the rooms affects the observers or their equipment.

In Fig. 27|2a we are looking at a universe where electric charge varies with time: let us assume for definiteness that it increases. Then the force between the two charges will increase with time and the spring between them will be compressed, adding to the potential energy of the spring—energy will not be conserved. If the magnitude of the fundamental charges should oscillate with time, the spring would flex with time and we could use that motion to operate a machine—a perpetual-motion machine! Energy is not conserved in this universe where the fundamental constants—such as the magnitude or strength of electric charge—vary with time.

The observer in Fig. 27|2b is watching the rotation of a dumbbell about its center, where the two weights are charged with equal and opposite electric charges. This universe is placed between the plates of a capacitor so that an electric field is directed across the universe. Of course this is an anisotropic universe: the potential energy of the dumbbell on its pivot will vary with the angle of inclination of the dumbbell. As a result of the forces on the charges, the angular velocity of the dumbbell will vary as it rotates, and angular momentum will not be conserved in that anisotropic universe.

In the universe of Fig. 27|2c, the potential energy of the set of two charges held by the observer will vary as the observer moves the system toward or away from the wall to our left. The electric field produced by the charge at the left will attract the

FIG. 27|2
Universes that change (a) with time, (b) with direction, and (c) with position.

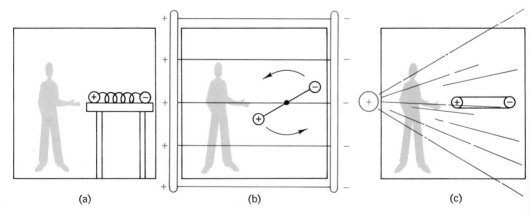

(a)   (b)   (c)

negative charge, which is closer, more than it will repel the positive charge. If the observer lets go of the pair of charges, the system will accelerate to the left. Even as the velocity increases,
the momentum of the system will increase, and momentum will
not be conserved in this universe where the potential energy of
the system will vary with position.

It is necessary to emphasize that while we have shown that in
very particular "universes," which do not display invariances
with respect to time, direction, and position, the dynamic quantities energy, angular momentum, and linear momentum are not
conserved: we have not proved (and will not) the much more important converse—that the conservation laws follow from the
invariances.

One might object that if we included the whole system in our
analysis—the external system that perhaps supplied extra charge
in the universe of 27|2a, or the capacitor plates of 27|2b, or the
external charge of 27|2c—the conservation laws would still be
valid. That is, energy, momentum, and angular momentum would
be conserved in our universe, but not in the observer's universes.
This is true, but is it relevant? If we discovered that energy was
not conserved in our universe, we could postulate an extra-
universal source of energy and say that energy was conserved
over-all. The man in the laboratories of Fig. 27|2, might, if he
were very clever, deduce that his system might be a subuniverse
in a whole universe in which the conservation laws did operate.
Although such a conclusion would be both interesting and important, it would not supplant the observation that energy is not
conserved in his universe.

This raises the question of the conservation of energy in our
universe: does our universe change with time? If our universe is
expanding from a beginning 10 billion years ago, a conclusion
suggested by astronomical evidence, do we not have an absolute
time, is the universe not changing fundamentally with time, and
is energy then really conserved in our universe? Perhaps not. On
a cosmological scale of time we do not know that energy is conserved. Many theories of the origin and character of the universe
contain implicitly a violation of the law of conservation of energy.
The conservation laws pertain to an ideal universe to which our
actual universe may stand only as a good local approximation.

27|2 *Microscopic symmetries—parity*

Our local environment contains a great deal of structure. Certainly much of the character of this structure is essentially accidental. Most men are right handed; most bears appear to be left handed; our heart is on the left-hand side of the body, or more properly the pumping of arterial blood takes place in the left-hand side of the heart. We feel intuitively that all of these characteristics are essentially accidental; we are loath to believe that the dominant selection of right-hand threaded screws by our technology is an indication of some fundamental character of nature.

However, the question whether a fundamental symmetry between left-handed and right-handed systems exists is valid and important. Is there any fundamental characteristic of nature that differentiates between left-handed and right-handed systems? If Alice passes through the looking glass, she finds a world where most men are left-handed and left-handed screws are used to holds things together—but perhaps this is only an accidental characteristic of this world, along with Humpty Dumpty and the Walrus and the Carpenter. Is there any observation Alice can possibly make that can tell her that she is in the looking-glass

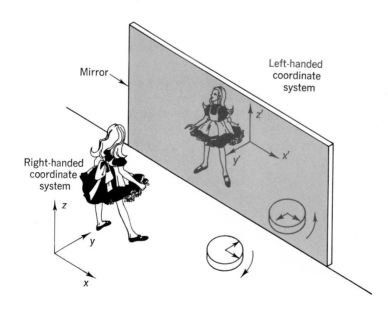

FIG. 27|3

Alice looking through a (tinted) looking glass.

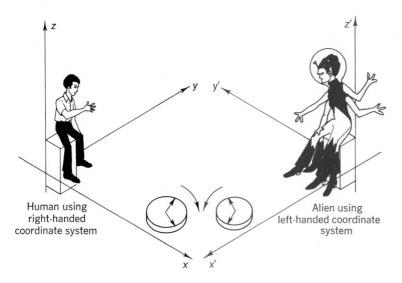

Human using
right-handed
coordinate system

Alien using
left-handed coordinate
system

FIG. 27|4
An alien from another
galaxy and a human,
where the alien, and
human use different
coordinate systems.

land; is there any fundamental character of the universe that differentiates between left-handed and right-handed screws, or between the world we know and a possible mirror image?

In Fig. 27|3 we see Alice looking into the mirror—or "Alice through the looking glass" looking out of the mirror. A coordinate system, labeled x, y, z, according to a convention we call a right-handed coordinate system, and a conventional clock are shown, together with their looking-glass counterparts. The hands of the "real" clock move in a manner that we call clockwise; the hands of the looking-glass clock move counterclockwise. The mirror coordinate system is labeled x', y', z', in a way we called left-handed. How can we tell the looking-glass world from our usual world?

We can further illustrate this question by considering a hypothetical problem. Let us assume that we have contacted some other civilization through some obscure means of communication such that symbols (words, for example) can be transmitted, but no material devices can be transferred. We can determine, easily enough, many of the characteristics of our alien friends; perhaps they have four legs, four arms, and feelers, as suggested by Fig. 27|4. We can even send pictures and exchange television programs. But there are also limits to our exchange of information. We have already emphasized invariances that suggest that we cannot determine the position of the other system, we cannot determine the orientation of that system, nor can we determine the time difference between the systems. The system may be a billion light years from us in the direction of Polaris; north in their geographic system may be west in ours; and they may be 10 million years in our future; but if the universe is invariant with respect to position, direction, and time, no measurements that we can perform and compare through our communication system can allow us to determine these relations.

Can we, however, determine whether the aliens use a right-handed or left-handed coordinate system? Do the hands of their clocks move clockwise, or counterclockwise; do they use the right-handed nuts and bolts, or left-handed ones? Can you find a way to tell whether you have passed into the looking-glass world? You might naïvely believe that you can make this determination by measuring the direction of the magnetic field near a wire carrying a current. Remember in the real world the direction of the field is in the direction of your fingers if your thumb is along the direction of the current and you use your *right* hand. In the looking-glass world we might expect that a *left*-hand rule would obtain: in the looking-glass world the direction of the magnetic field would follow the fingers of Alice's left hand. But how do you measure the direction of the magnetic field? Only by the force on a wire carrying a current. The definition of the direction of a magnetic field is a convention designed to express the force between two currents or two moving charges, and all physical results concerning the forces between the two currents are independent of whether we *consistently* use a right-hand rule for the direction of the field or a left-hand rule, so this technique is of no use to us. Indeed, it seems that as long as we consider only phenomena induced by gravity, the strong nuclear interactions, or the electromagnetic interactions, we cannot find any experimental result that differentiates between left-handed and right-handed coordinate systems, or between the real world and its mirror image. To the extent that we restrict ourselves to such observations, it appears that the universe is invariant with respect to mirror reflection or the choice of left-handed or right-handed coordinate systems, and we will not be able to determine which system the aliens use.

Until 1956 it was generally believed that the descriptions of all interactions were independent of the choice of coordinate system and thus that *any* observation of the universe was un-changed, or invariant, under reflection in a mirror. We label the operation of mirror reflection, *P*. Then indications appeared that details of the decay, through the weak-interactions, of the K meson into three pions was inconsistent with the decay into two pions and the hypothesis that no observation could dis-criminate between left-handed and right-handed coordinate systems. In the course of efforts to understand this result, C. N. Yang and T. D. Lee were able to show that nothing known about the weak-interactions was in contradiction to the hypothesis that the weak-interactions might generally proceed in such a manner as to define a screw direction and thus a coordinate system that was fundamentally different from its mirror image.

Shortly thereafter C. S. Wu and her collaborators performed an experiment that showed conclusively that the weak-inter-actions do define a coordinate system, and therefore nature does discriminate between left- and right-handed systems.

Cobalt 60, a radioactive isotope of colbalt that emits electrons, was aligned by a magnetic field so that the spin of the nucleus was in the direction of the field, somewhat as a small magnet is aligned in a magnetic field. It was then determined that the elec-trons emitted by the cobalt were emitted predominantly opposite to the direction of the nuclear spin and opposite to the direction of the magnetic field, **B**. It is useful to strip our description of any conventions of current direction or magnetic-field direction by stating that the decay electrons are emitted upward if the current electrons are moving counterclockwise. If the Co^{60} were placed on the face of a clock and the electron current were moving op-posite to the direction of motion of the hands of the clock, the decay electrons would move away from the face of the clock. We can then use the experiment to define counterclockwise, and thus, of course, clockwise. The diagram of Fig. 27|5 suggests sche-matically the character of this result.

Nature, then, does define a coordinate system, and we can use the results of such a measurement of Co^{60} decays to determine whether we are in a looking-glass world or not, or to determine the coordinate system used by the aliens with whom we are ex-changing information. In Fig. 27|6 we see the human and alien each performing the Co^{60} decay experiment, which can be used to define a coordinate system for them. If the moving electrons that provide the magnetic field that aligns the nucleus travel

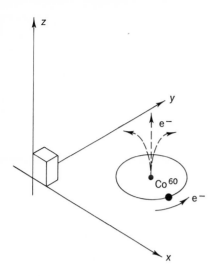

FIG. 27|5
*The decay of Co^{60}
nuclei polarized in a
magnetic field.*

opposite to the direction of the hands of a clock, and the decay
electrons travel primarily upward, a right-handed coordinate
system is in use; if the electrons travel downward, a left-handed
coordinate system is used—the clock convention is different and
we are in a looking-glass world.

The symmetry with respect to mirror reflection, P, of all of the
observations of nature that depend upon the strong-interactions,
the electromagnetic interactions, or gravity results in a conserva-

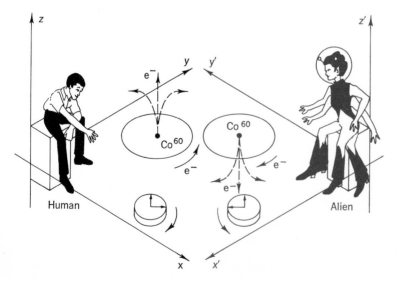

FIG. 27|6
*A human and an alien
observing Co^{60} decays.*

tion law—the conservation of *parity*. Parity is a more subtle concept than energy and momentum, and parity is obviously important only in the microscopic areas of molecules, atoms, and elementary particles. We will not examine the concept of parity and the importance of the conservation of parity carefully, but we will discuss the application of the concept to the very simple system of a particle in a one-dimensional box, which may serve to suggest some of the character of more complex and more general systems.

The graphs of Fig. 27|7 show the amplitude and the intensity of the de Broglie wave description of two particular states of a particle in a box, together with their mirror reflections. The amplitude A_a is unchanged by the reflection, which interchanges the coordinates x and $-x$: we say that the parity of the state A_a is even. The amplitude A_b is reversed by a mirror reflection, or by the interchange of x and $-x$ in the coordinate system: we say that the parity of this state is odd. Note that the intensity, the only observable, since de Broglie amplitudes are not measurable themselves, is unchanged by the mirror reflection. It can be shown (though not here) that the parity of a system will be unchanged or conserved if only forces act that are unchanged upon mirror reflection. If forces act that are not mirror invariant, the parity of the system need not be conserved, and amplitudes may obtain, such as shown in Fig. 27|7c, where the description of the intensity, an observable, is changed upon mirror reflection, or if the coordinates x and $-x$ are reversed.

FIG. 27|7

States of a particle in a one-dimensional box; the states have different parity.

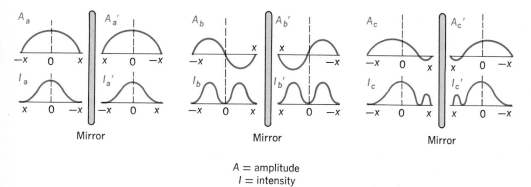

A = amplitude
I = intensity

(a)　　　　　　　　(b)　　　　　　　　(c)

27 | 3 *Microscopic symmetries
—charge conjugation*

In 1928, the British physicist P. A. M. Dirac developed the first wave equation for spin $\frac{1}{2}\hbar$ particles that was consistent with the Special Theory of Relativity. A number of striking results were implied by these equations. In particular, for each particle there must exist an antiparticle with opposite electrical properties— opposite charge and opposite charge distributions and currents. Somewhat later, similar results were obtained for bosons— particles with a spin of $0\hbar$, $1\hbar$, $2\hbar$, . . . ,—though neutral bosons could, in some cases, be their own antiparticles: There is no anti- photon; or better, the photon and antiphoton are the same.

A further property of the whole set of theories was the result that antimatter followed exactly the same laws as matter as far as electromagnetic forces were concerned. Later it was seen that matter and antimatter also behaved in the same way with respect to the strong nuclear forces and gravity. Perhaps this was the case for all interactions—the weak-interactions too. Then a uni- verse composed of antimatter, where antihydrogen gas, made up of atoms in which a positron or antielectron circled a negatively charged antiproton in a Bohr orbit, was used to fill antiballoons made of antirubber held by antichildren, would be just like ours. In the antiuniverse each particle would be replaced by its anti- particle.

Any interaction between universe and antiuniverse would be catastrophic, however. Since the conservation laws that operate so as to guarantee the stability of matter—that is, the conserva- tion of baryons and leptons—do not ensure the stability of mix- tures of particles and antiparticles, the matter in such mixtures will be largely annihilated to produce more probable or less con- centrated forms of energy. A nucleon and an antinucleon will annihilate to produce mesons with large kinetic energies; some of the kinetic energy will be dissipated in a manner that will eventu- ally be seen as heat before the mesons disintegrate to leptons with kinetic energy. And much of the kinetic energy of the leptons will eventually be transformed to heat. Then the leptons themselves will disintegrate into lighter leptons (and kinetic energy) or in- teract with antileptons, and be annihilated, again producing energy that is eventually transformed to heat. And the trans- formations would proceed with explosive speed.

The physical interaction between the two universes must be limited then. Friendships must be distant: any affair between boy and antigirl must be kept platonic. But if the symmetry between matter and antimatter were exact, and we made contact with some extragalactic civilization, like the aliens of the last section, in some manner so that we could exchange information but not material, we could not determine whether they were anticreatures living in an antiuniverse or creatures like ourselves. Girls and antigirls would thus be impossible to tell apart at a distance. A universe constructed of antimatter would be identical to ours: any fundamental observations (which, of course, does not include the length of feelers on the aliens' heads) would be the same in the two universes.

However, the experimental and theoretical work connected with the discovery of the nonconservation of parity by the weak-interactions, which was discussed in the last section, also showed that the weak-interactions do distinguish between matter and antimatter. The weak-interactions are therefore not invariant under a matter–antimatter exchange that is called "charge conjugation." In particular, it was shown that leptons and antileptons are produced differently by the weak-interactions. In the limit where they are produced at the speed of light, the leptons' intrinsic angular momentum or spin is directed opposite to their direction of motion, whereas the spin of the antileptons is directed along their direction of motion. A neutrino moving toward you is spinning clockwise; an antineutrino moving towards you is spinning counterclockwise. This behavior is suggested by the diagrams of Fig. 27|8, where the view in a mirror is also shown.

We can therefore use this information concerning the orien-

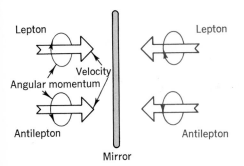

FIG. 27|8
Leptons and antileptons and their mirror images. The image is to the right.

tation of lepton spins to determine the relative particle–antiparticle character of our alien friends. They could observe
whether their neutrinos and other leptons are spinning clockwise
like ours, or counterclockwise. From this information they could
determine whether their local environment was composed of
particles or antiparticles. (Of course, like the label *alien,* the terms
particle and *antiparticle* are our nomenclature. They would call
us aliens and call our matter antimatter if it differed from theirs.)

Of course, in order to implement this exchange of information
we would have to teach the aliens what clockwise and counterclockwise mean, which means that we would have to determine
the relative coordinate system conventions of the strangers and
ourselves. Do they use a left-handed or a right-handed coordinate system? In the last section we showed that they could determine the relative convention by performing the cobalt-60 alignment experiment, or they could observe the relation between the
spin and direction of a neutrino.

But perhaps they do not have Co^{60} but anti-Co^{60}; perhaps they
live in an antiuniverse and would therefore observe antineutrinos
if they followed our prescription. Even as a neutrino behaves
like an antineutrino viewed in a mirror, anticobalt, in a magnetic
field produced by a current of antielectrons in an anticopper wire,
emits antielectrons (positrons) in a manner that is indistinguish-

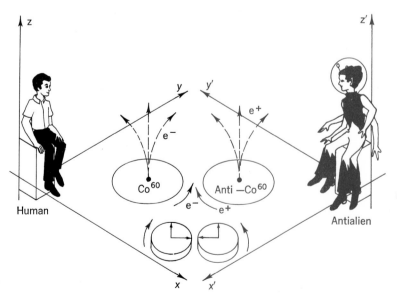

FIG. 27 ∙9

*A human and an anti-
alien aligning their Co^{60}
sources according to
different coordinate
definitions and observing
the decays.*

able from the corresponding particle experiment viewed in a mirror. As shown in the drawings of Fig. 27|9, antialiens, performing the Co^{60} experiment with anti-Co^{60}, in a universe of antimatter, will obtain results that will be described in the same manner as our results if they use a left-handed coordinate system.

The weak-interactions are not invariant with respect to the mirror-inversion operation, which we call P for parity. Nor are weak-interactions invariant with respect to the exchange of particles and antiparticles—the operation we call C for charge conjugation. However, to the extent that the description used here is correct, it appears that the weak-interactions are invariant with respect to the combination of operations, CP. It seems that if we substitute antiparticles for particles and observe the interactions in a mirror we cannot distinguish between these observations and observations of a particle reaction. The other important forces, gravity, electromagnetism, and the strong-interactions, seem to be invariant under the C and P operations separately.

Certainly to a high degree of accuracy the weak-interactions, like all other interactions, seemed to be invariant with respect to the combined operations, CP. Then quite recently, as a result of special properties of a heavy neutral meson, the K_2^0 meson, it became possible to test this invariance with considerable precision; results were obtained that showed, unequivocally, that violations of CP invariance do occur. The arguments concerning this interpretation of the original experiment are subtle and indirect, and we will not attempt to discuss them here. However, the interpretation of some later measurements is more obvious. If we run a beam of K^+ mesons into copper, or K^- mesons (anti-K^+ mesons) into anticopper, we know that we will produce a beam of K_2^0 mesons. We now know that K_2^0 mesons decay into positive muons and positive electrons slightly more often then they decay into negative muons and negative electrons. This result violates CP invariance, and we can show that it does by using the results of such experiments to determine whether our friend, the extragalactic alien, is an antialien living and experimenting in a universe of antimatter, which he describes using a left-handed coordinate system, or whether he uses a right-handed coordinate system and is constructed of the same kind of matter as we are. We will ask him to set up a beam of K_2^0 mesons and measure the curvature of the decay products, the electrons and

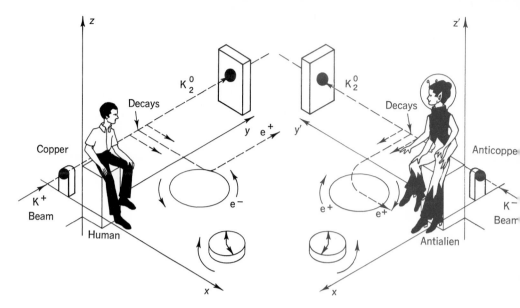

FIG. 27 | 10

*A human and an anti-
alien examining the
decays from K_2^0 mesons.
The observations show
them that they are
related as antibeings in
antiuniverses.*

muons, in a magnetic field derived from an electron current. The suggested setup and the results that prove that he is an anti-alien are shown in Fig. 27 | 10.

We take a K^+ beam from an accelerator and run the beam into a copper target to produce K_2^0 mesons. The antialien, in nominally following our directions, runs a beam of anti-K^+ mesons, or K^- mesons into an anticopper target to produce K_2^0 mesons that are the same as our K_2^0 mesons. We identify the dominant leptons from the K-meson decays as positive electrons and positive muons by passing them through the magnetic field produced by an electron current moving counterclockwise. The alien attempts to copy our procedures, but his electron beam is actually an anti-electron or positron current, and his version of counterclockwise is opposite to ours since he uses a left-handed coordinate system. But of course the main decay products of his K_2^0 beam are positive muons and positive electrons, just as ours are. But a little study of the relative charges and directions of the particles shows that the K_2^0 decay products in the alien's universe will be bent toward the negative y-direction, while the same decay products will be bent toward the positive y-direction in our universe. The difference is obvious and can be communicated. We now know that the alien is an antibeing using a left-handed coordinate system. And we now know that not everything in the universe is invariant under the combination of mirror inversion, or change of coordinate system, and charge conjugation; not everything is left unchanged by CP.

Since the weak-interactions, the strong-interactions, and the electromagnetic interactions all play a part in the decays of the K_2^0 meson, we do not know which interaction is responsible for this breakdown in the symmetry. Perhaps another force exists that is responsible that is much different from any of the well-known forces. We only know that the symmetry-breaking interaction is very weak, or a very small part of the other forces.

The probable importance of invariances of symmetries was emphasized particularly by Ernst Mach (1838–1916), an Austrian physicist and philosopher of physics. Einstein referred particularly to the influence of Mach in the introduction to his paper on the Special Theory of Relativity. Mach believed, essentially on philosophical grounds, that any basic description of the universe must be independent of the choice of coordinate systems. The discovery that nature did discriminate between left-handed and right-handed coordinate systems was disturbing to physicists, but the discovery of the approximate invariance under the combination of operations CP seemed to save this generalized Mach's principle. Even this is destroyed by the K_2^0 decay results, however. We have thus lost simplicities we believed we had found; nature is more subtle than we had thought.

27|4 *Microscopic symmetries*
—time reversal

Even as the descriptions of many fundamental processes have been found to be invariant with respect to reflection in a mirror, which is very much like a reversal in the direction of space coordinates, we might ask whether the descriptions of these processes are not also invariant with respect to a change in the direction of time—*time reversal*. Aside from the tendency for the universe to move toward a most probable situation or toward an increase in entropy, is there any fundamental process that determines the direction of time? We have noted that the collision of two billiard balls makes as much sense (fits the laws of conservation of momentum and energy) if the description of the event takes place backwards in time as it does if the description follows the actual course of events. If we observed a motion-picture projection of the event, we could not tell whether the film was being run backward or forward by observing the event. Likewise, the earth's path about the sun could just as well be reversed as far as the laws of gravity are concerned.

Until quite recently we believed that all interactions were invariant under time reversal and, aside from the second law of thermodynamics and considerations of increase in probability, no fundamental interaction could differentiate between past and future. The experimental evidence in this matter was never highly precise, and there is now some indirect evidence that not all interactions are invariant under time reversal. We have mentioned that we cannot understand the decays of K_2^0 mesons and hold to the thesis that the interactions are invariant under the combined operations of CP. However, there are good theoretical reasons (which we will not discuss further) that suggest that all interactions are invariant under the combination of the three operations C, P, and T, where T symbolizes time reversal. Then if the description of some interaction is changed under CP it must be changed under T if it is to remain invariant under CPT.

If all interactions are invariant under CPT, no possible experimental result that does not change probability or entropy would differentiate between two universes, *a* and *b*, that differ such that *b* consists of antiparticles, uses a left-handed coordinate system, and time runs backwards, while *a* is "normal."

Table 27|1 summarizes information concerning the invariance properties of the various interactions.

TABLE 27|1   *Invariance properties of the fundamental interactions[a]*

Interaction	P	C	T	CP[b]	CPT
Strong	+	+	+	+	+
Electromagnetic	+	+	+	+	+
Weak	−	−	+	+	+
Gravity	+	+	+	+	+

[a] + means conserved, − means not conserved.
[b] There is definite evidence for CP nonconservation, but the origin of the breakdown has not yet been located.

It is convenient to illustrate all these results in terms of observations of the projection of a motion picture strip made of any conceivable experiment, divested of cultural trimmings (such as right-handed men, conventional clocks, and so on). If all the interactions are invariant under P, we cannot tell whether the film strip is inserted in the projector with the wrong side facing the lens, or whether either the photography or projection is made by reflection in a mirror. If the interactions are invariant under C, we cannot tell whether the photographed experiment was performed in an antiuniverse or not. If the experiment did not result in a change of entropy, and if all interactions were invariant under T, we would not be able to tell whether the film was being run backwards or forward. If CP invariance holds, we cannot differentiate between a film of an ordinary universe and a film taken of an antiuniverse as seen in a mirror. If CPT invariance holds, we cannot differentiate between a film taken in our universe and a film taken of an antiuniverse, projected by reflection in a mirror, with the projector run backwards. We emphasize again that this assumes that the entropy does not change in the events we see—entropy is time's arrow for universes or antiuniverses. Of course, if the universe is not invariant under T as we suspect, there must be two different arrows of time, a thermodynamic arrow and an arrow from observations of the effects of elementary forces. One might then determine the direction of time in two different ways. Will the two methods always agree or are there two different times?

27|5 *The conservation of charge and particle numbers*

We have learned that the existence of conservation laws is usually, if not always, related to the existence of symmetries. We observe that electric charge is conserved, and that two kinds of lepton numbers are conserved. It is important—indeed, essential —that we learn to associate these conservation laws with other aspects of nature, and it is most attractive to attempt to connect the conservation of these quantities with a set of symmetries or invariances.

Although these quantities, charge and particle numbers, seem to be similar in that each conservation rule concerns the conservation of some integral number where individual particles can have either negative or positive values of the number, we have been successful only in relating the conservation of charge to an observed invariance of nature. The conservation of charge seems to be intimately related to the invariance of nature with respect to electrostatic potential: we know of no observable effect that depends upon electrostatic potential.

The two laboratories shown in Fig. 27|11 are supposed to be exactly equivalent except that they are held at different electrostatic potentials. This difference in potential is shown graphically by showing the laboratories at different positions between the large capacitor plates. The laboratory S is at a higher potential then the laboratory S' even as it would take energy to transport a positive charge from S' to S. We know of no experiment that can be performed in these laboratories that will allow the observers O and O' to determine the potential of their laboratories, and therefore no information they can exchange will allow them to deduce which of them is at the higher potential.

According to the picture of Fig. 27|11, the observers are each provided with a positive electric charge. Since the electric field is constant between the capacitor plates, the force on the charges in the two laboratories is the same if the charges are equal: only their absolute potential energy is different, but that is not measurable by any device we know. If the charges could be annihilated singly, and the energy of annihilation could be measured, the energy derived in S must be greater than the energy produced in S', however, even as the potential energy of the charge at S is

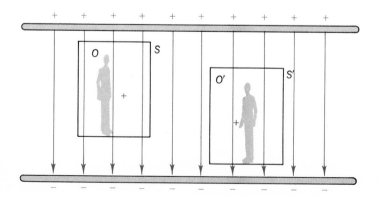

FIG. 27|11
Laboratories at different electrostatic potentials.

greater than at S'. Therefore, if charge is not conserved, but can be annihilated in such a manner, and if energy is conserved, one could measure the absolute potentials of the laboratories by measuring the annihilation energy. Conversely, if the absolute potential of the laboratory is to be meaningless and nature is to be invariant with respect to differences in potential, electric charge must be conserved.

It is important to notice that the annihilation of a pair of opposite charges is not forbidden by these arguments, even as the potential energy of a pair of charges is not different in S and S': even as the positive charge has greater potential energy in S than in S', the negative charge has less potential energy.

Although there have been attempts to develop similar relations between the particle numbers and invariances with respect to potentials, these have not yet been successful, and these conservation laws, the conservation of baryons and the conservation of leptons, stand now as isolated observations of the character of nature.

27 | 6   *Symmetries of the strong-interaction —charge independence*

A most serious complication concerning the strong-interactions lies in the very large number of particles, baryons and mesons, that take part in the strong interactions. The exact number of elementary particles depends upon the precise criteria used to define a particle, but the number can reasonably be given as of the order of 50 to 100. A hundred elementary particles is too many! Physicists believe, as a matter of faith, that the universe must be essentially simple—simpler than implied by the existence of a large number of independent fundamental entities. It is therefore imperative, and a central problem of physics, that we arrive at some simpler description of this aspect of nature. Perhaps many of these particles can be considered as excited states of a few truly fundamental particles, in analogy with the excited states of the Bohr model of the hydrogen atom. Perhaps we can construct a table of the particles, in analogy with the periodic table of the elements. Perhaps we can describe most of the elementary particles as consisting of compounds of a few fundamental particles, as the profusion of nuclei are now considered to be compounds of neutrons and protons. Some such simplification of our view is essential.

Recently great progress has been made in the classification of these particles through emphasis on the symmetry properties of the particles and their interactions. We may be very close to achieving a new, deeper level of understanding of fundamental particles and forces.

Soon after the discovery of the neutron it was noticed that the neutron and proton are surprisingly alike. They differ in mass by less than 0.1 percent, and have the same intrinsic angular momentum or spin. Since the mass of an elementary particle is closely connected to the strength of the charge the particle carries, the near equivalence in the mass of the two nucleons immediately suggests that the strong-interaction charge of the neutron and proton is the same, and that, in general, the nuclear interaction between particles is independent of the electrical charge of the particles: the nuclear forces are *charge independent.*

We might imagine that a microscopic observer has the task of differentiating between a neutron and a proton, as suggested by the drawing of Fig. 27|12. If he is using only a "meter" that responds to the strong-interactions, he cannot tell which is the neutron and which is the proton. No matter what observations or experiments he carries out, if he relies only on the strong-interactions, the neutron and proton will seem to him to be absolutely equivalent. Of course if he pulls an electric-field-strength meter out of his pocket, the difference will be immediately obvious: the two particles are not the same, of course; the proton carries a positive electric charge and the neutron is electrically neutral.

Certain sets of nuclei, as well as sets of elementary particles, exhibit a similar charge independence. The three nuclear states C^{14}, N^{14} and O^{14}, which were discussed in Chapter 25, comprise

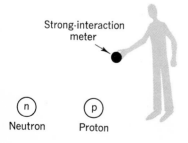

Strong-interaction
meter

Neutron   Proton

FIG. 27|12
*Observer examining a
neutron and proton with
a strong-interaction
meter.*

a family of nuclei that cannot be distinguished if nuclear forces alone are used. Like the neutron and proton, they can be distinguished by their electric charge: the C^{14} nucleus carries a charge of 6 units, N^{14} has a charge of 7, and O^{14} has a charge of 8. The three pions also comprise a charge independent multiplet: though the π^+, π^0 and π^- mesons have different electrical charges, they seem to be identical in their behavior with respect to the strong-interactions. Indeed, we find that all nuclear states, as well as all elementary particles, belong to families or multiplets with 1, 2, 3, or more members, where the members all have different electric charges but are not distinguishable through the strong-interactions. The members of such a multiplet do not have randomly different charges, but form an ordered set where the charge differs by 1 unit from member to member.

This charge independence of the strong-interactions, this invariance of the strong-interactions with respect to electric charge, this symmetry of the particles of a multiplet with respect to the strong-interactions leads immediately to some interesting restrictions on the decays and reactions involving nuclei and elementary particles, since these reactions proceed primarily through the agency of the strong-interactions. Symmetry immediately forbids the occurrence of some reactions and imposes definite ratios on the probabilities of others.

Rather than define particular rules, it is attractive to consider some simple examples that illustrate the character of the restrictions. We consider first the decay of a member of a multiplet of three particles into two states, each of which are singlets. In particular, we consider the decay of a particular excited state of Li_3^6 to a deuteron, D_1^2, and an alpha particle, He_2^4, where the superscripts represent the number of nucleons in the nucleus and the subscripts represents the charge or number of protons. Such decays, or breakups, of these excited states take place dynamically through the strong-interaction forces. The deuteron and the alpha particle are charge singlets: there are no other particles with the same strong-interaction properties but different charges. On the other hand, we are considering, for purposes of exposition, a state of Li_3^6 that is a member of a charge triplet. There are thus states of He_2^6 and Be_4^6 that are identical to the Li_3^6 state as far as all strong-interaction forces are concerned, though the three states differ in electric charge.

Since the Li_3^6 state is heavier than the sum of the masses of the alpha particle and the deuteron, we might expect that the decay relation

$$Li_3^6 \rightarrow He_2^4 + D_1^2$$

would take place quickly. No conservation law of any type we have discussed is violated by such a decay. Nevertheless, the decay is forbidden as a consequence of the symmetry with respect to the strong-interactions of the states that are involved.

Consider a collection of the three states that are identical with respect to the strong-interactions:

He_2^6
$Li_3^6 \rightarrow D_1^2 + He_2^4$
Be_4^6

The conservation of electric charge forbids the decays of the He_2^6 state and the Be_4 state to an alpha particle and a deuteron. If the Li_3^6 state could decay in such a manner, the decay itself, which proceeds through strong-interaction forces, would serve to distinguish the Li_3 state from the other states. If the reaction could occur, an experimenter using only the strong-interactions as a tool could assemble a set of the triplet states and determine which of them is a Li_3 state by observing the decays. But this is not possible if the symmetry is valid, and the three members of the triplet are indistinguishable through the strong-interactions— the experiment we have suggested would serve to distinguish one member from the others. The symmetry is therefore incompatible with the possibility of such a reaction, and the reaction cannot occur.

Restrictions of this type that result from the symmetry can be expressed in terms of a conservation law—the conservation of isotopic spin—which has very little to do with either isotopes or spin. We will not consider this conservation law in detail.

The fundamental indistinguishability of members of a multiplet also demands that the probabilities of certain reactions must be related. Again we consider a particularly simple example. An elementary-particle doublet exists such that one of the members is neutral and the other is charged positively; both of these particles decay through the agency of the strong-interactions to nucleons and pions. We can label these decaying states as p* and n* where p* has a charge of +1, like the proton, and n* has no charge, like the neutron. The decays that conserve charge, and therefore are possible are listed.

(a) $p^* \rightarrow p + \pi^0$ intensity 1
(b) $p^* \rightarrow n + \pi^+$ intensity 2
(c) $n^* \rightarrow n + \pi^0$ intensity 1
(d) $n^* \rightarrow p + \pi^-$ intensity 2

If we select a set of the doublet states, p^* and n^*, from a population that does not distinguish between them, by using strong-interactions, which do not distinguish between them, we must get equal numbers of n^* and p^*. Then if we let them decay we must end up with equal numbers of n and p, and equal numbers of π^+, π^0, and π^- mesons if our invariance is to hold. It is easy to see by trial and error that this will obtain only if the ratio of the decays of these states is as $a:b:c:d = 1:2:1:2$. That is, a p^* particle will have a probability of $\frac{2}{3}$ for decay to a neutron and a positive pion, and a probability of $\frac{1}{3}$ for decay into a proton and a neutron pion. Any other ratio would allow a selection of particular members of the pion multiplet or the nucleon multiplet through the strong-interactions alone, in violation of the symmetry or invariance we postulated.

Of course, the actual observation of forbidden reactions and the well-defined ratios for other reactions represent a large part of the evidence that suggested to us the existence of the symmetry. Also, since the electromagnetic forces are not negligible compared with the strong-interaction forces, the symmetry is inexact and corrections must be applied to actual measurements to take into account the electromagnetic effects.

The existence of the symmetry reduces our problem of many elementary particles somewhat, because now we can consider the charge-multiplet family as an entity instead of as individual particles and search for deeper relations between families.

27|7 *Symmetries of the strong-interaction —hypercharge independence*

In 1947, the English physicists G. D. Rochester and C. C. Butler were analyzing pictures of a cloud chamber exposed to cosmic-ray activity. A cloud chamber is a device designed to cool moist gas quickly so that a vapor trail of condensation builds up along the path of a charged particle moving through the gas. They saw two unusual events in these pictures; there were two tracks with a V shape. They deduced that these tracks indicated that a particle, which they called tentatively a V particle, had traveled several centimeters in their chamber and then decayed. A detailed analysis showed that the particles could not be quite like any known before. The most striking character of these V particles was the long distance they traveled before decaying. A particle that decays through the strong-interactions decays, almost always, in a very short time. The characteristic time for such decays is the time it takes for a particle traveling with the speed of light to cross a distance the size of a nucleon. The V particles traveled about 10^{13} times farther than this; they lived 10^{13} times longer than might have been expected if the decay took place as a result of strong-interaction forces. This extraordinarily long life was consistent with the hypothesis that the V particles did not decay as a result of strong-interactions but through the weak-interactions involved in such processes as the beta decay of nuclei, since the weak-interactions are known to be about 10^{13} times weaker than the strong-interactions. To the extent that we limit our discussion to effects of the strong-interactions, these particles are stable. Indeed, in a universe that differed from ours only in that there were no weak-interactions, these V particles would be stable.

Further study of the V particles showed that they decayed primarily into strongly interacting particles—into baryons and mesons. The only reason previously known for the absolute exclusion of decays of strongly interacting particles through the strong-interactions, when the decays are otherwise allowed, was by the operation of the constraint imposed by the conservation of electric charge. As far as we know, electric charge is absolutely conserved in all processes. A plausible explanation or description of the lack of strong-interaction decay of V particles was found in the suggestion that they held a new kind of charge, which was named *hypercharge*, and that the strong-interactions conserved this hypercharge. Unlike electric charge, hypercharge is not absolutely conserved: the weak-interactions do not conserve hypercharge. All the experimental data were consistent with this hypothesis and a suitable assignment of hypercharge to the various particles. The strongly interacting particles, the mesons and baryons, could thus differ in their hypercharge as well as their electric charge.

We find that we can create a consistent scheme of the elementary particles by assigning hypercharges to the particles to fit the following rules: strong-interactions conserve hypercharge; weak-interactions change the value of hypercharge by 1 unit or none. The absolute value of the hypercharges of the particles is still undefined by these procedures; we find the patterns are simplest if we give the neutron and proton a hypercharge of $+1$; the pion then has a hypercharge of zero. It is convenient to use the symbol Y for hypercharge. We examine two examples of reactions forbidden by hypercharge conservation.

$$\Lambda^0 \neq \text{p} + \pi \quad \text{and} \quad \text{K}^0 \neq \pi^+ + \pi^-$$
$$(Y) \quad -1 \neq +1 + 0 \qquad\qquad +1 \neq 0 + 0$$

where the hypercharge numbers are written below the particle symbols. Since hypercharge is not conserved, these particles, the Λ^0 and the K^0, live enormously longer than if hypercharge were conserved and they could decay as a result of the strong-interaction force. As it is, they live about 10^{-10} sec, a time that allows them to travel a few centimeters, instead of 10^{-23} sec, the time it would take them to travel the dimensions of a nucleus.

In any search for new simplicities it is attractive to consider an extension of known patterns. Even as the strong-interactions were found to be charge independent and do not differentiate between members of a multiplet that hold different charges, we might suppose that the strong-interactions would also be independent of hypercharge and should not differentiate between members of a supermultiplet that hold different values of hypercharge. One of the pieces of evidence that suggested that the strong-interactions are charge independent was the observation that the members of a charge multiplet have almost the same mass; since the mass is presumed to be derived from the energy stored in the force field, this immediately suggested that the forces are identical. Of course, the masses were not really exactly the same, but the differences were of a magnitude to suggest that the energy stored in the electromagnetic field resulting from the electric charges and currents accounted for the mass difference.

Even as sets of particles with different electric charges were

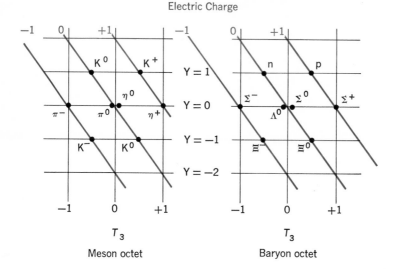

FIG. 27 I 13
The positions of the particles that make up the meson octet and the baryon octet, plotted showing electric charge, hypercharge, and the charge multiplets according to the scheme of Gell-Mann and Nishijima.

found to form families such that the members of the family are identical except for the value of the electric charge, it is possible to assemble larger sets of particles with somewhat the same properties—such as the same spin and same baryon number, for example—where the members have generally different values of electric charge and hypercharge. Two such augmented families, or *supermultiplets*, are shown in the diagrams of Fig. 27 I 13. The ordinate in the diagram represents the value of the hypercharge, while the electric-charge multiplets are spread out along the direction of the abscissa with the center of the multiplet at zero. (The scale of the abscissa is labeled T_3, which is called the third component of isotopic spin; but that need not concern us here.)

A pattern is formed by the class of all known mesons and baryons: all such particles have values of electric charge and hypercharge which fall on the intersections of the grid lines in Fig. 27 I 13. This rule of Gell-Mann and Nishijima is not at all trivial: as we change values of hypercharge, we change from odd charge multiplets to even charge multiplets. All particles with odd values of hypercharge, $Y = 1, 3, \ldots$, belong to even electric-charge multiplets with $2, 4, \ldots$, members; all particles with even values of hypercharge, $Y = -2, 0, 2, \ldots$, belong to odd electric-charge multiplets with $1, 3, \ldots$, members. Nature has shown us at least part of some comprehensive pattern of the elementary particles.

The particular supermultiplets shown in Fig. 27|13 serve to illustrate some of these relations. At $Y = 0$, in the meson octet, there are two charge multiplets: the pion triplet of π^+, π^-, π^0, and the singlet η^0. At $Y = 1$, there is the doublet K^0 and K^+; at $Y = -1$, there is the doublet K^- and K^0. (The patterns are important to us, the names are not.) Again, the members of an electric-charge multiplet are indistinguishable by the strong-interactions.

The baryon octet presents an identical pattern: at $Y = 0$, there is a Σ triplet and a Λ^0 singlet; at $Y = 1$, there is the n–p nucleon doublet, and at $Y = -1$, there is the Ξ^-–Ξ^0 doublet.

The masses of those members of a supermultiplet which have different values of Y, the hypercharge, are quite different. The K mesons have more than three times the mass of the pions, though they are all members of the meson octet supermultiplet. The baryons that make up the baryon octet also have quite different masses; the Xi hyperon (Ξ) has a mass almost half again as great as the nucleons. But even as the members of a charge multiplet have different masses because of the effects of the charge, it seems that there is an energy associated with some field connected to hypercharge, and the mass differences between members of the supermultiplet result from this "hypercharge force." Thus the strong-interaction can seemingly be divided into two parts: one part is independent of electric charge and hypercharge, while the other is independent of electric charge, but is somehow derived from the hypercharge. Our nominal group of four forces may really be five.

This classification of particles, and of strong-interactions into two separate forces, represents a considerable advance in the classification of elementary particles. Nevertheless, further simplifications are still quite desirable. The charge-multiplet structure of nuclear states is similar to the supermultiplet structure of elementary particles, though somewhat simpler. It is possible to show (though not here) that a very simple explanation for the existence of this symmetry in nuclei is to be found in the possibility (and of course fact) that nuclei could be (and are) compounds made up from two kinds of particles that are equivalent with respect to the strong-interactions but have different charges, one being neutral and one being positively charged. Of course we know that these are the neutron and proton, but one could have deduced that it was probable that such a neutron and proton existed merely from a survey of the symmetries of the nuclei.

Perhaps the elementary particles are made up as compounds of some "truly" elementary particle. Perhaps one can analyze the symmetries and predict the simplest set of such particles. Indeed, this is not extremely difficult, and these hypothetical particles turn out to have peculiar and interesting properties; the electric charge, the hypercharge, and the baryon number of these particles is nonintegral, either $\frac{1}{3}$ or $\frac{2}{3}$. There are three such particles—and three antiparticles—with the quantum numbers shown on the diagrams of Fig. 27|14.

These hypothetical fundamental particles have been called quarks (after a phrase in "Finnegans Wake," by James Joyce), and the hypothesis is that the baryons are compounds of three quarks, and that the mesons, which are not conserved, are compounds formed of a quark and an antiquark. The proton would thus be a compound of two β quarks and an α quark; a positive pion would be formed from an α quark and an anti-β quark.

Although the very many consequences of this scheme that have been explored fit observations made on the elementary particles with remarkable accuracy, there is now considerable doubt that quarks exist as simple free particles. Despite extensive searches for free quarks, which should be produced in the course

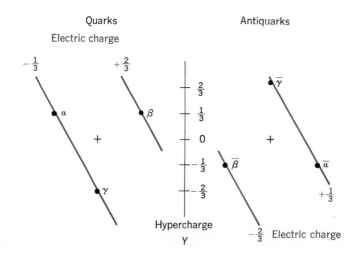

FIG. 27|14
The charge and hypercharge of quarks and antiquarks.

of very-high-energy interactions of the elementary particles that should break up these "compounds," no quarks have been found. Perhaps they do not exist as free particles but do exist in elementary particles in some way that is not now within our comprehension.

PROBLEMS

27 |1 The figure shows an elementary reaction such that a pion strikes a proton at rest and produces a lambda particle, which decays into a proton and a pion. The lines represent the trajectories of the particles as they might be observed in a bubble chamber or a cloud chamber. Assume that the trajectories of the incident pion and the lambda lie in the plane of the paper, and that the decay pion usually is emitted upward and the proton downward. That is, in a large sample of events the proton is more often emitted down into the paper. Show that this result is not consistent with the conservation of parity (mirror symmetry).

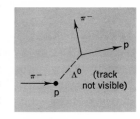

27 |2 Consider an antihydrogen atom made up of antiproton and a positron (antielectron). How would you expect the frequencies of light given off by this atom when it is excited to compare with the light given off from a regular hydrogen atom? Why?

27 |3 If we can receive signals from an alien universe, we can work out a way of sending pictures such as television pictures. But we will still not be able to exchange information as to whether we and the aliens are both right-handed if we do not compare weak-interaction experiments. Consider the character of the information required to construct a picture (as on a television set) and explain in detail why such a picture cannot be used to determine whether the aliens are left-handed or right-handed.

27 |4 Redraw the diagram of the spinning billiard ball striking the side cushion so that it represents the interaction with time reversed. Assume that the basic interaction is invariant under time reversal.

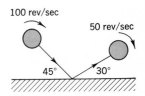

27 |5 A charge quartet of particles A^{++}, A^+, A^0, and A^-, where the superscript represents the electric charge, decays into nucleons and pions through the strong-interactions. What is the ratio of the probabilities for the decays of

(a) $A^+ \rightarrow n + \pi^+$ and $A^+ \rightarrow p + \pi^0$

(b) $A^0 \rightarrow n + \pi^0$ and $A^0 \rightarrow p + \pi^-$

27 | 6   Diagram (a) represents a reaction such that a particle *a* strikes particle *c*, which recoils as *a* is transmuted to particle *b*. The arrow represents the direction of the spins of the particles engaged in the reaction. Diagram (b) shows an inverse reaction in which the velocities of the particles and the angles of interaction are the same. Show that the occurrence of these two reactions implies a breakdown in time-reversal invariance, and change diagram (b) so that the result is invariant under time reversal.

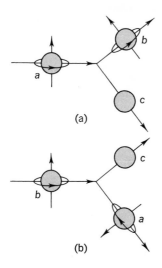

(a)

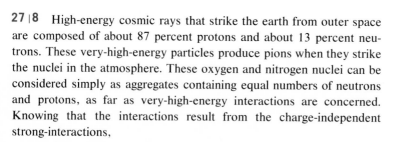

(b)

27 | 7   When a positive pion decays into a positive muon and a neutrino, the muon spin is always directed opposite to the direction of the muon motion, whereas the negative muon that is emitted in the decay of a negative pion has the spin in the direction of motion. Show that this result violates the conservation of parity and charge-conjugation invariance. The π^+ and π^- are antiparticles. Are the reactions invariant under CP?

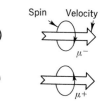

27 | 8   High-energy cosmic rays that strike the earth from outer space are composed of about 87 percent protons and about 13 percent neutrons. These very-high-energy particles produce pions when they strike the nuclei in the atmosphere. These oxygen and nitrogen nuclei can be considered simply as aggregates containing equal numbers of neutrons and protons, as far as very-high-energy interactions are concerned. Knowing that the interactions result from the charge-independent strong-interactions,

(*a*) Show that the number of neutral pions produced by a large number of such interactions will be equal to half the number of charged pions produced.

(b) An experimenter says that many positive pions are produced, but that no negative pions are produced. You answer that the ratio of negative pions to positive pions must be at least as large as $\frac{13}{87}$, though it could be larger. Are you correct? Why? or why not?

27|9 Use the quark model and the values of the charges and hypercharges from Figs. 27|13 and 27|14, to determine the quark composition of

(a) the Σ^+, and Σ^-, the neutron, and the proton;

(b) the K^+, K^-, π^+ and π^-, mesons.

Consider that beta decay of an elementary particle can always be described as the beta decay of one quark into another quark, an electron (or positron), and a neutrino (or antineutrino).

(c) Show that the decay $\Sigma^- \rightarrow n + e^- + \bar{\nu}^-$ is allowed, while the decay $\Sigma^+ \rightarrow p + e^+ + \nu$ cannot occur.

twenty-eight *Cosmology*

28 | 1 *Cosmological principles*

IN THE BROADEST SENSE, cosmology, considered here as the inquiry into the nature of the universe at large with special emphasis to cosmogony, the origin of the universe, has concerned man from the beginnings of recorded history. The Semitic cosmologies such as the Enuma Elish of Babylon, written in Akkadian, and the Hebrew Genesis, seem to have originated nearly four thousand years ago, while the Babylonian Gilgamesh epic, which contains a cosmology, probably originated with the non-Semitic Sumerians considerably earlier. These early cosmologies, together with their familiar Indo-European counterparts of Greece and Scandinavia, are closely tied to aboriginal nature myths and eventually to the higher religions. Archbishop James Ussher may have been the first to date the origin of the universe. From his study of the Old Testament he concluded, in work published about 1650, that the universe was created in 4004 B.C., a date that was inserted in the reference margins of the Authorized Version of the (King James) Bible. Modern cosmology, or scientific cosmology, cannot be traced back much farther than a century and has not yet attained either the definite character suggested by Ussher's calculations nor the precision.

Cosmology differs in an operational way from most other areas of physics in that the evidence from which one attempts to draw conclusions is purely observational. It is generally impractical to the point of impossibility to modify the gross conditions of the universe. Experiments, in the usual sense, are impossible; one can only observe carefully things as they are. As a result of this restraint modern cosmology proceeds intellectually in a manner that is slightly different from that followed in most other branches of physics. In general, there is more emphasis on axiomatic construction of theories. A set of axioms, chosen as aesthetically attractive guesses concerning the probable course of nature, is used as a basis of a well-defined theoretical structure. The conclusions or consequences of these axioms are then studied as thoroughly as possible, and these consequences are then compared with observations which then test the theory and the axioms from which the theory was constructed. Some philosophers of science consider that this axiomatic approach is contrary to the "scientific method"—a criticism that is cheerfully disregarded by astrophysicists.

A first example of a rotational axiomatic cosmology, and its disproof, was provided by Olbers in a remarkable paper written in 1826. Olbers investigated the simple assumption—or axiom—that the universe was infinite and unchanging in space and in time, and showed that this assumption was wildly incompatible with the simplest of observational facts; that the sky was dark at night.

The reasoning is basically rather simple: if the density of stars in the universe is the same everywhere, and if the universe is infinite, a line in any direction will eventually intersect with the surface of a star. This is suggested schematically by the two-dimensional diagram of Fig. 28 | 1. If Olbers' model were valid and if you looked in any direction at night, you would see the surface of a star, which would, of course, be as the surface of the sun. The brightness of the sky at that point, and thus at every point, would be equal to the brightness of the surface of the sun; not only would the sky not be dark at night, it would be intolerably bright. As a corollary result of this intense radiation, the temperature of the earth would rise to equal the temperature at the surface of the sun, 6000°C. Even this is an underestimate, which essentially assumes that the stars themselves are not affected by the extra radiation incident upon them from all the other stars. If this is taken into account, the temperature at any spot in the universe will be equal to that at the center of stars, or about 20,000,000°C!

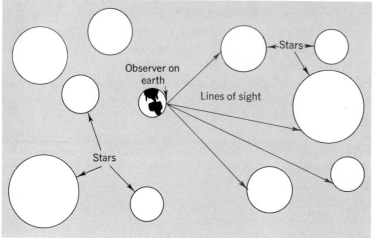

FIG. 28|1
*The lines of sight from a
point on earth
intersecting the surface
of a star according to
Olbers' hypothesis.*

This conclusion is not affected by the possibility that some matter, perhaps some dust suspended in space, would block the light from far off stars. Such dust can only reduce the amount of light by absorbing it, and this absorption of energy will result in the heating of the dust. From consideration of the second law of thermodynamics it is easily shown that the dust will increase in temperature until it radiates as much energy as it absorbs; at this time its temperature will be the same as that of the surrounding stars; it will be as bright as the surrounding stars.

What deviations are then required from this simplest of cosmological models in order that its conclusions will fit observations? We know from our observations that the density of stars is not the same everywhere but does have some structure. Stars are found in groups called galaxies (historically these were called nebulae, which is an observational term). Galaxies are, typically, disk-shaped, slowly rotating assemblies of stars of the order of 30,000 lt-yr in diameter and perhaps a tenth as great in thickness. The sketch of Fig. 28|2 illustrates the character of a typical galaxy. An average galaxy contains about 10^{10} stars. A light-year is a convenient cosmological unit of distance: it is the distance light travels in a year—about 10^{16} m.

The density of stars at the edge of the galaxy is much less than the density at the center. Our sun is very near the edge of our galaxy: the Milky Way is the dense center of our galaxy. The nearest neighboring galaxy, Andromeda, is about 1,000,000 lt-yr away, an average internebular distance, and is visible to the naked eye under the best of conditions. It subtends an angle of about one-half degree at the eye, but its brightness is low. The beautiful pictures of galaxies one sees are all the results of long time exposures, and galaxies are not so striking to the eye—a result (from the second law of thermodynamics) that cannot be improved by the character of the telescope used to view them.

The galaxies themselves appear to be grouped in larger sets. These supergalaxies seem, however, to be uniformly distributed throughout space. The stars themselves can thus be considered to be effectively uniformly distributed, though there does exist the double hierarchy or order, and our observational evidence concerning the density of stars does not violate the criteria of Olbers' hypothesis.

The formation we use to deduce the near uniformity of space comes from observations that do not extend to distances much beyond a billion light-years. The weakness of this result is evident when we consider that the most of the light incident on us, according to Olbers' model, must come from incredibly far away if

FIG. 28 |2

A typical spiral galaxy such as ours.

Axial view   Edge view

the density of stars is generally not very different from that within a few millions of light-years from the earth. In that case the average distance along a line from the earth to the surface of a star is about 10^{20} lt-yr! The largest telescope, the 200-in. telescope at Mount Palomar, can only photograph galaxies that are no farther than about 10^9 lt-yr away. Olbers' ideas are valid only if the universe is the same over a space that is a hundred billion times larger than the distance we can see with our most powerful telescopes. Clearly deviations from the ideal model of Olbers that are quite small locally can radically change the total results.

All of the scientific cosmological theories that have been seriously proposed to date have contained, implicitly or explicitly, certain assumptions or axioms similar to those proposed by Olbers. A most important assumption is that of the Cosmological Principle which states that, aside from local fluctuations, observers at different parts of the universe view essentially the same picture. The local fluctuations can be on a grand scale: as I write this I am in New Haven, Connecticut, which is a specific spot in the Northern Hemisphere of the third planet of a medium-sized star found in one of the arms of a particular spiral galaxy. All of this detail is regarded to be as particular as the specific chair in which I am sitting, and as irrelevant from a cosmological view. Olbers' theory used this assumption of the Cosmological Principle.

Since we understand that space and time are closely related as expressed in the theories of relativity, we might expect the Cosmological Principle to include time. We have, then, the *Perfect Cosmological Principle* emphasized by the English Astrophysicists Bondi and Gold, which carries the further assumption that the universe is the same for all observers at different times. This special assumption of a steady-state universe is not generally used by all cosmological theories. It is implicitly assumed by Olbers' theory.

Certainly if the universe began at some particular time, T, much less than 10^{20} years ago, the results of Olbers would be affected because the stars that would be farther than T light-years away would not shine on the earth. Their light would not have had time to reach the earth.

Even though most cosmologies are axiomatic in nature, if they are to have any meaning to us they must confront observation, even as Olbers' model confronted the observation that the sky is dark at night. It is therefore necessary that the theories concern observable quantities. Such primitive quantities as time and distance must be defined in an appropriately operational way in terms of real measurements. It is also obviously necessary that any cosmological theory must reduce to, or agree with, the description of the behavior of local objects that makes up the body of physical theory on the local level. On the other hand, cosmological theories need not follow local physical theory over the enormous extrapolations from experience involved in considering the whole universe. Laws such as the law of conservation of energy or the second law of thermodynamics need not be true for the universe as a whole. Our observational evidence, upon which such laws or summaries of experience are based, simply does not extend to the vast times, distances, and masses we must consider in cosmology.

28|2   *The red shift and the expanding universe*

About 30 years ago E. Hubble completed a series of measurements of the spectra of the light emitted by distant galaxies (or nebulae) that strongly suggested that our universe was expanding. Hubble examined the absorption lines in the spectra of the light from distant galaxies. Since these galaxies are made up of large numbers of stars, the light from a galaxy has very much the same character as the light from an average star such as our sun. There is an essentially continuous spectrum, such as that produced by the surface of our sun, marked by lines representing the absorption of light by specific elements in the atmospheres of the various stars, even as the absorption of the solar spectra by the atmosphere of the sun results in the Fraunhofer absorption lines named after the German optician who made the first diffraction gratings and the first accurate map of the absorption lines in the spectra of the sun early in the nineteenth century. Two very prominent absorption lines, or dark lines, are found in the near ultraviolet and result from the absorption of light by calcium atoms in the atmosphere of the sun. Hubble found that light from distant galaxies was just like the light observed from our star, or a typical star in our galaxy, in that the two calcium absorption lines were clearly visible, except that the lines were typically shifted slightly toward the red end of the spectrum—this is the red shift. Furthermore, the fainter, and therefore farther away the galaxy, the greater the shift. The diagrams of Fig. 28 | 3 show the character of the spectra seen from various far-off galaxies, showing the red shift in the spectra. The light from the galaxy is gathered by a large telescope, spread into the different colors by a prism, and then photographed using plates that are primarily sensitive to the blue and violet. The diagrams are rather more distinct than the original photographs.

The most plausible explanation of such an effect is that the other galaxies are moving away from ours and that the farther the galaxy is from ours the faster it is moving away. The shift in wavelength is then the *Doppler shift*.

The Doppler shift can be understood quantitatively from rather simple arguments. Consider that a light signal is sent from a source to an observer who is certain distance, x, from the source. The observer may be on earth and the source may be a galaxy moving away from the earth, as suggested by the diagram of Fig. 28 | 4. The light signal might be a certain wave vibration: for numerical convenience let us make the rather unrealistic assumption that we are dealing with signals that are sent from the source galaxy at a frequency of 1/sec. If the time of emission of the first signal is $t_s = 0$ sec, the signal will be observed on earth at a later time

$$t_0 = t_s + \frac{x}{c}$$

FIG. 28 | 3
The character of blue-sensitive emulsion negatives taken with a telescope and prism, showing the red shifts for distant galaxies.

Source of light	Distance (light-yr)	Velocity β
A galaxy in Virgo	2.2×10^7	0.004
A galaxy in Corona Borealis	4×10^8	0.072
A galaxy in Bootes	7×10^8	0.131
A galaxy in Hydra	1.1×10^9	0.203

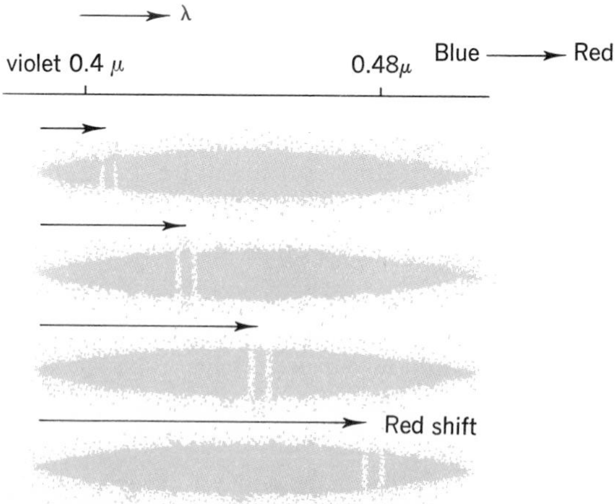

$\longrightarrow \lambda$

violet 0.4 μ 0.48μ Blue $\longrightarrow$ Red

Red shift

Signal received   Signal sent

$t = \dfrac{x}{c}$ sec  $t = 0$ sec

$t = \dfrac{x}{c} + \dfrac{v}{c} + 1$ sec 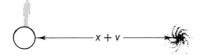 $t = 1$ sec

FIG. 28|4

$t = \dfrac{x}{c} + \dfrac{2v}{c} + 2$ sec ◯←————— $x + 2v$ —————→ ✦ $t = 2$ sec

Diagrams used to illustrate the Doppler shift: x is the initial distance in meters; v is the velocity of the galaxy in meters per second.

$$\Delta t = 1 + \frac{v}{c} \text{ sec} \qquad\qquad\qquad \Delta t = 1 \text{ sec}$$

$$\text{Frequency} = \frac{1}{1 + v/c} \text{ signal/sec} \qquad \text{Frequency} = 1 \text{ signal/sec}$$

Since $t_s = 0$,

$$t_0 = \frac{x}{c}$$

where c is the velocity of light and thus x/c is the time required for the signal to travel the distance x from the source galaxy to the earth. If the galaxy is moving away from the earth at a velocity of v m/sec and the second signal is sent at a time $t_s' = 1$ sec, the galaxy will then be at a distance of $x + v$ m from the earth and the signal will be received on earth at the time

$$t_0' = t_s' + \frac{x + v}{c}$$

$$= 1 + \frac{x}{c} + \frac{v}{c}$$

Two seconds after the first signal, the galaxy will be at a distance of $x + 2v$ m from the earth, and a signal sent at that time, $t_s'' = 2$

sec, will be received on earth at the time

$$t_0'' = t_s'' + \frac{x + 2v}{c}$$

$$= 2 + \frac{x}{c} + \frac{2v}{c}$$

Although the signals will be sent at times that are 1 sec apart they will be received at times that are $1 + v/c$ sec apart: if the frequency of sending is 1 cycle/sec, the frequency received is $1/(1 + v/c)$ per sec, and the frequency received on earth is thus lower than the frequency sent at the source.

If the frequency is greater, f_s vibrations per second, we can consider that the first signal was the electromagnetic vibration at the beginning of a second and the second signal was the electromagnetic vibration that marked the end of the second of time; f_s vibrations will have been sent during the second that elapsed, where f_s is the frequency of the source. These f_s vibrations will have been received by the observer over a period of time equal to $1 + v/c$ seconds. The frequency received by the observer will be less than the frequency f_s, since the vibrations will have been received over a longer time. The observed frequency will be

$$f_0 = \frac{f_s}{1 + v/c}$$

Since the wavelength is related to the frequency by the relation $f\lambda = c$, where λ is the wavelength,

$$\lambda_0 = \lambda_s \left(1 + \frac{v}{c}\right) \quad \text{or} \quad \frac{\lambda_0 - \lambda_s}{\lambda_s} = \frac{v}{c} \qquad (28|1)$$

In the particular case we have followed, where the source was moving away from the observer at a velocity of, perhaps one-tenth the speed of light, the wavelength measured by the observer will be about 10 percent longer than the wavelength he would measure if the source had been stationary. For convenience and clarity of exposition we have treated the problem from a classical view and ignored the time dilation, which we know will be important if the velocity of the receding source is near the speed of light. If the velocity of the source is no larger than one-tenth the speed of light, the classical result is nearly correct.

We should note for completeness that the Doppler effect can be observed more mundanely for sound waves, or for any other waves, if either the source or the observer is moving. The high-pitched scream of an approaching racing car followed by the lower pitch as the car passes the grandstand and recedes from the observer, represents an example of the Doppler effect: the frequency is shifted toward a higher pitch as the car approaches and to a lower pitch as the car moves away. For velocities of source or observer that are small compared to the velocity of sound, the arguments and conclusions are the same as those used in our example for light.

The changes in the observed frequency that follow from the Doppler effect do not suggest that there is any fundamental difference in the rate of passage of time. Unlike the time dilations that result from the considerations of the theories of relativity, the Doppler shift can be considered as a distortion of the observation and not a distortion of time itself. If a source of sound or a source of light moves away from the observer and then moves back again at velocities small compared with the velocity of light, the Doppler reduction of frequency, or slowing of observed time that is noticed as the source is moving away is just compensated by the increase in frequency or speeding up of observed time during the return journey. If you listen to the heartbeats of your identical twin as he speeds away from you, the rate will appear to slow down. But the rate you hear will speed up as he returns, so that the total number of beats you have recorded through his whole journey is just the same as the number of your own heartbeats. Of course if he travels very fast there will still be a relativistic time dilation—your twin will appear younger, and you will record fewer heartbeats—but it is possible to consider this as a separate effect that is unimportant at small velocities.

It follows from relation (28|1) that the shift in wavelength of any spectral line will be proportional to the velocity of the source. Hubble and his collaborators, followed later by many other astronomers, measured these shifts for a large sample of far-off galaxies and correlated the shift with the distance of the galaxy from the earth (and our galaxy). It is quite difficult to establish a scale of distance for distances of this magnitude. A rather long chain of measurements is required, and the possibility of an error in the absolute scale of distance (but not in relative distances) is easy to make. Measurements of the distance of nearby stars can be made directly by triangulation, just as a surveyor makes measurements of distances far from his base line. In this case the

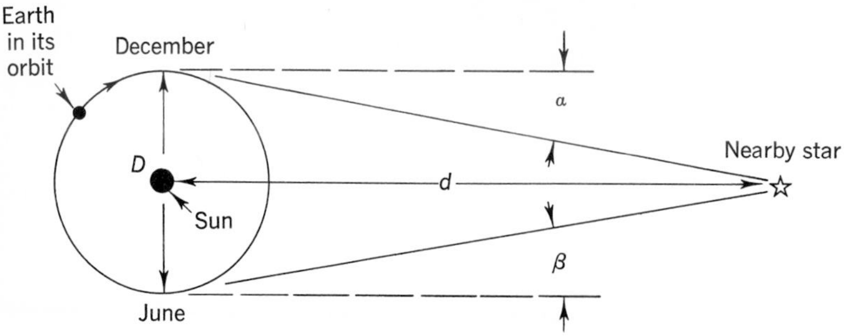

FIG. 28|5
A diagram showing the parallax of a nearby star.

base line is the diameter of the earth's orbit, and the different angular positions of the star as seen from the earth over the year are used to measure its distance in terms of the length, D, of that base line.

The distance of the star from the solar system can be measured in terms of the diameter of the earth's orbit, D, by determining the angle of parallax, which is the sum of the angles α and β of Fig. 28|5. The distance, d, is then

$$d = \frac{D}{\alpha + \beta}$$

If α and β are measured in seconds of arc (1/3600 of a degree) instead of radians,

$$d = \frac{1}{\alpha + \beta} \quad \text{parsecs}$$

where a *parsec* (*par*allax of one *sec*ond) is a convenient operational measure of the distance of an object from the earth: a parsec is about 3.26 lt-yr. Since even the nearest stars are farther away than 1 parsec, the angle of parallax is very small even for the near stars and this method is not useful for determining distances much greater than 15 parsecs, or 50 lt-yr.

Distances to farther stars can be estimated by using the measured distances to the near stars together with the assumption that most stars with the same surface temperature emit about the same amount of light. The temperature of stars can be estimated by determining their color; a hot star is blue, a comparatively cool star is red. Thus a star that is one-fourth as bright as a measured star is assumed to be about twice as far away; a star that is about a hundred times less bright than the measured star is assumed to be about ten times farther away from the earth. We assume that the observed brightness of a star varies inversely with the square of its distance from us even as the observed brightness of a terrestial source varies inversely with the square of its distance. Although such a technique is unreliable for any one star, it works well for the average of a large number.

Thus distances of nearby galaxies are estimated by assuming that certain bright stars in the galaxy (cepheid variables) emit about the same amount of light as similar stars in our galaxy and, again, that the observed brightness follows the inverse-square law. Then the distances of far off galaxies, such that individual stars cannot be resolved, are determined with respect to nearby galaxies by assuming that all galaxies emit about the same amount of light and again that the inverse-square law holds.

Hubble established a scale of distances based on such considerations and found that the wavelength, λ_o, that was observed for a spectral line was related to the wavelength measured in a stationary laboratory, λ_s, which was presumably the wavelength of emission of the distant galaxy, as

$$\lambda_o = \lambda_s \left(1 + \frac{R}{R_0}\right) \quad \text{or} \quad \frac{\lambda_o - \lambda_s}{\lambda_s} = \frac{R}{R_0} \tag{28|2}$$

where R is the distance of the galaxy and R_0 is a constant, which has the dimensions of a length, which we will call the radius of the universe. Hubble determined the value of R_0 to be about 2×10^9 lt-yr on the basis of this distance scale. More recent investigations have established that Hubble's scale was in error, and the present best estimate of R_0 is that it is about 10×10^9 lt-yr. If we accept that the shift results from the Doppler effect, by comparing (28|1) and (28|2) we have

$$\frac{R}{R_0} = \frac{v}{c} \tag{28|3}$$

and the result that all of the galaxies are moving away from us with a velocity that is proportional to their distance. If we extrapolate backward in time, we conclude that all of the galaxies began at one point at a time that is about 10×10^9 (10 billion) years ago; the age of the universe would thus be 10 billion years even as the radius of the universe would be 10 billion light-years.

Again, the relations, as expressed above, are only precisely valid if v/c is much smaller than 1. For very large velocities—

and recently some very large velocities have been measured—relativistically correct relations must be used that are somewhat more complex than the simple results of (28 | 1) and (28 | 2). The result that the velocity of recession appears to be proportional to the distance is retained, however. In the limit that v, the velocity of the recession, is equal to c, the wavelength received by the observer is infinite and no light signal or any other signal can be received. There is, then, no operationally defined existence beyond the distance R_0, and no distance greater than R_0 can be said to exist.

No acceptable explanation of the wavelength shift has been suggested except that of the Doppler shift, and it is this explanation and therefore this model of an expanding universe that is generally accepted.

This result does not, in itself, contradict the thesis of the Cosmological Principle that there is no privileged position or privileged observer. Though all galaxies are receding from the earth, to an equal degree they are all receding from each other—the earth, or our galaxy, is not a privileged point, nor are we privileged observers.

This state of affairs is easily understood with the aid of a two-dimensional model. Consider that the galaxies are mapped as points on a sheet of rubber; it is particularly convenient to consider that the rubber might form the surface of a balloon, as in Fig. 28 | 6, which is being blown up or expanded so that the diam-

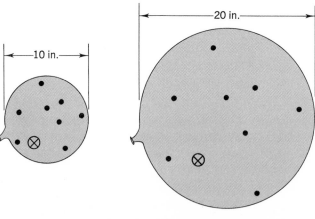

The universe at $t = 10$ min   The universe at $t = 20$ min

FIG. 28 | 6

The simulation of an expanding universe by an expanding balloon. The spots on the two-dimensional surface of the balloon represent the galaxies in the three-dimensional universe. The diameter is increasing at a rate of 1 in./min; t is then the age of the balloon universe.

eter of the balloon increases at the rate of 1 in./min. At the time that the diameter of the balloon is 10 in., the distance between any two points on the balloon will be increasing at the rate of 10 percent per minute even as the diameter is increasing by 10 percent per minute. Two points that are 1 in. apart will be receding from each other at a rate of 0.1 in./min: two points 2 in. apart will be receding from one another—that is, the distance between them will be increasing—at a rate of 0.2 in./min. If we consider one particular point as privileged by our presence—that is, representing our galaxy—all the other galaxies, or points on the surface of the balloon, will be retreating from us at a rate that is proportional to the distance from us. Indeed, we can express this velocity of recession in a formula like that of Eq. (28|3):

$$\frac{v}{c} = \frac{R}{R_0} \qquad\qquad (28|4)$$

where v is the velocity of recession, c is here equal to 1.0 in./min, R_0 is 10 in., and R is the distance to the ink-spot galaxy in question. But the Cosmological Principle still holds; every ink-spot galaxy is moving away from every other ink-spot galaxy, and relation (28|4) is valid for observers in any galaxy. There is no cosmologically privileged galaxy. The two-dimensional balloon surface or universe is expanding. In the same way, it appears that our three-dimensional space is increasing in size, and every point marked by a galaxy is moving away from every other point.

The usual view of this expansion, which considers that the galaxies themselves consist of matter that is conserved, is not consistent with the Perfect Cosmological Principle. Observers at different times will see a different universe. An observer viewing the universe a billion years after creation would see a universe in which the galaxies were ten times as close together as now. The density of matter in the universe would be a thousand times larger than it is now. On the other hand, an observer 10^{11} years from now would view a universe in which the spacing between galaxies would be ten times as great as now and the average density of matter in the universe would be a thousand times smaller.

This means that an absolute time must exist; time can be measured from some absolute beginning of the universe. Since the universe will be changing with time, we have no assurance that experiments in a laboratory will give the same result now as 9×10^9 years ago, or 10^{11} years from now. The invariance of physical laws with respect to change in time will not necessarily hold over the age of the universe, and such laws as the conservation of energy, which follow from these invariances, are not necessarily valid over so large a time scale as the age of the universe.

Another result of our observations of the character of the whole universe that differs from the description we have adopted from local information is the conclusion that absolute velocity must have a meaning. An observer in a space ship traveling with respect to the earth at half the speed of light could easily determine that he was moving with respect to the rest of the universe by measuring the spectra from the galaxies in front of the ship and behind the ship and comparing the Doppler shifts from the two sets of spectra. From the view of the ship, the galaxies behind the ship will exhibit a spectra strongly shifted to the red, the nearer galaxies in front of the ship will show spectra strongly shifted in the opposite direction—their spectra will be shifted toward the violet. The velocity of the ship relative to the universe can then be determined by measurements of these spectra. If the ship were stationary, almost all of the galaxies would show red shifts, and the degree of shift would be proportional to their distance. The absolute velocity of the ship can thus be measured and thus has an operational meaning. We can no longer be certain that the results of measurements of physical phenomena will not depend upon the velocity of the laboratory if that velocity is very large.

28|3   *The curvature of space and time*

The concepts of space and time are empty without the existence of matter: if there are no markers and no events, distance and elapsed time, defined operationally as the distance between events and the time between events, can have no meaning. We cannot, then, separate our inquiry into the nature of space and time without recognizing that we must deal with a space–time that contains matter.

Since the only force that seems to operate substantially between matter in the large—between stars and galaxies—is gravity, and according to the General Theory of Relativity gravity is an effect of the curvature of space–time that results as a consequence of the existence of matter, we may expect that the space–time of the universe, filled with matter as it is, will be curved.

In the course of our discussion of gravity and the equivalence principle we were able to show that the curvature of space in a gravitational field followed naturally from the equivalence principle. We emphasized that the natural definition of a geodesic, or shortest distance between two points, was the path of a beam of light in a vacuum. Using the equivalence principle directly, we found that the path of a light beam through a transverse gravitational field could be considered to follow approximately (within a factor of 2) a path that could be described by considering that the light was accelerated by the field even as a simple particle. We will use this approximation to discuss the magnitude of the curvature of the universe that we might expect from the effect of the matter in the whole universe.

In order to estimate the magnitude of the curvature effects we adopt a simple model that assumes the universe is a sphere of matter. The density of the matter is taken from our observations of the nearby universe. We can then find a radius such that a beam of light will travel in a circle about the universe. This radius will not have any very simple meaning, but its value should suggest to us the magnitude of the size of a universe such that the curvature of space is important.

The gravitational acceleration near a body of mass m is expressed by the relation

$$a = \frac{Gm}{R^2}$$

where R is the distance from the mass and G is the gravitational constant. If the radius of the universe is R, the mass of the universe will be equal to Vd, where d is the average density of matter in the universe and V is the volume of the universe, $\frac{4}{3}\pi R^3$. Then the acceleration of gravity at the surface of this universe sphere will be

$$a = G\tfrac{4}{3}\pi Rd$$

$$\approx 4GRd \qquad\qquad\qquad\qquad\qquad (28\,|\,5)$$

If the light travels in a circle of radius R, its path can be described by the familiar kinematic relation of centripetal acceleration,

$$a = \frac{v^2}{R}$$

where v is the velocity of the light and a is the acceleration toward the center of the circle. Equating the two expressions and using c for the velocity v,

$$\frac{c^2}{R} = 4GRd \qquad\qquad (28|6)$$

and

$$R = \frac{c}{\sqrt{4Gd}}$$

The value of the gravitational constant, G, is 6.6×10^{-11} N-m²/kg², and the value of d, the average density of matter in the universe, is estimated to be about 10^{-26} kg/m³. Substituting the numerical values into relation (28|6) we find

$$R = R_g = 2 \times 10^{26} \text{ m}$$

$$= 20 \times 10^9 \text{ lt-yr}$$

Since this gravitational radius, R_g, is of the same magnitude as R_0, the Hubble radius of the universe, it is clear that we shall have to consider seriously possible large-scale curvatures of space in the construction of a cosmology.

If the Cosmological Principle is valid, the curvature of the universe can be determined by plotting the number of galaxies observed against the square of their distance from the earth. Figure 28|7 shows the distributions to be expected for positive, negative, and zero curvatures. The abscissa is the square of the distance, r^2, and the ordinate represents the number of galaxies per unit interval of r^2.

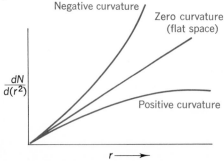

FIG. 28|7

The density of galaxies per unit interval of r^2 for variously curved universes.

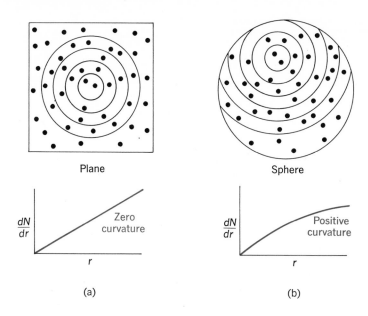

FIG. 28 | 8
*Flat and positively
curved two-dimensional
universes together with
appropriate density
plots.*

The character of analysis suggested above can be understood simply by considering a two-dimensional analogue to our three-dimensional space. If a two-dimensional cosmological principle holds, the density of galaxies on a two-dimensional space will be the same everywhere. If the space is flat, as suggested by the sketch of Fig. 28 | 8a, a plot of the number of galaxies per unit distance against the distance from some reference point will take the form of a straight line. This result simply reflects the fact that the area between r and $r + dr$ is equal to $2\pi r\, dr$ if the surface is a plane; the area per unit distance is proportional to r, so the number of galaxies per unit distance will be proportional to r.

If the two-dimensional surface is curved as the surface of a globe, the area between r and $r + dr$ will be nearly equal to $2\pi r\, dr$ if r is very much smaller than R, the radius of the globe, but for larger r the area per unit distance will be less than that for a plane surface. A measurement of the number of galaxies per unit distance might then tell the two-dimensional creatures who made the observations that their space was curved—they might call this particular curvature a positive curvature.

It is also possible to distort a two-dimensional surface so that the area per unit distance from a reference point increases faster than the distance from the point. The map of Fig. 28 | 9 represents such a surface. This surface has the character of a saddle, or a

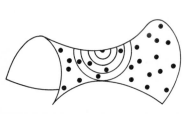

Surface of negative curvature

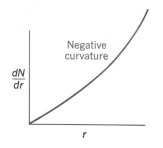

$\dfrac{dN}{dr}$

Negative curvature

r

FIG. 28|9

A negatively curved two-dimensional universe, together with a plot of the density as it varies with distance.

pass through the mountains, and its curvature is called negative. Using this analogy, the negative curvature suggested by the curve of density versus distance in Fig. 28|7 would represent the characteristics of a sort of saddle shape in four dimensions, while the positive curvature suggests a shape that is a four-dimensional analogue of a sphere. A flat or Euclidean space such as shown in Fig. 28|8a is said to have zero curvature.

Even as space may be curved substantially over so large a region as the universe, we might be concerned that time could be curved or distorted also. Even as space is curved in the presence of a gravitation field and thus in the presence of matter, we learned that time was changed by the presence of a gravitation field and thus the presence of matter. Although the curvature of space by local distributions of matter was small, the total curvature by all of the matter in the universe could be substantial. In the same sense the smallness of local distortions of time need not convince us that very large distortions might not exist on the scale of the universe.

In Section 4|6 we developed a relation between intervals of time in regions differing in gravitational potential:

$$dt' = dt \left(1 + \frac{ah}{c^2}\right)$$

where dt' is the time elapsed at the lower potential and dt is the time elapsed at the higher potential, a is the acceleration of gravity, and h is the distance between the two regions. Although this relation was developed for a constant gravitation field, it can be used to consider the order of magnitude of time distortions in the universe. For the purpose of making such estimates let us consider that we are at the edge of the universe in some sense and we wish to estimate the magnitude of difference in the rate of time flow at the center of the universe. We will treat the universe, then, as a large sphere of radius R and density d. Then we can estimate the relation between a unit of time, dt, in our system and a unit of time, dt', at the center of this universe as

$$dt' = dt \left(1 + \frac{aR}{c^2}\right) \qquad (28\,|\,7)$$

If aR/c^2 is of the order of 1, we might well expect an appreciable distortion of time. From our previous discussion of space curvature we defined a gravitational radius, R_g, such that $a = c^2/R_g$. Then for $R = R_g$, $aR/c^2 \approx 1$. And we know that the Hubble radius, R_0, is very nearly the same as R_g. Then, in the approximations we have made, we can see that a large time distortion, or curvature of the universe in time, would not be surprising.

If the Cosmological Principle is valid, the time flow at region a as seen from region b must be the same as the rate of passage of time at b as seen from a. Further, the concept of being at the edge or at the center of the universe could have no meaning. The estimates made of the distortion of time are thus only indicative of the possibility of differences in the flow of time, even as the calculations of the curvature of space only indicated the possibility of a large-scale curvature of space. Neither calculation establishes that any effect will exist. The calculations are important in that they show we cannot, a priori, neglect such possibilities.

Any look out to great distances is also a look back into time. Galaxies that are observed to be 10^9 light-years away are also observed as they were 10^9 years ago. From our elementary description of the expanding universe we would therefore expect that the galaxies would be about 10 percent closer together at a distance of 10^9 lt-yr simply as a result of the fact that we would be viewing that part of the universe 10^9 years ago when the expansion of the universe had not proceded quite to the extent that it has today. It is then important to differentiate between the *world picture,* which is the description of the universe as it would be seen or photographed by an observer on earth using a telescope, which necessarily looks back into time even as it looks out into space, and the *world map,* which would describe the whole universe as it might exist at some instant of time. The graph of dis-

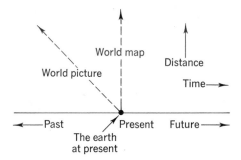

FIG. 28|10
*A diagram suggesting
the relation between
distance from the
observer and time for
the world map, which
represents the
universe as it is
everywhere at some
instant in time, and the
world picture, which
represents the universe
as it is viewed by an
observer who must look
back into time even as
he looks out in space.*

tance versus time of Fig. 28|10 shows one curve that represents the world picture and one which represents the world map.

It is usually the world map that we discuss, and it is always the world picture that we observe. As a result the interpretations of observations are not completely obvious. If the galaxies seem to be denser at great distances, does this result from the greater density of the universe in the past, or is it indicative of a negative curvature of space in the universe? In general we need more information to make a choice.

28|4   *Cosmological models*

Most of the many existent cosmological models are evolutionary models. These models assume that the character of the universe changes in time—the universe evolves. These theories consider that the universe had a beginning that is measured in time by the Hubble radius; that is, the universe was created in some sort of explosive process at a specific initial time, about 10×10^9 years ago, and has been expanding since that time. Obviously such a description violates the attractive Perfect Cosmological Principle. The individual models differ in their predictions concerning the curvature of the universe and the rate of change of the expansion. The spatial curvature of the universe and the rate of expansion of the universe are connected, in most models, through the logic of the General Theory of Relativity. It is not practical for us to discuss these rather abstruse results in any detail, but an analysis of some simple classical models might be helpful in suggesting the physical origin of the results.

Let us assume, then, for the purposes of such an exposition, that the universe is a Newtonian universe; that is, we ignore relativistic effects and consider gravitation simply as a force between masses that varies inversely with the square of the distance between the masses and not as an effect of space curvature. Then if all of the galaxies are present in some very small volume of space at a time very near the time of creation, $t = 0$, even as molecules of a gas might be held in a small container in a large evacuated room, the galaxies will disperse as time passes even as the gas molecules will disperse if the container is broken. After a time t passes, each galaxy will be found at a distance vt from the origin, where v will be almost exactly the original velocity of the galaxy. We assume that the galaxies do not collide and we assume implicitly that we are able to choose a time t sufficiently small so that the gravitational forces acting on the galaxies, as a result of the presence of all of the other galaxies, are not important.

Figure 28|11 shows two-dimensional representations of the distributions in space of the galaxies where the galaxies have different initial velocity distributions. Since the distance of a galaxy from the origin is just proportional to the initial velocity of the galaxy, the distributions in space shown in the diagrams of Fig. 28|11 are, equally, distributions in velocity. Figure 28|11a shows such a distribution in space of the galaxies if the initial velocity distribution were the same as the Maxwell–Boltzmann distribution of molecular velocities discussed in part in Chapter 17. Since very high velocities exist but are rare, the density of galaxies is much lower at large radii than at smaller radii, a result that would not be in accord with the Cosmological

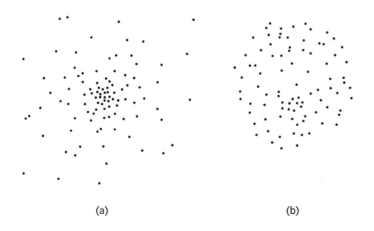

(a)   (b)

FIG. 28|11
The distribution of galaxies after a time t from a central beginning: in (a) the galaxies have a Maxwellian velocity distribution like molecules of a gas; in (b) they have a velocity distribution such as to preserve the cosmological principle.

Principle. In order to simulate our universe, in which we consider that the Cosmological Principle operates and that the local regions near any galaxy are equivalent, we must have a distribution like that shown in Fig. 28|11b, where the densities are the same everywhere out to some edge of the distribution. Of course this is a rather special initial distribution of velocities. We need not be overly concerned with this, however, as we are constructing a model to represent a more logical, four-dimensional, relativistic universe.

We can see, qualitatively that the expansion must slow down to some extent as a result of the mutual gravitational attraction of the galaxies: each galaxy experiences some gravitational acceleration toward the center of distribution or origin. It is easy to examine the character of the motion quantitatively using some of the results of classical gravitational theory discussed in Chapter 8. In particular, the escape velocity v_e, which is the minimum velocity an object must have in order that it be able to leave a gravitational system and not return or fall back, is given by

$$v_e = \sqrt{\frac{2GM}{r}} \qquad (28|8)$$

for the escape of an object from a sphere of mass M and radius r; G is the gravitational constant.

We can use relation (28|8) to consider the expansion of the universe of Fig. 28|11b, where the mass of the "universe" is M and the radius is r. First let us examine the course of the expansion if the velocity of the outer galaxies is v_e. These galaxies will continue to travel outward, but at ever slower velocities, until they stop infinitely far away. But what will happen to the inner galaxies? For convenience we can consider a galaxy that is half as far from the origin as the outermost galaxies, and therefore moving at half the initial velocity. The gravitational mass that affects this galaxy is derived solely from the sphere of matter at a smaller radius—we remember that the outer shells of matter exert no force. So the value of the effective mass is $\frac{1}{8}M$, while the radius is $\frac{1}{2}r$. Then the escape velocity v_e' for this galaxy, is just $\frac{1}{2}v_e$. So this galaxy will also travel outward forever, but always slowing down so that it will stop infinitely far away. At any time this galaxy will be half as far from the origin as the outer galaxy, and the homogeneity of the universe will continue to follow the imposed axiom of the Cosmological Principle. The

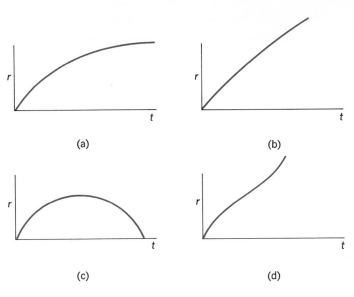

(a)

(b)

(c)

(d)

FIG. 28|12
*The radius of the
universe as a function
of time if the universe is
classical and the
expansion is bounded
by gravity: (a) if each
velocity is equal to
the classical escape
velocity from the
gravitational field of the
remaining galaxies; (b)
if the velocities
are greater than the
escape velocities; (c)
if the velocities are
smaller than the escape
velocities and the
galaxies fall back upon
themselves; (d) if the
initial velocity is near
the escape velocity but,
as a result of the
curvature of the space,
the gravitational force
falls off with distance
faster than $1/r^2$.*

diagram of Fig. 28|12a shows the variation of the radius of this expanding universe as a function of time.

If the velocity of the outer galaxy is greater than v_e, the expansion will not slow down as much. Again the universe will continue to be homogeneous, and the radius will vary with time rather as shown in Fig. 28|12b. If the velocity is less than v_e, the outer galaxy will eventually fall back toward the origin—and so will the other galaxies—and the radius of the universe will vary with time as shown in Fig. 28|9c.

If space is curved, the variation of the radius of the universe with time is affected by the curvature. If our three-dimensional universe is curved positively in four dimensions, in analogy to the curvature of a two-dimensional surface on a three-dimensional sphere, the surface area of a sphere of radius r, in our universe, will be a little less then $4\pi r^2$, even as the perimeter of a two-dimensional circle of radius r, on a three-dimensional globe, will be a little smaller than $2\pi r$. In such a curved universe gravity will not fall off with distance, r, quite as fast as $1/r^2$. We might think that the gravitational force is not spread so much even as the area of the sphere is not quite as large as in a flat space. In a negatively curved universe, where the curvature is comparable to the shape of a saddle, the gravitational force will decrease faster with distance than $1/r^2$, just as the surface area of a sphere will be a little greater than $4\pi r^2$. We might consider that the gravitational force is spread out over a larger area than in a flat space and is correspondingly weaker. If the gravitational interaction becomes stronger with distance, the universe will slow down its rate of expansion when it becomes very large, and we will have a variation of radius with respect to time rather like that shown in Fig. 28 | 9c. On the other hand, if the gravitational force falls off faster with distance than in a flat universe, the universe will effectively expand faster as it grows larger, and we can have a variation of radius with distance like that shown in Fig. 28 | 9d. The limited experimental evidence available as of 1968 suggests that the far-off galaxies are moving away faster than suggested by the Hubble relation of Eq. (28 | 4). Of course we are observing these galaxies as they were a long time ago, and the observations therefore suggest that the universe was expanding more rapidly a long time ago than it is now. If the expansion of the universe is slowing down, the description of Fig. 28 | 12c may be relevant. Thus we are living in a positively curved universe that is still expanding from a beginning about 10 billion years ago. But the expansion is slowing down, and eventually, in perhaps 60 billion years, the universe will contract again into a primeval fireball. As of 1968, such conclusions are hardly definite, however: much more information is required to establish the exact character of our universe.

Obviously these models, where the universe changes in time, do not conform to the Perfect Cosmological Principle. There is another theory that does conform to this axiom. This is the *steady-state theory* of the universe. According to this theory, the universe is constant or uniform in space and time; an observer will see the universe as the same from any position in the universe and at any time. The universe is thus the same as viewed from any point at any time—excluding local variations as usual. This must be reconciled with the observation that the galaxies are all moving away and the universe is expanding. These observational facts are made consistent with the Perfect Cosmological Principle by assuming that new galaxies are continually being created in any particular volume of the universe at a rate just equal to the loss from the volume that occurs when old galaxies leave it in the course of the Hubble expansion. For every galaxy that leaves the volume, a new galaxy must be formed, on the average. The new galaxies are presumably formed from the gravitational condensation of huge masses of gas that occupy the volume. We have some evidence now that the mass of the tenuous cold gas that occupies the space between the stars in the galaxies is greater than the total mass of all of the luminous stars. The mutual gravitational attraction of this huge mass of gas, which is almost wholly hydrogen, is sufficient to cause it to condense over regions of the magnitude of the distance between galaxies. According to the steady-state theory it is this process of condensation that leads to the formation of the cluster of stars that constitutes the galaxies.

Obviously this continual creation of new galaxies would use up the gas in the characteristic volume if new gas were not created. It is this startling hypothesis of the continuous creation of cold hydrogen gas that allows the observation of an expanding universe to be reconciled with Perfect Cosmological Principle. Although there is nothing in this theory as it exists at present that suggests any mechanism for the creation, there is also no mechanism for the instantaneous creation of the universe in the "big bang" that is the starting point of the evolutionary cosmologies.

The rate of production of this hydrogen necessary to balance the mass of the galaxies that leave a particular volume is sufficiently small so that it cannot be easily observed directly. About 1 atom per year must be produced in a volume equivalent to a cube a kilometer on a side. It is a little disturbing to some scientists that the production process that is violent enough to produce an atom that has a rest mass with an energy equivalent of 10^9 eV is so delicate that the atom is almost always produced in its ground state. If the atom were often produced in an excited state, with a mass of a few electron volts greater than the ground state, the radiation of the atom would be easily observed. Again the sky would not be dark at night; or, at least, not as dark as is observed.

A number of observations made recently seem to support the evolutionary model of cosmology rather than the steady-state model. In particular, if the universe began as a tremendously energetic—or hot—fireball, perhaps we can still see this flash. Remember, even as we look far out in space we look far back in time. If we look out far enough, can we see the origin of the universe? It seems that in some sense we can. Since the edge of the universe—which is also the beginning—is moving away from us at a high velocity, the radiation from the flash will have been shifted by the Doppler effect to very low frequencies and show up to an observer on earth as radio waves. These radio waves have now been detected and appear to have just the characteristics to be expected if they were produced in the origin of the universe. Perhaps we can now see this genesis!

Again, recently, some extraordinary objects have been found in the sky, which have been named quasi-stellar objects, or quasars. The Doppler shifts from these objects are characteristically very large, suggesting that they are receding with very high velocities and thus are very far away. If they are so far away, their observed brightness demands that they must be emitting an enormous amount of light energy—more than the light from 10,000 galaxies. We do not know what these quasars are: perhaps they are part of the primeval fireball that did not explode completely into smaller parts! It is possible, however, that they are much nearer, and thus not so large or intense. The large red shift may, then, not result from a Doppler effect but from a gravitational effect. Perhaps quasars are very massive and dense and their gravitational potential is very large. Then time would proceed slower at the quasars, and the vibrations of their emitted light would seem to us to have a lower frequency and be shifted in color toward the red, simulating a Doppler shift.

In either model—the evolutionary model or the steady state model—there must exist some mechanism for the production of heavy nuclei. It appears now that all heavy nuclei originate in dying stars and are spread through the universe by the supernova explosions of large dying stars. The last two supernovae to occur in our galaxy were observed in 1572 (described by Tycho Brahe) and in 1054 (described in some detail by Chinese astronomers). It is intriguing to consider that some of the very material that makes up our bodies had its origin in the explosion of such a supernova.

28|5   *Numerology*

The Greek mathematicians and philosophers were very much interested in the possible importance of integers or small ratios of integers in the description of the universe. The most profound work in this direction resulted from the school of Pythagoras,

centered in the Greek colonies of southern Italy. It was Pythagoras who discovered that the frequencies (or more properly, the
wavelengths) of the pleasing musical intervals were ratios of
integers. Though most of the conjectures of the Pythagoreans
concerning the relations of integers to the physical universe were
incorrect, the general concept that the real numbers of physics
must be related has always had a half-mystical attractiveness to
scientists. In this spirit modern Pythagoreans have shown that
there are some striking numerical relations concerning the fundamental quantities used to describe the universe.

The fundamental quantities that might seem to be important in
macroscopic descriptions of the universe can be listed:

G	the gravitational constant	6.6×10^{11} N-m^2 kg^2
R_0	the Hubble radius of the universe	10^{10} lt-yr or 10^{26} m
c	the velocity of light	3×10^8 m/sec
d	the density of matter in the universe	10^{-26} kg/m^3

We would like to connect these quantities with the microscopic
fundamental quantities.

ke^2	the strength of the coupling of the electric charge to the elec-tromagnetic field	2.3×10^{-28} J-m
m	the mass of the electron	9×10^{-31} kg
h	Planck's constant	6.3×10^{-34} J-sec
M_p	the mass of the proton (as a typical baryon)	1.6×10^{-27} kg

We could proceed to attempt to relate these constants to one
another by constructing dimensionless numbers from combinations of the constants. This would be most elegant, but might
tend to obscure some interesting physical consequences of such
relations, so we will discuss the numbers from a more nearly
physical orientation.

The ratio of the gravitational force to the electrostatic force
between an electron and a proton (as in a hydrogen atom) is

$$\frac{ke^2}{GM_p m} = 0.24 \times 10^{40}$$

The number of particles in the universe will be about equal to the total mass of the universe, which will be about equal to the density times the cube of the Hubble radius, divided by the mass of the proton:

$$\frac{dR_0{}^3}{M_{\mathrm{p}}} = 0.06 \times 10^{80} \qquad \text{or} \qquad (0.25 \times 10^{40})^2$$

The ratio of the size of the universe, R_0, to the nominal size of an elementary particle such as an electron is also of the order of 10^{40}. The classical radius of the electron is taken as ke^2/mc^2, which can be derived from equating the energy in the electric field about the electron to the rest mass energy of the electron. The ratio of these two numbers is

$$\frac{R_0}{(ke^2/mc^2)} = 3.5 \times 10^{40}$$

It is also interesting to note that the natural number

$$\frac{\hbar c}{ke^2} = 137 \qquad \text{and} \qquad 2^{137} = 10 \times 10^{40}$$

Many physicists consider that it is probable that the first three of these ratios are simply and fundamentally related. The recurrence of so large a number as 10^{40} in three separate ways seems unlikely to be a complete accident. The fourth relation is somewhat contrived and is more likely to be accidental in some sense.

We have shown in Section 28|3 that the ratio of the observed Hubble radius, R_0, and the gravitational radius, $R_{\mathrm{g}} = (c/2)/(Gd)^{1/2}$, is nearly equal to 1—another Pythagorean relation that might well be significant.

The total energy of the universe might be estimated by taking the energy corresponding to the rest mass of the universe and subtracting the gravitational potential energy. The mass of the universe is about equal to $M = dR_0{}^3$, and thus the total rest mass energy will be Mc^2 from the Einstein relation. If we use our simple picture of the universe as a sphere, a particle of mass m on the surface of the sphere will have a gravitational potential energy of $-GMm/R_0$. We can estimate the total potential energy of the universe by substituting M for m, and thus the potential energy will be about $-GM^2/R_0$. Adding the two energies to get the total energy of the universe,

$$\text{Total energy} = Mc^2 - \frac{GM^2}{R_0}$$

But the two terms Mc^2 and GM^2/R_0 are equal within a factor of less than 10, which is well within the accuracy with which we can measure these quantities or even define their meaning. So within the accuracy of our measurements and within the depth of our understanding of the meaning of such measurements, the total energy of the universe is zero! The energy that would be required to disperse the matter in the universe so that the mutual gravitational interaction of the particles was truly negligible would be about equal to the energy that could be obtained from the matter by changing it completely to energy.

Though we have no successful explanation of the relations between these numbers at this time, it seems likely that the numbers are deeply significant, and these relations may be a clue to some deeper understanding of the character of the universe.

PROBLEMS

28 |1 Assume that the whole universe is expanding in microscopic detail according to the Hubble observation. How much would a meter stick expand in our year? Do you think that this would be observable?

28 |2 (*a*) Assume that the universe is not expanding, but that the value of the electric charge is weaker at great distances. How must the value of e^2 vary with R to account for the red shift? Does this violate any of the cosmological principles? (Consider the frequency of light emitted by an atom according to the Bohr model.)

(*b*) Assume that the universe is not expanding but that the electric charge is increasing with time. Does such an assumption violate any of the cosmological principles? Can the red shift be explained in this way?

28 |3 If the universe is curved, the observed brightness of a far-off galaxy will not vary as $1/r^2$ where r is the distance of the galaxy. In a positively curved universe the galaxy will seem brighter, in a negatively curved universe the galaxy will appear less bright than in a flat universe. Consider the characteristics of two-dimensional universes curved in three dimensions and explain by analogy how these conclusions follow.

28|4   It is 40 billion years in the future, and the universe is known to expand and then contract as suggested in Fig. 28|12c with a total lifetime of 70 billion years. Discuss the variation of the Doppler shift with respect to the distance of far-off galaxies as measured by a scientist of this time.

28|5   How does the Hubble observation dispose of Olbers' paradox—that the nights are dark?

28|6   How would the observed red shift vary with distance if the expansion rate were constant? How would the red shift vary with distance if the expansion rate were increasing with time?

28|7   Consider the application of the theory of relativity to observations made by different inertial observers, and show that no unique world map exists. Nevertheless the concept is useful because there is a usefully defined special observer. What is the character of this special observer?

28|8   How should the density of galaxies appear in the world *picture* if the expansion rate is constant and the curvature of space is zero? If the expansion rate increases slowly in time and the curvature is zero?

Index